An American Genius:

THE LIFE OF ERNEST ORLANDO LAWRENCE

An American Genius:

THE LIFE OF
Ernest Orlando Lawrence

by Herbert Childs

E. P. Dutton & Co., Inc.
New York 🌿🌿 1968

Grateful acknowledgment is made to the following for permission to quote from copyright material:

Harper & Row for excerpts from *Now It Can Be Told, The Story of the Manhattan Project,* by Leslie R. Groves (1962).

Oxford University Press for excerpts from *Atomic Quest, A Personal Narrative,* by Arthur H. Compton (Copyright © 1956 by Oxford University Press, Inc.).

For my son
George

Contents

8 ❦ ❦ CONTENTS

Illustrations

Photographs

After the presentation to Professor Lawrence of the Sylvanus Thayer Award, West Point, 1958

The Lawrence children in 1958

Diagrams

Foreword

The idea of a biography of Ernest Lawrence was first mentioned in my presence in April, 1959. A New York editor and I had been invited to Mr. Edwin W. Pauley's home in Beverly Hills for lunch to discuss an unrelated matter. Mr. Pauley, who was chairman of the Board of Regents of the University of California, was much more interested in a life of the university's famous atomic scientist whose tragic death at fifty-seven had followed the 1958 Geneva Conference of Experts (on detection of nuclear explosions), which he had attended at President Eisenhower's request. "His is the story you ought to be interested in," Mr. Pauley insisted. "Ernest Lawrence was one of the most important men of our time. His life should be an inspiration to bright young people everywhere, as he was for those he worked with."

Mr. Pauley was eloquent and convincing—"youthful vitality," "genius," "humanity," "statesmanship" are terms I clearly recall, and even the editor seemed to forget the business for which we were present. Mr. Pauley telephoned to Berkeley and arranged for the editor to meet Chancellor Seaborg there for further discussion. I had been impressed, but as a bystander, for I was busy with another project.

Nearly a year later, and many months after I had last seen Mr. Pauley, he telephoned and asked if I remembered our discussion of Ernest Lawrence. I certainly did. Had I given any consideration to writing his life? I had not; I had assumed that the final decision on the project had long since been reached. Mr. Pauley explained that there had been much discussion among Ernest's friends, associates, and family as to whether the biography should be strictly scientific or written for the general public. The consensus now favored the latter. Did I think it could be done interestingly? I could only reply that I did not know, but agreed to discuss it with Dr. John Lawrence, brother of Ernest, over lunch at the Burbank Airport within an hour. If I did not wish to undertake the project myself, Mr. Pauley suggested, perhaps I could offer advice.

That was the first of several airport luncheon conferences. A plane arrived at Burbank every noon, another left there for Berkeley about three. We were joined once by Donald Cooksey, friend of Ernest Lawrence for more than thirty years, and his assistant for more than twenty. Late in April I went to San Francisco and Berkeley to discuss the project with Ernest Lawrence's adviser and friend H. Rowan Gaither, Jr.; Mrs. Ernest Lawrence; Chancellor Glenn T. Seaborg; Edwin M. McMillan, head of the Lawrence Radiation Laboratory; and other Lawrence associates; and to see the great laboratory complex which in itself is a monument to the man. I could not quickly determine that a biography of wide general appeal could be written; the activities of a scientist are predominantly mental, and however important, may seem far less dramatic than those of a so-called man of action—which I was later to learn Ernest Lawrence also was—but I was much interested, and agreed to find out. From a fund previously appropriated toward exploring a biography, the regents of the university would defray approved traveling expenses to make possible interviews with knowledgeable people involved in the story. After three months I would either proceed with the biography or withdraw and give such material as I had gathered to the university.

I soon determined that ample material for an interesting and exciting biography of Ernest Lawrence was available, that it would be the writer's fault if it were not presented in readable form. I also learned that controversial areas could not honestly be avoided, that excellent scientists may be no freer of envy or prejudice than are other intelligent human beings, and that I could undertake the task only if completely free of any university or family supervision or right of approval. There was no difficulty in reaching agreement on these terms: the work would be entirely mine and my responsibility. It was up to me to be as objective as I could be. My only contractual obligation to the university would be to deliver collected material (within the limits of confidence) to the archives when I had finished the job. I would continue to be reimbursed for necessary, and approved, travel expenses within the limits of the original appropriation. I was promised cooperation and access to necessary files. Optimistically, I thought it might take two years to complete the biography; instead, almost seven years have elapsed.

The work would have taken longer without the cooperation and assistance of many people, particularly people in the university's Lawrence Radiation Laboratory and Mrs. Lawrence. No biographer could be more fortunate than I in his relationship with the one nearest and dearest to his subject. Molly Lawrence's objectivity, her frankness and cooperation, were not only unusual but were essential to the task.

My deepest thanks, both for his assistance and for his patience, must go to Donald Cooksey, whose letters introduced me everywhere, who chauffeured me, answered questions without number, was more objective than might be expected of so devoted a friend and faithful assistant, and who, with his wife Milicent, made me welcome in their home more times than I can possibly enumerate.

I am grateful, too, to Dr. John Lawrence, who turned over to me the correspondence that passed among his brother, himself, and their parents over many years. John and I spent almost a week in South Dakota: in Canton, Vermillion, Springfield, and Pierre, the locale of Ernest's early years. Many people who knew him as boy and young man were ready with information. Amy (Mrs. John) Lawrence dug up old scrapbooks and albums and was in every way helpful and encouraging.

No interview of the some eight hundred conducted was more delightful than that with Mrs. Lawrence's parents, Dr. and Mrs. George Blumer. Mrs. Blumer—Mabel to Ernest—had rare insight and many humorous recollections. She was very proud of being the mother-in-law of two Nobel laureates, Ernest Lawrence and Edwin McMillan. Elsie McMillan, who had known Ernest for as long a time as had his wife, her sister, was also a gracious source of information otherwise unobtainable. Edwin Mattison McMillan, Ernest Lawrence's successor and present head of the university's Lawrence Radiation Laboratory has been helpful in every way. Perhaps my chief debt to him is for his review of my manuscript for scientific errors likely from a writer not himself a scientist.

So many people at the laboratory smoothed the way toward information! First and foremost in any possible enumeration of them is Eleanor Irvine Davisson, Ernest Lawrence's secretary for many years, and now secretary to Dr. McMillan. Her day-to-day help as I went through files —which often seemed inexhaustible—was incalculable, and her willingness to check names, facts, and dates, in fact to respond quickly and cooperatively to every request, is beyond recompense. I must also mention Business Manager and Engineer Wallace B. Reynolds, and Assistants to the Director Harold A. Fidler and Daniel M. Wilkes. Dan has not only tracked down facts and information, his help in securing photographs has also been most valuable. I wish there were space to list others in the laboratory, from office girls to doctors of philosophy. They all have my gratitude.

I am equally at a loss for words to express adequately my appreciation of the help of hundreds of other people, many of whom not only generously submitted to interviews—often taped—answered my letters, and gave me pictures and permission to quote what they told me and to quote from their correspondence with Dr. Lawrence, but who entertained me in their homes, and often made possible further access to information I would otherwise have missed. I can only say that in addition to material for the biography, I have been enriched personally through such associations. I regret the necessities of space that force me to acknowledge my debts by an alphabetical list of those to whom I owe most. Proper mention of all with whom I have talked would require another volume. To all I am deeply grateful, and especially to the following:

Philip H. Abelson, Paul C. Aebersold, Lewis E. and Myra Akeley, Luis W. Alvarez, Dr. Walter C. Alvarez, E. Amaldi, Clarence Anderson, Gladys Alvarez Archibald, Hugo Atterling, Robert F. Bacher, Barney Balaban, Sidney W. Barnes, Charles S. Barrett, Rexford W. and Marybelle Barton, Jesse W. Beams, Jay Bedsworth, Pedro G. Beltran, Robert Beringer, H. J. Bhabha, Wilfred S. Bigelow, Raymond T. Birge, Ward Blackmon, Felix Bloch, Dr. James L. Born, George McN. Bowles, Norris E. Bradbury, Hugh Bradner, James J. Brady, Gregory Breit, William M. Brobeck, William Brower, Harold Brown, J. W. Buchta, Vannevar Bush, Melvin Calvin, Owen Chamberlain, William R. Chambers, Edward G. and Mrs. Chandler, Ralph W. and Mrs. Chaney, Albert K. Chapman, E. P. Churchill, Sir John Cockcroft, Frank Collbohm, Arthur H. Compton, James B. Conant, Richard Connell, Mrs. Charlton D. Cooksey, A. Crawford Cooley, W. D. Coolidge, Karl K. Darrow, Walter C. Dean, William D. Douglass, Robert Dressler, Lee A. DuBridge, Walter F. Dudziak, Priscilla Greene Duffield, Jesse W. DuMond, Charles Dunham, Dr. Patricia Durbin, Edward and LaRue Dwight, V. P. Dzhelepov, Niels E. Edlefsen, Ann Eggers, Sidney M. Ehrman, Horace C. Ellis, Lorenzo Emo, Herbert M. Evans, George Everson.

Also George Felbeck, Paul C. Fine, John Flaherty, John Stuart Foster, John Stuart Foster, Jr., H. F. Frankenfeld, Walter and Christine Frederick, H. Rowan Gaither, Jr., Warren Garrison, F. William and Muriel Ashley Giauque, Dr. John W. Gofman, J. D. Gow, George Kenneth Green, General Leslie R. Groves, Morgan Gunst, Jr., Lawrence R. Hafstad, William and Elizabeth Hamilton, Borge Hansen-Møller, W. T. Hanson, Jr., Lawrence and Margaret Haugen, Curtis R. Haupt, Leland J. Haworth, Admiral John T. Hayward, Randolph A. Hearst, Leo Heck, John C. Hecker, A. Carl Helmholz, Caroline Hemmingson, Malcolm C. Henderson, George de Hevesy, Norman Hilberry, Alexander Hildebrand, Joel H. Hildebrand, Roger H. Hildebrand, Robert and Lois Hipple, Dr. Fred J. Hodges, Oren House, Frederick T. Howard, E. D.

Hudson, Eugene Huffman, Albert W. Hull, Charles Gilman Hyde, Franklyn Hyde, Dr. Leon O. Jacobson, Henrietta Jenkins, Verne and Elizabeth Jennings, Dr. Arthur L. Jensen, Mrs. Ardis Johnson, Lyall Johnson, Thomas H. Johnson, Warren C. Johnson, Bart Jones, Dr. Hardin B. Jones, David L. Judd, Martin D. Kamen, Elmer Kelly, Bernard B. Kinsey, L. Kowarski, Marietta Kuper.

Also Louis La Roche, Clarence E. Larson, L. Jackson and Barbara Bridgeford Laslett, Charles C. Lauritsen, Barbara Hundale Lawrence, John Eric Lawrence, Margaret Lawrence Casady, Mary Kimberly Lawrence, Robert Don Lawrence, Susan Lawrence, Oliver Laxon, Chauncey D. Leake, John Leermakers, Victor Lenzen, J. J. Livingood, M. Stanley Livingston, Robert S. and Mrs. Livingston, Leonard Loeb, Edward J. Lofgren, Alfred and Manette Loomis, Don H. Loughridge, Walter W. Ludeman, Anne Cooksey Maes, W. G. Malcolm, John Manley, Wilfrid B. Mann, Lauriston C. and Mrs. Marshall, Stanley E. and Mrs. McCaffrey, Louis W. McKeehan, Donald H. and Mrs. McLaughlin, C. E. K. Mees, Melville and Marion Akeley Miller, Joseph C. Morris, Burton J. Moyer, R. F. Mozley, Eger V. Murphree, Raymond L. Murray, Thomas E. Murray, Basanti Nag, Henry W. Newson, Amos Newton, John Francis Neylan, F. Y. Nikitin, Ben and Gus Noid, C. E. Norman, John H. Northrup, James S. Norton, Sir Mark Oliphant, Frank F. Oppenheimer, Robert Oppenheimer, Maurice and Mrs. Overseth, Oliver E. Overseth, Mrs. John Overseth, W. K. H. Panofsky, William E. Parkins, Jr., Helen Parsons, Linus Pauling, Jenny and Paul Paulson, Isadore Perlman, O. O. Piccioni, Gerald Pickavance, Francis Pinckney, Kenneth S. Pitzer, Polly Plesset, Langley Porter, Wilson M. Powell, Josephine Priestley.

Also I. I. Rabi, Paul Raiborne, J. T. Ramey, Frances Randolph, Vladimir A. Reichel, J. Reginald Richardson, Chaim Richman, Ernest and Iva Anderson Rowe, Glen Ruby, Ryokichi Sagane, Winfield W. and Mrs. Salisbury, Ira Sandefur, Glenn and Helen Seaborg, Emilio Segrè, Duane C. Sewell, Charles and Mrs. Seymour, C. Donald Shane, R. S. Shankland, Dr. John Sherrick, Kai Siegbahn, David H. Sloan, Lloyd Smith, Samuel B. Smith, Arthur H. Snell, Frank H. Spedding, Robert Gordon Sproul, Chauncey Starr, Walter A. Starr, Harold E. Stassen, Cyril J. Staud, J. MacWilliams Stone, Dr. Robert S. Stone, Lewis L. Strauss, Edward W. Strong, C. Guy Suits, Walter Sullivan, A. L. Swanholm, W. F. G. Swann, Alfonso Tammaro, Edward Teller, Charles A. Thomas, Lowell Thomas, Robert L. Thornton, Leonid M. Tichvinsky, Cornelius A. Tobias, Arthur Tobiason, Robert Traver, Harry S Truman, Elwin Tuttle, Merle Tuve, Robert M. Underhill, Harold C. Urey, James T. Vale, T. Gentry Veal, Vladimir I. Veksler, Lionel Viales, E. S.

Viez, Dr. Shields Warren, Dr. Stafford Warren, Glen Watson, William W. Watson, Warren Weaver, Julian H. Webb, Lester Wegner, Vernon M. Welsh, John A. Wheeler, Harvey E. White, Milton G. White, Rolf Wideröe, Maggie Williams, Robert R. and Mrs. Wilson, Jean C. Witter, Louis Wouters, Byron Wright, Chien-Shiung Wu, Herbert F. York, Rebekah Young, and Luke Yuan.

I am very grateful to Ralph W. Chaney for conducting and taping interviews for me in Hawaii and Japan, and to David L. Judd for taping an interview with Rolf Wideröe. My friend and neighbor, Lydia Takeshita, interrupted her own researches in Indian art to ask questions for me in India.

Mr. Philip Jacobsohn helped fill a void with copies of his brother Samuel's 1924–25 letters from Yale to members of his family; to him also my thanks.

I am also indebted to Frank Barry of *Movietone News* and C. B. Stratton of *Hearst Metrotone News* for enabling me to see newsreels.

Donald Cooksey took most of the photographs made at the Radiation Laboratory that appear in these pages. Credits for some others appear in their captions. I am indebted to the skill of George Kagawa and Douglas McWilliams of the Lawrence Radiation Laboratory for restoration of many old snapshots.

Limericks and other verse by men associated with the laboratory are credited where used. Portions of Arthur Roberts' "The Cyclotronist's Nightmare" are reprinted by special permission.

How can one realize and acknowledge his debt for information gleaned from files? It would be as futile as to attempt to acknowledge every book and article in the vast literature of science. Many sources for any work so long as this must lie below the level of conscious classification, but one can be grateful in spite of the fact.

Some I have interviewed may think I have ignored much that was said or advice that was given; I must deny such charges. Everything was considered, all has been helpful, if only to force deeper search. I have had to resolve conflicts as best I could, with my own judgment where empirical evidence was lacking. I have purposely refrained from the use throughout the text of footnotes and keys to specific references. To many general readers these are distracting. Sources, by chapter, may be found in the appendix.

Finally, I would thank my sister Gertrude Childs Shrock for the sort of editorial tasks on the manuscript that can be so tedious for a writer too familiar with his story to notice error, and in this regard I must add my gratitude to William Doerflinger, my understanding editor at E. P. Dutton and Company. To Rachel Anne Sadler and Juanita Shields goes appreciation for secretarial assistance. Nor can I conclude this incomplete compilation of debts without mention of Marjorie Leonard Childs, patient partner who must be aware of the enormity of my debt to her and, I hope, of my undefinable gratitude.

HERBERT CHILDS

La Crescenta, California
September 2, 1967

An American Genius:

THE LIFE OF ERNEST ORLANDO LAWRENCE

CHAPTER I

Born Grown Up

[1901–1918]

Ernest was born grown up." His mother said this so often that it became a family cliché, anticipated whenever Gunda Lawrence spoke of her eldest son. She said it before he was ten, and again when he won the Nobel Prize at thirty-eight; it was her response when questioned about his youthful enthusiasm at fifty—without thought of the contradiction in terms. It was her explanation of the inscrutable. It would have served had she heard the scholar whose business it was to assess the brilliant, call him "Perhaps the only real genius I've ever known," and as readily for the summation of a successful businessman: "The most normal egghead I ever saw!" Nor did it surprise her that a President of the United States called him a "statesman." Of course he was a genius, and as normal as any successful American—an American genius.

An *American* genius: of immigrant stock, rural prairie, small-town schools, and Midwest universities until graduate work in the East; all in America, at a time when the luster of Cambridge or Göttingen was important in physics. Then, in so short a time, he created his own bailiwick in the Far West, a center to which physicists of every enlightened nation gravitated, the while remaining a "regular fellow," at ease and at home with dignitaries, scientists, politicians, military men, students, and Rotarians; courageous, optimistic, in a hurry, and as extroverted and happy as the normal American male is supposed to be. A *success* in the true Horatio Alger genre.

He had his "winning manner, smile, and definite personality" by the time he was in elementary school, according to Mary Cooper, his first teacher, who wondered if the charm, or whatever made him singular, was attributable to big blue eyes, eager attentiveness to whoever addressed him, determination to understand the reason for everything, or just a happy combination of factors. He was not an outstanding student in the sense reflected by grades, and in no way distinguishable as a prodigy. Taller than his classmates, gangly and a bit awkward, his ready smile camouflaged any unusual seriousness. To most people he was just another boy of the small Dakota town on the expanse of the American prairie.

South Dakota had been a state only a dozen years when Ernest Lawrence was born on a hot August 8, 1901, in Canton, Lincoln County seat since statehood but first settled in 1867, four years after Dakota Territory was opened for homesteads. The town had prospered because of thrifty farmers and the best soil of South Dakota; the area along the southern end of the Big Sioux River supported two lines of the "Milwaukee" railroad, which crossed at the Canton station. By 1901 there was a stone courthouse in a central park; a church, two public-school buildings, and a Lutheran academy. There was also a state asylum for insane Indians, named for Hiawatha. A number of people in the town and its environs, when Ernest was old enough to be interested, remembered Indian raids to the west. Those after the Treaty of 1869 never quite reached the Big Sioux Valley, but had been close enough to put some homesteaders to flight, leaving crops and cattle behind. Most of the Norwegian settlers had remained. There were fresher memories of droughts and grasshopper plagues, though even with these scourges, Lincoln County settlers had been among the more fortunate people of the state. At the turn of the century, the Norwegians of Lincoln County had improved their lands; sturdy houses and big barns had replaced sod huts. Many farmers had houses in Canton, too, as a newer generation took over actual conduct of the farm. If there was no great wealth, there was no real poverty, though people considered poor lived across the main-line tracks, as other than Norwegian influences came with growth. Pastor Rasmussen even considered Masonic and I.O.O.F. lodges evil, and tabooed public dances. Fortunately there was the Augustana Academy, where adolescents could have proper Lutheran Christian education, and it was the academy that brought Carl Lawrence to Canton. Professor Anthony Tuve hired young Carl to be the academy's professor of Latin and history, at sixty-five dollars a month, the summer following Carl's graduation from the University of Wisconsin in 1894.

To leave Madison, Wisconsin, for Canton, South Dakota, had not been an easy decision for him to make; he had started to work in the offices of Senator Robert La Follette, whose political philosophy had appeal; politics had interested him since, as a twelve-year-old boy, he had been a messenger boy in the Wisconsin Legislature. The job also paid $100 a month which, with tips, was more than he earned for several years even after graduation from the university. He had had to work hard from the age of ten; his father, in trying to help a drunken man from a gutter, had been kicked in the spine and permanently crippled, and conversion of their home to a boardinghouse, even when supplemented by his mother's wages as a carpet weaver, was insufficient to raise and educate children.

Ole Hundale Lavrens had been a teacher in Telemark, Norway, where the family was known for their "good heads." In 1846, three years after his arrival in Wisconsin Territory, he was granted a certificate of qualification as a teacher. He seems to have Americanized his name in two stages; first to Larence and finally to Lawrence, by the time he married Bertha Hull, an immigrant from Kragero, a dozen years after he had come, thus uniting in America, his countrymen said, the two most beautiful valleys of Norway. Though Bertha never learned to write, she was an avid reader, and could speak German as well as her native Norwegian and adopted English. They had six children, two of whom died before the age of five, and before Carl Gustav, their youngest, was born in January, 1871. John Hundale, thirteen years Carl's senior, had been able to achieve his goal and was a Lutheran pastor. Ellen, four years older than Carl, was with John in New England when Carl was ready for the university. Carl's oldest sister, Emma, a schoolteacher, was able to contribute a little toward his education, not expensive since the state university was in Madison. The summer he was ten Carl had carried water for a thirsty railroad gang, laying rails to Milwaukee; his father had fashioned a yoke for his shoulders to enable him to carry two pails more easily. In school months, he found time for baseball, debating, ice-boating, or sailing on the large, nearby lake.

When he was graduated from the university, Carl was six feet, four inches tall, strong—he had spent his last summer vacation pushing tourists in big rolling chairs around the Chicago World's Fair—and he was concerned about the community and nation in which he lived. This concern, and his interest in La Follette, vied with a natural inclination toward, and respect for, teaching—as high a calling in his father's opinion as the ministry was in his mother's. Pedagogy won, and in late summer of 1894 he bicycled to Canton. He secured room and board in a private home for fourteen dollars a month, and with quiet enthusiasm Carl Lawrence entered the life of the academy and the community. He returned to Madison during the summers of 1896 and 1897 for graduate work in history and physics—to make himself more useful. After four years at the academy, he resigned and became Superintendent of Canton

City Schools. It meant an increase in income of a little more than eighteen dollars a month, and, more important, the opportunity to be of greater service to the community. He had already helped organize and had become the first president of the South Dakota Luther League.

Extracurricular activities were not confined to religious associations; he was the prime mover in the organization of the Athenian Debating Society, in which good citizens, not necessarily either Norwegian or Lutheran, each Monday night debated political problems, current affairs, or philosophical questions in orderly fashion. In true Athenian spirit the society also fostered games—Carl was pitcher for the Athenian baseball team. He built a house on Third Street, on the academy side of town, and was a respected and leading citizen.

As superintendent, Carl was expected to teach in the high school. The one other high-school teacher, whose specialty was mathematics, was Gunda Jacobson, pretty, fair, and five years his junior, who almost reached his shoulder. They had met; Gunda had been an enrapt member of his Bible class, and he had bicycled out to her father's farm near Moe, east of Canton, ostensibly to visit her brother Knute, who had been a student at the academy.

The senior Jacobsons were also from Norway, where men of the family were famous throughout Gulbransdalen as artistic. Gunda's father Erik had carved a noted altarpiece for the church at Garmo. He and his wife had come in 1871 to Iowa, where a brother was a homesteader near St. Ansgar. Three years later Erik and Marit had crossed the Big Sioux River into Dakota Territory, and to a homestead of their own; they were among the earliest settlers of Norway Township. Gunda was born in 1876, a few months after the defeat of General Custer, in a sod hut, before Erik could build a proper house. She attended a country school and a state teachers' college, excelling in mathematics. Though a member of Lands Parish—one is still directed to this or that parish to locate a resident in the environs of Canton—she attended the Canton church during the school year. As it was the center of social activities for Canton Lutherans, there were picnics, sociables, and various meetings— dancing was taboo—where young people became acquainted, and she knew Carl well enough by the time he proposed marriage to be certain that he was the most desirable of all possible husbands. So superior in fact did she consider him to anyone she had known, so distinguished and important, that, to be more worthy to be his wife, she hired out, the summer before their marriage, as a servant in a great house in Minneapolis, to observe the arts of housekeeping and social conduct proper for an important man's wife. When she returned to Canton to be married, on August 22, 1900, she was determined that Carl should never regret his marriage to a country girl.

Gunda was equally determined to be a good mother when Ernest was born the following August 8, but nothing she had learned, or that physicians could advise, helped her to cope with so independent a child. Years later when it seemed that rather than having been born grown up, he had never outgrown boyish *joie de vivre,* she wrote: "Ernest was always of a happy disposition and life to him seems still to be one thrill after another. But was he persistent and insistent!!! Often when I opposed something he wanted to do, he would say, 'Now, Mama, if you can give me just *one* good reason why you won't let me do this or that, it will be all right, I'll not ask for it any more.' I agreed, and in most instances I found that the only reason I could give was that I was his *Ma* and so was *boss* (which I realized was no valid reason at all).

"Perhaps one reason might be that I couldn't nurse him after the first weeks. I got typhoid fever and the poor babe was on his own. He was a very thin baby too, but always very cheerful. Merle Tuve, who was born just across the street from us six weeks before Ernest put in his appearance, had the colic for months and often we were awakened at night by his crying. Mrs. Tuve used to bring him over and say she envied us our smiling baby. Those two babies became fast friends before they were in the grades."

The initials of the Lawrence firstborn were determined before the names with which he was christened, as, according to Norwegian custom, they must derive from a given name of each grandfather. Why Ernest was chosen instead of Erik is not known; Carl thought there were enough Oles, and he remembered having been teased as a white-headed Norski, so Orlando was chosen for the O, perhaps from Shakespeare; he was to be teased later as the character so named in *As You Like It.* In spite of her son's cheerful disposition, Gunda worried over his inability to put on weight and attributed it to what seemed excessive activity for so young a child, though she was certain also of his "obvious intelligence, and inquisitiveness." Curiosity about matches and fire might have destroyed him, a week before his second birthday, had not Gunda been able to quench the blaze and strip him of his burning clothes. He was very sick for a few days but by his birthday, though far from well, was happy and cheerful again, the *Sioux Valley News* reported. A small scar near the corner of his mouth remained for the rest of his life. He was seriously ill again for several days with pneumonia, just after his fourth birthday, but though he was slow to gain weight as a child, and, as he increased in height, was a little stooped, was generally healthy. The usual childhood diseases and a tonsillectomy were not serious.

A second son, John, born on January 8, 1904, completed the family. Gunda was delighted with ". . . the fat little butterball. Ernest was so very thin and so we were surprised and pleased that John was so chubby." She could cuddle John, who did not resist being held as Ernest often had, and she was able to nurse him—perhaps because of this, and Ernest's independence, she was always somewhat closer to John. "While in the grades and high school John had somewhat of an inferiority complex—which his dad and I bent every effort to combat. He seemed to feel that he could never come up to Ernest in ability. We always praised him and complimented him on his work and tried to make him realize that he had just as good a mind and could do anything that Ernest could—only he was almost three years younger . . . until he was awarded the Phi Beta Kappa key. This was a surprise to him, and was the means, I think, of giving him the self-confidence he needed. . . . From their father they both inherited a keen sense of *right*—and like him are simple, unassuming and sincere," Gunda wrote some years later. Carl credited their mother with being the source of any bent toward science they inherited: "she was the mathematician."

Whatever the combination of inherited tendencies and the differences between the boys, they were close members of a tightly knit family. Though young John was a serious responsibility who slowed Ernest when in tow, there was little conflict between them. Gunda could remember, but never understand, Ernest's ability to make John angry simply by staring at him across the table, nor could John explain it other than that his brother "looked at me." This usually occurred after grace before a meal, an ancestral grace said in Norwegian until Ernest protested that he was "not Norwegian, but young." When it was explained that Norwegian had nothing to do with age, he protested: "But I am an American!" His father, to Gunda's amazement, thereafter allowed his son to ask the blessing in English, though he continued to attend Norwegian classes after regular school.

Ernest engineered another triumph of reason over motherly concern —aided by fatherly belief in self-reliance—when seven-and-a-half years old. He suggested that Easter vacation would be a good time for him to visit his cousin Tommy Clapp in Sioux City, Iowa, some seventy miles from Canton. Gunda laughed, but he persisted, as usual, until she said it was out of the question, since neither she nor his father could take him. "But you don't have to, I can go by myself." Gunda threw up her hands in horror. "Alone? You're much too young!" "Of course I can, it's easy. You get on the train at the station. If there aren't enough seats, you stand up. At Sioux City you get off and walk to Aunt Anna's. Then you do the same coming back. What's difficult about that?" Gunda stared at him: tall, thin, he did look older, and such intent blue eyes beneath the shock of fair hair, reddish as the sunlight touched it. So sure of himself—such grown-up attitudes. Before she could defeat reason with motherly fiat, Carl interposed, gently. "He's right, Mother, let him try his wings." Gunda went on with her supper, suppressing fears; if Carl thought it wise, it must be. Aunt Anna, prettiest of Gunda's sisters, was also surprised to see him come alone. Tommy was delighted; he was to die of leukemia in a few years at the age of twelve, a factor in Ernest's intention to become a doctor.

There was no question in the Lawrence household as to where authority rested, and it rested easily with Carl. Gunda would not think of arguing with her husband when she knew his will, though she often got her way by gentle indirection. Discipline was strict but light—perhaps because there was little need to exercise it. Ernest was spanked twice by Carl, who each time regretted it. Nonviolent by instinct and theory, Carl always hoped to avoid corporal punishment whether for his sons or adolescents under his charge. The first chastisement was for a misdeed forced by another, but an important principle was involved—poor excuse, Carl thought in remorse, for whipping. A neighborhood boy, seven or eight years older and something of a bully, used to hitch Ernest and Art Tobiason as a team to a wagon and make them pull him around town. At Kelly's dairy farm, near the academy, he once made them join in teasing the Irishman, as he milked. Kelly pretended to ignore them until they were within range, when he squirted fresh milk in the ringleader's face. The boy was so angry he made Ernest and Art stamp down several rows of young corn in Kelly's field. Kelly failed to catch them, but he reached their fathers.

Carl Lawrence was intolerant of intolerance, and of wanton destruction. It was what a man was himself that was important, not whether he was Norwegian or Irish, a schoolman or a dairy farmer; that must be understood. He was restrained and ingenious in handling student difficulties, a fact remembered to this day by ex-students—as fair with them as with his sons.

Ernie, as his contemporaries called him, was too busy to get into much mischief but had his share of pranks, particularly when they seemed called for. One Halloween, with Merle Tuve, more and more his favorite companion, he threw rubbish on Mrs. Sorum's porch, next door to the Lawrence house. It was late dusk but Mrs. Sorum was unpredictably on the porch. Ernie escaped, but Mrs. Sorum caught Merle by the seat of his pants and pulled him back through the fence hole through which he hoped to disappear. Such conduct was not condoned, but was understood, nor did it happen often enough to cause alarm. The terrible sin would have been to lie for any reason whatever; honesty was the great virtue. In the Tuve household it had been stressed that dishonesty included helping oneself to neighbors' fruit, and Merle refused to join Ernest and Oliver Overseth in picking apples from someone's tree. Oliver remembers that Merle "preached us a regular sermon about stealing." Ollie was Ernest's cousin and a year older, but Ernie was taller and could run faster. He and Merle, as professors' sons, were sissies to a group of crosstown toughs who sometimes ambushed them. One would grab a professor's boy by the hands, another by the feet, to swing him, sometimes against a tree or a telephone pole. Ernest outran them a time or two, and Merle accused his friend of having a peace treaty with the toughs. He was intensely teased shortly after his seventh birthday, following an item in the *Sioux Valley News* of August 14, 1908: "Master Ernest Lawrence, Miss Bernice Byrnes and Miss Margaret James attended primary classes a number of times this week and did some paper cutting, braiding, etc., which showed how readily the little folks can and will take hold of the industrial work."

He had been too young to be troubled by previous press notices—not infrequent about the son of a superintendent whose fame had spread from town to county to state after his election as Lincoln County superintendent of schools in 1906. Carl Lawrence's ideas for developing interest in corn culture, with clubs and contests for rural boys, was so successful that in the second year of the program many high-school boys surpassed their fathers in quality and quantity production. Not only did Superintendent Lawrence receive the plaudits of the governor, he was asked to speak and to help initiate the program in other counties. A similar program for girls was initiated with the introduction of domestic science into rural schools. Student displays were judged by experts and state officials, who noted, with pleased parents, that the incentive engendered also heightened interest in regular schoolwork.

Ernest and Merle decided early that they did not wish to become farmers. Ollie was less certain; his father had a fine profitable farm, as well as a stone house in town. As they assessed leading citizens, and Merle remembers several who "made Canton a good place for a boy to grow up in," the physicians of the community seemed the most worthy models. "We were all going to become doctors," Merle said. There were admired businessmen too, but for interesting, worthwhile work, the doctors seemed to surpass all others. It was taken for granted that teaching was a fine profession, though perhaps Ernest and Merle were too close to that to find it glamorous and too young to credit it with doing much good.

The only farm attraction for Ernest was the heavy draft horses— though there had been fun hiding in haylofts, until he worked at haying. It was easier for him to leap onto a horse than it was for shorter boys, and exciting to ride off, bareback. He once frightened John almost into hysteria when he was pitched violently onto a concrete floor after he had leaped onto an unbridled horse inside a barn. He was stunned for a few minutes, after which he calmed John and convinced him that Mother should not hear about it.

It was most unusual to keep anything from their mother or father, and, as far as the boys knew, their parents kept no secrets from them. Everything was shared in the family, and each one's interest, however minor, was an interest for all; even after the boys were in college, members of the family opened and read each other's mail. Carl often did not have to see letters addressed to him at the house, since their contents might already have been revealed by one of the boys. Secrets were discouraged and even politeness was no justification for deceit.

It was not only memory of early days in the sod hut, before her family prospered, which made Gunda more practical than her sometimes overly generous husband; thrift was a characteristic of a good wife, and if Professor Lawrence would "give the shirt off his back," she saw to it that her sons' clothes were mended and mended and made to last. Their knickers were neat and patched, and the long, black, ribbed cotton stockings the boys detested as they grew older were well darned. "We couldn't any of us wait to be confirmed so we could wear long pants," Oliver remembers. The Lawrences were frugal by instinct and in order to save toward their sons' education, but also to teach the value of things—a lesson Ernest learned so well in the case of water that he could never tolerate a dripping faucet or any careless use of water. Water had been the difference between good years and those of failure—even, at first, with Gunda's family, whether they could stay on their land or give up and go to work for others. Carl had carried water too far as a boy not to respect its conservation, and Ernest had pumped from wells to keep the kitchen supplied, or to water small trees which otherwise would succumb to a dry summer.

Frugality was nicely balanced with the father's large sense of generosity—another trait that characterized Ernest throughout his life—and both parents were liberal with their time. No question was put off, and if an answer was not readily known, time was taken to find out, however demanding on the parents. Ernest's curiosity kept both busy until he learned to find answers for himself. Gunda thought his inability to get questions and statements spoken as fast as he could think them caused his increasing tendency to stammer, which became an embarrassing affliction when he was in the fifth or sixth grade. It was another thing to be teased about, but it never hampered his enthusiasm, cheerfulness, or the aggressive drive that worried his mother. "You don't have to go so fast," she remonstrated. "You have plenty of time." Stammering was no hindrance at spelling bees in which he, Merle, and a schoolmate, Katherine Lyboggen, vied for honors.

Before they were nine years old, Ernest and Merle became engrossed in electricity. They spent hours winding motors. Old dry-cell batteries were collected and, with holes punched through their zinc casings, were recharged in Mason jars filled with sal ammoniac. "When they were hooked in series, we got a lot of juice out of them," remembers Merle, "enough to run a six-volt motor." Verne Kennedy, who had graduated from M.I.T. and whose father owned the local telephone company, was a willing source of information about volts, ohms, amperes, and the like. He showed them *Electrical Experimenter* and *Modern Electrics* magazines, the ads in which were as fascinating as the editorial content. Spark coils, bells, buzzers, and motors littered the Lawrence house and the Tuve basement; a less devoted mother than Gunda would have been exasperated. The boys did not practice their piano lessons an instant beyond the required time, they raced through their regular chores, and Ernest seemed unable to get home from school fast enough to get back to his electrical apparatus. There were many "logical" reasons for staying up beyond bedtime. In vain did Gunda try to slow his pace; one might as well have tried to check his physical growth.

The boys' overriding interest and close companionship were interrupted in January, 1911. The success of Carl Lawrence with the Lincoln County schools caused a statewide demand that he be a candidate for the nonpolitical office of state superintendent of public instruction. Carl, who considered himself a Progressive Republican, left no doubt of his position in other than educational concerns in a stirring address at the 1910 Republican State Convention in Huron, after which he was referred to as the "La Follette of South Dakota." He won the election handily, sold his house in Canton, and moved his family to the capital, Pierre, and became a much respected member of the state administration. Though by law he could serve no more than two terms of two years each, the break with Canton as home seemed complete.

The shock of severance from Merle and abandonment of their joint projects—linkage of their houses by telegraph wire was the latest—was somewhat relieved by Ernest's anticipation of adventure. Not only was Pierre the state capital, it had been the first permanent settlement in South Dakota. An outpost fort against Indians, it had become a lusty point of departure for gold-seekers and adventurers, and a sometimes brawling trading post for hunters who had all but stripped the plains of their once great herds of bison. Though warlike Indians and lusty adventurers might have vanished with the buffalo, what would Pierre's present youthful inhabitants, all strangers, be like? If only he did not stammer!

Ernest anticipated even more eagerly the train ride halfway across the state; two train rides, in fact, for transfer to the Northwestern Railroad would be necessary to reach Pierre. He tried to conceive a plan that would permit him to ride in one of the locomotives—always so intriguingly alive with restrained power as they panted impatiently at the Canton station—with no success; that was taboo even for the son of a state official. He had to remain more or less immobile by a window in a coach, "because I'm your ma and I say so." The scenery was not very exciting, the past summer had been dry; even in midwinter little snow covered the parched countryside of the Missouri plateau. He could only watch and envy the conductor and brakeman, with freedom to move from car to car—even to the engine itself—and to get out at every stop.

Pierre itself did not seem very exciting, except that it was built on hills, or rather on a sometimes steep slope rising from the river bottom below the station, up Main Street toward the statehouse and on above it to the small residence on Summit Avenue which Carl had rented. There were Indians, too, but they scarcely resembled the erect, skin-clad, and feathered chiefs Ernest had envisioned. They lounged lazily in groups near the station, or on corners in the lower part of town. In that section, too, below the intersection of Main and Capitol Streets, were groups of boys who stared at the newcomers in their Sunday best. The statehouse was imposing with its high dome, and even the courthouse seemed larger than that at Canton; Pierre was about twice as populous.

It was at school, which Ernest had to start the day after his arrival, that scrutiny was inflicted on him—as only schoolboys can scrutinize a newcomer. He was not even allowed to take his seat without being introduced as the son of the new state superintendent! He stammered more the more he tried to control it. Even his usually ready smile was somewhat forced when he was questioned at recess and his prowess tentatively gauged. He missed Merle and Ollie, yes, even the bullies of Canton, who knew him well enough to avoid probing, and whom he knew well enough to know what to expect. He quickly learned that, since he lived on the hill, other young residents there could become allies in the presence of gangs from other areas: "The Flats" from near the railroad tracks, or "The Tigers," who were toughest of all. Some of the Hill boys considered him a sissy, for it soon became evident that he was serious and smart in the classroom, but he was not easy to tease successfully. He could smile and ignore taunts, or leave with the calculated necessary speed, if violence seemed imminent.

Ernest was soon tolerated, and then accepted, by Hill peers on pioneering ventures across the Missouri, or to Hilger's, or Snake, Gulch. Not very adept, he was sometimes allowed to participate in football games which were played in the streets where arc-light suspension wires served as goals. He played more regularly after he acquired his own

football, one of the few in the neighborhood, and could take it home if
he were excluded. After a few rough experiences in the Pierre brand of
pump, pump, pull-away, he became a respected adversary; one of his
long legs could suddenly project to surprise and upset an opponent trying to get through the line, and he was good at swimming in a river
pool deep enough for diving. He entered into many activities when he
would have preferred to remain at home with his electrical apparatus;
sometimes it was important to conform. He noticed that most of the
boys in his class wore shirts with detachable collars of a certain style,
and he told his mother that afternoon that she simply had to get him
"store-bought collars. I looked around the class and only one other boy
had homemade shirts and collars like mine." Gunda purchased the
proper collars. Another time he came home beaming with excitement.
"Oh, Mother, the boys really like me; they have given me a nickname."
Asked what it was, he answered with pride, "Skinny!" Gunda did not
think this complimentary, but he assured her that it meant acceptance;
all the regular boys had nicknames.

After about a year in the Summit house, the Lawrences moved to
Prospect Avenue, nearer to the statehouse, and directly across the street
from the courthouse with its wide lawns. Though a caretaker was likely
to chase the boys off the grass that had suffered after a particularly dry
summer, it often was a place for play, and there was a vacant lot between the Lawrences' and the old red Hyde house, where Frank Burris
lived with his grandmother. They erected poles with a crossbar, and
Skinny became adept at vaulting, excelling his less gangly companions,
as he did in running. The Prospect place, being on the hill, involved
no change in gang status; there were occasions when he had to stay with
members of the group and even use his fists, contrary to his instinct and
home training. His legs were still his best defense if he was outnumbered; his disarming smile, genial charm, and intelligence usually
sufficed to avoid conflict with a single, possible opponent. He quelled
scraps between younger, smaller boys in the neighborhood, particularly
if John, or a weaker neighbor, needed help, and was rescued once or
twice himself by Franklyn Hyde, a smaller boy who loved to fight.

Hyde had decided that there was merit in knowing the answers in
school, in never getting mad, and in being resourceful enough at games
to overcome awkwardness. To have his approval, as the best fighter on
the Hill, was in itself a status symbol with meaning even in other gangs.
One day, after a welcome rain accompanied by a fierce electric storm,
Franklyn picked up a fallen 2,200-volt power line and only miraculously
escaped death. His head, shoulders, and right arm were severely burned,
and everyone thought his fighting days were over. The idea was quickly
dispelled before his badly and permanently scarred arm was completely

healed, and he later became welterweight champion at the University of Minnesota.

Skinny further demonstrated his prowess by fashioning a canoe of canvas stretched over barrel-hoop ribs held in place by a single long board. After he had proved its worth on Capital Lake, everyone wanted to join in paddling, but the fun for Ernest had been in making it. As his special friends, the Wegner boys and Bob Hipple, the mayor's son, all had flocks of barred homing pigeons, Ernest developed his own good flock, kept in coops he built near the alley at the back of the deep Prospect Avenue lot. He soon had the largest male of all, one that had been despised by most boys and that Ernest had picked up cheaply because of leg injury. He had noted the bird's other qualities and reasoned that the limp would not affect him as a breeder, and soon he had an enviable flock of young birds.

As relationships with his peers became settled and could be taken for granted, Ernest became bold enough to refuse some pastimes for solitary pleasure with electrical apparatus brought from Canton. One afternoon his mother, who worked at the statehouse for a time, came home to find wires in holes drilled through her old dining-room table and a telegraph key screwed firmly onto it. Ernest persuaded Bernard Murphy, who lived next door, to let him install a sounder and key, run wires between the two houses, and practice code with him. Soon coils, batteries, and wires again cluttered Gunda's kitchen, and Ernest's experiments were seldom solitary. Even younger boys nearer John's age, like Francis Pinckney and Joe Byrne, the governor's son, hung around the kitchen in awe—and sampled the zwieback always available in a big barrel; no other house had such a luxury. Skinny constructed a motion-picture machine from odds and ends collected from the dump, or by trade, and entertained an increasing number of boys after word of it got around.

He was always on the lookout for jobs by which he could add to his savings or purchase desired equipment. Wire, less easy to come by than it had been from Canton linemen, had to be purchased. There was often snow to shovel in winter, and he had a regular job taking a neighbor's cow to and from pasture. In good weather he could almost always find someone for whom to caddy; he had learned enough golf from his father to make helpful suggestions to many of the beginners for whom he worked. He delighted in increasing his savings, but never hesitated to spend for something important, which usually meant an item of electrical apparatus. Candy, toys, and games were extravagances he easily avoided; he had little time for the usual toys in any case. He was allowed as much electric current as he wished, though the Lawrences were as thrifty in its use as they were with water.

In addition to jobs for money, there were regular household chores, which, however much Ernest begrudged the time away from "important things," he carried out quickly and cheerfully—whether the regular Saturday housecleaning, clearing the sidewalks of snow, or carrying out ashes. He seldom had to be urged to perform regular duties. His industry and sense of responsibility gained as much approval as his curiosity and inventiveness. Only once in the four-year period at Pierre was he severely disciplined. The neighbor whose cow was Ernest's charge reported her missing long after she was due back from pasture. Ernest was not present to answer, and, since it was so unusual for him to neglect duty, Gunda became worried. He came home very late from an expedition across the river at old Fort Pierre; the cow had been completely forgotten. Father Lawrence, who considered responsibility almost as important as integrity, spanked Ernest for the second and last time. Gunda discreetly left the house during the chastisement; she was so relieved at Ernest's safe return that she could have forgiven anything.

She frightened her family badly herself one afternoon; John found her unconscious on the back porch—and ran crying to neighbors for help. She had regained consciousness by the time Ernest and his father arrived, but was still pale. She had been nearly overcome by gas escaping from the range in the closed kitchen, but somehow had reached the porch and fresh air—which undoubtedly had saved her life. The incident had a profound effect on Ernest, who had seen his father running toward the house, and a crowd of neighbors in the yard. The terrible intimation that his mother was in danger almost overcame him, and, in spite of the sudden seeming collapse of his stomach, he almost caught up with his father. Mother was not taken for granted for some time afterward; life without her was beyond imagination.

Ernest knew that his father had been frightened, too; it was not running that had paled his face. When weather prohibited regular golf and tennis, Carl kept his body hard and trim with walking and exercise. He only occasionally smoked cigars, and never in public where it might be a bad example. Few people knew that he usually had a bit of chewing tobacco between jaw and cheek; no one ever saw him chew it, and no one ever saw him spit. Perhaps his mother's accident and his father's betrayed concern inspired the first conscious assessment Ernest made of his parents. He felt, as much as saw, his mother's real beauty, and sensed, too, her great love and whatever else it was that made her the heart of the family. He had taken for granted, too, those qualities in his father that made him an honored and important man in the state government, and the family anchor. He realized that it was more than position, or mere democratic custom, that caused his advice to be sought by the governor, Senators, and Congressmen. Never awed by title or position, and as much as he valued achievement, Carl impressed upon his sons that character was most important. Pierre was much less oriented toward religion than Canton, yet Carl, unostentatiously but with conviction, upheld his principles and regularly attended the Lutheran church—though it was not on the Hill. He was never profane, nor was Ernest, whose strongest expletives were "Sugar!" and "Oh, fudge!" Ernest was confirmed at the Lutheran church in the spring of 1914—and got his first long pants.

What loomed most importantly that spring, however, was the possibility that he could be cured of stammering. In an educational magazine, he saw an advertisement for the Millard School of Stammering, in Milwaukee, which promised a free course to any stammerer who sent in a certain number of names of students with speech impediments. He asked his father for a list of school superintendents in the state and wrote to each for names in his jurisdiction. By the end of the summer he had more than the required number and the promise of the course for himself, free of charge, the following summer.

Before summer arrived, however, the Lawrences were back in Canton. Superintendent Lawrence's second term would end with the year 1914. In order to accept again the position of city superintendent of schools for Canton, he resigned the state position early, and the family moved in November. Skinny became Ernie again and entered the eighth grade with old friends. "Gosh," he said, "I'd like to go to school sometime where my dad isn't the boss."

The return to Canton was not the happy homecoming Ernest had expected, only because it did not include the familiar house that had been home. The Lawrences had to accept a small apartment over a downtown store, a poor, cramped place for electrical experiment and, more disastrous, beyond the possibility of telegraphic connection with the Tuve and Overseth houses. Those houses were as familiar as they had been, except for the growth of trees around them, and Ernest was as welcome as ever; with Merle and Ollie there, it was homecoming. Nothing seemed to have changed in the relationships, nor in their appearances. Canton, too, was much the same; the major difference, the new Carnegie Public Library.

It was Merle who suggested a solution to the telegraph problem, and providence that made the solution possible. Wireless telegraphy was the answer, and providentially there were wonderfully mysterious boxes in the Tuve basement that supposedly contained wireless equipment. Professor Tuve and other citizens had organized a boy scout troop soon after the Lawrences' departure for Pierre, and had produced a minstrel show to raise money for uniforms. The show was so successful that a substantial sum remained after each boy had his outfit, and it had been decided to invest the remainder in wireless equipment to provide worthy occupation for winter months. By the time the boxes arrived, interest had subsided, and they had remained unopened in the Tuve basement, strictly taboo to Merle's curiosity.

With Ernie's persuasive help, permission was obtained to open them and attempt to put their contents to useful purpose. No unearthing of buried treasure could have been more exciting than the revelation of those contents. There were such things as patented detectors, a "Wollaston wire," a "Radiosen," and other items of glamorous trade name equipment. Professor Tuve's fear that an aerial over his roof would attract lightning was overcome by digging the ground into the earth to a depth of thirteen feet. It did not matter that they were unable to make some items function, even after poring over such journals as *The Wireless Experimenter* and *QST*, which supplanted electrical magazines. Without them they were able to pick up intelligible code with galena and cat's whisker. Ernest had mastered Morse code in Pierre, and Merle soon picked it up. The only flaw in their delight was that they still could not communicate with each other, nor could they respond to code from elsewhere. It became imperative that they acquire sending apparatus, and a second receiver.

Ollie persuaded his father, who liked nothing better than to barter, to drive them several miles into Iowa to bargain for equipment of which they had learned; much was acquired, including an interrupter, which magazine ads had persuaded them was a fine, advanced piece of equipment. Ernest thought he had solved the problem of attaching one end of an antenna to a standpipe near the Overseth house, but twine which a specially constructed, six-foot kite carried over the top of the standpipe always broke before the antenna could be pulled over after it. Not discouraged, they made a support of old gas pipe and two-by-fours, and, with the help of Merrill Williams and his father, erected it back of the Overseth house and hung a five-strand antenna between it and the chimney. That was connected to the newly assembled receiver in the attic. It never worked quite as well as the set at Merle's, but they could always receive time signals from Arlington, and sometimes ships at sea could be heard. Equipment for sending was still beyond their means, but they got to try a set after the exciting day they picked up signals from an orphan's home across the river at Beloit. Nineteen-year-old Christian Christiansen had remained at the home longer than most children, to help with the farming and run the light plant. He had built a complete outfit by himself, and right after Sunday school a few days after they had heard him, the three boys crossed the river to see Christian's outfit. They thought it pretty fine and after trying it hurried back across the railroad bridge to listen at a prearranged time; Christian's code came in perfectly, whether in Merle's basement or Ollie's attic. They immediately undertook construction of parts such as he had made, and they gave much thought to schemes for earning money for what must be purchased.

For Ernest, that had to be postponed for the summer; even more important than wireless was the determination to be free of stammering, and he largely succeeded. When he returned from Milwaukee, his speech was very precise, and most of the time he spoke without hesitation. What he chiefly remembered of the school in later years was that its concern for rhythm had involved dancing, frowned upon in Canton Lutheran circles—certainly by Pastor Henry Rasmussen.

Superintendent Lawrence thought Rasmussen too harsh with his own and his parishioners' children and did not always stand behind the pastor's statements if Ernest questioned them at home, though Carl firmly believed in the word of God as revealed in the Bible. His Bible classes were generally thought to be more interesting than the pastor's; religion was less harsh as Carl understood it. Belief was important, but absolute honesty, ethical conduct, and compassion for others were the essentials of its practice on earth, as Carl taught his sons and exemplified it in his own life—honest, simple, full of effort, but with room for wholesome fun too. Gunda probably would have been stricter by Lutheran tenets, but a principal rule for every Christian woman was obedience to her husband. What Carl said was final and likely would have been even without Biblical admonition.

There were boys, including Ollie, who had gone off to nearby towns to dance. Ernest had tried it only near Geneva, before Milwaukee, but he had yet to become interested in girls; there was no special one, though he and Merle usually gravitated toward Kalma Graneng and Palma Thompt at picnics, or other social occasions when it was thought necessary to pair off. A couple of times when Ollie's mother was out of town and Ollie had her car, they drove Olga Skartvedt and Polly Jewel as far as Inwood, Iowa—but having the car was more exciting than being with girls. Girls were somewhat awed by a boy who spoke of such esoteric things as tuners and interrupters. Ernest had few social graces as an adolescent, and was somewhat careless in his dress. He became less bashful as he learned to control his speech, and when he did attempt dancing, his pace was as fast as though it were a race. Al Swanholm, a nephew of Carl's widowed sister-in-law, visited the Lawrences when Ernest was in high school and asked him to get dates for a dance at Masonic Corner—"hell's corner," in the words of Pastor Rasmussen, who forbade it to his charges. Al thought Ernest a prude because he pulled himself straight and very solemnly said that he certainly would not go to that dance, and did not know the type of girl who would be interested in such a thing.

He rebuffed hints to take girls in the canoe he built after the Pierre model. He and Ollie carried it the mile or more to the river as soon as the paint had dried on the canvas, and found it a good one, but after that trial it remained on props beside the Overseth house. Sometimes in winter the boys went to the slopes near the river to ski—Ernest's skis were pine, with improvised straps for his feet—but this seemed to Ernest and Merle a small-boy pleasure, as were prolonged swimming and rabbit hunting. Ernest never shared his father's keen enjoyment of fishing as John did, though he occasionally joined him more for companionship than sport. None of the three friends found delight in the pool hall that attracted some of their peers, many of whom considered them, if not sissies, a bit odd—at least in their ideas of pleasure. The most fun socially was to be had in the Hi-Y group Professor Lawrence organized in the high school, particularly when they went to another town for a joint meeting or competition. A long-remembered Hi-Y excursion was one to Sioux City when Merle and Ernest visited the home of a surgeon in which there was what seemed the ultimate in wireless equipment: meters, heavy copper switches, a spark-gap beeper in a glass case, and real De Forest audion tubes. It was hard to think of the subjects of the Hi-Y meetings they felt bound to attend.

How to acquire audions, always expensively listed in advertisements? Would it be possible to make passable substitutes for apparatus that should be sealed in evacuated glass tubes? Money once more became all-important, and they spoke of little else than schemes to earn it. Merle got a job that summer working on a golf course Professor Lawrence had persuaded Canton men to lay out on land near Kennedy's cow pasture. Ernest spent the summer on the Overseth farm, except for a week of recuperation at home after absentmindedly allowing his team of horses to pull a wagon over his foot. He disliked farm work almost as passionately as he wanted the money it earned, for wireless equipment. Years afterward he spoke of farming as the only really hard work there is. So tired at the end of the day he could scarcely get himself to bed, he was certain, when shaken awake each dark morning, that he had just turned in. Work before breakfast, work all day, work after supper. No wonder farmers all wanted to build houses in town and let their children do the work. It seemed to Ernest that his only enjoyable times that summer were the occasional instances when he had energy enough to jump on a tired horse and gallop around for a few minutes. Uncle John Overseth, who considered farming the only worthwhile occupation, stated emphatically that Ernest would never amount to anything. "He can't farm worth a nickel, can't even hit the bangboard with an ear of corn. They all fall back on the ground. Now John, he's much better at it. He could amount to something."

Neither Ernest nor Merle made enough money that summer to do more than improve their receivers. The following summer Ernest preferred work on a concrete crew. It was hard, too, but only ten hours a day, and the pay was better. It was his hand that he hurt this summer, when it was caught in a cement mixer. When it healed, the little finger crooked away from the others, which did not disturb him. "See how handy it is for scratching the inside of my ear," he would laugh, with a demonstration.

However awkward he seemed at such ordinary tasks, he was clever with more delicate wireless equipment, and he could make Ollie's Maxwell run. Ollie's bargain-loving father had purchased the old car for twenty-five dollars somewhere. It was a wonder no boy's arm was broken, trying to crank it. Somehow in 1916 they managed to make sending sets, and even acquired secondhand tubes. They made cabinets out of mahogany and walnut scraps from Satram's planing mill, and Merle's set was assembled on a bench from an old rosewood piano. Ernie got his and Ollie's sending apparatus to work first, and the elder Overseths were amused that Ernest would tap out a message and rush down from the attic and telephone Merle to learn how well the signal had been received. But it was only a matter of days before Merle could answer in code, and communication by wireless was established at last. "Ernie never stuttered with the key; he had a good fist for sending," Oliver remembers. Then exciting news from warring Europe was received, and lucky guests listened to dots and dashes from submarines and battleships.

The boys became the talk of the town. Mr. Gemmil, the grain merchant, wrote for the *Canton Leader* about hometown boys transmitting across state lines, without wires and with apparatus they had made and assembled themselves. The article was picked up by other papers, and other stories about them appeared in Sioux Falls and Sioux City papers. Ernest and Merle were separated in their second year of high school when Merle transferred to the academy, but most afternoons, as soon as they were within hailing distance of each other, one would shout, "Hey, want to monkey wireless?" And each would run to his respective set. There was still much to be added or improved, however, and means to earn money for college as well as wireless concerned them both. Higher education was taken for granted in both families. Ernest felt that, if he were to have money enough for both, it would have to be earned by other than ordinary means.

He answered an ad for salesmen of aluminum ware that promised large commissions. Future salesmen, however, first had to purchase a complete set for demonstrations, at a cost of seventy dollars. Ernest and Ollie persuaded their parents to advance the money, on Ernest's argument that selling would not only be lucrative but valuable training in meeting the public. The demonstrator sets did not arrive in time to permit much effort that summer, but Ernest was enthusiastic about an early start the next year, and the possibility of a "small fortune." He had learned that most of the countrywomen were sympathetic and eager to give advice—which taken gracefully paved the way for sales. His first cake-baking demonstration was a complete failure because he had forgotten the baking powder. But his chagrin over his "flatter than a platter" cake was quickly salved by maternal advice, and purchases enough to convince him that farm and construction jobs were a waste of time and effort.

It was not lack of money for high-priced equipment that brought wireless construction to a halt. When the United States entered the war, amateurs were requested to shut down sending sets. The boys reluctantly obeyed, but continued to listen with their receivers. Much of what they heard was exciting; Merle actually copied the German declaration of war against the United States from Hanover before it reached Canton otherwise. A few days after they had stilled their senders, Professor Tuve appeared in the basement, horrified to find them listening.

"When the President says something, you obey!" He ordered everything dismantled and packed in cases he himself sealed. Ernie and Ollie dismantled their sets, too.

The boys' inventive brains were not long idle; dogfights over the Western Front had aroused interest in aviation, and Ernest and Merle constructed wings hinged to a ring which could be fastened around a young body. Loops and grips enabled extended arms to manipulate wings. They tried the device on the golf course, taking turns jumping from the rear seat of the Tuve car moving at thirty miles an hour. Each was certain he had been suspended in air for a few seconds at each attempt, and each thought another try would extend the time. There was little agreement from the large audience that gathered, first children, then older boys and girls, and finally, adults. What would they be up to next?

Plans for making a fortune from sale of aluminum became another war casualty because of restrictions on the metal. In despair Merle and Ernest decided that all that could be done was to help get the war over with as soon as possible. When school was out that 1917 spring, they went to Sioux City to enlist in the army—without notifying their parents. It was neither the first nor the last time that Ernest was told he was too young. When his parents heard about it, they were careful not to ridicule but to congratulate the young man for patriotic motives. Ernest thought it stupid they had not been accepted; they certainly could be useful as wireless operators. They were forced to think of other things, to understand that there were insurmountable deterrents, even for ambitious and resourceful young men. "We sort of grew up that summer," Merle remembers.

Ernest took more than the required number of courses in school that year. Gunda thought he still was trying to proceed too fast with his schooling, as with everything, however she admired scholarship. He caught her about to tell him that he was born grown up, and made her laugh—after which she managed to reiterate that there was no reason to continue growing too fast and to be in so much of a hurry.

Carl tried to arouse greater interest in his son for sports, but Ernest thought there was no time for more than a minimum of play until after college. He played occasional tennis with his father, and had been pressed into service as a substitute tackle on the undermanned high-school football squad. Tall and rangy enough, he was too light to be effective and was overpadded before a game to make him look stockier. His reward for the effort was a blow that left a solid, small lump on his forehead for the rest of his life, though at the hairline it was scarcely noticeable. He was glad when the season was over, and he did not attempt basketball or baseball—though the latter was a favorite with his father, who as star pitcher of the Athenian team had broken his arm in a game with the Canton Merchants. Ernest calculated that time saved from extracurricular activities, and devoted to study, could cut a year from the usual high-school four, and help compensate for the extra years of medical school.

Ollie was able to persuade him to join in taking John and a group of younger boys to a big Y.M.C.A. encampment at Geneva, Wisconsin. He enjoyed it until the main event, which was a thunderous oration by the celebrated John R. Mott, whom Ernest thought far surpassed Pastor Rasmussen in the depiction of life as a dismal affair. When the evangelist in his tirade harangued the audience on the evils of dancing, Ernest said "Oh, fudge!" and walked out. His companions followed him; Ernest took them to a dance. They went to Yerkes Observatory and Chicago before turning homeward, John and young Chuck Barrett trying to keep up with the older boys, and marveling at Ernest's confidence and audacity. He even knocked on the door of the director of the Observatory, to get his questions answered; he was as bold and curious at the Art Institute and the Lincoln Park Zoo.

As roustabout for one of the Chautauqua groups whose tent served as theater and lecture hall for a solid week of cultural attractions in outlying communities, he saw performances of standard plays and listened to musical performances and lectures—some more than once, as the tent moved from town to town. Main attractions were with the group for only a scheduled day in any one community, but might be billed with it again in another town. Ernest noted that a lecture usually seemed less important a second time; oratorical flourishes had less impact and what was said could be more readily assessed. He became critical of standardized thought, and listened for originality. He observed that the same high-sounding phrases won applause in each community, and that speakers took advantage of popular opinions that were peculiar to a town. Patriotic phrases were applauded everywhere, but harsh references to Germany were avoided in predominately German areas.

After school began again, it became evident that there was irrational anti-anything-German agitation even in Canton. Stories of Prussian atrocities were favorites, and it was not long before boys of German descent, who had been popular, were somehow suspect because of their parents' or grandparents' origin. Products with German names were automatically inferior; it was as silly as changing hamburger to liberty steak!

It was anything but silly to the Lawrences when otherwise good citizens succumbed to the extent of exerting pressure for the removal of German from the high-school curriculum. Superintendent Lawrence first ridiculed the notion as absurd; somewhat later he had to defend its study as essential for students whose college plans required two years of the language. Each resolute refusal to be influenced by bigotry quieted outspoken opposition for a time; Carl and his sons knew that agitation continued throughout the school year 1917–18, if not always openly. It was Ernest's third and last year of high school; only one classmate, Oliver Laxon, graduated in June, 1918, after completing the course in three years, though Merle accomplished as much at Augustana Academy.

The end of the school year only spurred anti-German factions; pressure was exerted on members of the school board to overrule Superintendent Lawrence and remove German-language courses. Handbills were circulated accusing him of pro-German sympathies, and of having betrayed the trust and friendships of members of the Board of Education. It was no longer sufficient to discuss and make his views known at Athenian meetings; Carl demanded a public hearing and resolutely defended himself and his principles, concluding by challenging anyone who thought him pro-German to stand up and say so. No one stood. There was silence which it was hard for Ernest not to break with applause, he was so proud of his father. After a sufficient interval Carl strode from the courtroom. His family were not alone in their admiration; members of his adult Bible class presented him with a leather-bound Bible.

Ernest learned personally, too, that all men are not always honest and just, that one may be blamed for another's mistake. He lost a job as a hotel night clerk because a patron who responded when called at a requested hour had gone back to sleep. Angry that he had missed his train, the man loudly accused Ernest of failure to call him. Because of this, another salesman, for whom Ernest drove during the day, also fired him. At the State Fair in Huron, where he sold tickets, he was scolded for calling attention to insufficient change given by another to a customer, thinking it an honest mistake—after which the shortchanger explained how to do it deliberately. It was not a very lucrative summer; he did not realize that it had been educational in knowledge of humanity. His thoughts on education were focused on admission to a university.

He knew that his mother considered him too young for that, though his age was not mentioned at home, at his request; he had been embarrassed at being considered young at sixteen to graduate from high school. He fully expected to be allowed to attend either Minnesota, Northwestern, or Chicago, as he usually had his way with reasonable desires, and certainly study at a university was reasonable. His mother was proud of the fact that her husband had graduated from one. Ernest and Merle filled out applications, and discussed which school might be preferable for premedical work. Medicine was still their most definite ambition, though to be a wireless operator on a battleship seemed pretty exciting! Ollie was already enrolled for the fall at the University of South Dakota in nearby Vermillion. Ernest and Merle wanted wider horizons and thought longingly of larger universities in cities like Chicago or Minneapolis.

Ernest would gladly have compromised on South Dakota and Vermillion after his mother adamantly refused to consider the desired universities, and had persuaded Carl that their son must not be allowed to overcome her instinct about it by reasoning. Ernest had to settle for St. Olaf College in Northfield, Minnesota, where he was offered a scholarship, though the state university would have been as inexpensive. Gunda could not be swayed this time; at sixteen he would be much better off in the atmosphere of a Lutheran college, named for the patron saint of Norway, than in a secular state university where worldly temptations might entrap a curious boy. In vain, Ernest argued: he would be seventeen by the time classes started; he had no interest in "worldly temptations"; he would have to go to a university later in any case, to become a doctor, or a good professor like his father. It was hard to resist him, but Gunda did. "I thought at seventeen he was too young to be sent into the wickedness at the state university," she later told an interviewer. Also, Professor Glasoe, who had been at Augustana for two years, was to teach chemistry, Ernest's intended major, next year at St. Olaf, which would be a link with home.

Merle, too, was disappointed, and in a far larger sense; his father died that spring. He would have to work to help support his mother, sister, and younger brother; his older brother, Lew, had two more years of university work. He promised to continue study by himself and get to a university later. Ernest's disappointment over his friend's misfortunes almost equaled his own at being denied a great university. But he refused to bemoan that which he could not change, and was his usual optimistic self when he left Canton for Northfield and St. Olaf. He promised his mother that he would go to church on Sundays, and his father that he would make the most of his talents in the halls of higher learning. "Remember," his father told him, "those who make a success in life are those who know they are not the smartest, but who are working hard to compensate for what they lack."

CHAPTER II

Young Man in a Hurry

[FALL, 1918 – JUNE, 1922]

The fall of 1918 was not an auspicious time for a young would-be scholar to initiate himself into the realm of higher education. No college in the country, it seems likely, could have presented the idealized peaceful grove of Academe Ernest and Merle had envisioned. St. Olaf was no exception. Classes were held, textbooks acquired, and courses prescribed, but study was difficult, even for a serious student. The fever of war was at its highest—American troops were winning laurels in France at the expense of casualties; young men in the comparative peace and luxury of campus life must be prepared. Ages for selective service had been extended in late August, and, during the first months of the college year, students of eighteen or over were inducted into the Students Army Training Corps. Ernest, just seventeen—still too young—could not draw the soldiers' wages the older ones received, but he did have to wear the uniform and drill and train with those who could. Added to this were the terrible flu epidemic, the rumored armistice and the real one, and the continuation of drill in spite of the cessation of hostilities.

Professor Glasoe, who a few years later was the only teacher to remember Ernest at St. Olaf, admitted that even the faculty was "kept agitated, making it difficult to keep individual students in mind." Glasoe's chemistry class provided the only instruction Ernest really enjoyed, "And I am afraid that it was about the only course that I studied," he later wrote. The records show, however, that he started well in both mathematics and English—he got B's in these as in chemistry. He felt that Bible instruction was a waste of time; it had been much more interesting under his father in the Canton Sunday school. Compulsory chapel consumed too many hours, and it seemed to Ernest that an inordinate amount of time was spent in military and physical training—drill, and gymnasium. He got a C in religion the first half year and just "pass" in drill and gym.

There were other distractions, too, that first term, during which he twice went home. In spite of the fact that his father had come away from the hearing on pro-German sympathies without a challenge and with increased stature in the eyes of Canton's more reasonable citizens, agitation against him had continued. And, to some of those reasonable taxpayers, the superintendent's efforts to get a new high-school building were less than popular. The old building, however, was badly overcrowded—for a whole term Carl had his desk in the hall so that his office could serve as a classroom. More teachers were needed; often, in addition to his administrative duties, the superintendent had to teach classes in physics, algebra, Latin, and German. There was no athletic field; the county fairgrounds had to be rented for contests with other schools. More important than the shortage of facilities was the fact that the outdated brick building was a fire hazard; even this seemed unimportant to many prosperous citizens.

At home Ernest sensed his mother's unhappiness for her husband and was proud that neither parent complained or revealed concern. When with either or both of them in town, he walked with pride. He talked with Merle chiefly about chemistry; it could be exciting. Merle was envious, but aside from laboratory work, perhaps had gained as much from home study as Ernest had from the disrupted St. Olaf regimen. Both felt frustrated and far from their goal of becoming doctors of medicine. For Ernest, at least, chemistry was a requirement—as well as a lot of fun. He played down any sense of disappointment in college except to complain of drill to Merle. With others he joked that S.A.T.C. stood for Saturday Afternoon Tea Club.

The war over, he felt that he might get more from college, but there was little change; drill and physical education were stressed as much the second term, and the general atmosphere seemed as hectic as it had been before the armistice, perhaps more, since there was no apparent reason for continuing the wartime schedule. At the end of his freshman year, Ernest's marks had fallen below those for the first term, from B to C in mathematics. He was graded only C in chemistry, as he was in English and psychology. More important at home than to him was the D in religion, though there was little comment about grades. He said nothing of his determination to continue education at a university where he would have more freedom in selection of subjects. What disappointment his parents felt over his lack of success at St. Olaf was overshadowed, and in

Gunda's mind somewhat compensated for, by preparations for another move from Canton, a move tinged with both regret and pleasure.

The conclusion of the war had made little difference to bigots who finally had forced the removal of German instruction from the Canton curriculum. In spite of this success, agitation against Superintendent Lawrence and reflections upon his patriotism continued—always behind his back. He had been determined to stick it out with dignity after the hearing, but the continuance of gossip even after the war, and failure of the school board to consider a safe and adequate high-school building, seemed indicative that his usefulness had ceased. He had discussed resignation when Ernest was at home for Christmas, though the possibility of a similar position elsewhere was not promising. Ernest had not protested, though it would undoubtedly interfere with plans for taking his sophomore year at a university; he was quiet about personal desires in the face of his father's problem. That parental convenience had priority was unquestioned. The university could be postponed if the family needed financial assistance. He declared for the first time that he was young enough to wait. Schemes for earning sufficient money to encompass both aid to the family and tuition occupied, perhaps, too much of his thought until April, when the family problem was happily resolved. The state regents selected Carl as the new president of Southern State Teachers College at Springfield. It was clear vindication for Carl and an enhancement of his prestige; it also paid a higher salary. The family moved to Springfield soon after Ernest's return from St. Olaf. Happy for them, he had no regret over leaving Canton; Merle and his family moved that spring, too, to Minneapolis.

Gunda rejoiced not only for her husband but also because Ernest could live at home and attend the Springfield college. Ernest was careful not to protest, or to press arguments for a larger school, to the point of forcing a final decision by the unquestioned head of the family; his father did not reverse thought-out decisions easily. Ernest would wait until more than reason could be used to sway his mother. He left Canton before the family moved, for a construction job at the University of South Dakota in Vermillion.

Ten hours a day, six days a week on a concrete gang were still pretty hard at first, but his muscles developed and the pay was good. Before the summer was over he had enrolled at the university, paid the twelve-dollar yearly tuition, and rented a room for the coming year in a private home, a room he would share with Arthur Tobiason of Canton; his cousin Oliver had transferred to the state college at Brookings. The *fait accompli* was simply announced when Ernest went to the new Lawrence home in Springfield for a few free days before the start of the university term in the fall. However disappointed Gunda may have been, Carl was pleased that his elder son had shown determination and initiative.

Ernest brought, on his visit to the new home, a $2,100 Navy surplus two-way radiotelephone set he had purchased for $165, and in less than a day had it set up. Everyone in Springfield was aware of succeeding visits; a loudspeaker in a window of the Lawrence house broadcast phonograph music that could be heard half-a-dozen blocks away. The recorded music was also fed into his sending apparatus for other amateurs to pick up at greater distances. "There were wires strung all over the house," Gunda remembered, "It's a wonder we weren't all electrocuted!" Ernest wrote Merle of his "beautiful outfit" and that his enthusiasm for wireless transmission was greater than ever, especially since it had developed into radiotelephony that amateurs could understand and use. He urged Merle to get a set so they could converse; there was no doubt of the great future of wireless communication.

There was so much to be done, so much to be discovered in the frontiers of the "ether"! Who could tell, it might even be possible to transmit pictures over radio waves. He left the set with reluctance, even for long swims in the Missouri River with his father and John, though they were great fun, especially when they went upriver and rode logs down current, finally steering them into a bank for a lazy mud bath before swimming home. The brief vacation was much too short, though he was eager to get started at the university and another chance at advanced education, determined to find out if learning could be as exciting and rewarding as he and Merle had expected it to be under normal circumstances. He had to give up wireless again. He couldn't accomplish all he desired if he were two people, or find out all he wanted to know! He protested having to pick up wires in the hall at home, and having to put his room in his mother's idea of order before he left. It would just take that much more time from more important work when he came home some Saturday—Vermillion was only about fifty miles away.

Ernest's obsession with lack of time continued to be a goad when he entered the University of South Dakota in the fall of 1919; there was that first year of hectic college life to make up, even though it was credited as complete and he was a full-fledged sophomore. He knew that he had learned little, except perhaps in chemistry, and he had no idea of merely completing the required time; he wanted to learn, to know, whatever he became after college. Medicine still seemed the most worthwhile profession, though teaching, so honored by his forebears, could be made more interesting than he used to think possible, and would take less time before he could undertake its practice. He had seriously considered radio as a career; it had received such impetus during the war that it would be an exciting field—one might go a long way advancing that. Success as a goal, in whatever field, had never been questioned, but neither had service to humanity, and the possibility of contributing to health, perhaps even of understanding baffling disease and discovering remedies for it, could be as adventurous as radio. Besides, there was no wireless equipment of any kind at U.S.D.

He decided on a premedical course—flexible enough to permit change. Chemistry was his first choice as a major, followed by mathematics. German, even at the university, was frowned upon, so French was elected as a language. Military drill was required for another year and provided $30 a month, now that, at eighteen, he was a proper S.A.T.C. recruit. To improve his speech further, he enrolled in public speaking that first term, and, to add further resistance to stammering, in a course called "Voice."

He and Art Tobiason fixed up their room in "collegiate" fashion, hanging pennants on the walls, and Ernest put his growing collection of "worthwhile" books, bound in red Fabrikoid, on a shelf over his table. He took snapshots of his landlords, "my second family," and sent them to Springfield. He dismissed fraternities as frivolous and undemocratic, though he was sought by those considered best. "We knew he had brains," his contemporary Ed Dwight remembers, "and figured our chapter could use a few." He did join the Y.M.C.A. His mother would be happy about that and perhaps less worried about evil influences at the bigger school.

There were many he knew among the students, from Pierre as well as Canton. He attended the get-acquainted party for new students, and had seventeen signatures on the card declaring who he was and asking in large print "Who Are You?" before getting that of Ruby Patterson, after which he sought no more names. He squired Ruby to Dakota Hall after the party, the first of many times he was to walk with her to her dormitory. There was something about her that made him stammer as he had not done since Milwaukee. In the days that followed, he walked to the river's edge to practice speech with pebbles in his mouth as Demosthenes had done in ancient Greece.

But not even Ruby—whose company was so exciting that Ernest wrote ecstatically, "She's SOME girl," to Merle, who had entered the University of Minnesota—prevented concentrated attention to his courses. He finished the first term with A's in chemistry and math, and B's in both French and public speaking. His efforts at voice merited his only D; he even managed a C in military drill. He dropped public speaking and voice the second term, substituting a second chemistry course in which he also earned B, and with effort managed to get B in military drill, so that the second report he sent home had all A's and B's. All of his junior and senior grades were A's. "Fine work, Old Man, to get A's in all your subjects: if you were at this U you'd be hailed from one end of the campus to the other," Merle wrote from Minnesota.

But he was in no sense a "grind." He quickly grasped the subject at hand—if he was interested—and, after sophomore drill, never took a course he considered a waste of time. He developed habits of study and concentration that enabled him to learn without any sense of tough work, and after a few weeks there was time for speculation, and a hunger for more than his courses offered. "Some gal" though she might be, Ernest could not be wasteful of time even with Ruby, for whom he usually walked too fast when they went riverward. Canoeing was fun, as were discussions common to intelligent young people attracted to each other. From Ruby's letters, it seems that he did a good deal of sermonizing on such subjects as waste of time, worthy goals, jealousy, fidelity, and promiscuous necking. His ideas of good and bad appeared fixed, without gradations between those limits.

On several weekends Ernest went to Springfield. At least once the first year at U.S.D., he and Art Tobiason hiked the sixty-odd miles from Vermillion to Springfield along the Missouri River, but usually he hitchhiked along the road, striding rapidly between rides that sometimes merely lasted from one farm to another, or to a nearby town. He never just waited for a ride, any more than he could dally between classes on the campus. He may not have been exactly certain just where he was going in life, but he was determined to waste no time in getting there.

He toyed with the idea of taking his radio equipment to Vermillion, but decided instead that the university should have an outfit of its own. The more he thought about it, the more it seemed a necessity, if the university was to be up-to-date; Merle had written of fine equipment at Minnesota. He left home earlier than expected one Sunday, forgetting to pick up wires in the hall, and marched off for Vermillion, formulating plans and often forgetting to signal for a ride when a car approached him. He decided that Dean Lewis Akeley of the College of Electrical Engineering would be the logical person to understand the importance to the university of wireless communication. The dean, considered a "rare bird" by many students, was an independent individual to say the least. Ernest had listened to an amusing lecture by Akeley, director of the Student Army Training Program. He knew that, like his father, Dean Akeley had suffered abuse during the war for his insistence that all things German were not evil because of hostilities. Indeed, Akeley's hearing had been more like a trial, as though he himself were a German spy.

Ernest did not find Lewis Akeley free until Monday afternoon, but then found him in a receptive mood, as, with little stammering, he proceeded to argue the wisdom of university interest in all forms of wireless communication, and its future importance. His enthusiasm was so infectious, and his presentation of the subject so sound, that the dean was tempted to grant funds then and there for the purchase of at least minimum equipment, for Ernest had clear, written outlines of what could be had for various sums, and what might be accomplished in each case.

Lewis Akeley, however, was much more interested in the persuasive young man who had prepared his case so well, and who obviously had scientific curiosity, than in any scheme for wireless. He put the impetuous young man off until the following day and went home to enthuse about Ernest Lawrence to his wife, wondering aloud repeatedly why a student with such natural scientific interest was in neither physics nor electrical engineering classes. He had never been so impressed with a student, at first meeting, in his long career. Myra Akeley knew better than to ask her husband why he didn't invite Ernest; Dean Akeley had a solid rule against proselytizing; if a student did not realize what could be learned in his classes, that was the student's hard luck. Before their next meeting Akeley looked in the registrar's file and noted that Ernest was a premed, that chemistry was his science, and that he was doing well in mathematics. When Ernest later entered his office, Akeley asked, with a twinkle in his eyes, if he had not understood Ernest to say that his ambition was to "advance the new science of wireless" and perhaps become an operator on a battleship.

Ernest, convinced that he had succeeded with the dean the previous afternoon, was nonplussed for only a moment before explaining that medicine had always seemed the most worthwhile field, but lately he had wavered between that, wireless, and the high profession of teaching; that no wireless course was offered at the university, and that the premed course could easily be adapted to preparation for a teaching career. Akeley asked if he did not think physics would be helpful in pursuing wireless. Ernest confessed that he had studied, a little, in high school, under his father, but doubted that he had the ability to accomplish anything in physics. Dean Akeley noted that this was the only indication of doubt the young man had revealed. He granted $100 from engineering funds for the purchase of radio equipment and allotted space in the attic of Science Hall for the installation.

Ernest's impatience until the apparatus arrived in Vermillion was contained by work beyond assignments in his studies, so as to have more time when the equipment did come. He also tried to interest other students in working on the project and found one, Louverne Beaumont, who had been a naval wireless operator during the war; others had nothing to offer but the interest Ernest's enthusiasm aroused.

The receiving apparatus proved to be good, the sending equipment quite weak. Ernest tried everything he could think of to improve the sending and further enhance the receiving device. Various types of aerial were constructed and tried. Coils were wound and rewound. Often, long after others had gone to study, or for dates, Ernest continued to "tune" for signals from distant areas. Reception was usually better near midnight, and Ruby, that girl of girls, discovered that a date with Ernest often consisted of little more than sitting nearby while Ernest worked over the set, quietly, until the search was successful and he would call excitedly that he had code from Mexico, a ship, even Paris, Nauen or Hanover, Germany. It was frightening and exciting for her at first, when he displayed the pyrotechnics of sending, the rotary spark gap beating out a staccato, and sparks playing around the metal ceiling of the room.

Ruby was not the only one impressed by the emanations of the apparatus; Chuck Barrett, an amateur of Vermillion—who had been with Ernest on that 1917 trip to the Y camp at Geneva—remembers that when the university transmitter was in operation, no one in the Vermillion environs could pick up anything else. Young Ed Freeman of Elk Point, who had a fine amateur set, often engaged in code conversation with Ernest and later went to Springfield to meet him. Amateurs within range recognized Ernest's "fist" before he gave his name, it was so individual. Something of his "jubilant vigor" came through with the crisp code, Barrett remembers. The sending outfit was brought up to the one kilowatt legal limit for university stations in 1920, and was given the call letters 9APC. Dean Akeley had seen enough to know that wireless could be an exciting and worthwhile feature of the science department with one like Ernest in charge, and left it pretty much in his hands.

Akeley was still more interested in the young man himself. He could not understand and was piqued that one so eager to learn and experiment had not registered for physics or electrical engineering the term following installation of the wireless outfit. He was convinced of Ernest's personal regard, and that his genius lay in those fields—and he was convinced that more than any student he had known, Ernest had genius. He so often fretted over the situation at home that Mrs. Akeley finally asked if her husband's rule against seeking any student couldn't be overlooked, under the circumstances, but the dean was adamant; a good man should know where he could get the kind of knowledge he needed without being proselytized. And who knew? Perhaps he was wrong, and Ernest had equal or greater genius for medicine; he often thought Ernest might be great whatever he decided to do with his life.

He may not consciously have attemped to influence the eager young student, but he often spoke in inspiring terms of the great men of physics. He made Heinrich Hertz's work seem great adventure, and his discovery that light and electricity are similar as important as the discovery of a continent. Did Ernest know that Hertz was the first to generate and receive waves by wireless? He recalled how he himself had witnessed the first exhibition of long-distance transmission of electric power in Frankfurt, and how this had inspired him to begin the organization of the College of Engineering upon his return to the University of South Dakota, from which he had taken a year's leave in 1890 to study at Leipzig. He told of the controversy over Einstein, whose bold theories opened new vistas; of another Ernest, Sir Ernest Rutherford, also a country boy, who had won the Nobel Prize for his exciting experiments.

Rutherford had left New Zealand for the Cavendish Laboratory at Cambridge in 1895, the year often considered the first of modern physics because of Roentgen's discovery of X rays. The next year radioactivity was discovered by Henri Becquerel, working with uranium. Rutherford then found that some of the natural radiation of uranium was similar to X rays. In fact he, and others, found three kinds of radiation: alpha and beta (streams of electrically charged particles) and gamma (like X rays). Studies of radioactivity led to Rutherford's formulation, in 1911, of the structure of the atom—not as an indivisible, solid particle like a minute billiard ball as it had been considered from the time of Democritus, in the fifth century B.C., but as a largely empty shell with a relatively tiny, electrically charged core which contained practically all of the atom's mass, and which was electrically balanced by negatively charged electrons orbiting around it, as planets orbit the sun. Think of Marie Curie, who first used the term radioactivity, and her discovery of radium! Must not such exploration lead to new concepts of the structure of matter? Did they not suggest tremendous forces in the tiny units which held everything in place, determining and maintaining each particular elemental structure? Could anything be more excitingly adventurous? Why, in just the past year, Rutherford had first disintegrated atoms with alpha rays from radium, and changed one element into another. True, it was not the gold that ancient alchemists had sought from lead—but who could tell what might follow? If the structure of the nitrogen atom could be altered so that it was no longer nitrogen but oxygen, could the transmutation by man of other elements be any longer thought an im-

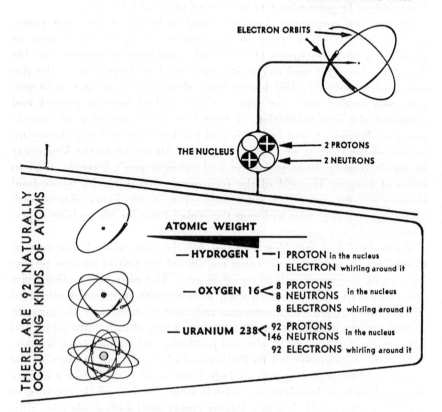

THE HELIUM ATOM ENLARGED
100 MILLION TIMES
WOULD LOOK LIKE THIS:

ELECTRON ORBITS

THE NUCLEUS
2 PROTONS
2 NEUTRONS

THERE ARE 92 NATURALLY OCCURRING KINDS OF ATOMS

ATOMIC WEIGHT

—HYDROGEN 1— 1 PROTON in the nucleus
1 ELECTRON whirling around it

—OXYGEN 16< 8 PROTONS 8 NEUTRONS in the nucleus
8 ELECTRONS whirling around it

—URANIUM 238< 92 PROTONS 146 NEUTRONS in the nucleus
92 ELECTRONS whirling around it

The structure of the atom. (*Lawrence Research Laboratory*)

possible dream? What adventure could equal that of searching for such long-hidden secrets of nature—more sophisticated and exciting to the mind than golden isles or new continents sought on the seas of a world? There was all of space—and the smallest particles that made up matter. Think of bygone explorers: Galileo, Newton, Maxwell, and those whose names are honored in scientific terminology: Watt, Faraday—the list was long. Often Ernest walked with Akeley to his home, was kept for supper and taught other things than physics: the value of a trained mind, for instance, with which one could learn in any field. But Akeley's lure was the great adventure of physical research.

Akeley thought the greatest experiences of his youth had been the occasions when explanations had dawned spontaneously on his mind, in country schools where all the grades were in one room, and the teachers explained little. He had gone from such a school to the state normal school at Brockport, New York, at the age of sixteen. He had won a master's degree in classics at the University of Rochester in 1887 and gone at once to Vermillion to teach mathematics when enrollment at the University of South Dakota was about three hundred students. He said he became a scientist in the laboratory of Wilhelm Ostwald, the German chemist, in Leipzig, but that the impetus toward education had come in rural schools, that it was in these that he had been inspired to become a teacher rather than to farm his grandfather's sixty acres, "As I'd have had to in older times."

The friendship of Akeley and Ernest developed naturally, and before the end of the school year the dean could refrain no longer from urging the study of physics on the young man he had never had in the classroom. "If you come back here and spend the month of August with me, before school opens, I'll interest you in physics. If I can't, I'll never speak of it to you again."

Ernest agreed without hesitation, though he had planned to devote the summer to selling aluminum ware, available again. Farmers' wives had money after profitable war years and he had arranged for rights to a large territory for which he had recruited students as salesmen. He could not himself continue to sell when he came to Akeley in August, but he could continue to direct his salesmen and earn 2 percent of their commissions. The venture was very successful; he not only earned more than he had expected in commissions, he parlayed a $125 Ford through a series of better ones, fixing each before selling it at a profit, until by August he had a new Ford, paid for from the profit of the other car sales, and before September and the regular term, he sold that, too, at a profit. Such industry left little time for Ruby, except for sales trips near her home in Gary, South Dakota, near the Minnesota state line. There was not even time to write as often as she did—letters full of her activities that often involved other young men. But Ernest apparently showed little jealousy or concern. He had two free weekdays that summer and spent them fishing at Lake Andes with his father.

Akeley had been right; Ernest became so engrossed in physics that the major portion of each day for six weeks was spent in intense study and laboratory work with the dean, at the end of which a year of sophomore physics had been completed. He enrolled in third-year physics for the fall term, in addition to chemistry, math, French, zoology, and economics. He found Akeley's classes as stimulating as the private sessions had been. Students who did not respond to the excitement of physics, as taught by Akeley, were kept awake by his pungent personal comments from which no one was exempt. "Mr. Smith," Dean Akeley once called to the baseball star of the university, "I understand you are a pretty good ballplayer. I suggest that you drop physics and spend your energies on baseball." Ferdinand Smith, who became a major-league professional, and Dean Akeley remained friends.

Ernest once received a different citation. "Class," said the dean, "this is Ernest Lawrence. Take a good look at him, for there will come a day when you will all be proud to have been in the same class with Ernest Lawrence." Another time Ernest was completely unaware of the dean's comment. He had had no sleep the night before, due to exceptional wireless reception, and had dozed off. The dean observed that others in the class were amused that the prize member should be so caught. "Never mind," said Akeley. "Let him be! He knows more physics asleep than the rest of you do wide awake."

The fact that he was considered a brilliant student did not affect Ernest's popularity. He was again urged to join fraternities, and again refused. He protested openly against secret societies in a state institution and went so far as to write state legislators and editors urging the wisdom of banning such organizations in South Dakota's university and colleges. Ruby had joined a sorority, whatever Ernest had to say on the subject, and was teased by her sisters for dating a man, however important on the campus, who not only was opposed to sororities, but often had to be phoned and reminded of a date. The girls knew, too, that he often changed plans for a movie he had asked her to, because of an important program from Pittsburgh, or some other place that just had to be listened to—not informing her until they were on the way to the wireless. Perhaps they did not know that he then sometimes forgot her presence in the room.

He did like to dance, and was considered good, though some girls accused him of running a race around the floor. He made no effort to be popular, or to cultivate social graces. Girls usually thought his smile charming; his open countenance, under a shock of light brown hair, was handsome enough, and he always showed interest in other people to an unusual extent, which was winning. Though he now wore glasses, his blue eyes were as direct in their gaze as ever. He was good company at a picnic, on swimming parties, and canoeing—when he had time. Ruby occasionally protested his attitude of proprietorship toward her; he did feel that she was his girl—perhaps because, liking her, it was easier that way than seeking a variety of dates. It certainly saved time. Letters went back and forth after dates, apologizing for arguments, hurt feelings, or just for explanation. For part of one summer there were daily letters from Ruby, in a challenge, though of course Ernest did not write so often nor so much. All through college they had steady dates.

He was elected treasurer of the Y for his junior year and was a prime organizer and one of the first officers of the University Tennis Association, and was in charge of construction and care of the courts. He and a friend reached the finals in a doubles tournament in June, but were defeated. In the consolation match he defeated his doubles partner. Tennis, which he had first tried with his father at Pierre, became his sport, the only one that aroused his enthusiasm as a participant.

He helped to organize a Boosters Club, for fostering university activities, and was promptly elected its vice-president. Naturally, one of the first items the new club undertook was drumming up interest in the university wireless. With its help, and Ernest's persuasive tongue, a "wireless telephone" was added to the equipment, and dance music by the best orchestras in the country was promised for the fall of 1921. He also stressed the fact that fine concerts could be heard, and that football scores from all over the country could be known almost as soon as made. He prophesied that entire games would soon be broadcast.

Through these activities Ernest was able to select better prospects for aluminum-selling crews for the summer. Raising money, taken in stride with everything else, seemed simple enough if one were willing to work—even though a postwar depression made selling more difficult in agricultural areas than it had been the year before. But, again, the second summer vacation from university work was profitable!

When Ernest had started at St. Olaf, his father had made arrangements with the bank to honor Ernest's signature on checks, trusting his son not to take advantage of his confidence that the account would be used carefully. Ernest added to it considerably during the summer vacations of 1920 and 1921, a good deal more during each of those months than his father deposited as salary. Carl, always overly generous, lent money when he thought it wise for the borrower and boasted that he had never been bilked by students, not all of whom were enrolled in his institution. As the account increased, Ernest advised investments. Apparently there was more than advice, for there **is** an extant typewritten note over Carl Lawrence's signature:

"On February the sixth, nineteen twenty-two, I told Erny that I wouldn't get sore at him for the way he handles my finances, or apparently bosses me."

To his curriculum for his senior year, when he also taught freshman mathematics, Ernest added further studies in economics, a course in geology, and an Akeley course in electrical engineering. He was the only student in advanced physics, and Dean Akeley tried an innovation. He handed Ernest the material and prescribed course at the first session. "You will be the teacher," he said, "and I the student. You will prepare the material for each session, give me the required assignments, and you will deliver the lectures, ask the questions, and prepare the examinations. You will, in fact, be the instructor." So it was for the entire course. Dean Akeley never interfered; Ernest prepared lectures for each of the required five hours a week and mounted the rostrum in the auditorium of Science Hall as the teacher, while Dean Akeley occupied a student's seat. He was so pleased with the quality of Ernest's lectures and talked so much about them at home that Mrs. Akeley often attended. Dean Akeley later wrote for the South Dakota Education Association *Journal*, "Someone once told me that my job was to discover Michael Faradays. I am sure I never discovered one. Ernest Lawrence discovered me, and taught me how to recognize a Michael Faraday when I saw him. I am deeply indebted to him."

Dean Akeley had used the bait of interest in wireless to lure Ernest into physics, and its study had greatly enriched his understanding of such communication, and how it might develop. But physics had ceased to be an adjunct; it was an exciting, demanding, and rewarding thing in itself, aside from what it could contribute to radio. Merle Tuve, who had caught up at Minnesota and would graduate the following June, was also deep in the subject. "I am carrying eighteen hours of what amounts to only math and physics," he wrote, in a letter urging Ernest to join him for graduate work at Minnesota in the fall of 1922. Though at Akeley's suggestion Ernest had already applied for a scholarship at the University of Chicago, with glowing recommendations from President Slagle and faculty members of the university, he immediately followed Merle's suggestion and applied to Minnesota. Chicago had a more formidable name in physics, but C. R. Englund, of Westinghouse, who had lent Ernest 50-watt tubes and sockets for the university station, had written, ". . . it won't be the same with [Robert] Millikan gone." If he were to have a choice, the presence of Merle at Minnesota made graduate work there seem ideal.

The issue was settled with the offer of a teaching fellowship at Minnesota which paid tuition costs and $600 and enabled him to work toward a master's degree. Perhaps more than Akeley's and other recommendations, Merle's insistence at Minnesota that Ernest was brilliant and would go far in physics had been the determining factor. Ernest thought so; years later he wrote, "Through Merle's interest in my behalf, I obtained a teaching fellowship in physics at Minnesota." He had been swept along by events, particularly that busy senior year at South Dakota, and with his course for another year determined, felt twinges of disloyalty to medicine, which he had not given a chance. Engulfed in his own and Akeley-inspired enthusiasm, he had more or less acted as though physics had been the goal from the beginning. True, he had never enjoyed anything more than the experience, but he occasionally wondered if it would be as exciting without Akeley. It would also be weighted toward enjoyment with Merle. He kept an unspoken reservation in mind: he could still switch to medicine, after a year of graduate work, without losing much time. He should be able to be definite about his career after another year, and he would be equipped to teach physics if it became necessary to interrupt study for a job. He had found teaching it interesting, too, though he could hardly expect students as stimulating as Akeley had been as a pupil.

He felt no remorse over wireless; that dream of operator on a battleship had been adolescent—anyway wireless, or radio as it was being called with increasing frequency, was in physics. He could always play with it, whatever his vocation. He did want to ensure its future at South Dakota. Without much effort he persuaded the dean to order radio-telephone and other equipment that made the station quite complete within Federal restrictions governing university sets. Now, not only were concerts received from elsewhere, but the university broadcast its programs within a radius of over 600 miles. During its first concert from the chapel stage, which was conveyed by wire to the transmitter in Science Hall, cards were written testifying to the good reception, and there was a phone call from Pipestone, Minnesota, thanking Ernest for "splendid entertainment."

He wrote articles of explanation for the school paper, and ensured continuity of interest by inducting underclassmen Charles Barrett, Ed Freeman, Ross Bardell, and Sydney Lawton as future operators. This, the first station in South Dakota, has continued uninterruptedly, though it is now known as KUSD.

Ernest received his bachelor's degree—with high honors—in June, bade the Akeleys and the university farewell, and returned to Springfield, eager to see what physics might have in store for him, eager to earn money in the months before he'd go to Minnesota, and eager to join his old friend Merle.

He was not often at home that summer, but, when he was, he worked at experiments in physics, just for fun, often going to the shop at his father's school to construct apparatus. Physics was getting into his blood.

CHAPTER III

Cut-and-Try

Ernest made the journey to Minneapolis—by way of Gary—in his old, fixed-up, Model T Ford as fast as he could, considering the amount of bumpy, rutted, or muddy dirt roads traversed. Even Ruby had been unable to detain him long in Gary, he was so eager to get to Merle's and the University of Minnesota. Merle's directions from the highway bridge over the Mississippi River were so explicit that he reached the Tuve home without any pause for inquiry, and for all the new environment it was as near home for Ernest as any except that of his parents could be. Though it had been three years, and much had happened to each, Merle was still without a doubt, "my best friend." Mrs. Tuve's welcome was more vocal and elaborate, after the interruption, but otherwise it was as though he had run in from across the street, as in Canton. Rosalind, as near to being a younger sister as Ernest would ever have, had grown up enough to be an undergraduate at Minnesota, where Merle's older brother Lew was already an instructor. Ten-year-old Mark was the only member of the family who had changed much. Ernest would be one of the family for the school year, though he would see little of any of them except Merle between hastily eaten morning breakfasts, unless there was time to come back for supper.

There were few formalities that first afternoon before the old friends were engrossed in their common old and new interests, wireless and physics. Merle had no doubts about the latter; it was so all-encompassing an interest that he had taken little time from it even for wireless, though he had rigged up a continuous wave and phone set at the start of the summer quarter and regretted, a little, that he had not been able to take a regular turn at the station. His extra units of physics and his jobs—singing at a church and library work—left little time for anything but necessary sleep. For more than a year he had taken only Friday nights off to hear Minneapolis Symphony concerts. "If I had had more time I wouldn't have spent it much differently," he said. "I never felt I was accomplishing so much in such a short time, and I never so thoroughly enjoyed myself, although they handed it to us pretty stiff sometimes."

He gladly took time to show his friend some of what, to Ernest, was a metropolis. The nearly 700,000 population of Minneapolis–St. Paul (the Twin Cities) was greater than that of all South Dakota, and in addition to stores, industries, and other enterprises that served it and the whole Northwest, there were art galleries, theaters, libraries, and the fine symphony orchestra whose concerts Merle so enjoyed. There were beautiful parks, drives, numerous lakes among wooded hills, and imposing residences. The sight one was most eager to show and the other to see was, of course, the tree-studded, 750-acre campus of the university, above the Mississippi River, already one of the larger universities in the country. With more than ten thousand students, compared with about five hundred at South Dakota, it seemed a city in itself. The facilities of the physics department made Ernest feel quite humble, and a bit doubtful of his ability to keep up with graduate students like Merle who, he felt, must be far better prepared than he for advanced work. And where Dean Akeley had been the only teacher of physics and engineering at Vermillion, here were many professors and instructors who devoted full time to physics. Merle introduced him to Professor H. A. Erikson, the chairman of the department, with whom Ernest had corresponded; to Professor John T. Tate, who had taken his doctorate in Berlin, and under whom Merle would work for his advanced degree. He met Professor Anthony Zeleny, who had had a year in Göttingen, and who startled Ernest, not with physics lore, but with a discourse on the evils of tobacco, and was pleased that Ernest did not use the weed in any form. But the professor who caught Ernest's fancy was William Francis Gray Swann, whose quick appraisal of the new student made that attraction mutual. It was Swann to whom Ernest was assigned for guidance as a candidate for the master's degree, and under whom he would study electromagnetic theory.

Professor Swann was a dynamic little Englishman whose love of music had nearly cut off his career in physics. An accomplished cellist, he might have become a distinguished concert artist. The issue had been resolved with the solution of a particularly difficult classical problem that "aroused my stubbornness," and led to an immediate job as an assistant demonstrator in physics at the Royal College of Science. Two years later he became assistant lecturer at the new Sheffield College. He had come to the United States in 1913, as chief physicist of the department of terrestrial magnetism at the Carnegie Institution, in Washington, and, four years later, moved to the Bureau of Standards. He had come to Minnesota as a professor in 1918.

Swann, though well versed in the classical, mathematical, and theoretical aspects of physics, was a progressive whom some thought radical. He had no patience for the ivory towerism which he said old-line physicists clung to in mystical pride; he had less use for those who said that the great discoveries had been made—that all that was left of the secrets of nature was the unraveling of lesser aspects of those discoveries. A pioneer in cosmic-ray research, he had early accepted the theory of relativity. He encouraged scientific rebellion both as a popular lecturer and in the classroom. In the laboratory he stimulated rather than dictated, and listened to every idea offered by a student without ridicule or disparagement. Let the inquirer find out for himself, seemed to be his motto. A born showman, and prophet of the "new physics," and the older physics in the new raiment, he naturally attracted bright young students, who found in him a scientific ideological and spiritual leader. If Swann was overly critical, as some physicists thought, it was of the conservatism of "old physics," never of the spontaneous enthusiasm of youth. He has been considered by others to have been a prima donna; certainly he seems to have exerted anything but a calming influence on any faculty of which he was a member. He was given to extravagant statements. "People are divided into two categories," he told Ernest. "Those who understand electrodynamics and those who don't, and the people who do understand can explain it to the others, but they aren't able to understand it." Such remarks did little to make him popular with his colleagues, but for young Ernest Lawrence, Swann fanned the spark which Akeley had ignited, and Ernest never forgot to credit Dr. Swann for his part in setting him on his course. Ernest received, under Swann, the thorough grounding in electrodynamics and magnetism that was basic to his future achievements.

In 1922 Professor Swann was reformulating his ideas on electrodynamics, and had just verified conclusions on unipolar induction with an experiment in which he had rotated a sphere in a magnetic field. He was eager to extend the research by rotating an ellipsoid in the same way, and he assigned this project to his new student as a subject for his master's thesis, after discussing the theoretical problem already worked out, concluding confidently: "Every two years someone comes up with an experiment in which he rotates a magnet or something and expects to get the effect he wanted, but he doesn't, and can't understand why. We'll shed some light in the darkness."

Ernest's task was to construct apparatus for rotating the ellipsoid in a suitable magnetic field attached to a variable motor, with gauges for reading results, and experimentally verify the theory. Swann, always available for advice, never interfered, leaving it entirely to his pupil. The laboratory mechanician, named Dane, was available for necessary help in construction, and another student could be relied upon when more hands were necessary, but the working out of the problem and the design and construction of the mechanism to determine the charging effect produced were left entirely to Ernest.

Ernest familiarized himself with what was known about the problem and designed apparatus he felt would determine the validity of the theory. Then the fun began for Ernest, in laboratory and shop, constructing his device. With the help of Dane, he machined an ellipsoid of steel twenty centimeters long and two centimeters in diameter at its thickest. He fastened this on a brass shaft and mounted bearings for the shaft in a brass tube, from one end of which the shaft extended sufficiently to engage a high-speed motor and an electric tachometer. He wound wire over another tube, enough larger to maintain, uniformly, the magnetic force over the ellipsoid. He attached suitable rheostats, a galvanometer, and an ammeter in such a way that he could keep an accurate check on results.

Swann pronounced the apparatus "beautiful" and called Professor H. A. Erikson, who joined in the accolade. Professor John Tate, in whose class Ernest studied electrons and their impact in gases, concurred, as did Professor Anthony Zeleny. That it had been accomplished in unusually short time was generally conceded, even by those students whom Ernest had considered better prepared than he for graduate work.

For him the work had been more pleasure than anything he had done—even with wireless. And the work of others in the laboratory excited him almost as much as his own. With all his industry and long hours, he took time to observe the exciting things going on around him, and every experiment had an element of excitement. He was able to make helpful suggestions, and other students quickly recognized his native ability; he, too, was gaining confidence in himself.

One of the other projects that particularly fascinated him is significant. J. William Buchta, also under Swann's direction, worked on a device for development of high-energy particles, based on the same "physics" which Robert Van de Graaff later used in developing his electrostatic generator. Buchta's device, made of glass, was too fragile to approach the efficiencies of later machines, but the possibilities so intrigued Ernest that he all but offered Buchta "a price" to turn the project over to him.

Swann was much interested in the possibilities of high energy and had written a paper on a device remarkably like that now called a betatron. He and Buchta never were able with their apparatus to develop the tremendous energies required for nuclear work beyond that initiated by Rutherford, who used radium radiations for energy—energy insufficient to affect any but the lightest elements. Physicists in several laboratories were attempting to devise means for the generation of very high voltages, and development of tubes capable of withstanding the required pressures. Swann, who sensed the theoretical possibilities, encouraged Ernest to consider what might be accomplished with very high energies, and how they might be generated. Ernest and Merle, also fascinated with the subject, discussed it often and at length—as they discussed most of the work of laboratory and classroom.

When construction of his apparatus was completed, Ernest settled down to long hours of observation that would confirm or disprove the theoretical conclusions of his problem. The experiment was repeated many times, the ellipsoid rotated again and again at varying speeds in different degrees of magnetic induction, and for each he noted complete data, from all of which conclusions were derived. The ultimate results were considered experimental confirmation of the theoretical formula. Ernest explained it in a paper for presentation to the committee that would determine whether or not he should be given a master's degree. Swann was proud of the work, and of his student. The other physics professors of the committee agreed, but old Professor George D. Sheperdson of electrical engineering, whose approval was necessary, turned down the thesis. "You'll simply have to educate the old chap," Swann told Ernest. "Your thesis is good, sound in every way, a real contribution. Beard him in his den. Of course he doesn't know anything about electrodynamics, and what he thinks he knows just isn't so." Ernest, who had no hesitation in approaching anyone for information, hesitated to dispute one who had been teaching at the university for thirty years. But Swann was insistent that Ernest do it.

Professor Sheperdson was a stickler for detail who tended to judge one by whether or not he smoked or drank. A sign on his desk confronted anyone who entered his office: "Please do not waste my time! Every minute of time that you take means that I must work that much harder at the end of the day to catch up." Swann reported, "He made you feel that you were sucking his life's blood if you opened your mouth at all, to speak to him." Sheperdson realized why Ernest presented himself. "It's wrong!" he snorted before Ernest could speak. "Where, sir? What part?" Professor Sheperdson thundered, "It's all wrong!" Ernest asked, in his naturally friendly manner, if he would be good enough to explain, and, after wasting a couple of minutes of the good man's time in silence, began himself to explain enough electrodynamics for the old engineer to enable him to understand the thesis which, to use Swann's words, had been "completely beyond his comprehension. Ernest had a dickens of a time educating him enough to get his approval."

Ernest not only received a master's degree, but Professor Swann also communicated the paper to the Philosophical Society and the thesis was published in the *Philosophical Magazine*. Thus Ernest, by that paper, first won the attention of scientists outside the institution where he was a student.

There had been little time to question whether physics would be the most desirable career, and little inclination to think of another. "It's the most exciting thing in the world!" he wrote his brother John, a freshman at Springfield State Teacher's College, and living at home. "Study hard, get good marks so you can go on to graduate work, whatever you decide to do. There's nothing like research, and nothing more worthwhile." John was planning to study medicine, and Ernest wondered if he too would change. He felt sympathy that John had so far to go before he could have the fun of graduate work.

For it had been fun, so much so that he had rarely thought of the usual forms of recreation, certainly had not missed them. He barely noticed winter sports and university athletic events; he attended, and enjoyed, one Big Ten football game. When weather permitted in fall and spring, he played tennis, usually with Iwao Fukushima who had the desk next to his, and whose talk about Japan was fascinating. He usually shared Friday night symphony concerts with Merle, and from him learned something of the art of music. He went to the Haugens' on occasional Sundays for dinner; it was Aunt Emma who had financially helped his father when he was a student. She had visited in Canton with her children, Lawrence and Elizabeth, whom Ernest liked. Lawrence was at the Naval Academy that year, though Elizabeth was present on those Sundays when Ernest visited. She and Rosalind Tuve were almost the only girls with whom he talked that winter. He saw more of Minneapolis driving Gregory Breit around in his Ford, than he had all year. Breit, who had just completed two years as a National Research Fellow at Leyden and Harvard, was to join the Minnesota faculty. Swann had introduced Ernest to Breit with rather extravagant praise and then left them in an interesting discussion. Ernest offered to show the stranger something of his new environment by car, thus holding him captive while questioning him about the Dutch university, Europe, and Harvard.

Merle had wanted to go to Cambridge, and Rutherford's Cavendish Laboratory, for further graduate work, but had accepted an instructorship at Princeton where he would work toward a Ph.D. Positions offered to Ernest were solely for teaching. He went to Swann's office to discuss them. Swann, who was to leave Minnesota for Chicago, was scornful of them. "You have no right to quit now," he said bluntly. "Your family must support you, if necessary, until you get your doctor's degree. You come along with me to Chicago next fall! Fill out the papers; you'll get in." Ernest complied, and before he left for Springfield had been accepted for further graduate work at the University of Chicago. He was glad that he was leaving the world of physical research only for the summer.

He went home by way of Gary and found Ruby much as she had been. They had corresponded regularly—at least she had. Certain that she was still his girl, he promised to see her frequently during the summer, and did, as he toured the area that had been so profitable to him as a salesman before he had surfeited it with aluminium ware. He attempted to sell radios this summer, not so successfully as he had aluminum. The radios were expensive, and farmers were not so well-to-do as they had been immediately following the war.

He was in and out of Springfield all summer. He saw much of John, who with Stanley Tobiason painted the wooden trim of the masonry buildings at Springfield State. When they had finished, near the end of the summer, they joined Ernest and Oliver Overseth, a teacher now, at Iowa State College, for a brief vacation. They pooled money for supplies, lowered the top of Ernest's Ford, and drove to the Black Hills in the western part of the state.

They pitched their pup tents near the Game Lodge that was to become famous in the next few years as the Summer White House of Calvin Coolidge, who had just become President after the sudden death of President Harding. The attractions at the lodge in the summer of 1923, however, at least for the four campers, were the waitresses, all college girls, including the daughters of the state governor. Also, there were often dances, which the boys managed to crash. They even organized an impromptu band for nights the regular musicians were idle, Ernie at the piano: "He faked it well if the noise was loud enough," Ollie, who was on the drums, remembers. Stan was a good player of both piano and clarinet. John played saxophone. They were popular with the waitresses; there was no one who whirled them around the floor faster than Ernie, who seemed to be making up for his rather austere winter months. They were not popular with young male regular guests, particularly with one boy whom they knew well, and who was thought to "be sweet" on the governor's daughter. He was suspected of instigating the manager's request that the four campers leave, and not return. It was time to return to Springfield, anyway, and it had all been great fun. There was time enough after their return for a few swims and mud baths in the river with their father and Dean Walter Ludeman of the college, and for a few sessions with the radio, which had been so neglected.

There were many friends at the station when Ernest left for Chicago, and he amused them all; as the train approached the station, he discovered that he had left his ticket and money at home!

The University of Chicago, in existence just over thirty years when Ernest enrolled in its Ryerson Physical Laboratory, enjoyed a reputation many ancient institutions could envy. No other university in history had been conceived and inaugurated on so grand a scale. President William Rainey Harper, chosen to organize it, had millions of Rockefeller and civic-minded Chicagoans' dollars to work with, and he used them unstintingly and well, for handsomely equipped gray stone English Gothic buildings, grouped around quadrangles, and for a very distinguished faculty. Determined that Chicago should at once rank with the best European universities, and be patterned after them, he placed at the head of each department a man distinguished in his field. "Harper's Raid," as it was called, with high salaries, and unusual opportunities for research and scholarship, brought to the initial faculty nine college and university presidents and other eminent scholars.

For the physics department, Harper could scarcely have chosen more wisely had he been able to divine the future; Albert A. Michelson became, in 1907, the first American scientist to win the Nobel Prize. Already famous for measurements of the velocity of light, and controversial conclusions on the ether, thought to fill all space and provide the medium on which light traveled, he was a living example of the American success story.

An immigrant of Polish descent, whose parents had fled persecution in Germany when he was two years old, Michelson had spent his boyhood in the Mark Twain-Bret Harte country of gold-rush California and Virginia City, Nevada. His realistic father had considered college impossible for any of his numerous children, but Albert, with the determination he later showed in science, won an appointment to the Naval Academy that cost his parents nothing and paid him $500 a year. It had not been easy; when he passed the examination but lost the appointment to the son of a crippled Civil War veteran, he appealed to President Ulysses Grant by letter. He did not wait for an answer by mail, but by foot, horseback, carriage, and train made his way to Washington. There he stayed on the White House steps until President Grant emerged with his dog, when Michelson personally made his plea. "I'll make you proud of me if I get the appointment," he told the Civil War hero. Further persistence won him admittance to the academy—by "an illegal act," he liked to say, as he was "eleventh of a legal ten special appointees."

Known at the academy as "Mike the Fiddler"—and as the best lightweight boxer—he ranked ninth among twenty-nine survivors of an original class of eighty-six. After two years at sea, he returned to the academy as an instructor in chemistry and physics, and here commenced his experiments on the speed of light. Five years later, granted leave of absence, he studied at Berlin, Heidelberg, and Paris under admired European scientists, among them the great Hermann Helmholtz, and later resigned from the Navy to become the first professor of physics at Case School of Applied Science. After further European study and a stint at another institute, he had accepted Harper's call to Chicago.

He spoke at the dedication of the Ryerson Laboratory in 1894, and in the speech lent support to Lord Kelvin's assumption that all great discoveries in physics had probably already been made, and that what remained involved more precise measurements. He later regretted this strange support for a prevalent notion—strange from one whose work seemed so radical to old-school thought, and whose experiments were fundamental to the theory of relativity and the newer physics. Michelson was not much of a theorist; he was imaginative in the design of precise instruments, and with optical problems—a superb experimentalist.

He brought good minds to the Ryerson Laboratory and made it outstanding. But he had little love for administrative detail and as soon as possible handed the details of administration and thesis work—he had never worked for a Ph.D.—to others. He avoided faculty meetings and social gatherings; at lunch in the Quadrangle Club he sat alone, dignified, handsome, and immaculately dressed. His recreations were the violin, walking, and tennis, though he would play chess at times. His own work was the important thing. In 1920, he had further distinguished himself and the university by making the first determination of the size and brightness of a star: he found Betelgeuse to be 240,000,000 miles in diameter, or 250 times larger and 1,200 times brighter than our sun. But the welfare of the Ryerson Laboratory was on his mind and he never failed to back a professor or to argue the laboratory's cause with the university administration. He had supported Robert Millikan's effort to augment staff and facilities, so necessary to attract National Research Fellows, this time in vain. Harper was dead and his successor's administration disapproved of the suggested expansion, and Millikan had departed. Michelson, who in this year of 1923 had received the high honor of election to the presidency of the National Academy of Sciences, was aware of growing interest in science, and knew that if Ryerson was to maintain its standing, its faculty would have to be kept at a high level.

Professor Swann was one of the new men recruited in 1923, though he had lectured during summer quarters when most of the regular faculty gave way to visitors. Swann had been a sort of spiritual leader of the summer group, which had included such men as Ludwig Silverstein, the German theorist; H. A. Wilson, who had been a Rutherford associate at Cavendish under J. J. Thompson; and theoretician Leigh Page of Yale. Perhaps the solitary Michelson had overheard the lively discussions of Swann's group at their lunch table, as they argued about how many molecules of perfume could be detected by smell, or how many quanta were required for visual perception. Perhaps Swann's appointment had been suggested by Millikan, who later wrote in his autobiography: "No one else in America or England, save Dr. Swann and myself, paid any serious attention to it [the 'Cosmic Ray Problem'] prior to 1931. . . ." In any case, Swann did not prove to be as popular with the regular faculty as he had been during summer quarters. Outspoken, no respecter of tradition, he was resented by some of those whose entire academic life had been at Chicago.

There were no difficulties with Henry G. Gale, acting administrator of the department, who had helped Michelson with experiments as a graduate student. A lovable man and a fine classical physicist, he was a good leader, but faculty feuds continued below the surface, and the somewhat flamboyant, irreverent Swann thought some of the professors were "scarcely touched by the atomic era." There was no rapport between them and Swann. Some of their irritation was directed at Ernest, who was called "Swann's Pup" by Associate Professor Harvey Lemon. Fortunately Lemon, in charge of undergraduate students, had little to do with Ernest's work.

Professor A. J. Dempster, an excellent mathematician and a brilliant, if somewhat conservative, physicist, was in charge of research. Though he kept clear of feuds, and was scrupulously fair, he felt that Ernest's thesis problem approved by Professor Swann was much too ambitious and difficult for one who had had only one year of graduate work. Both Ernest and Swann were insistent, however, and Ernest proceeded to study the photoelectric effect in potassium vapor. Two years before, Albert Einstein had won the Nobel Prize for his photoelectric effect formula; Millikan had done a beautiful experiment on the effect with potassium metal. Still, little enough was understood of the precise nature of the emission of electrons by light striking solids, in which the impact tore electrons from the atoms; would the same be true with atoms of a vapor? The photoelectric effect in vapors, experimentally demonstrated, would also have significance in view of certain theories of Niels Bohr, the great Danish physicist who had won the last Nobel Prize for quantum theory work.

Ernest's experiment had been tried previously, but there was doubt as to the accuracy of the conclusions in which some electrons counted were more apt to have been freed by light impinging on the apparatus than from vapor within it. After but a few days of paper work and a rough design of his apparatus, Ernest wanted to get to the laboratory and experiment on various methods for avoiding any possibility of spurious effects. Again he encountered reluctance on the part of Professor Dempster, who felt that much more thought and paper work should be applied before work on apparatus was undertaken.

Dempster had studied under Wilhelm Wien in Germany, indeed had had to escape, at the outbreak of the war, just as he was to take his doctorial examination. He then had had to spend two more years before obtaining the degree at Chicago. To him, understandably, the thorough, laborious, German methods were normal. A man so shy that he usually faced the blackboard while he lectured, without so much as a glance at his class, he was happy with the Chicago tradition of maintenance of proper distance between professor and student, as in Germany. He disapproved of women students in physics, and had just been embarrassed when Ann Hepburn (Hilberry), who became the fourth woman to earn a Ph.D. at Ryerson, apologized for absence from a class, because he had not missed her. It was natural that he, whose work involved measurements to "the last decimal," would not respond to Ernest's rapid approach.

"Often one has to work out a problem to the last, theoretically," Swann argued on Ernest's behalf, "but cut-and-try sometimes is more efficient than too prolonged theorizing." There were, Swann thought, too many, at Chicago and elsewhere, who spent months trying to work out on paper what a good experimenter might solve in a fourth the time in the laboratory. "It might have taken Ernest two years to work out his problem mathematically at Minnesota, and when he saw that, he went to work on the lathe and in three days had a satisfactory spheroid." Dempster reluctantly assented but balked at granting Ernest's request for a casting to support the apparatus that included a furnace for heating potassium. He said that an academic physicist should use apparatus available for teaching, rather than seek it elsewhere. Ernest made his support of wood, using asbestos to insulate the small furnace he made of brass tubing wound with resistance coils. He had to blow glass to form the vapor jet, reservoir, and Pyrex flask for liquid air. He used wax to seal the glass to an ionization chamber fashioned from brass, to which were fixed brass tubes to carry the beam of light into the chamber, and from it, after it passed through the vapor, to a photoelectric cell. Such items as a monochromator to control the wavelength, or color, of light used, a light source, and meters were all available in the supply room.

According to rules, long unobserved, a student had to get a key and permission to take something from the supply room, signing a card kept in the case containing the equipment. To save time, graduate students for many years, judging by the last signatures on sign-out cards, had each made his own key, as Ernest did. He entered the room at will, nights and Sundays, as well as on class days.

He was with Professor Swann in the hall one day when Professor Lemon interrupted their conversation to ask Swann's advice about an experiment, and Swann told him that a certain piece of apparatus would simplify his problem. Ernest, in his good-natured, helpful manner, offered to get the apparatus and went off at his usual rapid gait. He returned shortly with the item for Lemon with his key still in his hand. Instead of thanking Ernest, Lemon stared at the key, demanding to know where Ernest had procured it. "Why, I made it," Ernest replied frankly. "You made it!" Lemon stormed. "You should be expelled." Lemon went off without another word. Swann made a wry face and told Ernest not to worry, but it was not long before he was summoned by Professor Gale.

"Lawrence, what's this I hear about your making a master key? Don't you know that's a criminal offense?" Gale boomed in his gruff voice. "I'm sorry, sir," Ernest said, "I don't think it is quite as serious as all that." Gale, who must have known of the practice, scolded him a bit, got up from his desk, and patted Ernest on the shoulder, saying it was all right this time, but not to let it happen again. Ernest was not quite sure whether Gale meant not to use the key again, or not to let Lemon catch him again. Lemon would not let it go at that. He insisted that Lawrence should be kicked out of the university as an example, and threatened to take the matter to higher authorities. Swann protested; he realized that his position was awkward since he was nominally in charge of the laboratory, but, with eighteen thesis subjects to worry about, he had ignored the key situation. He knew that every graduate student had one, and he was sure that Lemon knew it. He did not propose to have his bright student pilloried for something everyone had taken for granted for years. He called a faculty meeting and suggested that Ernest collect everyone's key and personally present them at a later meeting; that if he could not get them all, he be required to answer when asked whom he had seen with keys who had not come forward with one. "Either you'll have to tell a lie, or we'll get all those master keys back," he told Ernest. That seemed a sensible solution to everyone, including Gale. Not even Lemon wanted to be forced to expel every graduate student, though he said he did not believe others had keys. Ernest soon collected twenty-six keys, and one student, who had become alarmed at the ruckus and had thrown his key into Lake Michigan, made another in order to turn one in. That was the end of the matter, though Swann bragged a bit over what he called his "judgment of Solomon." But America, and the world, had come close to losing a great physicist.

There were times when Ernest thought that he was not cut out to be a physicist. Problems arose at almost every step in the construction of his apparatus, each of which he ultimately was able to overcome, though some of them might have discouraged even an experienced experimenter. When he failed to get adequate light from quartz-mercury lamps, he found that he could from a type of iron arc properly resolved —and noted that even relatively small bands of wavelengths from the arc produced effects as large as those obtained from the whole spectrum of the quartz-mercury lamp. He had to calibrate his photoelectric cell with a thermopile and a galvanometer to be certain of the light intensity. He found it necessary to blacken the interior of the tubes leading the light beam to and from the vapor to prevent its striking the tubes or electrodes, and releasing electrons from sources other than the vapor. He made diaphragms in the tubes to keep the light beams parallel, and calibrated them. When his wax joints melted from the heat of the vapor, he devised an air blast to cool them. Trying one method after another, he finally got the apparatus so that a proper light beam left the monochromator, passed correctly to the ionization chamber—kept exhausted by mercury diffusion pumps—and on through a jet of vapor from the furnace and out through the second tube to a photoelectric cell. With some trepidation he prepared to take the first data from meters and gauges, after keeping vacuum pumps going to exhaust the chamber while distilling potassium metal into the boiler of the furnace. He adjusted the arc and monochromator to get maximum intensity of light and turned on the furnace, brought the temperature up to about 300 degrees centigrade, and adjusted the potentials of the electrodes. All seemed to be working correctly. As he made a final adjustment prior to noting data, he was bumped by a passer-by and the apparatus exploded.

It was a dark moment, and for a day or so Ernest decided he should have studied medicine. It would all have to be done over, if the year was not to be wasted. Perhaps Dempster had been right. Perhaps Lemon would have done him a favor had he succeeded in getting him expelled. Swann consoled: "These things happen; they should not discourage one." Ernest missed Merle and their intimate discussion of each day's events—had Minnesota seemed a more friendly place because of that? Less an apparent array of suppressive forces? He had quickly learned that at Chicago a graduate student was entirely "on his own"—he received his assignment, and only as a last desperate resort would admit to a professor that he was in trouble. No faculty names appeared on

Chicago graduate papers, signifying help from that quarter. Rarely would one ask assistance even of a more advanced student. A classmate, Norman Hilberry, summed it up: "You had to think for yourself and trust no one, not even God, unless He answered in the laboratory." Everything seemed designed to hold one back, at least to a slower pace than Ernest felt necessary.

Finally he accepted them—disaster and system—as challenges. Though he had neglected some other required studies for the long hours in the laboratory, and most of his three quarters at Ryerson had passed, he set to work again and was able to rebuild the apparatus before the quarter's termination. And it worked!

There were indirect sources of encouragement, besides Swann's approval, which were inspirational beyond any single experiment—from the oldest and the newest members of the staff. The great Michelson often came to his laboratory on Sundays and noticed the young student hard at work. "I see you're desecrating the Sabbath again," he'd say with a rare smile. And in a laboratory next to Ernest's, one of the new professors was more like a friendly fellow student than a professor. Ernest never asked for help, though he was full of questions about the experiment on which Arthur Compton worked, and there was also professional interest in Ernest's problem. Compton had experimented with the photoelectric effect using X rays. More important for Ernest, Compton welcomed him into his laboratory at night when both were at work.

Arthur Compton, at Washington University, St. Louis, the year before, had carried out his famous experiment on the scattering of X rays. But his discovery had been discounted by such authorities as William Duane of Harvard, and Ernest learned that students were not the only ones in physics with difficulties! Compton explained that one of the great aspects of physics was that every theory, and every experiment, had to stand further verification by other physicists to gain acceptance—a wonderful way to arrive at fact! Compton was endeavoring to extend and verify his experiment at Chicago with more precise instruments. His enthusiasm and persistence were an inspiration to Ernest; they seemed proof that experimentation was worthwhile, however difficult, and whatever the odds against finding what one sought.

Ernest could not stay away as the critical time approached when Compton's theory would be verified, or not. Compton stayed with it, regardless of time. Mrs. Compton brought sandwiches and coffee to the laboratory, and spoke encouragement from her great faith in her husband's genius. Ernest intuitively sensed the importance of the work, though there was not much faith around the laboratory in what Compton hoped for. Student watched almost as eagerly as professor during the final, crucial runs, far into the night—more than twenty-four consecutive hours were required—and with his own eyes Ernest saw the electrometer spot move in the right direction, verifying beyond any doubt Compton's conclusions. And Ernest joined him, as the professor literally danced with joy. Now known as the Compton Effect, its discoverer won the Nobel Prize in 1927. More immediately, he had inspired a young physicist.

"I derived tangible evidence and assurance that not all the important discoveries had been made but that science was alive and throbbing with growth, that I might indeed be able somehow to contribute in the never-ending search for knowledge," Ernest remembered later. And Arthur Compton, in *Atomic Quest*, was to write of Ernest Lawrence and this year at Chicago: "He had an extraordinary gift of thinking up new ideas that seemed impossible of achievement and making them work. In our conversations in the laboratory our relations had been more those of research colleagues than those of student and teacher."

Ernest found new values in the many hours he spent recording data indicated by various adjustments of his apparatus. Even Professor Dempster, always fair, admitted the success of his experiment. And the great Niels Bohr, visiting at Chicago, whose theoretical interpretation seemed inconsistent with Ernest's results, was brought by Swann to see Ernest at work on the readings. Bohr patted Ernest's back and muttered approval. The wonder of physics was further impressed on him after a discussion between Swann and Bohr pertaining to excited states of atoms. Ernest missed the conversation, but he eagerly watched and helped a bit, as Arthur Compton set up a cloud chamber test and proved his mentor correct and the great Bohr wrong. Compton explained that the discrepancy was likely due to differences in other experiments, Swann deriving his conclusions from the more satisfactory one.

Charles Barrett, following Ernest with the radio work at South Dakota, visited him in Chicago that spring and found him bubbling with enthusiasm. Perhaps for the first of many times, Ernest commented: "There's no greater work than research, and no finer title in the world than professor of physics." Barrett thought Ernest had no other interest, except tennis. As at Minnesota, his usual opponent on the court was a Japanese fellow student, Kuma Kawasaki, with whom he would correspond for years, after Kuma's return to Japan.

John and their cousin Oliver also visited Ernest but could not tear him away from his work, though Ollie wanted a night on the town. It was one of those times when exploding glass interrupted the experiment. Ernest would not leave the laboratory until a new glass part had been blown and waxed in place. John and Ollie gave up and went to bed. When Ernest finally returned to his room, and found both beds occupied, he went to sleep on the floor. "All he thought about, except for

now and then a question about Ruby Patterson, was work, and that's all
he ever did except for a little tennis to keep in shape," Oliver relates.
Ernie showed them an engagement ring he had acquired, and asked if
they thought Ruby would accept it and wait another year for him. "It
was the tiniest diamond I ever saw," Oliver reported. He teased Ernest,
saying that he could not find the stone. Ruby had written about the
possibility of a year's journey around the world on a "floating university."

Ernest realized that it was going to take another year to get his Ph.D.
He had completed his experiment, but had not had time to write his
thesis on it properly. He had somewhat neglected German, a language
requirement. He passed the physics examinations satisfactorily, including Swann's, which was the toughest—written examination, from eight
to twelve o'clock, and oral from one to six. Ph.D. or not, Ernest knew
that it had been a good year for him. There were no symbols for some
elements of growth, but he felt he had been successful.

When Swann announced that he had accepted a professorship at Yale
for the following year, Ernest was crestfallen for only a moment. Swann
suggested that Ernest apply for a Sloane Fellowship at Yale, and "come
along to New Haven. You'll get your degree after another year. Get
your language requirements in shape. With you, physics will take care of
itself. Before you know it you'll be a *Herr Doktor* professor of physics
yourself!"

Ernest had no organized business activity that summer. The Sloane
Fellowship, which was granted, would be adequate for his needs at Yale.
He did earn money during the vacation, apparently at odd jobs, as he
could find them. He also studied the German he had been denied in
high school, and French. He worked and played with his radio, and
made apparatus for an experiment, in the shop of Springfield State,
where members of his father's faculty remember that he talked of little
else than physics, and how important it was, and would become, and of
new discoveries and discoveries to be made. From science, he said, would
come the modern Columbuses and Magellans. Most people in South
Dakota that summer were talking about Robert La Follette and his new
Progressive Party, formed after he was denied the presidential nomination at the Republican Convention. La Follette advocated, among other
things, recognition of agriculture as the basic business of the country.
The farmers liked that, and Carl Lawrence was still an ardent La Follette admirer. Ernest saw Ruby a number of times, but there is no evidence that she accepted, or even saw, the diamond that had so amused
Ollie in Chicago. Ruby was not certain that she loved Ernest, though
she admitted to tremendous admiration for his "brains," his "smile,"

and—perhaps added with *double-entendre*—his "industry." Anyway, he was still her best boy friend. She wanted more education before committing herself, but assured him there was no one else at present to worry him while he was away. She would be proud to have her beau at Yale.

The rain which, throughout the morning, had obscured all the countryside but that closest to the tracks, had increased in force when Ernest got off the train at New Haven in September, 1924, but his ebullient spirits were as little dampened as his wonder at being there. Though his father's faculty and friends had reported it with pride, Ernest had, until this day, given little attention to the prestigious aspects of the famous university, founded three-quarters of a century before the country's independence. He had thought chiefly of continuing with physics under Professor Swann, and of his Ph.D. Beyond that he had considered what he might contribute to the understanding of nature, the excitement of experimentation in the unraveling of her mysteries, and the effort to render the complex simple. And here he was on the Eastern seaboard, about to enroll in the third oldest institution of higher learning in the country, a university not only fashionable but high in rank among the universities of the world. Now he was curious about it, eager to see its buildings and environs. It was exciting; as a boy, bent on education and success, he had no more dreamed of Yale than of Oxford or Cambridge. He felt pride now, and hoped that Yale might be as proud of him.

He could make out little of New Haven as he waited for a streetcar; nor could much be seen from the water-streaked car windows as he rode up through the city, past The Green with its three old churches, beyond the college proper, to the spacious area around the physics and chemistry buildings of Yale's Sheffield Scientific School. The wet baggage in either hand failed to stoop his squared shoulders as he strode toward and entered the Sloane Physical Laboratory—a wet young giant—and sought the director's office.

Professor Swann welcomed him, commented about the miserable weather, and voiced concern over his state of dampness. Ernest brushed such concern aside as easily as he removed his sopping coat. Swann thought he seemed eager to go to work at once, but suggested that the newcomer meet the department head, Professor John Zeleny, a younger brother of Anthony Zeleny, under whom Ernest had studied at Minnesota, and who himself had studied and taught there before moving to Yale in 1915. Zeleny got up from his desk, greeted Ernest warmly, and said that Swann had reported great things about him. He apologized for the weather and promised many fine days before snowfall, days when the balmy autumn air and Indian summer colors would lure thoughts from books and laboratories, making doubly difficult the work of students within the building. Startling to the new student was an invitation to lunch with the head of the department later in the week! Ernest stammered his appreciation and thanks.

Swann conducted him on a tour of the building, which Ernest thought a "beautiful, well-equipped, spacious place." He met urbane Professor Charlton Cooksey and his younger brother Donald, a research fellow whose studies had been interrupted by the war, busy at an interesting device for measuring X rays. Ernest's interest in the device, which Don explained was a specially designed X-ray spectrograph, was immediate. With this instrument the Cooksey brothers were to make the most precise measurements of X-ray wavelengths of the time. The Cookseys were cordial to the damp young man from the country. Professor Cooksey told Ernest he must come to his house for tea some Sunday, soon. "Gee whiz! These professors welcome you as warmly as do church elders. The first two professors—two invitations!"

The invitation reminded Swann that tea and cookies were always available at this hour at Sloane, and that it might be good for Ernest to drink something hot. They found Samuel Jacobsohn, another Chicago student who had followed Swann to Yale, enjoying refreshment with others, both professors and graduates. Jake did not have to point out the difference in atmosphere from that at Ryerson, but he remarked on it. Tom (T. H.) Johnson, who had been at Chicago before Ernest, and was a teaching fellow at Yale, concurred—and made a date with Ernest for tennis. Everyone so cordial and interested! In such an atmosphere, how could one fail?

It was late in the afternoon before Ernest remembered that he would have to find a place to sleep. He was advised to hurry to the Y.W.C.A., "which at this boys' college," Swann said, "takes care of the matter of finding rooms," but Sam Jacobsohn suggested that Ernest come to his room, at least for the night; perhaps the landlady might let them share the room for the year. Each would be studying identical subjects, each knew enough of the other from Ryerson to think they could get along, and it would be cheaper than separate rooms. "It's close," Jake said, "only a block if the street were cut through, but, as it is not, we have to walk two blocks to get there."

It stopped raining when they left Sloane Laboratory for the white clapboard house, number seventeen Compton Street, where Mrs. Rice said they might share the room for $2.75 each, per week, whereas Jake had agreed to $4.25, alone. She promised to find any needed extra furniture, and the boys climbed two flights of stairs to a dormer room next to the attic.

The room was fairly large, with two side-by-side windows from which

Ernest and John Lawrence, three years old and six months respectively.

An early Lawrence family portrait. *From the left:* Gunda, John, Ernest, and Carl Lawrence.

(*Above left*) In Pierre, South Dakota, Ernest's nickname was "Skinny." (*Above right*) The young scholar-salesman.

From the left: Stanley Tobiason, Ernest, and John on the South Dakota prairie en route to the Black Hills.

Ernest Lawrence *(left)* and Jesse Beams with their Kerr cells in Ernest's office in Yale's Sloane Laboratory. *(Courtesy of Jesse Beams)*

California's young associate professor. *(Lawrence Radiation Laboratory)*

Robert Oppenheimer *(left)* and Ernest at Robert's New Mexico ranch.
(Courtesy of Mrs. Ernest Lawrence)

The first "cyclotron," constructed by N. E. Edlefsen under Ernest's supervision early in 1930 to test the Lawrence principle of magnetic resonance acceleration.

The second cyclotron, built by Ernest Lawrence and his graduate student M. Stanley Livingston. Between the poles of a four-inch diameter magnet, on January 2, 1931, with the application of 2,000 volts, this device produced 8,000-volt hydrogen molecular ions. *(Photos: Lawrence Radiation Laboratory)*

The 11-inch cyclotron, with assorted controls, in a laboratory of Le Conte Hall, University of California, Berkeley. With this instrument, which cost approximately $800, the million-volt electron energy range was surpassed for the first time in the artificial acceleration of particles. (*Lawrence Radiation Laboratory*)

H. A. KRAMERS   N. F. MOTT   G. GAMOW P. BLACKETT   M. COSYNS   Aug. PICCARD

E. STAHEL   P. A. M. DIRAC   J. ERRERA   C. D. ELLIS   E. O. LAWRENCE

HENRIOT   F. JOLIOT W. HEISENBERG   E. T. S. WALTON P. DEBYE B. CABRERA W. BOTHE   Ed. BAUER J. E. VERSCHAFFELT J. D. COCKROFT   L. ROSENFE

F. PERRIN   E. FERMI   M. S. ROSENBLUM   W. PAULI   E. HERZEN   R. PEIERLS

E. SCHRÖDINGER Mme I. JOLIOT N. BOHR   A. JOFFÉ Mme CURIE   O. W. RICHARDSON Lord RUTHERFORD M. de BROGLIE   Mlle L. MEITNER   J. CHADW

P. LANGEVIN   Th. DE DONDER   L. de BROGLIE

Absents : A. EINSTEIN et Ch.-Eug. GUYE

The Solvay Conference at Brussels, Belgium, in October, 1933, which Ernest attended as the only invited American member, with some of the world's most distinguished physicists. *(Benjamin Couprie photo, Lawrence Radiation Laboratory)*

Jake pointed out the towers of Sloane Laboratory across the rooftops of houses on Mansfield and Prospect Streets. A plate of fresh Concord grapes from the yard below were on the small table. The white enameled iron bed seemed sturdy enough for two, and the old dresser against the wall, adequate. There was a good bookcase, and room enough for another table or desk with a second straight chair. On two of the cleanly papered walls were colored prints: the "Angelus," a Dutch scene, and a calendar. An extension cord connected the center light with a small electric plate in a corner. "Handy for grilling eggs. We can have breakfast here. Mrs. Rice will order milk for us." Jake then produced zwieback, cake, and cookies his mother had made. His hunger roused, Ernest suggested they go out for supper rather than consume Jake's meager stock. There was much to see: a brief survey of the university grounds and downtown New Haven. Jake noted at once that Lawrence was not one to postpone what could be done "now."

Half a block up Compton to Winchester Avenue was one of "the cheapest looking restaurants" Jake had ever seen. They could wait; it was still light and one could eat after dark when the sights were shrouded. They strode down Winchester toward the campus, at Ernest's pace. A streetcar passed. "It goes downtown, if one doesn't want to spend fifteen minutes or so walking the distance," Jake said.

They continued along the wall of the old New Haven cemetery to the university Commons, where they might eat well and cheaply if they chose. Jake had eaten breakfast of cereal, toast, and coffee there for sixteen cents, cafeteria style, though there were tables with white cloths and busboys to clear them. Lunch had cost the "exorbitant sum of forty-one cents," but Jake had been so full after that sumptuous repast that he had gone to his room for a half-hour nap. Graduate students might dine there whenever they wished, and pay only for what they chose, whereas freshmen had to pay for three meals a day at the Commons whether they ate there or not. "A privilege of rank," Jake said, "but we can beat even the breakfast price in our room."

Neither hunger nor frugality detained them long in the Commons and, after a peek into Woolsey Hall, they crossed Memorial Quadrangle with its tower, walked through the Old Campus surrounded by dormitories, halls, and chapels, through the traditional Yale fence, and onto New Haven Green. Jake pointed out the Taft Hotel across the street from the Green at a near corner. "We'll dine there sometime when we've something to celebrate—and after we've been paid for our duties." They crossed the Green and wound up at Childs Restaurant in town. They walked back, too, in the dark, Jake pointing out old colonial residences he thought might be worth a tourist's while. They talked long after returning to the room: about courses and duties, examining undergraduates' laboratory work, helping them, and "flunkin' deserving students," as Jake added facetiously.

The first requirements of their degree work in which they were to be examined were the languages, one of them in two weeks. Ernest, doubtful about his German, was confident of success in French; Jake knew German but was concerned about his French. Each agreed to coach the other in his troublesome language. Jake would take the German examination first while Ernest took the French, to allow each more time for his less familiar language. Then the principal examination for the doctorate had to be passed, followed by thesis requirements. Jake's project had to do with temperature radiation and thermal equilibrium; Ernest's, a continuation of his Chicago experiment on the photoelectric effect of potassium vapor as a function of the frequency of light. Neither had serious doubts about any requirement. It had been an exciting and auspicious day in spite of the rain that had ushered it in.

The days that followed were as stimulating. Lovely and sunny as the first had been wet and gloomy, they failed to distract Ernest from the work at hand in Sloane Laboratory, whatever the nature of the task. If there were subjects less interesting than others, they were those that did not directly pertain to physics; only the language cramming for the early examinations could have been called a grind. It was difficult for Ernest to understand why some of the students whom he assisted failed to find everything pertaining to physics exciting, and some of them did catch a little of his enthusiasm. "You didn't have to do more than see him to get some of his drive," Thomas Johnson remembers. "He was a dynamo! Always walked with his head and shoulders back—as though preparing mentally and physically for aggressive approach. He only relaxed when he sat—unless preparing for action."

He passed the French exam the last week of September. As Jake also passed in German, they treated themselves to a piano recital—for twenty-five cents each. German was also passed satisfactorily, and, on October 29, Ernest took the doctoral examinations. He got off to a bad start in the oral examination when asked why the sky is blue, a question any undergraduate should have been able to answer without hesitation. Ernest, careless of detail that held no particular interest for him, hesitated only a moment before replying cheerfully, "You know, I've often wondered about that myself." Perhaps his boldness and disarming manner caused the board to overlook his ignorance; more likely Ernest's ready grasp of more important facts enabled him to pass. He was now free to work on his thesis and the experimental problem concerned. Jake had also passed, and the two were now in their room only for sleep, as a rule spending the hours from eight in the morning to midnight in the laboratory.

Ernest again constructed the necessary apparatus, this time with castings, whereas at Chicago he had used wood parts. He was able to simplify the design somewhat, and, when it was suggested that his method might produce specious results, was able to prove himself correct. Not only his own uncomplicated apparatus but also his help to others soon proved him a good experimenter. No student failed to listen to his views, and he was as quick to praise and encourage as to make suggestions. Tom Johnson remembers that he always seemed as excited and happy over another's success as one of his own. It was all a great adventure—to do things that were new, or to do something differently. He seemed unique, not only because of his enthusiasms, his clever, simple apparatus, and good experimentation, but because of his open frankness and readiness to admit ignorance. He had no use for bluff and was intolerant only of "weak sisters" who wouldn't work, or who didn't want to dispel ignorance by finding out. He sometimes became so excited in his own quest that stammering was evident; if the subject was science, he seemed to have lost any sense of embarrassment this might once have caused. In his first report to the Physics Club, he "brilliantly summarized the existing knowledge of cosmic ray phenomena, while discussing a current paper on the subject, without notes," Don Cooksey remembers. By the time he had passed his doctoral exams, he was spoken of around Sloane as a "comer."

The results of his experiment corresponded remarkably with those he had noted at Chicago in his first photoelectric experiment with vapor. He completed the written dissertation by the end of January. This not only impressed the faculty, but was communicated by Professor Swann to the Philosophical Society and printed in its journal, as his master's thesis had been. The name Ernest Orlando Lawrence was becoming known in the world of science, though he was not yet twenty-four. His doctorate assured for the June convocation, there was too much to find out for him to loaf. Before the thesis was finished, he was at work on experiments designed to resolve questions that had arisen with his photoelectric problem: to measure initial velocities of photoelectrons, and devise a system for analyzing positive ray ions in the hope of better understanding the nature of photoelectric ions. But this and the interesting experiments of others were not enough for his eager mind.

Early in November he had read an article about an inventor, C. Francis Jenkins, who claimed to have formulated a device for the transmission of moving pictures by radio. Jenkins would not completely describe it, since he felt that the idea of the phonograph had been his, and that Edison had stolen it. Ernest and Jake first discussed the possibilities of transmitting pictures by wireless during one of their long walks. By the time they were back at the laboratory, they had a device in mind which Swann, who made a few suggestions, considered excellent, and the young men stayed up all night experimenting, with hopeful results. Idea followed idea in their discussions of transmission and reception, until, by December, a crude apparatus "to demonstrate and sell the thing" was able to transmit and receive silhouettes. Even the long Thanksgiving weekend had been given over to the work—except for time out to enjoy Mrs. Rice's fine dinner *and* supper! As though that were not sufficient, the kind landlady left a pumpkin pie and stuffed dates in their room.

Ernest argued for a patent application, but his more conservative friend thought their device should first be put in better shape, though both knew that it might take years to perfect. An attorney they consulted thought they would need two patents and about five hundred dollars, and that there might be litigation afterward, as often happened, so the young men carefully wrote down their ideas, had them dated and witnessed by several professors—and saved their money. Jacobsohn also took the precaution to write all the details, listing his contributions and those of Ernest, in letters which members of his family preserved.

Ernest, whom Don Cooksey had invited to drive with him to the Washington meeting of the American Physical Society during the Christmas holidays, promised to discuss the idea with Alex Nicholson at the Western Electric laboratories in New York. "I'll go see Jenkins himself when I'm in Washington." Jake, who planned to attend the meetings and stay in Washington with his brother, a chemist at the Bureau of Standards, wouldn't think of "barging in on Jenkins."

"Barging in" had never bothered Ernest if he wanted to learn something. In class he would interrupt a lecturer to clarify a point, and would persist until it was thoroughly understood. Though this could be annoying, and at times disrupted the continuity of the talk, some of the less bold students appreciated the resulting clarification.

Education was not confined to Sloane Laboratory. Professor Swann invited Ernest and Jake to his house for dinner with Professor Zeleny, after they'd been at Yale but a month, and the young men were enrapt as the older ones discussed their days at Göttingen and Cambridge, and the great men of physics at these universities. Talk of Rutherford at Cambridge and his work with the atom and radioactivity, in some of which Yale's Professor B. B. Boltwood, discoverer of the element ionium, had a part, drew questions from Ernest that kept them at Swann's house beyond the time they should have left. But with Ernest, according to Swann, the professor-student relationship always quickly became that of friends and colleagues.

Swann often shared Ernest's and Jake's habitual walks, walks always laced with talk—usually of physics. Ernest was a great believer in a fit body as a requirement for an alert mind. There was rarely a noon that he and Tom Johnson didn't play tennis, or, if weather was forbidding, squash, indoors. Jake had not brought tennis gear with him but sent home for it posthaste when Professors Swann and Page challenged them for doubles. His equipment arrived in time for a day or two of practice singles with Ernest, who trounced him. Jake had barely recovered from the ensuing stiffness when they met the professors. "I'd much rather have spent the time talking with them," Jake opined, but even contact with the professors on the court was worth the effort.

On their walks, Professor Swann, who by his own admission would "talk the hind leg off a donkey," spoke of anything from philosophy to music—he constantly practiced with his beloved cello—but Ernest usually got the conversation back to physics, if topics became too abstract. Once, when Ernest had a brilliant idea concerning an experiment, Swann had to tell him that it had been done before, was not original. Jake said: "I'm beginning to think most of a physicist's life is doomed to be spent forgetting ideas he has thought of, or even developed, only to find they have been done before."

Swann ventured that not all explorations resulted in the discovery of an America. The adventures of science, more precise and as exciting, need never be limited, because someone else had, unbeknownst, charted the course. Frustrations were bound to occur, but what of it? Swann was given to philosophizing.

"A true researcher should enjoy the battle of overcoming difficulties. He should be delighted to learn of the successes of others. Think of the trouble it saves him in the long run; he doesn't have to go all over it. And there is always comfort in the fact that none of the work is completely wasted. A good man cannot live completely in the realm of mental bliss; sometimes he's happy and sometimes despondent. A plotted chart of his activities would show many peaks above an axis and many below. But I would rather occasionally be condemned to the dungeons of despair if I am also sometimes allowed to see the mountains, than to live on a plane where there were no mountains, no crevasses."

Swann had very little use for outside pressures in getting something done—"except in the case of a poor student, or crass laziness, and then it isn't worth the bother anyway. Worthwhile pressure must come from within one, inspiration may come from without. That's the combination of a good researcher: inspiration from without and pressure from within. It's a mixture that doesn't always seem consistent, superficially, yet there is consistency. The strong desire to find out the truths of nature, as distinct from playing about with apparatus, is from the inside."

Neither Ernest nor Jake felt pressure as far as physics was concerned; they wondered that Swann called the desire to learn by such a term. They had no hesitation in foregoing the football game with Georgia when Swann that afternoon invited them for a walk in the brilliant countryside. Yale had squeezed out a one-point victory, but they felt they had gained far more from their afternoon, though they enjoyed football. Ernest particularly liked the Harvard and Army games which he attended with Jake. He had written to Ruby suggesting that she come to New Haven for one of them. But she was wrapped up in plans for the "floating university," with classes aboard between interesting ports. Ernest was satisfied with her plans; they would keep her occupied until the establishment of Dr. Lawrence.

Social life in New Haven had little effect on busy students, but what he saw of it revealed new vistas to Ernest. Dinners at the Zelenys' house, as at the Swanns', were rather more formal than he had known previously—until the men got lost in physics. He learned that conversations at the table were usually kept general for the sake of members of the family. Teas at Professor Cooksey's house up on Huntington Street were elaborate, and neither dinner nor supper was like anything Ernest had known, and if he was unconscious of the fact that he was somewhat lacking in social grace, the Cooksey daughters were not, though he was always neat, kept his hair trimmed and his clothes pressed. The older people generally found him most interesting. Mrs. Zeleny liked him at once, but Elizabeth, the eldest Cooksey daughter, accepted an invitation from him only after pressure from her father. New Haven was full of brilliant students, many whose backgrounds made them more appealing to young ladies of some social sophistication. "I don't know how long it was before he got the idea that a man seated a lady before he sat down himself," Elizabeth remembered. And her sister Ann observed that he ate as rapidly as he walked, as though it were a job to get done as soon as possible. He always started a conversation as though curious about, and interested in, his companion and her interests, but once the polite young lady had turned conversation to his own interests, Ernest was off on physics "for good." He squired the Zelenys' daughter, Caroline, a few times, but by and large he had few dates as a graduate student.

Ernest did take one of the young ladies to the play *What Price Glory?* and, as the language got rougher and the situations involving two Marines and a French girl, franker, he tried to persuade her to leave. She refused and they saw the entire performance. When Ernest visited Princeton during the Christmas holidays, and the conversation turned to girls, he amused graduate students there by exclaiming over this incident, because the girl was a *"nice girl,"* Joe Morris, then at Princeton, remembers his saying, "and she *liked it.*" He was glad he had gone with Jake to a pre-Broadway version of *Artists and Models* in New Haven; even Jake thought it was being tried out on the New Haven police before being subjected to censorship in New York. The New Haven tryouts of

Broadway productions may have added to his knowledge but had little effect on his conduct; even after *What Price Glory?* his strongest epithet was still, "Oh, fudge." The New York Philharmonic Symphony and frequent twenty-five-cent concerts and recitals deepened his musical appreciation. Most of his efforts with radio, he wrote to Merle, were pulling in good programs in the lab, nights, when they didn't interfere with work. Jake sometimes tuned in the Chicago Symphony and could usually get the New York orchestra, or the Brunswick concerts. Jake, brought up on classical music, was a ready teacher, when Ernest asked about composers, conductors, or artists involved.

On election night, Ernest and Jake had turned, at intervals, from music to news, for there had been interesting discussions on politics and parties. Jake, who had studied the *Literary Digest* poll, had wanted to wager that the next President of the United States would be decided by Congress; Ernest, an ardent La Follette supporter, did not think the glossing over of the Teapot Dome scandals could be offset by the fact that Coolidge once settled a Boston police strike. A Japanese student who was studying economics gave the Democratic Davis a chance, despite resentment against the Ku-Klux Klan. Ernest found it difficult to believe many people would tolerate either dishonesty or bigotry in a great national party. Jake twitted him for his innocence and said that, as a firm believer in Success, he should be a Republican as were the great industrialists and successful corporation administrators who, after the results were in, had proved successful again in politics. Ernest argued that he believed in success, but with principle. His father had gone to the top of his field in his area, not at the expense of anyone else, and with willingness to risk all for his ideals.

Jake told Ernest that his interest in the Japanese student was based on the fact that his grandfather had been Premier of Japan. Ernest agreed that it was an interesting fact about his friend, but reminded Jake that he had had Japanese friends at Minnesota and Chicago, that he was curious about people and had known no Oriental prior to his year at Minnesota. Jake laughed, and suggested that his interest in Kawasaki at Chicago might have been influenced by the fact that his family was one of the few great industrial dynasties of Japan; indeed, as his letters to Ernest attested, Kawasaki was even now learning the business in the submarine section of his family's shipyards. Well, that was interesting, was it not? Kawasaki had learned enough physics to get into Ryerson. He was starting at the bottom, not the top, of his family's industrial empire, and, furthermore, wrote of his deep concern that they were making submarines instead of something constructive. Despite the general American worship of success and of power or wealth, Ernest felt that he didn't necessarily respect these in themselves. But he certainly intended to become a success himself and could see nothing wrong with wealth honestly come by. Look at all that had been done for the common good by the Carnegies, Fords, Rockefellers; most American millionaires had given everything, from libraries and hospitals to laboratories, for universal benefit. How about Ryerson and the University of Chicago? Or the Sheffield Scientific School, and Yale itself? Jake chuckled; he knew as well as anyone else around Sloane that Ernest knew wealthy students whom he classed as "weak sisters." Wealth, as with so many advantages, depended upon who had it and how it was used.

There was Professor Cooksey's brother Donald. Don had money, but was so interested in physics for itself that he wasn't much concerned about getting his degree; not enough anyway to work on the language requirements. Yet he worked hard in the lab, and wanted instruments so precise he would design them himself and get them machined by such experts of close tolerance as Pratt and Whitney up in Hartford. Jake agreed that Don was a fine fellow, an individual and a good scientist, but couldn't resist suggesting that Ernest cultivated Don because of his Duesenberg roadster—and Chrysler sedan. Ernest reminded Jake that Don had asked him, not he Don, to drive to Washington. And if Jake wanted to see an example of success being achieved, and recognized, let him watch Arthur Compton. His experiment on the increase of the wavelength of scattered hard X rays would prove correct, Ernest was certain. It would be the big issue at the coming meetings of the Physical Society in Washington, and Compton would win, whatever the opposition. It was ridiculous of men like Professor Duane to protest that Compton hadn't had enough experience or patience to prove his statements, just because Duane had tried the experiment and failed to reach satisfactory conclusions.

The excitement of going to their first Physical Society meeting offset, somewhat, any homesickness Ernest and Jake felt on Christmas Day, which was gloomy and rainy when they awoke. Jake suggested they could have afforded the trip home if they'd used the money spent on presents for Swann's son, the landlady, and her husband and granddaughter. But by the time they left for Professor Swann's home for a fine Christmas dinner, the rain had turned to snow and their spirits were high again.

Snow did not prevent Don Cooksey from driving to Washington, and Ernest forgot physics long enough during the drive to learn something of his friend, and to tell him more of his own background than Don had known. Ernest thought his background pretty limited by the time he had pumped Don, even though Don, nine years older than Ernest, did not feel any further advanced in science. He was, he said, in physics because he loved it, and thought it important, and for no other reason. Ernest could say that he was in physics for the same reasons, but that he hoped to make a living from it.

To Ernest, Don's life had been full of fascinating, varied experience —the traveling, the faraway places he'd been—crossing America as a boy in his grandfather's private railroad car to live in Montecito, or in the San Francisco area, crossing the Atlantic in great liners, to live in England with a tutor from Oxford, punting down the Isis River and the Thames with his father. What fun it must have been to drive into Yosemite Park in a spring wagon, to penetrate and camp in the wild Trinity Mountains of California, and to pan gold! Yet Don, who could do just about as he pleased, preferred physics to anything else.

Ernest smiled, thinking how, when he told Jake about his friend, he would chaff him about being impressed, but Jake knew that he had liked Don at their first meeting, before he had known anything about him, or his sporty cars and fine bachelor quarters on St. Ronan Street. Ernest was to learn much of the ways of the world from his friend— starting with this trip.

As for Donald Cooksey, he had at once been attracted by the genuineness of the South Dakotan, and had been continuously impressed with his work, his attitude toward science, and his almost instinctive ability to get to the heart of a problem. "I knew that I would never be a great physicist," Cooksey said later, "but I thought I might be of some help to one who, it seemed obvious to me, would become one. He was different, he was aggressive, interested, and knowing. He was fun to be around. He had an engaging naïveté about the East, and the social life of the East. He had never seen a skyscraper."

Certainly Ernest had never slept as high up as they did at the Yale Club in New York; it was as amazing as being able to dine two floors higher, on the roof, where he could look out across the city between other, taller buildings. His unself-conscious exclamations over things new to him, and the manner in which he frankly gawked, had a charm —perhaps, Don thought, because it stemmed from honest curiosity and a mind exceptionally aware and anxious to understand every facet of new sights and experiences. Situations that might have embarrassed one less genuine Ernest took in stride, as he would an experimental failure from which he learned something.

Don saw that Ernest met people who were important in the world of physics, and not only at meetings of the society. He had introduced him at commercial laboratories on the way down—Ernest would have introduced himself, but it was helpful to have Don do it, and at Princeton's Palmer Physical Laboratory where everyone present was entertained by Ernest's account of Arthur Compton's verification of his theory, and Ernest's insistence that it had been proved and must win acceptance. Arthur's older brother Karl, head of the department at Princeton, was as impressed by the young man's explanation, as by the bold way in which he championed Arthur. And at the meetings themselves, though the young man was properly silent during sessions at which Compton's theory was vehemently attacked, Ernest was as much the advocate in corridors as he had been at Princeton. He was also shocked at the tone and attitude of noted physicists in the controversy; he had not imagined that good scientists could appear so petty. He met a number of young men who would become friends as well as colleagues, at the meetings, at Princeton, and at Johns Hopkins, where he had two days with Merle Tuve, thanks to deep snow that prevented Don's car from traveling beyond Baltimore. Merle was interested in the scheme for radio pictures, which had seemed so promising in New Haven, and which had been so deflated in New York.

Alex Nicholson, at the Western Electric Laboratory in New York, had shown Ernest a roomful of devices, similar and otherwise; at the Bell Telephone Laboratory it was the same. In both, experimentation had gone beyond the conceptions of Ernest and Jake. In Washington, he had not been overly impressed by C. Francis Jenkins, or his ideas, after learning what had been done in the big New York laboratories. The distraction of Jenkins' blonde secretary may have been partially responsible for the impression. Ernest tried to get her to join him for New Year's Eve festivities, without any luck. Her refusal was so polite that he thought it might have been due to the presence of Jenkins in the office, and he telephoned from the hotel to ask her again. She refused just as politely over the phone.

Jacobsohn wasn't at all surprised to learn that commercial laboratories had been considering motion pictures by radio. Both young men decided it would not be very long before some device was successfully developed to bring pictures into homes, as radio had brought sound. But Jake thought they were lucky to be out of it before they had wasted a lot more time on the project. Ernest, full of his adventures with Don, thought they ought to go to New York frequently, not only for the museums and symphony concerts, but to visit the laboratories he'd seen and keep in touch with what was happening in the world of practical science. "We ought to get a secondhand flivver so we could run down there, and up to Boston, without much expense," he argued. Jake was more conservative. "Considering wear and tear on tires, clothes, and nerves," he reasoned, "it will be cheaper to turn our money over to the New York, New Haven and Hartford than to Henry Ford and Standard Oil."

Ernest's letters to his parents were so full of the excitement and interest of New York and Washington that his mother worried again about his moral and religious health. He admitted he had not attended any church regularly, but mentioned a Universalist service he had attended with a friend. Gunda Lawrence was quite firm about that. "They don't believe in Jesus," she wrote. "Isn't there a Lutheran, or an Episcopal church, in New Haven? Pick out one you like and go. John goes to church regularly in Vermillion." "You ought to go with me," Jake said. "You'd make a good Yid." But more than once during that winter, Jake called Ernest a Christian Scientist because of claims to be well when he suffered severe colds.

Ernest had not thought about Jake as Jewish until they had been living together almost a month and Jake had gone to New York for Rosh Hashanah services. A few days later, he had helped Jake break his Yom Kippur fast with a fine dinner at the Taft Hotel. Ensuing discussions about religion had resulted in agreements by Ernest to go with Jake to shul, and Jake to accompany Ernest to an Episcopal service—since moving to Springfield where there was no Lutheran church, the Lawrences had become stalwarts of the Episcopal Diocese of South Dakota. The boys did not visit each other's services until April, when Ernest attended a Passover service at New Haven's Reform Temple on what happened to be the Christian Good Friday. This was followed by dinner at a kosher restaurant where Ernest kidded Jake that even for a ten-dollar bill he could not have bread and butter with his meat. Two days later, after Easter Mass at a "high" Episcopal church, Jake kidded Ernest about the "holy smoke." On the Saturday between the services, a box of Pesach goodies had arrived from Mrs. Jacobsohn, and Jake wrote home that he'd had few of the macaroons because "Lawrence had seen them first."

One of the most exciting events of early 1925 had been provided by nature herself; the total eclipse of the sun on January 24, and the boys had very nearly missed it in spite of study and preparation for it. Jake had taken observations of atmospheric electricity from nine to midnight the night before, and Ernest from midnight to three in the morning. He had fallen into bed half dressed for a few hours of sleep, and when the alarm went off about six, Jake turned it off without fully awakening. Ernest, who had barely heard it, sat up about ten minutes later, and being already partly dressed, nudged Jake to get up and start the oatmeal cooking. Jake groaned and turned over, suggesting that Ernest "go to the devil." Ernest rose up enough to look out the far window, the curtain being drawn on the near one. "Shucks, it's cloudy," he said and got back under the covers.

"No!" Jake mumbled and jumped out of bed to see for himself. "It's all off," he sighed not too unhappily, and sleepily got back into bed. About ten minutes later, Ernest could stand it no longer. He got up and looked out the window again. "It's clearing up!" he shouted. "It'll be fine by nine!" Jake was skeptical. "Pull up the near shade and let me see." Ernest refused; he turned on the hot plate under the cereal. Jake had to get up and look for himself. They dressed, had their oatmeal, and hurried out. It was a few degrees above zero as they walked to the streetcar. After they left the car, they passed Professor Swann's house. He invited the boys to ride with him and his family the rest of the way, but they were afraid of crowding them and soon started the four-hundred-odd-foot climb up East Rock. They were warm and puffing when they reached the top, where already a fair-sized crowd had gathered, some with telescopes, some with cameras, all with smoked glass or exposed film to protect eyes.

There was little view of the city, normally almost complete from East Rock, or of Long Island, nearly twenty-five miles across the water. Enough clearing to reveal the eclipse was still doubtful. There were only a few patches of white cloud overhead, but the sun was hidden, except for occasional glimpses. Heavy clouds were moving along the horizon. About ten minutes after eight, the sun could be seen, and everyone got out his darkened glass to look at it. A piece on the upper right-hand edge was obscured. Fifteen minutes later about a fourth of the sun had been blotted out. As it shrank slowly, almost imperceptibly at first, the sky darkened. Ernest and Jake jumped up and down as it became colder, waving their arms and doing a regular dance between observations.

The clouds remained tantalizing. Though there seemed little doubt that they would be able to see the sun, moon, and corona, the clouds might cover the whole at the moment of totality, spoiling the view from the rock and observations down at the observatory. The disk of the sun became more and more a narrowing crescent; daylight became less and less bright, as shadow deepened on the western horizon, covering first the hills, then the towers of Harkness, and the town. Trees below had no shadows. Soon the western horizon took on the colors of a sunset. Then there was no sun.

"Ernie! Totality!" Jake shouted. Where the sun had been was a black disk surrounded by a white shroud, the corona, so rarely seen! About a degree below the spectacle were clouds. It seemed almost a miracle that they had receded enough to permit the observation. It was almost as dark as a moonlit night. Stars were visible, and the temperature fell three degrees. But the young scientists did not feel the cold then; they were scarcely aware of anything but the indescribable corona—like a white veil with streamers off from either side. And as the edge of the sun began to come into view, the clouds took on the aspect and colors of beautiful mother-of-pearl. Gradually the crescent enlarged, the stars faded, and daylight returned. Silently, they started down the hill toward town and hot coffee—even Ernest was subdued. Perhaps never again would they be where a total eclipse could be seen.

In February, Professor Swann nominated Ernest for a National Research Fellowship. Established after the war, these fellowships provided opportunity for a select number—from the top 5 percent of Ph.D.'s in science—to spend two or three years in independent research at a university of their choice, before having to take jobs in industry or as teachers. Fellows were to receive about $2,000 the first year, with the possibility of as much as $3,000 for a third year. The plan had been conceived by members of the wartime National Research Council as an effort to bring the standard of American science more nearly abreast of that of Europe. By Executive order of President Woodrow Wilson the council had been made a continuing peacetime body, supported by funds from the National Academy of Sciences. The actual fellowships were supported by the Rockefeller Foundation.

By winning one of the fellowships, Ernest was relieved of the necessity of choosing among offers he had received from universities and from an industrial laboratory. He was fortunate even in the offers; there were not many good positions for physicists at that time. That he could continue with research for at least another year was all that could be desired—until he learned that rules required fellows to do their postdoctoral research in an institution other than that which had granted the degree. The thought of leaving Professor Swann at this stage took much of the joy out of the award; regardless of better offers of employment, he had taken it for granted that he would stay at Yale, with his old professor, as an instructor. Swann was equally downcast; neither had realized what close friends they had become. After a long walk together, neither very clear-eyed as they discussed it, Swann said he would try to think of something, and he did; he persuaded the Research Council that Ernest had moved around too much already, had experiments in progress at Yale, and should be allowed to remain there for his fellowship. The council made an exception for Ernest. Joy and excitement reigned again.

In March, at a fine banquet, Ernest and Jake were elected to full membership in the physicists' fraternity, Sigma Xi. Ernest wrote home of his great luck in getting into physics, of the worth and adventure of research, but he still had rare moments of doubt of his worth as a scientist. "You'd never know it," Tom Johnson said. "Maybe sometimes his erect striding around and eager attitude were to bolster his own morale." Shortly before commencement, Ernest was at work on what seemed a hopeless experimental problem of his own, and he was somewhat discouraged. Perhaps he was not, after all, capable of original work! Professor Swann entered the lab with Michelson to see Ernest's work. "Still desecrating the Sabbath?" the old man joked, remembering. He became so interested that he wanted to know all about the experiment, unashamed of his ignorance of certain ideas involved. Ernest did not confess his difficulties, but was able to answer Michelson's questions. His gloom disappeared, and, as soon as his visitors left, he told Jake, "If so great a physicist has to ask such questions as he asked me, then there's hope for us."

Cognizant of all he had learned, in and out of the laboratory, during the months in New Haven, he resolved never to give up, no matter how difficult the problem, and to continue to learn in all areas, as in science. He wanted Professor Swann to be proud of him, and Akeley, and his family, too. Carl and Gunda were coming to New Haven to see him get his Ph.D. They were to stay at the home of Paul and Ann Benedict on St. Ronan Street, where Tom Johnson roomed in exchange for tending the furnace and doing other chores for the invalid Paul Benedict. The Benedicts had been good friends to Tom's fellow student before, and Ernest had taken time to talk with the invalid, and had been able to discuss questions concerning New Haven social conduct with the young wife.

He suggested to Jake that they stop calling each other Jake and Ernie, that Sam and Ernest would be more dignified for doctors of philosophy. Sam agreed with a chuckle. But Ernest seldom thought about dignity. On the great day of commencement, June 17, Ernest was as busy as usual right up to the time to prepare for the ceremonies. At one time he had to get over to the laboratory in a hurry before donning cap and gown. The way around seemed much too long for an about-to-be Ph.D. For the first time he cut through the two intervening lawns and gardens. He negotiated the first without notice, but in the garden of the second house, facing Prospect Street, an elderly gentleman popped out of the shrubbery and challenged the hurrying young man. "Who gave you permission to pass through here?" he demanded angrily. "Oh, go to the dickens!" Ernest replied after a moment's hesitation, and rushed on to Sloane Laboratory.

A short time later that day, Ernest found himself marching beside the old gentleman in the academic procession of Yale University's two hundred and twenty-fourth commencement.

CHAPTER IV

Not Work—Great Fun

[JUNE, 1925–AUGUST, 1928]

D r. Ernest Orlando Lawrence, National Research Fellow, not yet twenty-four years old, did not return to Springfield with his mother and father after the commencement in June. The general, happy, vacation-bound exodus from New Haven affected him little. Sloane Laboratory was quieter with undergraduates gone, and many graduate students and professors away—even Swann had gone off to give his cello preference over laboratory instrumentation for a few months. Tom Johnson was around for a while; he was to be a Loomis Fellow for the coming year and had an adjoining laboratory on the upper floor of Sloane. Don Cooksey and his brother the professor were often to be found in the laboratory.

The chance to return with his parents, vacation leisure, even the possibility of seeing Ruby Patterson could not dissuade Ernest from continuing work to determine whether or not his apparatus was practical. Not until he was reasonably certain did he leave New Haven. He knew, of course, that the finest-sounding theory may have a flaw; that experimental projects may prove useless. It had been noted that one of the factors contributing to his ability as an experimenter was his readiness to put aside an idea, or, without a qualm, discard apparatus that seemed unlikely to produce results. Swann thought too many physicists "hugged their experiments to their bosoms" when reason and trial should have indicated their uselessness. Though Swann did not believe in telling a student that he was on the wrong track if he might discover it for himself, he had always been willing to let one find out in discussion, if the student came to him. It had always pleased him that Ernest usually had come for discussion already aware, and simply for verification. Now

Swann was away but he had not been needed much of late, even when present. Professor Page, who had always welcomed Ernest's queries in the theoretical field, was gone. Don Cooksey and Tom Johnson marveled at the young man's apparent grasp of his problem, but in this instance he was involved in a proposition beyond their ready ken. Tom was busy with molecular beams, and Don with instrumentation for X-ray measurements.

When Ernest did leave for a brief vacation at home, he went by way of Chicago to see Arthur Compton and to stay with Jacobsohn, whose home was there. Ernest was to visit his former roommate often in the years to come; Sam remained all of his career with the Gaertner Scientific Corporation, eventually becoming its president.

Compton was again impressed by Ernest's understanding of his problems and by his enthusiasm: "It was as if brakes had been removed from a fast, smooth-running machine."

Ernest seemed somewhat preoccupied when he visited Ruby Patterson and was glad that her university cruise around the world was at last to become a reality. He agreed to meet her in New York upon her return. He still took it for granted that they would ultimately marry, once he became a professor; meantime there were other interests that seemed quite as important.

At home he preached tirelessly to John of the rewards of good scholarship, the happiness that success brings. John, who had another year at South Dakota, wanted to get into Harvard Medical School. "You can do it if you want to badly enough," the older brother emphasized. "There's *nothing* you can't do if you work hard enough."

For the most part, it was joy and optimism that Ernest radiated at home, and the proud parents, indeed the proud community, marveled at him—so young, so energetic, and so full of talk about things impossible for them to comprehend. Even his uncle, Oliver's father, had to admit that the boy he once predicted would never amount to anything seemed to be making his way, though he still thought that anyone who couldn't be a good farmer didn't quite measure up. Only Carl and Gunda knew that he was sometimes so withdrawn that he could look at one as though unaware, his mind divorced from present conversation, oblivious to direct questions. He seemed never to forget his work. Had he perhaps taken something for granted? He knew that while much of past physical laws and assumptions must be accepted, there may be a point in new work when only by questioning the accepted can an experimenter hope to work out his own theory and design. New questions continually occurred, suggesting fresh inquiries into old as well as new problems. So much to do; could he crowd much of it into one life? He experienced periods of depression when he questioned his ability to accomplish his high aims. Strangely, these were similar to the dark moods that always threatened to engulf him immediately after the elation following successful conclusion of an experiment—depression that lifted once he commenced a new project. Work was the cure. Hard work and success, he kept repeating to John, were the greatest things in the world. Enthusiasm and optimism always marked his conscious behavior, and certainly they were his predominant moods wherever he happened to be.

When he left for New Haven again, Ernest went by way of Minneapolis. Professor Tate had devised a Faraday cylinder that showed a somewhat lower absorption rate for slow velocity electrons than had been assumed. It was good to talk with him about it. Physicists at Minnesota who had read Ernest's doctoral thesis, just published in the *Philosophical Magazine,* commented on the tricky, "beautiful" experiment, as did those at Chicago and Johns Hopkins—where he stopped to see Merle. At Princeton, Karl Compton was complimentary, and so were Ernest's contemporaries, Henry Smyth, Joe Morris, and Joe Boyce. Fred Mohler, at the Bureau of Standards in Washington, working on photoionization of vapors, was glad to discuss their common problems. Everywhere Ernest was willing to share his findings, and happy over the successes of others. He could not understand the secrecy with which some physicists guarded their special interests from others. Ideas to him were not private possessions that could be stolen. One of the beauties of science was its openness, an openness that knew no boundaries of laboratory, campus, or nation in the quest for the truths of nature. One of his preoccupations while at home had been catching up on the current literature of physics, articles from Europe as well as America, in a variety of languages—but all expressive of ideas that might help others besides the originator.

He did not go at once to Sloane Laboratory when he reached New Haven this time; he telephoned Caroline Zeleny and made a date for the evening. He would return to his solitary room ready for sleep, and be fresh in the morning for the laboratory. Perhaps Tom Johnson would be there, and Don Cooksey. A good game of tennis after the trains and the visiting would be beneficial; Don might invite him for a ride out into the country.

There was plenty of activity and interest at Sloane; Ross Gunn was back, and Joe Henderson, and George Gardner. Tom was in his lab next to Ernest's. It did not take Ernest long to become engrossed in his experiments. Discussion of them with Professor Tate and summer reflection quickly determined changes in apparatus. Before the December Washington meetings, he was able to show that Faraday cylinders of usual dimensions, despite having been commonly regarded as complete absorbers of electrons, do not retain all of them, and that current-retarding measurements generally do not indicate accurately the distribution of velocities in an electron stream. He discussed the paper at the meetings and it was published in the *Proceedings of the National Academy.*

Long before the meetings, however, Ernest was at work trying to produce an electron beam of homogenous velocities, and developed a method of magnetic analysis that produced such a beam of about ten-electron-volt energy, with which he bombarded mercury vapor, resulting in interesting "information on the nature of the probability that an electron will ionize an atom." The experiment also showed correspondence in the behavior of electrons and light quanta in atomic processes. It was referred to as an elegant piece of work, and he remembered how Jake had laughed, when they first heard the term so applied, because Ernest thought it more fitting for a tailor's sales talk. Results of the experiment were published later in *Science.*

While constructing the apparatus, Ernest wrote a rather theoretical dissertation, based on accepted data and results of his own photoelectric studies, to show that photoelectric and thermionic phenomena from solid surfaces may be considered experimental confirmation of the ratio of absorption to emission, evaluated in statistical equilibrium theories. The ensuing publication in the *Physical Review* credited Professor Page as well as Swann for advice.

But it was his following experimental proof that an electron will ionize an atom that placed him securely in the forefront of the new generation of physicists before his degree was a year old. He actually measured the ionization potential of the mercury atom by the electron impact method. It was the most accurate measurement of its kind that had been made, and made possible the calculation of the value of Max Planck's constant h, one of the most important constants of nature, and fundamental to quantum theory.

Though he postponed writing the results for publication, word got around. At the April meetings, professors from all over the country indicated interest in his future plans. Significantly, one of these, Professor Leonard Loeb, whom Ernest had met with Swann at Chicago, went on to New Haven where he was further "fascinated by Ernest's technical ability. He's the man we want," he told Swann. He urged Ernest to consider the opportunities for bright young scientists at the University of California. Under Gilbert N. Lewis, California had developed a chemistry department of repute; he, Professor Armin Leuschner, and younger scientists were eager to bring physics up to a like standard. Loeb urged Swann and Tom Johnson, who had been his student at Chicago, and other young physicists whom Ernest respected, to "do propaganda for

California with Lawrence." He wrote Professor Elmer E. Hall, chairman of the department at California on May 8, 1926:

". . . On my own initiative, I felt out one of the most brilliant experimental young men in the East—a lad whose name is on everyone's lips on account of his recent papers on Ionizing Potentials—that is Ernest Lawrence, a student of Swann's at Yale. Lawrence has succeeded in measuring ionizing potentials with an accuracy and certainty which gives a new value of h comparable with Millikan's. His work, which utilizes the magnetic separation of electrons with unique and known velocities for determining ionization potentials, has also shown the astounding fact that the probability of ionization by an electron is greatest right at the ionization potential and not at higher values, as had been previously assumed from work with heterogeneous velocities. He is personally one of the most charming men I have met—a first class mathematician and thoroughly alive. He is tied up at Yale as a research fellow. When asked whether he would consider an Assistant Prof. at Berkeley following the termination of his fellowship, he was quite enthusiastic and I said that as things progressed here we would let him know."

Even the Secretary of Agriculture and sometime member of the National Research Council, the Honorable William M. Jardine, expressed curiosity about the much-talked-of experiment, and was conducted to Ernest's laboratory. Tom Johnson, born in Michigan, and Jesse Beams, a National Research Fellow from the University of Virginia, born in Kansas, whose laboratories adjoined Ernest's on either side, were present. Jardine, born in Idaho, was interested that none of these brilliant researchers were Easterners. "The equipment may come from the East," he said, "but it's obvious the brains come from the Middle West."

Don Cooksey brought Professor Karl Manne Siegbahn of Uppsala, Sweden, Nobel Prize winner of 1924 for his work in X-ray spectroscopy, to meet Ernest and see his apparatus. Siegbahn was chiefly interested in the X-ray work of the Cookseys, but this meeting initiated a long and fruitful association for both Ernest and Siegbahn.

Among less distinguished visitors, except perhaps in appearance, was a young lady with whom Ernest had had a date. While riding with her, an idea concerning his work suddenly occurred to him and he persuaded her to drive to the laboratory on the grounds that it would be interesting for her to see his apparatus. They surprised Jesse Beams, shirttail out, bending over his own device. The quiet, bashful Jess blushed, stammered worse than Ernest now ever did, and withdrew to right his clothing. "Next time you do that," he cautioned Ernest, "stomp on the stairs so I'll know you're coming!"

Jess always wondered how Ernest, who worked so hard and such long hours, could have energy left for a date. Jess led a fairly monastic life; a movie, possibly an occasional road show, and church on Sundays were all he could squeeze into his busy life, and still get enough rest; yet he was sure Ernest spent more time working without ever tiring. "It's because you're younger," he would joke. Jess was not quite three years Ernest's senior.

Ernest found outside activities not only pleasant and broadening but a useful stimulant to his work. He and Tom Johnson kept up their tennis or squash. On Sundays they often rode horses from the Yale R.O.T.C. stables for a few hours, Ernest preferring spirited or rough mounts "to make it interesting." They swam together. Now that he received a monthly check from the Research Council, and was no longer restrained by Jake, Ernest purchased an old, dilapidated-looking Model T Ford roadster with good engine and running gear, but which had to be pushed to start if it had been idle more than a couple of days. Parts of its body were so rickety that the windshield once fell into Tom's lap while they were driving to Savin Rock for a shore dinner. They never partook of the amusement features of the park or paid much attention to the people. The main thing was to get out, but even on rides, as on walks, Ernest "was always talking and thinking physics. He was good company."

Ernest often visited Tom at the Benedicts', would entertain Paul, and sometimes take Ann to church, a movie, or a lecture. "He was so generous with his time, as with anything else," Tom recalls. It became customary for him to have Sunday dinner at their home, and Ann continued to be a fine mentor in the ways of New Haven society. Ernest felt he ought to learn these customs; Tom thought that one of the reasons he went out with girls was because he thought he ought to, but there is no doubt that he usually enjoyed such outings. He had very little use for bridge or other card games, and seemed to enjoy some of the mothers as much as he did their daughters.

Early in June, 1926, Ann Benedict asked Ernest to take Mary Blumer, of nearby Gateway School, to her commencement dance. The daughter of Dr. George Blumer, professor of clinical medicine and recently dean of the medical faculty at Yale, Miss Blumer had written to ask a cousin to escort her and had received no reply. Too shy to ask another, Mary Blumer had announced that she would not attend the prom. Miss Reynolds, the Gateway headmistress, appealed to her friend Ann; it was unthinkable that her prize pupil should not attend. Ann was sure that Ernest would find the tall, brilliant, and attractive "Molly" interesting; certainly he would like her family. Ernest thought it might be an exciting adventure, certainly no ordinary "blind date," and Ann announced that she had a prize man for Miss Reynolds' prize student. A few days later Ernest received a note from Mrs. Blumer inviting him to a pre-dance dinner party.

He was the first guest to arrive at the Blumer house on Whitney Avenue, just a door beyond the New Haven boundary in Hamden on the edge of East Rock Park. Mrs. Blumer received him in the living room, curious about the young man who had been so highly recommended. She explained that, due to weather, the Gateway School's Shakespearean play had been postponed until that afternoon, that her daughter had played Falstaff and been late getting home; graduation, play, and dance all in one day! Molly would be down in a few moments.

When Molly, just sixteen, descended the stairway, Ernest noticed first the coppery glints the late sun brought out in her brown hair. Then, as she moved between him and the sun, her slender figure was silhouetted through the material of her dress. He dropped his head a moment as Mrs. Blumer turned to look at her daughter. When she turned again to Ernest, he gave her an amused smile and wink that endeared him to her. The gentle manner in which Mrs. Blumer prevented embarrassment for the young lady earned Ernest's respect; he knew he liked the mother. After the introduction, she eased her daughter upstairs for a longer slip. He liked the daughter, too, serious, shy, and obviously, he thought, above the average—mature for her age.

Molly was impressed with her escort—"None of the boys I knew were Ph.D.'s, and had done all those impressive things"—but thought him too old, not at all handsome, and for one over six feet tall, "terribly thin." She was amused at the dinner table when he asked why the doily on the dessert plate, should he eat that? And what about the finger bowl with the lemon verbena leaf floating in the water? At least he was frank and unpretentious. At the dance Molly explained the cards listing dance partners, which the girls had filled in beforehand, exchanging escorts with girl friends for all but the first and last dances. He enjoyed the party, but when he asked if he could call, she thought it was merely for politeness' sake. He meant it, and appeared the following Sunday. Molly was not much interested and decided she did not like him. He was unaware of it; he liked her and liked her parents.

Ann Benedict told him that if he were to move in such circles he must have calling cards engraved, and instructed him in their proper use, much to Ernest's and Tom's amusement. Leaving three cards at the door, one each for Molly, her mother, and father, seemed a silly business when the servant could announce you, or report your call if they were "not at home." But he had the cards made.

The Blumer family moved to their house at Haycock Point on Long Island Sound at the end of June, and Ernest visited there a few times before he went to Springfield in August. On his first visit, Molly, a school friend, her mother, and younger sisters were fishing a short distance from shore in two rowboats. He was visible to them on the shore, but Molly pretended not to notice him. Her sisters would not let her ignore the visitor, and Mrs. Blumer insisted that she row ashore and be sociable. Her friend was appalled that she should meet a beau in old khaki bloomers, and, as they neared the shore, hissed, "At least take off that horrible old hat." Molly said she did not care how she looked; she didn't like him. Her sisters, particularly Elsie, three years younger, had teased her about her "old Ph.D." since their meeting. Ernest, unaware of any tensions, thought she looked fine, bloomers, floppy faded hat, and all. He stayed for dinner, served on the wide front porch looking out over the Sound. They danced afterward to phonograph music. He could see lights in Jesse Beams's laboratory when he got back, so he went up and told Jess what a wonderful girl Molly was.

Jesse and Ernest had quickly become close friends, stimulating to each other whether experimenting or just talking. Beams had chosen Yale for his fellowship largely because of Professor Swann. He had heard so much of Ernest that he had asked about him immediately upon arrival, and had been assigned an adjoining laboratory. His experimental work with Kerr cells, short-time intervals, and the spectra from sparks interested Ernest, who was fascinated by quantum problems. From his own experiments, it seemed that quanta were very small particles, yet considering the Compton Effect and other known data, quanta might be expected to be three or four meters long. (The indeterminacy principle was then unknown; there was much contradictory evidence as to the nature of quanta.) The two young research fellows thought that by combining apparatus a light beam might be chopped into small enough segments to be measured discretely. Possibly they could devise an interval so brief a quantum could not get through.

They started designing the setup of apparatus while continuing their individual experiments through the hot July. In the fall, needed portions of each could be quickly assembled for their joint venture. Ernest left for Springfield at the end of the month, stopping at various laboratories en route. In Philadelphia he had his first airplane ride with his cousin Lawrence Haugen, who had graduated from the Naval Academy and was stationed at the navy yard.

Ruby was somewhere in the Mediterranean—her last letter had been from Cairo—so he spent the time in South Dakota with his family. John, going to Harvard Medical School in the fall, was busy selling hosiery and trying to capture a bonus that would add to his profits. Ernest explained how he and Joe Holleman, also going to Harvard, could get as far as New Haven the cheapest way while sight-seeing en route.

An upper berth could be shared for a dollar and a half a night—much cheaper than any hotel—while traveling between cities, and could be occupied until a reasonable time in the morning, whatever the time of arrival.

Gunda was curious about Ernest's life in New Haven and the girls he saw. Ernest told her about Molly, and another girl whom he had seen frequently during the past year. Yes, he had spent some time with Professor Zeleny's daughter Caroline. Gunda, still opposed to dancing, hoped they were all nice girls. She thought Molly, whose family must be fine considering her father's position, might be accustomed to too much extravagance for a poor boy. Ernest laughingly assured her all the girls were very proper, and that he was still a free man. Gunda was not sure the "floating university" was a proper place for Ruby. With his father, he played a little golf and fished. Much of the time he spent writing his paper on ionization of atoms for the *Physical Review* and reading current scientific journals.

He left Springfield the last week in August and stayed a few days in Chicago. Then he went to Washington to see Merle, who had given up going to Rutherford's laboratory and taken a fine position in the Department of Terrestrial Magnetism of the Carnegie Institution. "Dr. Fleming asked me if I could put a million volts on a vacuum tube," Merle had written Ernest, "and I told him I thought I might. 'Come and do it,' Fleming said."

At Sloane Laboratory he found requests from as far away as Europe for reprints of his treatise on the ionizing potential of mercury, including one from Karl Darrow. Dr. Darrow regretted that the work had come to his attention too late for inclusion in a forthcoming book, in which he had cited Ernest's work with potassium vapor. Ernest was pleased, too, with a quick acknowledgment of the receipt of his finished article by the editors of the *Physical Review* and their statement that it would be printed, as written, in the November issue.

He found Professor Swann preparing to leave for a month of cosmic ray research on Pikes Peak. Professor Zeleny told him how he had made the lowest score of the season on a golf course in the White Mountains, demonstrating what he had learned about correct form, as Ernest enthusiastically wrote to his father. He regretted he could not practice himself. When he might have found time is hard to tell, unless he cut sleeping hours still further than was his habit. He and Beams were soon so immersed in experiment that light from the top floor of Sloane shone almost every night until one or two o'clock. "Lawrence was so full of ideas; he was so energetic—actually he worked me to death, practically," Jesse reported. "Often our experiments required running all night, and actually sometimes a day or two at a time. We couldn't leave the apparatus. I declare! We'd run all day, all night, and all the next day, and Lawrence would have a date that night. It was just an amazing amount of energy," Jesse repeated. "Just a boundless amount of energy. And such keen physical insight. It was mostly his idea; he was the main push behind it. He always did more than his part. He could do it a lot faster than I could. Wonderful all-around experimentalist. Good glass-blower—and this genius with apparatus! I declare! When he went out, I got some well-needed rest. At the same time—he was such a generous fellow—he would give his time freely to help people. He could work a little while with a piece of equipment and find what was wrong with it. I know one student—I'm not mentioning his name—Lawrence found out what was wrong, helped him with it, helped him take his data, and was responsible, really, for his getting his degree. I don't think this man ever mentioned that Lawrence did this, yet he has become a very good physicist."

Though portions of their apparatus could be used as constructed for individual experiments, much work was necessary to join it for the exciting problem at hand. Glass had to be blown for new Kerr cells, Beams's optical shutter had to be developed to turn on and off in minute fractions of a second. Don Cooksey lent them fine Nicol prisms. Most delicate photoelectric cells were set up. When assembled, the apparatus functioned as planned—with most startling results. Light quanta, generally thought to be at least three meters in length, were not affected when cut into segments of ten centimeters. Repeated trials caused the investigators to trust their data. Though not immediately accepted everywhere, this proved to be one of the experiments that forced physicists to look at phenomena in the new way. The length of time it takes for the photoelectric effect to take place was then determined. Niels Bohr and J. C. Slater of M.I.T. had suggested that this might take considerable time. With their apparatus and Ernest's knowledge of photoelectric technique, Ernest and Jesse were able to let light fall on various surfaces for extremely short intervals and determine, beyond doubt, that the time required is less than a billionth of a second!

This worked out in agreement with theory, but they had never expected to find the time interval so short. They repeated the experiment over and over, but the results always seemed to violate basic ideas of the time. They stuck by their data in the face of a good deal of criticism. Beams admired the apparent ease with which Ernest remained detached from expected or desired results and the influence of accepted theoretical interpretations.

When Ernest read the ensuing paper at a Physical Society meeting in December, his audience overflowed so into the hall that Dean Akeley's son, Edward, who had attended because of Ernest, could not get close enough to hear or see him. He did hear much favorable comment, which he relayed to Akeley, who was ill in a hospital in Minneapolis. It was considered by many physicists as the most important research of the year—though there was criticism, too, of course. It was by far the most discussed issue of the meeting and was reported in the New York papers, which Ernest clipped for his parents. After the meetings, he stayed with the Haugens over the New Year and attended the Naval Ball with them. "I especially enjoyed seeing the gay pomp of naval dress uniforms from the Admiral down, and had some good dances, including the Admiral's daughter," he wrote home.

Criticism of their experiment hinged chiefly on the possibility of faulty results through the use of Kerr cells, so the intrepid experimenters devised another, completely independent method, to check the experiment. A mirror was rotated at a sufficient velocity to flip light through a narrow slit with enough rapidity to permit observation of extremely short light segments. Data recorded verified the former experiment in which Kerr cells were used. The mirrors were spun on whirling jets of air; at one time, when about six thousand revolutions per second had been achieved, a mirror disappeared. They could not find it anywhere, nor could Swann. Professor Zeleny thought it ridiculous not to be able to locate it, or fragments of it in a closed room, but his search, too, proved unsuccessful. Months later the mirror was found, embedded in a wall corner.

"Have been working very hard," Ernest wrote his parents near Christmastime, "many nights till one or two. Not work in one sense of the word—it has all been great fun. We have a good time most of the time. Besides I have concocted a mathematical investigation to explain a host of mysterious things and hope to bring it to some kind of conclusion someday. I am not as skilled at juggling equations as I am at glassblowing, so the job is a bit harder for me. A great life. Went to church with Beams and made social calls in the afternoon before usual Sunday supper at Benedicts'. I read the remainder of the evening. I notice references to my work popping up in current periodicals."

Ernest was able to drag Beams out to a movie once in a while. It is doubtful that work was completely forgotten even then. On one occasion they talked physics right into the theater, after leaving the Ford on a street. A physical problem that must have been given some thought in the theater was discussed before they got out of the door after the movie, and was continued all the way back to the laboratory. The Ford was forgotten for two days. Then neither could remember where, in downtown New Haven, they had parked it. When found, it had been ticketed several times. It had to be pushed to start it. Just as they got it moving, a policeman stopped them. "Where do you think you're going?" he demanded. "To the jail," Ernest answered, laughing, showing the tickets. "You're damn right you are," the officer snarled. "You'll learn to make fun of the law!" They had to phone Don to come down and get them out.

Ernest could not persuade Jesse to drive to Haycock Point before Molly left for Vassar. He went a time or two by himself, and when John arrived with Joe Holleman en route to Harvard, he took them there unannounced, for an afternoon. But since, "you could hear the old Ford coming three blocks away," Elsie Blumer remembers, she, then fourteen, Bertha, nine, and Peggy, six, to tease Molly, were near the entrance to greet them. All kidding ceased when they saw the two younger men with Ernest. Molly was dragged out of hiding and everyone had a good time, swimming, at supper, and dancing on the porch. The girls agreed that John was much more handsome than Ernest—*and* three years younger. When Ernest drove John to Boston the next day, he insisted that John write to Elsie, thanking her for a good time. When he returned to New Haven, he wrote to Molly at Vassar. There was no answer.

He wrote again, later, asking her to go with him to the Harvard football game. She accepted, with a formal, "Dear Mr. Lawrence" note that invited him to a Blumer dinner party after the game. He scolded her for her formality and offered to meet her at the train. This time she wrote, "Dear Ernest: (Please note how nicely I began this time.)," and asked him to lunch at her mother's before the game. "Nice to offer to meet me but Mother said she'd be on hand." They rattled off in the flivver after lunch and parked some distance from the Yale Bowl, and after the game Ernest had completely forgotten where. It was Molly who found the car. She invited Ernest to a Vassar dance to be held in November. Serious Molly, whose idea of a beau was a handsome, pipe-smoking young man with a sports roadster, was glad to have even an "old" Yale man asking her to big games—to enable her to hold her own with girls who bragged continually about conquests of West Point cadets and Dartmouth beaux. His invitations also provided reasons for seeing her family—and she liked football.

A letter from Ruby in Siam told of exciting times in Japan, China, and the Philippines, and of romances and parties aboard ship. If Ernest was concerned that she might meet someone she preferred to him, he gave no indication. He never mentioned Ruby to Jesse or Tom; he talked only of Molly to them. They knew he went out with other girls —with Elizabeth Cooksey to the theater after a dinner party at the professor's home, and to another party after that "where I met and danced with lots of nice girls," as he wrote to John at Harvard, telling him in the same letter to "stick to your work and get to the top of your class." He had a Thanksgiving dinner at Professor Cooksey's at noon and another in the evening at the Benedicts! He was an usher at a dinner dance at the Lawn Club. He drove into the country a few times with a young lady who had a Franklin—to Woodbury, or to Lake Quassapaug. After a dancing party Dr. and Mrs. Blumer gave for Molly in January, Ernest wrote John more about Molly's Vassar roommate than about Molly.

In December, through Don's good graces, Ernest and Jesse were appointed proctors, Jesse in a freshman dormitory of the college, and Ernest in Vanderbilt Sheffield (Van Sheff), where undergraduates of the scientific school lodged. Ernest furnished his two rent-free rooms, one of which had a fireplace, with two beds, andirons, rugs, chairs, and even a piano. He wrote John that he could now visit him comfortably during the holidays, but that he should bring his books along so that he could study, and insisted that John send his grades. He never failed to congratulate him when they were good. John consulted Ernest on everything from joining fraternities to accepting dinners with faculty members, and always Ernest's advice concerned the effect any decision would have in advancing his brother in school, or his future career, insisting in every letter that John could get to the top if he worked and kept alert. He provided a good example for what he preached so continually. John, in Boston, kept hearing discussions of and seeing items in papers about his older brother's work. *Scientific American,* which in December had sent a man to photograph the apparatus constructed by Ernest and Jesse, in February asked Ernest for a two-page article, offering fifty dollars. "Good for popular reputation," he wrote John. "Our work is very important but becoming very hard."

Professor Loeb wrote from California that Ernest was being considered for an assistant professorship, and Professor Swann had inquiries about Ernest from the department chairman at Berkeley. This was more effective than the medicine prescribed for the flu, which had left a lingering cough for weeks but did not curtail his activities for more than a day or two. In February, Professor F. A. Osborn of the University of Washington, Seattle, asked Ernest to become an associate professor there at $3,500 a year, promising that he would have half of his time for research. Yale countered with the offer of an instructorship at $2,500 and the promise of promotion to assistant professor the following year at a minimum of $3,000. He decided to stay at Yale, as did Beams. He was happy there and liked New Haven. To celebrate, they invited Swann to New York for the opening of the Ziegfeld Theatre, where Beams's niece was to play in *Rio Rita*—and to visit the Bell laboratory. They visited the laboratory as planned, but substituted a movie for *Rio Rita* when they found prices for the opening ranged from $11.00 to $27.50 a seat. In March, however, Professor Osborn came to plead the advantages of the University of Washington. He explained how Ernest might achieve the rank of full professor in three years and promised much time and equipment for research. Ernest decided to accept. "I nearly pinched myself to see if I was dreaming," he wrote John. "A full professor at twenty-nine years of age!"

Yale then offered an immediate appointment as assistant professor at $3,000, the first time Yale had offered an assistant professorship to one who had never been an instructor. The advantages and prestige of Yale outweighed the greater salary and title. Ernest wrote politely to Osborn of his many friends in New Haven and of his happiness there. He had barely made his decision when a telegram arrived from California offering an assistant professorship there. He had known it was coming; Loeb had written copiously about the department at Berkeley: the new physics building, the fine younger men of the staff, including Raymond Birge, Frederick Brackett, John Hopfield, and Samuel Allison, all of whom could expect promotion on merit without waiting for older men to retire, as at so many other institutions. And James Franck, Nobelist from Göttingen, was to be lecturer in physics and chemistry. Professor Birge would attend the Washington meetings of the Physical Society in May and could answer any questions Ernest might have about advantages for research and promotion at California. "If I can stay at Yale with the same rank," he wrote John, "I wouldn't go to California if they offered to make me president of the university." He had scarcely rejected the California offer when one came from Cornell, offering him the same position but at a $3,500 salary. Cornell would pay expenses to go to Ithaca and look over the laboratory, and would he speak at a colloquium? Ernest went to Ithaca, spoke, and rejected the offer, as he had known he would. He wrote the good news to Ruby, too, at Aden, but said nothing about marriage now that he was a professor. She had talked of spending the summer in New York after her return, about the first of May. Ernest promised to meet her ship.

Not least among the incentives for remaining at Yale was the presence of Professor Swann, who presently announced his resignation to assume directorship of the Bartol Research Foundation of the Franklin Institute of Philadelphia in September. He would leave Yale in May, go to France with his beloved cello for study with Pablo Casals, and visit Cambridge en route. Ernest, after initial disappointment, reacted with characteristic optimism. Why not, he argued with Jesse, make the most of it and go to Cambridge with Swann? Then, while he devoted his time to music, they could visit the great laboratories of Europe. He advanced reasons enough to justify the trip; in the muggy summer weather electrometers would leak, making readings questionable. How much they would learn, in the European laboratories, perhaps talking with great physicists! It need not cost much; they could go tourist class and were assured of salaries for a year. Jesse agreed and Swann concurred happily. Ernest told John not to tell their parents; he himself would, when everything was settled. There would be a month at home in September after his return. "I see where President Coolidge is going to vacation at the Game Lodge in the Black Hills. Maybe we should drive out there again."

They worked later hours than ever preparing for the April meetings in Washington, Jesse finally taking data, while Ernest wrote the paper. That paper, with its startling conclusions that the lag in the Kerr Effect is no greater than a very minute fraction of a second, again created a stir. The quick succession of outstanding experimental proofs made Ernest celebrated in his own professional society. Professors Ernest Merritt and Osborn of Cornell and Washington urged him to reconsider their universities. Dr. Albert Hull, famous General Electric Company scientist, invited Ernest and Jesse to come as guests of General Electric to visit the Schenectady laboratories for several days. Professor Birge introduced himself and regretted that California had not succeeded in attracting Ernest. He expected to visit at Yale en route to Boston, and Ernest invited him to speak at Yale's colloquium, promised to meet him at the New Haven station, which he did, crowding the professor, Mrs. Birge, and their two children into the Ford—young Robert Birge had to sit on Ernest's lap while he drove.

Ernest visited Merle at the Carnegie Institution and was impressed with his friend's efforts to get high voltages for nuclear experiment. Ernest was doubtful that satisfactory high voltages could be made to work without electrical breakdown from voltage concentrations across the discharge tube; there must be some method of attaining high voltages without high costs in current, too. Many laboratories were at work on the problem; at General Electric, for example, there was W. D. Coolidge with his X-ray tubes. Merle and Ernest had quite an argument, "got quite hot" about the question. Merle insisted to the end that Ernest ought to get into the field, that it was far more important than "spinning tops." Ernest realized the importance of high energies and the excitement of nuclear work, but he felt that experimenters had yet to find a way to get those energies cheaply enough to be practical, and devise means to control them when they did. He gave much thought to a reasonable solution, feeling there must be a more practical way than had yet been suggested.

When Ernest and Jesse returned to New Haven, there were letters about their paper. Ernest had one from A. Soltan of Prince Maurice de Broglie's laboratory, asking for copies of all his papers. Ernest replied that they expected to be in Paris during the summer with Professor

Swann. An invitation to visit De Broglie's laboratory came by return mail. Jesse and Ernest tried to find time to bone up on French and German; they even tried conversing in the laboratory while working, but what had to be said, as a rule, required too precise a statement to risk an error of language. They thought it would be useful to visit the General Electric Laboratory, and they drove to Schenectady in the Ford, trying to limit themselves to French and German as they rode. Hull, Coolidge, and Irving Langmuir gave them a fine few days and invited them to spend that summer, or the next, at the laboratory. It appealed to them—for the following year.

When Ruby wrote the date of her expected arrival in New York and said she was "almost in love—but not sure," and must hurry home to her mother who was ill, Ernest sent her a telegram, regretting his inability to meet the ship.

"On the Nature of Light," by Lawrence and Beams, was published in the *Proceedings of the National Academy of Sciences* in the April issue, "On the Lag of the Kerr Effect" in the July issue of the same journal. Ernest and Jesse jointly prepared two other papers for publication, before their departure for Europe. Ernest's own dissertation—"Ultraionization Potentials of Mercury" was also published in July, in the *Journal of the Franklin Institute.*

Ernest did not get around to packing until late at night before sailing from New York. He arranged with a Loomis Fellow to take over his post as proctor and left his Ford on a slope outside Sloane for John to pick up and drive to Springfield for his vacation. "You'll have to push it downhill to get it started. Otherwise it's in fine shape." He got off a note to Molly, giving an address in England. Don Cooksey came by with his "hole-in-one," the golf ball with which he had made it, to give to his English brother-in-law, by way of introduction. Tom Johnson's farewell had a touch of sadness; he, too, was moving to Bartol and would not be in the laboratory next to his friends in the fall. It was early in the morning, May 28, 1927, when Ernest got to bed; there were but a few hours for sleep, before entraining for New York with Swann and Jesse, to board the ship.

The crossing to England provided rest and relaxation; it was also, in itself, a grand adventure. The S.S. *Minikada* had to be explored in every area open to a tourist passenger, and there were even intrusions above tourist limits; Ernest was ordered off the bridge—after a good look around and a brief conversation with the helmsman and the officer on duty. He had better luck in the lower sections and was fascinated by the great pistons, cranks, and condensers—the smooth transference of power from coal through steam to propeller. There was dancing at night and

Ernest lost no time making friends. He made a date for Paris with Peggy Read, who was traveling with her mother and who seemed to enjoy fast rounds of the deck with him as much as dancing.

In England Ernest and Jesse went directly to Cambridge with Swann, and at the Cavendish Laboratory met Sir Ernest Rutherford, who introduced them to Peter Kapitza, the Russian scientist who, with Rutherford's support, was experimenting with magnetic properties of matter. The brilliant, idiosyncratic Kapitza was as curious about America as the young travelers were about his work—and Russia. Rutherford also introduced them to his predecessor as head of the Cavendish Laboratory, Sir Joseph J. Thomson, who in 1897, with his discovery of particles now called electrons, had challenged the centuries-old idea of an individual atom as the ultimate unit of matter. Now Master of Trinity College, he was still active in the laboratory. The most interesting conversations were with younger physicists, such as John Cockcroft and James Chadwick. The British physicists seemed wise in ways of experiment with clean, simple apparatus; even the device with which Rutherford had first disintegrated the nucleus of lightweight elements was no larger than a shoe box.

After Cambridge, Ernest and Jesse parted from Swann, whom they would later rejoin in Paris. They saw the sights of London like any tourists, Ernest as frankly curious about the venerable as he had been about the tall in New York. Shops and shopkeepers' ways intrigued him; he purchased a rug for his rooms in Van Sheff, five yards of suiting, and articles of haberdashery. He persuaded Jesse that a rented car would give them freedom to see much more of the country, more reasonably than otherwise. An old Dodge, well running and neatly polished, was hired cheaply; not until the time to drive it from the garage did it occur to either of them that in England one drove on the left side of the street. Jesse absolutely refused to drive it out into London traffic, so Ernest took the wheel, on the unfamiliar right side of the car, and drove out into and down the street "as though he'd always driven that way." They looked up Don Cooksey's sister and brother-in-law, Dorothy and Arthur Flowers and delivered the golf ball. Don had said they would like his relatives, but they had not dreamed of being entertained so royally in the English home, and, indeed, in much of England. The Flowerses offered to show them as much as time would permit, and they covered a good deal of country, visiting, besides laboratories, historical sites, ruins, castles, and cathedrals—York Cathedral and Fountains Abbey most impressed Ernest. In Chester Cathedral he looked in vain for a prayer said to have been inscribed there, a copy of which Dr. Blumer had given him and which he kept on his desk—as he did the rest of his life:

Give me a good digestion, Lord, and also something to digest.
Give me a healthy body, Lord, with sense to keep it at its best. Give
me a healthy mind, good Lord, to keep the good and pure in sight,
which seeing sin is not appalled, but finds a way to set it right. Give
me a mind that is not bored, that does not whimper, whine or sigh;
don't let me worry overmuch about the fussy thing called I. Give
me a sense of humor, Lord; give the grace to see a joke, to get some
happiness from life, and pass it on to other folk.

They drove north to Richmond to see the eclipse, but, though it
darkened, nothing was to be seen of the eclipse, itself, hidden in cloud
and fog. Don's brother-in-law particularly liked Derbyshire and its
people, but Jesse and Ernest could scarcely understand them, though the
dialect they spoke was said to be English. It was not easy to leave these
generous hosts, but dozens of laboratories waited their inspection.

They crossed the North Sea to Denmark. Niels Bohr was away, but
they had a good look at his laboratory. Among several interesting physicists visiting at Bohr's institute, Ernest was particularly pleased to find
Meghnad Saha, the Indian physicist, whose formula for calculations of
degree of ionization had given him one of his earliest intellectual thrills
when he had read of it at Chicago. Saha's ionization equation had been
most useful in Ernest's work. In Hamburg, they talked with Otto Stern,
who had read of Ernest and asked him to speak to a group of students.
Ernest did—in English interspersed with German words. He and Jesse
booked a North Sea round trip from Hamburg, stopping in Belgium
and in Holland. At Leyden and Eindhoven, the Dutch had the finest
equipment they were to see in any of the European or English laboratories, and better than the average in the United States. Professor
Ehrenfest of Leyden also asked them to talk. Ernest told Jesse it was his
turn; Beams insisted that Ernest could do it better. At almost every laboratory they visited, they were asked to talk, and Ernest usually complied. "It never bothered him at all. He always just loved it, but mostly
he asked one question after another. If there was any physics involved,
at the laboratories or anywhere, he was right there," Beams remembers.
"He always stammered a little bit if he got excited, but it didn't bother
him." In Sweden, Ernest tried to revive the Norwegian he had discarded
as a boy because "I am an American." It may have helped, but Beams
thought not.

In Berlin, where they made a prolonged stay, Ernest negotiated for
bed and breakfast at a pension for something less than a dollar a day for
the two of them. He was so proud of his ability to make inexpensive
arrangements that he bragged of it to Professor Saha, whom they met
again at the University of Berlin. Saha, too, planned to stay a few weeks

in the German capital and asked how much Ernest was paying. "They're cheating you!" he said, when Ernest told him. He was paying about a third as much at his equally good *pension*.

Ernest was very eager to see Walther Nernst, director of the Physical Institute, but the *Herr* Professor seemed always to be unavailable, until they met Professor Pringsheim, who after listening patiently to their faltering German, startled them with his excellent English. He had been an internee in England during the war. He took the young men to Nernst immediately. Their German was sufficient to understand Pringsheim's German introduction: "Here are two young men who can speak neither English nor German."

Nernst was amused, but was most cordial, when he learned they were from "Yawl." They were amused that he "knew all about Yawl"; he had given the Silliman Lectures at Yale and had enjoyed it very much. He went out of his way to give the young men from "Yawl" a good time, and an interesting one. He took them to his home, introduced them to many physicists, not only at the institute but elsewhere in Germany, professed great interest in their work, and asked for reprints of their published papers.

Leipzig and Munich—there were so many places where physics was regarded as important, and where important work had been and was being done. It was understandable that Germany was considered the center of modern physics, though one must include England and Denmark, too. At Göttingen the director of physics, Nobelist James Franck, was as difficult to see as Nernst had been; it was not easy for junior men to meet the great *Herr Doktors*. Ernest was persistent. Franck was most cordial, once they met, and talked long with Ernest about the photoelectric effect in potassium vapor. Noted Max Born, who was in the forefront of new quantum theory, joined in the conversations and discussed his work. Franck was going to California the next year as a special lecturer and was interested that Ernest had been asked to join that faculty. In Munich, the later home of Wilhelm Roentgen, discoverer of X rays, Edward Condon talked of Berkeley, where recently he had taken his degree, and where he expected to return. He thought Ernest should give California serious consideration.

In Paris they located Professor Swann on the Rue St. Jacques and settled down in a nearby *pension*. Swann, happy with his music, spared time from it to introduce them to Madame Curie, who showed them the old-fashioned apparatus with which she had done her important work. Again the simple, humble device deeply impressed Ernest. She, like so many others, used various waxes to seal things, and to hold them together, and yet accomplished so much. Swann reminded them that it was only in the last quarter century that a physics laboratory could be distinguished from any other classroom. The inventor of the electronic valve, J. A. Fleming, stated that when he took over as professor of electrical engineering at University College, London, in the eighties, his entire laboratory equipment consisted of a piece of chalk and a blackboard. Swann introduced them at the Sorbonne, and, on their own, Ernest and Jesse visited Charles Fabry and his laboratory. Soltan, who had written Ernest about his work, introduced them to the Prince de Broglie, whose suggestion of the wave nature of electrons, and therefore of matter, would be first demonstrated this year, in America.

In many of the dozens of European laboratories Ernest and Jesse visited, they met American students, drawn by the great names and reputations. Among some a degree of snobbishness toward the visitors, all of whose training had been in American institutions, was evident. But, "I'm satisfied," Ernest said emphatically to Jesse, "not only because of our superior facilities, but our training. We are not behind except in fame. It won't be long before all these people will be going to the United States; physics is on the move there, too."

Ernest was not particularly nationalistic, certainly not at that time. He had chosen to visit the numerous laboratories of Europe, and to see and talk with respected men who worked in them. He was well aware of their tremendous contributions to physics, in modern times as well as in the past. He could be thrilled as perhaps a more sophisticated scientist would not be—at least not admit to being, or show—by a Rutherford with his little apparatus that, with alpha rays, bombarded targets, with resulting transmutations; in a Madame Curie; by the theoretical probes of men at Göttingen, Copenhagen, Berlin—everywhere on that side of the Atlantic from the British Isles to Vienna, where erudite Erwin Schrödinger had recently suggested a theory of wave mechanics different from those suggested in Göttingen, Copenhagen, and by Paul Dirac in Britain. Whose theories were more nearly correct—more workable? Such eminent explorers could only draw tremendous respect and admiration from the young men so recently turned to science from the prairies of the Middle West.

But it was not, Ernest was certain, because these persons were Germans, or Austrians, Frenchmen, or Englishmen; if the United States had done less it was because it was a young nation, while the environment that encouraged scholarship in Europe was centuries old—with, by and large, a long tradition of excellence. There were many good laboratories in his own country, and men of science there, the famous and those about to achieve their reputations. They borrowed from the past no more than did Europeans; science always built on what had already been made known. Nor should science, he thought, observe boundaries; it was one great system that applied to all men, everywhere.

Democratic to the core, he resented any form of snobbishness or arrogance and believed such manifestations revealed weakness. With so much to know, to discover, how could an intelligent person set himself above another because of place, or advantage of birth? It was not the Europeans who caused his resentment, but his own countrymen. It was as Emerson had felt about his contemporaries who thought one could not be cultured without the grand tour. It was not study in Europe, but the man himself that made the great scientist. The dedicated man would contribute, whether his degree was from Göttingen or a young, public university.

A letter from Molly expressed the hope that Ernest would see something besides laboratories, and indeed he did. He wrote to her about cathedrals, ruins, and from Switzerland, particularly, mountains. There was not a famous place he had read or heard about that he did not visit—the Eiffel Tower, all the famous tourist attractions were included. In Paris he visited the Left Bank with his shipmate Peggy Read, and in the city she helped select a Spanish shawl for his mother, and gallivanted about Paris and its environs at Ernest's pace—from the Louvre to Versailles to Notre Dame Cathedral. Beams marveled at Ernest's ability—and sometimes nerve—in keeping expenses down while accomplishing more than they had dreamed possible. He even ventured to lecture Swann on money, when their professor bought a new cello. Ernest thought he was paying too much and proceeded to explain to his mentor how interest on such an amount would accumulate in a few years. Swann said Ernest was much too business-minded to understand a musician.

It was not his business mind, but all-engulfing science that prevented Ernest from understanding how so fine a physicist as Swann could find a stronger appeal in another art. During the years at Yale, Swann had often left everything to go to New York to play in a quartet. Ernest had never thought that strange, but in Europe, for a brief few weeks, there was so much to see, so many laboratories with their exciting explorers of nature's frontiers, all in so small a radius, yet it was the cello and music that occupied all of Swann's attention. Many scientists found solace in music, but it was hard for Ernest to imagine an Einstein or a Michelson giving predominance to their violins. Only regard for his young friends could lure Swann from his cello, or a laboratory. There had been a few fine Parisian dinners and evenings together, but if the young men saw Swann during the day it was briefly. They realized that their intimate association with Swann was at an end; they realized how much they had gained through working with him and had thought of the days in Paris as a sort of farewell party. He had always been available for endless talk if they went to him, and, perhaps as importantly, he had left them alone with their work. Perhaps he was deliberately casting them adrift on their own. Swann laughed at the idea; he was devoted to them also. They did not need him anymore so far as their work was concerned; he would see them often anyway; he was not moving his family from New Haven at once. Philadelphia was not at the end of the world. If they did not go to Bartol to visit him, he would be often enough in New Haven to visit them.

It was Ernest who first left New Haven after their return from New York, where they had docked on August 16. He picked up much-needed checks, including one from *Scientific American*, and, after a couple of trips to Haycock Point to see Molly, went too Springfield for a few weeks with his parents.

Mother Lawrence was pleased that he had gained weight. "If you keep it up they won't be able to call you 'Skinny' anymore," she said, recalling her son's pleasure at being accepted by the boys in Pierre. No one had called him that for years, Ernest told her, and very few used the nickname Ernie; Merle did, and sometimes Jesse and Tom Johnson. He was Lawrence to most of his associates, Dr. Lawrence to those he knew less well, and soon would be addressed as Professor. She was proud of him, so successful, so talked about, though only twenty-six. A professor at Yale, one who had traveled in so many countries in Europe, who spoke of incomprehensible things and seemed so much a man of the world. But she was not surprised that he could stand up and talk with famous professors and doctors of the great universities of the world; his curiosity and insistence on "just one good reason" had baffled her too often to amaze her now that he had gone so far with his "schooling." Some of the pride Carl felt lay in the fact that his son was a teacher in a great university—the third in a succession of teachers since the Lawrences had come to America.

Ernest did not see Ruby when he drove to Gary; she was in Kansas City. But just before he left to return to Yale, he had a letter from her, which came right to the point: "I'm desperately in love—and if you're going to look cynical and say 'I told you so,' you can stop reading this. . . . You did say something of the sort would happen on that cruise because of all the 'intense situations,' but you can't call it just another shipboard romance . . . out of all perfect spots in the world [I] chose the zoo at Kansas City to become engaged. I tried hard to be in love with you because you were so frightfully nice I really thought I must be crazy not to be. . . . Of course I adored your brains and your smile but a brain and a smile can't make one really dizzy. . . . You wouldn't like each other at all because you are both so disgustingly conceited. As I said before I adore one and love the other and there you are. Somehow I'd like for you to tell me you are glad."

If anyone knew at the time, it is not now remembered whether he was glad, or sad. He had had his doubts during the past year because of increasing interest in Mary Blumer. But Molly did not appear to care very deeply for him. Only seventeen, with three more years at Vassar, where she was an exceptional student, she might get over the idea that she would never marry. He talked of her with his mother—still cautious and practical in her advice. Take Merle, whose marriage, while Ernest was in Europe, had been a surprise; he knew something of his bride and her background. The niece of the Reverend ("Uncle Henry") Rasmussen, the Canton pastor, Winifred Whitman was "their sort of people." Ernest thought it more interesting that she had received an M.D. degree at Minnesota before becoming Mrs. Tuve. Molly talked of becoming a doctor. It was amusing to think that the two physicists, who, as boys, had planned to become physicians, should be interested in mates with that ambition. Ernest returned to New Haven in time to see Molly a few times before she left for college.

Molly's greeting was as casual as usual when he arrived at Haycock Point, unannounced. Her family, as always, were cordial, Elsie and Bertha elaborately so. Ernest never knew how much amusement he afforded the sisters—at Molly's expense. Peggy, only eight and a quiet child, was always pleasantly polite, nor did she join in teasing Molly. The entire family were very likable, it did not matter much that he seldom saw Molly alone at the shore; even in the canoe Elsie or Bertha always managed to be along. When John visited him on his way to Boston, he took him again to Haycock Point. The water was so cold that day there was little swimming and no canoeing, and Molly was completely engrossed with plans for returning to Vassar. He had little time or inclination to wonder about Molly's casual attitude. Reasons enough to explain it seemed apparent to one whose own mind was concentrated on science, without damage to romantic notions concerning her. It was admirable that she was interested in her studies to the exclusion of other interests; he wanted no flighty girl for a wife, however much his mother might worry on that score.

Research, in any event, was an overriding interest before which all others could be pushed easily to the periphery of his thought. No concern entailed so much delight as a complex laboratory problem, and no conversation quite equaled the give and take of theoretical or experimental discussion. Conversation often raised further problems of promise, sometimes of more interest than the original issue. Thus, in addition to the work with Beams, there were always two, or even three, other experiments running concurrently with the main project. It was always a wrench to leave experimentation for the necessary preparation of classroom assignments, though he had looked forward to the challenge of teaching, hoping to inspire others as he had been inspired by Dean Akeley and Professor Swann.

He enjoyed the work at first. Though he had eight o'clock classes, often hard to awaken for after a long night in the laboratory, his teaching assignments were fairly light out of consideration for his important research, and elementary courses required little preparation. After a couple of weeks he was able to write John that he liked teaching, that it took about "half my time, research the remainder, and social matters a bit of time too." But he did not find the elementary classes stimulating. No matter how hard he tried, he seemed unable to arouse enthusiasm in his students, most of whom were taking physics because it was required rather than because of real interest in the subject. Even among science majors he found little of the joy he had himself known in comprehending some aspect of nature. A great questioner in his student days, he was irritated more often than pleased by questions put to him; irritated because of the nature of the question, and he was reminded of Rutherford's admonition, "Go home, my boy—and think!" He tried to pick out those who were really inquisitive, without finding the spark that could be fanned to creative fire. With his usual optimism he decided that teaching would be more challenging with upper division and graduate students. There had been fewer "bums" and "weak sisters" in graduate courses he had taken.

His disillusionment was nearly complete when students were caught cheating during an examination, two of them majors in physics. How could one hope to understand nature, to experiment successfully, and push forward the frontiers of knowledge, if he was not completely honest! Though he did not have to discipline the culprits who were "flunked and dropped from the course" by a student committee, it bothered him for days. Certain colleagues were amused that he took it so seriously; there had always been dishonest students who would do anything to get by. It was not amusing in any sense to the young professor. Honesty had been a principal virtue taken for granted in his family —how could one seek truth if he himself were not true? And how could there be degrees of truth, subtle shadings of veracity! One might be wrong about a fact but never deliberately dishonest. A mistake of fact should be admitted and corrected; one might learn thereby. To put forth a wrong fact deliberately, to cheat for advantage in however small a matter, was as evil as to steal or to lie. Not usually given to philosophizing, or generally concerned with problems of good and evil, Ernest

was deeply disturbed by the event. Was the habit of honesty more rare than common? It was good to forget it in the deep involvement of research where there could be no compromise with truth.

The gentle Beams, so unquestionably moral in every way that he understood Ernest's distress, was a little more aware of human nature. The war had upset values for many people, and the present prosperity had made the easy way seem smart. Religious influence had declined, perhaps. Though Ernest sometimes attended church with the more faithful Jesse, he did not consider religion necessary to cultivate the habit of truth. Millikan had lectured at Yale on religion and science, finding no necessary cleavage between them. Ernest talked with Millikan afterward and came away with other ideas than he had clarified for himself. Intellectual honesty, for instance, was a quality that might necessitate some training, and for a scientist this was of prime importance. Beams thought Ernest had this beyond any doubt; he did not rationalize mistakes and never seemed to harbor a pet idea simply because it was his. Neither man made excuses; it was about this time that Ernest wrote to Dean Floyd Richmeyer at Cornell in response to a query about a young physicist: "I am usually suspicious of a person that excuses lack of research activity because of other obligations."

While there could be no compromise with truth, it is interesting to note that when Carl Lawrence wrote about a respected man's involvement in a paternity case, Ernest's written reply mentioned only amazement that so intelligent a man should have been so careless. And in other correspondence he warned that a certain girl was not the kind one would "go so far" with as to involve her too seriously. He had rebuked students for bringing girls to Van Sheff but had not actually found misconduct. William Watson, who was to join the faculty and eventually become head of the physics department, and Ernest were leaving Van Sheff for dinner one evening, when Ernest noticed a young woman being escorted into the building. He excused himself and after a quick check rejoined Watson. "It's an instructor, so it's all right," he reported with a laugh.

He spent very little time in his rooms and sometimes made his presence known there by playing the piano, even if for only a few minutes before leaving. His charges were not so wild as some of Beams's were; Jesse had had to hide in his own closet guns corraled from Western students. Oliver Overseth, who spent a couple of nights with his cousin, noticed a splotch on the wall over the sofa and asked about it. "Oh, a student threw an egg in one night." "Why? Were they mad at you?" Oliver was incredulous. "No. They're all my friends," Ernest replied. After midnight Ollie was awakened by what sounded like chairs being thrown down the stairs. He called out to Ernest, who did not awaken and who in the morning said he had not heard anything. He seldom used the rooms for study; even his letters were written in the laboratory where he had books, typewriter, and a clasped Art Steel file the size of a large dictionary in which he kept receipts and personal letters from Ruby, his parents, John, and those offering positions. His increasing correspondence took too much time, except for the almost weekly letters to parents and those of encouragement and gossip to John at Harvard. Answers to academic people about positions, experimental problems, requests for papers, and congratulatory letters pertaining to his work had to be more carefully written, but he liked to hear from others and tried to answer promptly.

Professor Loeb wrote that it was still hoped that he would cast his lot with California, indicating that he expected that a position Ernest might find attractive enough to make him leave Yale would soon be forthcoming. Loeb also continued to write others to "do missionary work with Lawrence," including Edward Condon, who spent a few days with Ernest at Yale, and Muriel Ashley, a graduate student from California who was later to become the wife of the California Nobelist and expert on very low temperatures, William Giauque. "We can have the leading department in the U.S. if we can get the best young men." Professor Swann was not only urged by Loeb to persuade Ernest to consider California favorably, he was queried by other faculties. Swann reported that Columbia was considering his protégé and soon an invitation came for Ernest to speak at Columbia. Ernest gave the lecture before a large audience of physicists from the environs of New York City, was dined by the dean and full professors of the Engineering College, but did not seriously consider a move to New York. "Too many attractions here, ha, ha," he wrote John. Condon, briefly at the Bell Laboratories, learned, and reported to Loeb, that the fact Ernest had no graduate teaching, and no graduate students to help with experiments was a minor cause of dissatisfaction on his part. There never was time enough for experiment, and there was so much he wanted to do, much of which could have been done by graduate students under his direction, as it was for more senior professors.

Some of these older men resented Ernest's appointment as assistant professor without a proper apprenticeship as an instructor. Ernest also found that being a Yale professor did not automatically confer status with the entire faculty; he detected an element of snobbishness in questions about his family and background. He sputtered about that a bit to Beams and to Swann, whom he saw frequently. Such snobbishness could be ignored—if it did not prevent one's advancement. The Zelenys accepted him, and the Cookseys, among other respected families who invited him to their homes. And who in New Haven could feel superior to the Blumers?

If the George Blumers were more democratic than some of the Yale elite, they, too, had questions concerning Ernest's background, though these had nothing to do with South Dakota or parents who were only second-generation Americans. Dr. Blumer was himself an immigrant, but his English birth was, to some of the socially exacting, an advantage. He was no social snob, but did remark to Mrs. Blumer one night after Ernest had been to dinner: "That young man has had no decent education, and he seems always to have done just what he wanted to and nothing else." Mrs. Blumer agreed that it seemed "pretty much true," but she liked him just the same. His frank admission, often, that he didn't know what was being talked about was refreshing to her, however surprising that a Yale Ph.D. should be ignorant of subjects even the children knew about. "Is this a custom?" he still often asked. Mrs. Blumer, however much amused over the delight Elsie and Bertha took in teasing, cautioned them about staring when Ernest showed a lack of sophistication, or committed some *faux pas,* and she herself learned to check quick looks of surprise directed toward Ernest after she was sure he noticed them. And he had noticed, had been embarrassed, and had forgotten them. Mrs. Blumer thought Ernest a "bit clumsy" at first but said he had improved in social manners. It never occurred to her that Molly, whom the whole family regarded as "something very special," could take his attentions seriously—any more than it did to Molly herself.

Dr. Blumer was not averse to joining the fun. Serious of mien, but with twinkling eyes, he asked Molly: "What were his parents thinking of when they gave him such a name! Ernest Orlando! If they had to have such names, it should correctly have been either Ernesto Orlando, or Ernest Roland. How could they have arrived at this confusion?" Molly tried to ignore it, but from then on she was Rosalind and he, Sir Orlando, or even Sir Lawrence. Too polite to refer to him thus in his presence, the sisters sometimes dared to use "Rosalind" in addressing Molly in his hearing, and Elsie might go so far as to say, "As you like it, Sir," without Ernest ever realizing the Shakespearean connotation. Dr. Blumer habitually wrote to his daughter on Sundays, a day Ernest usually called—early if invited for dinner, otherwise after dining with the Benedicts. Dr. Blumer would close his paternal letter with a post-script that the "faithful Orlando will post it on his way home."

Ernest invited Molly to both the Army and Princeton football games, after which there were dinners and dancing parties, and once, after she had come for a wedding, Dr. Blumer let him drive Molly to her train in the family car and return for dinner at the Blumer home. He now had a rival in a Yale senior who liked to dance but, to Ernest's advantage, hated football. Since he waited until after a game to call Molly, he failed to get her for dancing on these occasions. It was Ernest whom she asked to a New Year's Eve party at the home of one of her friends, and John, who was with Ernest for the holidays, went along with Elsie.

Once, after a day at the General Electric Laboratory in Schenectady, where Don Cooksey had driven him, Ernest asked Don to return by way of Poughkeepsie and allow him to call on a Vassar girl. When Don learned that the girl was Mary Blumer, he insisted that Ernest take the sporty La Salle by himself, and show Molly a good time. Don, who knew the Blumers well and admired Molly, took a train to New York, and Ernest took Molly for a Saturday afternoon drive to West Point. To return to Vassar by sign-in time, Molly suggested a shortcut, and they got lost. While she tried to become oriented, Ernest tried to tell her his feelings for her. He was rebuffed; Molly said she definitely was not interested in love, did not intend ever to marry, and was as dedicated to a career of meaning and service as he was. They drove in silence in a supposedly correct direction and were shortly stuck fast in mud. Ernest had to get a farmer and a team of horses to extricate the car. Molly was very late signing in at Vassar. Nevertheless, she was able, and willing, to drive into the country north of Poughkeepsie with Ernest Sunday morning and have lunch with him before he drove back to New Haven—in three hours, "Some car!" He went directly to the Blumer residence and told them he had been with Molly, which he thought pleased them. He did not mention his declaration of honorable intentions, though Molly was no longer able to pretend, at least to herself, that his interest in her was not romantic.

Beams was not in the laboratory when Ernest later stopped by Sloane, so he went to his rooms, which turned out to be fortunate. Ernest and Jesse had been using a high-powered oscillating circuit which caused much interference with radio reception in New Haven, so much, in fact, that a newspaperman had tracked the source to the Sloane Laboratory. Radio merchants had lodged complaints to the effect that the static would force them out of business, and the two experimenters had agreed not to use their oscillator at night. On this particular Sunday night, radio reception had been practically impossible due to static, and the following day's paper accused the experimenters of violating the agreement. Jesse and Ernest were able to prove that they had not been in the laboratory on Sunday. Professor Boltwood was so incensed at the accusation that he made the paper retract its statement and declare the young men innocent. Such publicity was amusing to Jesse and Ernest, who had become used to seeing their names in the papers for more creditable reasons. Ernest had another article, on light, in the *Scientific American,* and the New York *Herald Tribune* asked him to do an article. He replied that he was too busy to consider it until after the February meetings of the Physical Society.

Al Swanholm, that nephew of his uncle's widow who had thought Ernest a prig ten years before in Canton because he would not help him find a girl for a dance at "hell's corner," stopped in New Haven. He suggested that Ernest was becoming famous, judging by the frequency of articles by or about him, and that if he were smart he could land a high-paying job with a big company. Ernest showed Al an offer of a very profitable position with a major company which he had recently rejected. "But you can't ever make money like that at a university!"

"No, I've dedicated myself to service, to the good of mankind." Al thought that sounded a bit pompous, despite the grin that followed. He was impressed by the apparatus in Ernest's attic laboratory and spread out in two basement rooms that had also been made available for Lawrence-Beams experiments.

Those experiments went "swimmingly," as Ernest wrote John. "Our lucky star seems to stay with us." They prepared another paper for the February meetings of the Physical Society. Just as Ernest was leaving for their meetings on the twenty-fifth, he received a long letter from the chairman of the physics department at the University of California. Professor Elmer E. Hall wrote that he had been authorized by the president of the university to invite Ernest to join the faculty as an associate professor, at a salary of $3,300, with a $300 allowance for moving expenses. The letter detailed many advantages: graduate courses and graduate students, generous funds for research, and a weekly teaching load of no more than nine hours of lecture work, probably less, depending on the nature of the work and the extent of graduate work directed. In the same mail came a very long letter from Leonard Loeb listing faculty members—Robert Brode, whom Ernest had met at Princeton, had been added to the staff—facilities and advantages and describing the great charm of the campus at Berkeley. Ernest left for New York elated but with mixed feelings. He did not want to leave New Haven for many reasons: chief among those he voiced would be his separation from Jesse Beams, the perfect research partner. Though Swann was not at Yale, he was frequently in New Haven, where his wife still maintained their home. Ernest would certainly miss the Blumers, however adamant their daughter might be that her interest could never be more than friendship; there were so many friends and ties; and he liked Yale and the Sloane Laboratory. Professor Louis McKeehan, who had taken Swann's place as director of the laboratory, had been helpful in every way. Loeb's letter assured him that the democratic spirit of California would be to his liking, that his research facilities would equal, if not surpass, those at Yale, and emphasized again, as had Hall, that promotion was strictly on merit, regardless of age or other factors such as might stand in one's way at Yale and some other Eastern universities.

The Lawrence-Beams report of experimental proof that it takes less than three-billionths of a second for an electron to be knocked out of a potassium metal film when struck by light in a photoelectric cell, caused excitement at the meetings, but Ernest had California on his mind. He consulted several men about the situation, some of whom thought a move to Berkeley would be beneficial, while others thought that however good, it was too far from the center of science—by which they meant the Eastern seaboard and Europe. Some thought exchanging a famous school for a state university across the country would be folly for one so promising. Others agreed with Beams that Yale would never let him go. Franck of Göttingen, who had just spent a month as special lecturer at California, told Ernest that the Berkeley department was every bit as good as Yale's.

The impending visit to New Haven of his parents was also on Ernest's mind, and he left New York after a short visit with Oliver Overseth, who had a new job there, to prepare for their arrival, and to discuss the California offer in further detail with Professor Zeleny, who had been startled to learn of it at the meeting. Awaiting Ernest at Yale was a letter from Professor Birge urging the merits of the California position: "I am very sure that anything you do here will be appreciated for its own worth, and your age, family connections, etc., etc., will not be taken into consideration in such appreciation." Birge added that an immediate decision was not necessary: ". . . get all the information possible, both as to your present place and prospects and as to ours." Ernest wrote the California professors that the offer was extremely tempting and appreciated, and that he had been asked by Professor Zeleny to wait for a Yale verdict on his immediate future there.

His father and mother stayed at the Benedicts' the three nights they spent in New Haven. They were entertained for dinner at the Swanns', where all the talk was of California, for chocolate and cookies at the Zelenys', where the professor argued that Ernest should remain at Yale. Zeleny took John, who had come for his parents' visit, to a corner and asked him to use what influence he had to prevent Ernest from making "the terrible mistake of leaving Yale, just as he was becoming famous, for California." Zeleny also tried to impress the advantages of Yale on the parents. That they might meet Molly, Ernest invited her to New Haven for a Maria Jeritza concert. The Blumers entertained the Lawrences for dinner before the event, and Dr. Blumer later drove them to the Benedicts'—where Gunda sat down at once to write to John, who

had returned to Boston: "Say, Elsie certainly is a peach! She is absolutely the most attractive girl I ever met. She is the kind of girl who
would make an ideal wife. Better cultivate her friendship, John. I can't
say as much for Molly. She is too cold and intellectual, and I can't see
how anyone could fall in love with her. But Elsie, to my mind, is an
ideal girl." In a later letter to John, she wrote: "Blumers are a very nice
family—and Elsie beats them all. We were not so much impressed by
Molly—though I am sure she is a fine girl—but she hasn't the personality that Elsie has." John was inclined to agree about Elsie but wrote
his mother that she and her younger sister thought "Moll *the* super
person!!"

Gunda's comments to her eldest were less direct, more revealing in
what she did not say. "You have to think twice before taking a wife who
is rich and has been used to everything," she said, with similar remarks
which were in no way consistent with her comments about a sister raised
in the identical atmosphere. Perhaps Ernest's interest in Molly had some
bearing on Gunda's pleasure that Ernest was seriously considering a
move to California from "great Yale," of which she had been so proud.
"A son at Yale and a son at Harvard" had been a source of satisfaction
not to be surpassed. The New Haven warnings that her son's move
would be a tragic mistake seemed not to bother her at all.

Molly, too, seemed pleased about Ernest's offer. When he confided
that he had about made up his mind to accept, she showed no sign that
she would regret his absence—for games, dances, and dinners. He assured her, with his big smile, that she would not be entirely rid of him.
Professor Loeb had written that he could probably go East for meetings
at least every other year, and perhaps more often, with university support. Dr. and Mrs. Blumer did not believe that Yale would fail to meet
or better California's offer, considering the reputation Ernest had already earned. He told them he did not want to leave but had to be
practical about it.

Beams was the person most upset when Ernest finally made his decision to go to California, after Zeleny said he could do no more for him
at the time. Jesse stormed into Zeleny's office and said permitting Ernest
to leave would prove to be the biggest mistake Yale had ever made, that
Ernest would soon be one of the greatest physicists of this or any other
country, and that they could keep him simply by making him an associate professor and allowing him graduate courses and students. "I'll bet
that within ten years Ernest wins the Nobel Prize. He has the clearest
conception of fundamental problems of anyone I know. The work he is
contemplating is really inspiring." Zeleny said that he was inclined to
agree with what Beams said, but that he had been unable to convince
the dean, chiefly because of Ernest's youth. (He did not tell Jesse what

he and others involved believed, that Ernest would never leave Yale for a Western state university.) What bothered some of them, Beams argued, was that one so young could do so much. Zeleny agreed that there were people who thought Ernest too aggressive. "Because he wants to get things done!" Beams stormed. "Anyone who's trying to do new things, and has new ideas, is going to be criticized. But look at all the people here he has helped so generously; he doesn't care if it is the lowest student with an idea, or a Nobel Prize winner." Jesse, the modest, quiet one, surprised Zeleny with his outburst of loyalty and admiration, the expression of which was not confined to Zeleny. But the dean's decision was final.

Ernest wrote to Professors Hall, Birge, and Loeb that he was delighted to accept their offer and looked forward to joining their group. To Loeb he added that he had been influenced by the promised light teaching schedule—"I am more interested in finding more of Mother Nature's secrets than telling to someone else things I already know about her" —and the chance to teach graduate students and have them work with him experimentally. His chief regret in leaving Yale, he added, was that it would separate him from Jesse Beams.

The two continued with their experiment concerning relaxation of electric fields in Kerr cells, spurred on by the hope of getting results in time to send an abstract of their findings to the April Physical Society meetings in Washington. Each was conscious that this would likely be their last experiment together, and they worked hard. When Molly was in New Haven, instead of going to a show, Ernest took her to the laboratory—being careful to tromp noisily up the stairs in warning—and sat her up on a table to watch them. A question of chemistry came up that stumped them momentarily, and, when Molly answered it, they looked at her in surprise. "My golly, aren't you the wonder!" Ernest exclaimed, rushed over and grabbed her around the waist. "How do you know so much?" Molly thought they must be pretending ignorance. It was not difficult. "I study chemistry," she answered. "For heaven's sake, isn't she something!" Ernest said.

In the middle of March the experiment suddenly "went bad on us," and there was all-night work and a full weekend in the laboratory with a glassblower, getting things right. But what lifted the exhausted experimenters' spirits was a letter from the University of Virginia, offering Beams an associate professorship and charge of experimental research. Ernest was so happy that he insisted on a celebration. Jesse thought the best celebration would be sleep, but there was no denying his friend. The following day Ernest wrote to Professor L. G. Hoxton at Virginia lauding Beams and congratulating the department at Virginia for obtaining so outstanding a person and physicist. Hoxton replied that Ernest's letter had pleased everybody: "We are happy at the thought of having that Beam of sunshine with us again, both as a psychological and optical asset." Professor Zeleny tried to dissuade Jesse, as he had Ernest, from leaving; in vain he offered Beams an assistant professorship as inducement to stay. A few weeks after Beams's acceptance of the Virginia offer, it was announced at Sloane that assistant professors' salaries were to be raised $500 in the fall. Zeleny kidded Beams about salary differences, "trying to rub it in that we had both made mistakes. Our retort," wrote Ernest to John, " 'There are things which money can't buy.' "

In March Ernest bought a Reo "Flying Cloud" coupe with rumble seat, less than a year old, that had been driven only seven thousand miles: "A wonderful bargain, guaranteed to go seventy-five miles an hour. I've already gone sixty-three," he wrote John. Shortly thereafter Ernest drove to New York and on Saturday showed the car off to Oliver Overseth. Ollie drove it down Broadway, and near 86th Street a truck pulled alongside and the driver called out that they had brand-new tires "very cheap." Ollie shook his head, but Ernest said he needed tires for the trip to California, that the Reo had an unusual size tire, and maybe they could dicker for a couple. "Ernest always loved to dicker," Ollie claims. They were asked to pull around the corner. The men wanted fifteen dollars apiece for Reo size tires. Despite Ernest's efforts, they refused to lower the price and peeled the paper off a tire to show that it was a good new one. "Let's skip it," Ernest said, and they got back in the Reo and started off. The truck caught up. They could buy two tires for $10 each. Ernest had to borrow ten dollars from Ollie, and two wrapped tires were put in the rumble seat. After driving a few blocks back up Broadway, Ernest was suddenly skeptical. They pulled up to the curb and tore off the wrappings; the tires were old, with little remaining tread. Ollie laughed. "You may be a tremendous genius, but you can still be taken like any ordinary sucker." Ernest refused to chuck them; he needed tires for his trip and might trade these for new ones in New Haven. Since the car would be too crowded with students who had been promised rides, he expressed the tires back to New Haven.

Much correspondence went back and forth between New Haven and California all spring. He was asked to list items needed for his research so they might be obtained if not presently in the laboratory, about living quarters, and the amount of room needed for his work. Loeb spent a couple of nights with Ernest after the Washington meetings, and in May, Ernest, who had driven to Lynn, Massachusetts, to price optical equipment, met Loeb in Providence and drove him to New Haven for another stay. During the visits, Ernest learned much more of what seemed to be the happy situation at Berkeley. He decided to live on the campus, at the Faculty Club, which Loeb thought one of the best, at least as far as food was concerned, in both quality and price, and where the company was often stimulating and always pleasant.

When the final experiment was completed, except for the writing, he drove Mrs. Swann to Philadelphia, where his parting from Swann brought tears to the eyes of both men. Swann prophesied that they'd meet at least once a year. Since the California academic year terminated the middle of May, there would always be time for Ernest to attend spring meetings of the Physical Society in Washington, and, Swann thought, Ernest would always have good reason to attend—with or without expenses paid by the university. There would also be the long Christmas vacations, allowing time for other meetings.

The wrench in leaving Yale would be great indeed. There were many close friendships and associations besides Beams and Swann, both in and outside Sloane: Don Cooksey, who had opened so many doors to him— "It was only necessary to open any door a crack for Ernest," Cooksey said—young men on fellowships or others in graduate school; professors; the spirit of the laboratory generally; and New Haven itself. All were meaningful. Dr. Blumer, who had interned in San Francisco, and later, in 1905 and 1906, taught at the University of California Medical School before starting his long tenure at Yale, thought Ernest would like California. He said, in Ernest's presence, that Yale had made a mistake in letting him go. Mrs. Blumer, who had grown fond of the "rather raw young man who had developed a good deal socially in two years," appeared to be the only Blumer genuinely sorry that Ernest was leaving, though the younger girls thought he was a little better-looking, now, and approved of his better car. Molly, her feelings colored by the continued teasing of her sisters, refused to admit publicly that he particularly liked her and maintained to them that she did not like him at all: "All he can ever talk about is physics and chemistry."

The university, as though eager to terminate the association, asked Ernest to vacate his rooms early, for alumni arriving for reunions. The last articles by Lawrence and Beams were finished and sent off: "On Relaxation of Electric Fields in Kerr Cells and Apparent Lags of the Kerr Effect," to the *Journal of the Franklin Institute;* and "Element of Time in the Photoelectric Effect," to the *Physical Review,* for publication during the summer. As soon as classes were over and the last examination papers corrected, Ernest and Jesse left their laboratories for the last time together, refusing to say good-bye—they would meet often, perhaps work together again in some university. ("I consider Ernest probably my best friend, certainly one of the best friends I ever had," Beams said in 1960.)

Ernest went to Boston, taking various articles of his furnishings to John. The brothers came back to New Haven for two fine days at the shore with the Blumers before starting for South Dakota by a rather circuitous route, loaded down with Ernest's belongings, including the English rug and his andirons for their parents. The first stop, in New York, was to console Oliver, whose wife had died shortly after the birth of a son; then to Washington and the Tuves, General Electric in Pittsburgh, where Ernest was given a specially made gas-filled cesium photoelectric cell; Cleveland, Ann Arbor, Chicago, Madison, and Minneapolis.

Since the fall semester at Berkeley would open on August 17, and Ernest wanted to be established and have his research started, there were only a couple of weeks in Springfield. However, he took his parents with him for a few days in Yellowstone Park, John riding in the rumble seat, with luggage in and around it, and getting soaked with rain a couple of times. After seeing the park and doing some fishing, the parents were put on a train at Leander, Wyoming, for their return to Springfield. Ernest and John continued on to Berkeley, crossing the Sierras over Donner Pass, thrilled by the mountains and the winding descent to Sacramento. Berkeley seemed a paradise after the summer heat of the Sacramento Valley. John stayed a couple of days at the Faculty Club with Ernest before returning to South Dakota. He reported Ernest well situated in a beautiful place and eager to get to work.

CHAPTER V

How to Get a Million Volts

Associate Professor Ernest Lawrence forgot his twenty-seventh birthday on August 8, 1928, nine days before the opening of the academic year at the University of California in Berkeley; he was too engrossed in his new environment. He and John had driven with interest around the area, had even tried to find a girl in Piedmont whose name someone had given them. (She was not at home that first time, and, when Ernest found her later, he was disappointed. "She's the kind that likes the rah rah fraternity type," he reported to John.) They had ferried across the bay to wonderful San Francisco with its hills, wharves, and Golden Gate Park; had crowded into long days all the sight-seeing possible before John's return eastward. Now it was the campus, more than five hundred acres on the slopes of the Berkeley hills, facing, across the bay, San Francisco and the Golden Gate—truly golden in the setting sun, especially from the big concrete C on Charter Hill that overlooked the campus. Immediately below the 60-foot by 27-foot initial lay the classic Greek Theater, the first of modern times, designed after that at Epidaurus and seating 7,500. A little south of that was the 75,000-seat stadium. Spread out among trees below these were the university buildings, dominated by the 307-foot campanile, modeled after that of St. Mark's in Venice. Some of the bells in that tower weigh more than two tons, and the lightest weighs about 300 pounds. Huge clocks near the top face in four directions; between those and the chimes, no one on campus could fail to know the time, day or night. About the campanile plaza, other buildings spread for blocks, with winding paths, streets, and areas of green interspersed. It was truly beautiful, from the hill to the eucalyptus grove near the western end. Sixteen buildings of granite or plastered concrete set the adopted style of Italian Renaissance architecture, with older buildings of wood or brick-covered ivy in no way spoiling the general attractiveness of the campus.

The Men's Faculty Club, east and south of the campanile, in the midst of Faculty Glade—a wide, parklike area of grass and live oak trees, with Strawberry Creek running its length—was a rambling redwood building of Maybeck design completely blended into the trees and shrubs. Upper floor rooms were adequate for sleep and study while sociability and quiet reading rooms were provided for in lower areas. A high, peaked hall, after the fashion of some European colleges, served for dining and as a pleasant meeting place for nonresident faculty as well as for those domiciled above. Ernest shunned the card rooms but tried his hand again at billiards for the first time since his days as a salesman of aluminum in South Dakota and Iowa. More often he frequented the tennis court or, if it were occupied, one of the many all university courts nearby.

The spacious physics building, Le Conte Hall, one of the newer group about a hundred yards from the Faculty Club, faced chemistry's Gilman Hall across a narrow court. About a block west of Le Conte was ivy-covered South Hall, the oldest building on the campus, part of it still used by physical experimentalists. Perhaps a hundred feet north and west of that, the large main library—a good one—was the other building of special interest for Ernest.

The new young professor was made to feel at home from the first; indeed some at the Faculty Club as well as in the department said that it was an honor to have him on the faculty. The cultured Armin Leuschner, professor of astronomy, and director of the on-campus observatory, went out of his way to talk with Ernest and make him feel at home. Gilbert Lewis, dean of the College of Chemistry, at once invited Ernest to a soiree at his home where there was much wit and elegant conversation among a select group of professors.

Capable physicist Dr. Hall, very devout and a nonsmoker or drinker, proved to be an honest, fair chairman who understood and recognized good work. He said that he had never before greeted a new associate about whom there had been such excellent reports, and, as he considered himself a good judge of men, he was inclined to agree that they were valid. Birge, oldest of the so-called younger group in the department, who only appeared to be delicate in health, was solicitous to help acclimate the newcomer, and Loeb was no less complimentary and enthusiastic than he had been in his letters. Brackett, a spectroscopy man —he had published a paper with Birge—was cordial, as was W. H. Williams, a West Pointer who had backed Birge in forcing consideration of the quantum theory at Berkeley; even Gilbert Lewis and the former physics department head had been skeptical of Bohr's theories of electron orbits, the quantum of line spectra, and the correspondence principle. John Hopfield, formerly an assistant under Birge at Syracuse, expressed curiosity about Ernest's work. Ernest often had seen Brode at Princeton before he had come the previous year, and Samuel Allison had worked with Compton at Chicago. Professor Victor Lenzen told Ernest how enthusiastically Loeb had talked about him one night on a ferry returning from a joint meeting with Stanford physicists in San Francisco, two years before. Ernest had never felt more welcome, not even on that first rainy day at Yale when the atmosphere of Sloane had seemed so much warmer than that at Ryerson. There was disappointment in the department that Edward Condon had accepted an offer from Princeton. This was offset by the promise that the brilliant young theoretical physicist, Robert Oppenheimer, would join the staff the next year. In all, the staff seemed a well-rounded and excellent group, and Ernest happily set about planning his experiments before the students arrived for the new term.

The facilities seemed every bit as good as those at Sloane, and there was room to spare. A good machine shop had three mechanicians devoted entirely to working on research equipment. There were also student shops in the basement and on the third floor near the glass-blowing room. Two permanent assistants were in charge of setting up laboratory equipment for lower division classes; a third, specially trained, set up demonstrations for lectures, relieving instructors of responsibility and saving them much time. A curator and his assistant took care of supplies and inventory. Two full-time stenographers and a part-time library assistant were available to researchers for typing scientific papers. Thus, since assistant and teaching fellows handled necessary paper work for courses, all time free of preparation for and the conduct of classes and lectures could be devoted to research.

Ernest started the term with five hours a week of teaching, two in undergraduate recitation and three with seventeen graduate students in electromagnetic theory—"Going well," he wrote, "and giving me a wonderful opportunity to develop understanding of theoretical physics and ability to present abstract concepts in clear manner." He was also chairman of the Ph.D. examinations committee in electricity and magnetism. "Not the least homesick for Yale (remarkable thing). I have a relative importance which I could never have attained at Yale in years."

Whatever his "relative importance," everyone seemed curious to see his work, the elegant, unusual apparatus he devised with usual and available materials, as well as ingenious constructions that incorporated the unusual. His beautiful experimental jobs would outdo what had been done before by uncanny instrumental intuition. His use of ordinary materials in overcoming difficulties was very important, and one of the reasons some found it difficult to believe his work correct. "His Kerr cell shutter method was absolutely fascinating," Loeb recalls. Physicists and chemists alike eagerly looked, discussed, and nodded approval; obviously he wanted to be a credit to the department and the university. He told Lenzen: "The attitude at Yale was what they could do for me; here it seems to be what I can do for California."

The closeness of the physics and chemistry departments intrigued him. Of course, he thought, they should be close, there was so much in common, particularly in light of newer discoveries. He thought few places elsewhere recognized the wisdom of this relationship in practice. At Berkeley, chemistry and physics people sat in each other's seminars, and were in and out of each other's laboratories. This had not always been the case even at Berkeley; when Birge arrived in 1918, the chairmen of the two departments were not even on speaking terms. Physics was no more than a poor relation to Gilbert Lewis's strong and noted chemistry department. When Birge, supported by Williams, dissuaded Lewis of the validity of his proposed static atom, physicists increased in stature on the campus. As Birge became something of an authority on atomic structure, and new men joined the staff, rivalry ceased, and by the time Ernest arrived Birge could say that the only difference between physics and chemistry at California was that one was practiced in Le Conte Hall and the other in Gilman Hall.

There were mutual interest and stimulation, too, in the monthly dinner meetings with Stanford physicists in San Francisco, just forty-five minutes from Berkeley. There was also frequent intercourse with the California Institute of Technology in Pasadena. Professor Linus Pauling of the southern institution spent two months each spring at Berkeley, and Oppenheimer, when he came, was to spend a couple of spring months in Pasadena. Ernest met Pauling at a Gilbert Lewis party and saw a good deal of him afterward. Professor Pauling particularly remembers their dining together in San Francisco and discussing Millikan and the reasons for his success; another time the entire discussion revolved around the question of why almost all fields of research proved to be so important.

If there was faculty approval, it could not compare with the enthusiasm inspired in his graduate students: he convinced Curtis Haupt that the strange probability laws of photo-ionization on mercury vapor could be demonstrated by other means than he had used at Yale. "The way he put things, the way he struck me with his enthusiasm—well, I did it. It was not that he was a slave driver, though he kept you going at full speed, and the pressure was on, but his own innate enthusiasm. He sort of imparted it to people and they of their own accord gave their maximum. I never knew when he might come into my laboratory on the second floor; he frequently did, but he never got people angry or upset; just suggestions, help. A ball of fire, energy, and—well, I never knew anyone else with what he possessed." A description of Haupt's experimental demonstration was published, without Ernest's name.

Niels Edlefsen, half a dozen years older than Ernest, liked him at once. Though, as an assistant in physics, he helped other professors, he asked to do his degree problem with Ernest, and was set to work on photo-ionization of cesium vapor. He found Ernest a "tremendous spur." Strong and eager, Edlefsen soon had his furnace constructed and his glass blown. He worked late at night, often on Sundays. One night Ernest found him busy in the basement of South Hall. "Mind if I work with you awhile?" he asked Edlefsen. About midnight, beads of sweat standing out on his forehead, Ernest suggested they go out for a snack. They returned to the laboratory, as full of enthusiasm as before—maybe too enthusiastic for tired men, because about four in the morning Ernest broke some of the glass. "Oh, for heaven's sake!" he said and left. But he was back many other nights, and the experiment was finished before the Christmas holidays and was worth reporting at April meetings of the Physical Society in Washington, after which it was published.

"Let's see what we can do with rubidium," Ernest said, and Edlefsen went to work refining the metal and setting up for that. The experiment was finished in six months. Though either problem was sufficient for a Ph.D. thesis, there was no thought of quitting laboratory work, as far as Edlefsen was concerned. "Let's do potassium," Ernest said, and they did that. "On we went," Edlefsen remembers. "That was done in less than six months, before the second Christmas." "I'd sure like to see what we could do on sodium!" Ernest sighed, but there were too many other problems.

He was equally interested in experiments done with other graduate students, particularly Leon Linford's problem on the behavior of alkali films on tungsten under intense electric fields. Soon there was always a group of students around him. "There was always something happening. You got the impression he was alive from his fingertips clear through. He just radiated an atmosphere of excitement, but of peace, too, wherever he was," Lauriston Marshall said. Larry Marshall, getting his degree under Loeb, was told by the professor that Lawrence was the brightest prospect among young physicists in the entire country. Marshall was as curious about what went on in Ernest's laboratories as in his own; he particularly remembers the "largest hydrogen plasma tube built at that time, for the study of ultraviolet. It had windows in it."

There seems to have been some envy on the part of older men in the department over the attention given Ernest so soon by faculty and stu-

dents, and that so young a newcomer could start as an associate professor, but among the more active younger professors there was cooperation; Loeb gave up his darkroom so that Ernest and Edlefsen could use
it. When objections were carried to the superintendent of grounds and
buildings about high voltage wires strung along the basement corridor
in South Hall, Professor Hall quieted them with assurance that high
voltages would be carried only at night, or at such other times as outside
doors were locked and marked with warning signs. When someone objected that Lawrence's work was not very practical, he told a story he'd
heard: "When the Wisconsin Legislature was considering a budget one
year, it was argued that professors did not work many hours a week and
got few practical results, until a farmer legislator protested: 'I have a
fine bull at home. I don't think he works three hours a week, but he
sure gets results in the long run.'"

No one ever accused Ernest of not working hard, or for long hours.
Often when he wasn't in the laboratory, he could be found poring over
the current literature of physics in the library or trying to work out
some problem in his office. With all this he found time for tennis about
three times a week. He was thrilled to watch Helen Wills and Henri
Cochet, the French champion, play at the Berkeley Tennis Club. When
Lawrence Haugen visited him, Ernest promised that, with the advantage
of winter play, he would be able to beat his cousin by the time he went
to Washington in the spring. Haugen was surprised that Ernest took
time some evenings after dinner at the Faculty Club for three-cushion
billiards. Ernest pointed out several older gentlemen. "Those are important professors outside of science. I get to know them at billiards."

He found time for social activities, too; it was remarked that he
seemed to need little sleep. There were teas, dinners, and dances, and
horseback riding on Sundays in the hills, usually with some young lady.
During the nearly five weeks' vacation at Christmastime, he played golf
as well as tennis with a girl "I've seen a good deal of," at what was then
called the Berkeley Country Club. Correspondence with Molly was brief
and infrequent, though he continually asked about her in letters to
John, who saw the Blumers—and Elsie—when he could. But activities
with new friends in California seemed to his parents to have dispelled
any idea that Ernest still had Molly on his mind. In fact so many girls
were mentioned in his letters that Carl Lawrence was moved to write, in
a joint letter to his sons, in the spring: "Note Ernest is now going with
another girl. That is all right, Ernest, but I wonder if you did not get
too intimate with one, leading her to believe you might propose to her. I
am wondering if you shouldn't put on the brakes a little when you start
going with a girl. It is not fair to her if you show her too much attention, and then suddenly take up with some other girl. A girl's feelings

are too sacred to trifle with, and therefore I suggest that you be careful in such matters. You may take this suggestion for what it is worth, and possibly may laugh at it, but nevertheless I give it in all seriousness." Similar sentiments were reflected in letters between the two brothers, Ernest's full of advice and John's of his "interests."

Ernest drove to Pasadena for the Physical Society meeting in December and wrote his parents, not of girls but of the stimulating meetings, of flowers in December, fine weather, and of his work. "I can honestly say that there isn't anything (within reason) that I would prefer doing to what I am now. My position appears to me to be as nearly ideal as one could reasonably hope for. The longer I am in scientific research work the more fascinating it becomes and I am more and more appreciating the willingness of men to forget larger salaries for the privilege of living in an academic atmosphere, free to carry on research as one pleases."

He spent Christmas Day with the family of his cousin Mildred Beatty at French Camp, originally a forty-niner gold-rush settlement, now a center of what seemed to be one vast orchard and farmland. Most interesting was the dredging of the San Joaquin River to permit oceangoing vessels to come right into nearby Stockton. There was no doubt in his mind, he wrote, that California was the most progressive and forward-looking state as well as "the most scenic." Another day he ferried across San Francisco Bay to Sausalito, the quaint town north of the Golden Gate, and hiked over Mount Tamalpais. It was such a glorious day that it seemed odd to come down with a bad cold that night; he had hoped to escape such periodic ailments in California.

The new term was a delight, not only because more graduate students chose him for their thesis work but also because Tom Johnson was present, replacing Professor Brackett for the remainder of the school year. The old friends had much to talk about; it was as if they had not been parted, the way questions arose and were discussed. Tom was on leave from Bartol, where he worked with Swann. Ernest showed off his experiments and talked of those he planned to initiate—he had six graduate students this term—and of attempts in the East and in Europe to achieve high enough energies to disintegrate and reveal secrets of the atom. Ernest was still doubtful that the difficulties involved could be overcome in any of the current efforts, even with the giant Tesla coil, surrounded with cooling oil, that Merle and his associates at the Carnegie Institution were developing. How control, or direct satisfactorily, the tremendous voltage, even if achieved?

Yet of all the adventures of exploration, even including that of the vastness of space, Ernest felt that the most exciting and important was in the microcosm of the tiny atom, a million times smaller than a hairbreadth, yet similar to a universe with electrons as planets orbiting around a nucleus one hundred thousand times smaller than the tiny atom itself—yet containing most of its mass. And relative to the universe of sun and planets—everything in it, to be sure, made of uncountable atoms—containing more space by far between nucleus and orbiting electrons than that between planets and sun. Telescopes might explore the latter, which was exciting enough, but to penetrate the atom and discover the secrets of all matter—neither navigators nor astronomers had faced such a challenge and such possible adventure. Who could tell? The secret of life itself might be revealed. If Rutherford had shown that the centuries-old belief in the atom as the indivisible unit was invalid, and with radiations of radium had actually changed one basic element into another—something alchemists had dreamed and labored over for centuries—who knew what controlled power, sufficient to break atoms of every element, might accomplish? But without a practical method of generating such energies and devising tubes that could take them without breakdown, the attack on the minuscule atom, Ernest felt, could not be accomplished by artificial methods. That a method could, and eventually would, be devised had intrigued him since his days at Minnesota when Swann and Buchta had worked on a high-energy generator.

The challenge was being accepted in laboratories all over the world. Three German physicists had attempted to harness lightning attracted by a 700-meter chain stretched between mountain peaks. One of them had been killed. Millions of volts had been registered on gauges, but discharge tubes had been unable to withstand such potentials, even briefly. To wait for lightning was as unreliable as waiting for a fortunate strike of cosmic particles; and to strike a tiny atom with a single charge of however great energy would certainly be fortuitous. And the nucleus, that positive, central core, in size compared to the atom as a mosquito to a vast cathedral—how strike and study that? Tom agreed that it would take an as yet unachieved, continuous, intense stream of highly charged particles to get results. It was great to have Tom for such exciting discussions—not all of them in the laboratory. Ernest drove Tom to see the redwood giants north of the bay, and as far as Yosemite National Park, on talkative trips to see marvels and majesties of nature that were visible without laboratory equipment, but that were wonderfully related to both the infinite and the infinitesimal.

In a sense some of Ernest's experiments had altered atoms: the ionization potential of mercury is actually the energy necessary to pry an electron from the atom, thereby changing it, and photoelectric phenomena do likewise. There were challenge and excitement in all the experiments with his graduate students, but the problem of energies and a deeper study of the atom remained always in the background of his mind. With

Leon Linford he discovered a new photoelectric effect; with Edlefsen one element after another was subjected to photo-ionization experimentation—he was to report one of these experiments at the April meetings in Washington. Haupt was successfully verifying results Ernest had obtained before coming to Berkeley, and other new students showed promise and industry as they came under the inspiration and example of their industrious mentor. Though he expected interest and hard work from all, each was treated individually.

James Brady remembers his frustration over finding his thesis problem already described in a German journal, even to details of the experiment as he had planned it. Ernest dismissed the disappointment lightly and suggested another problem. Brady went often to Ernest for advice until the teacher, after a moment's study of the question, turned to the student. "You know as much about this as I do. Why don't you make the decision?" Years later Brady told Ernest he considered that the turning point in his graduate work, for after that he did make his own decisions. Nor were the students allowed to become narrow through concentration on a particular problem. Ernest initiated a weekly "Five o'Clock Journal Club" where anything could be informally discussed, including reports from laboratories all over the world. No one escaped having to give a report. Ernest stressed how much he had learned using "my limited knowledge of German and French" to scan foreign periodicals.

On about April 1, 1929, while perusing scientific journals in the main library with Tom, Ernest noticed an article in *Archiv für Electrotechnik* by a Norwegian engineer, Rolf Wideröe, on the acceleration of potassium ions. He scarcely glanced at the article in German—not even enough to note that Wideröe's idea was based on a suggestion of a Swedish professor, G. Ising. With growing excitement he studied the accompanying illustrations as the possibilities of the method became clear. Wideröe had placed two tubes (electrodes) in line, injected potassium ions into the first with damped high-frequency oscillating voltage, and, as the ions passed between the tubes, given them another boost with the same voltage, in synchronism with the first. The ions, on emerging from the second tube, had therefore twice the energy with which they had entered the first. With a series of tubes, increasing in length to compensate for the greater velocity from successive boosts, why not multiply the initial, and reapplied potential, thus boosting the energy to many times the original input? Instead of a tremendous voltage applied once, repeated applications of low and easily controllable voltage applied at the right times would boost the energy even higher, as a child in a swing is pushed higher and higher by repeated pushes, rather than by one tremendous heave.

Ernest quickly calculated how much longer each successive tube would

have to be and realized that to get to extremely high energy with protons would require an apparatus of an unwieldy length for most laboratories, though such a device for up to million-volt heavy ions might be
practical without being too long. Protons, however, seemed to be the
most potent particles for assault on the nucleus. He immediately tried to
figure out a way to reduce the length necessary. If it were possible to use
the tubes over and over again, as one used the same low power for repeated kicks . . . of course, that would require bending the tubes to
form a circle. The idea of a magnetic field to hold the ions within such a
circle occurred to him at once, for the angular velocity of an ion is constant in a magnetic field, regardless of its speed. Theoretically, then, one
should be able to circulate ions within hollow semicircular electrodes,
applying repeated boosts each time they crossed the narrow space that
separated them along the diameters, if the electrodes were within a magnetic field. It would not matter that the radius of the circular path
would increase with each boost; the increased speed from each successive
kick would always compensate for the greater distance.

In an hour or two, Ernest was bubbling over to Tom, filled with the
excitement of discovery. Johnson could see no flaw in Ernest's equations
and diagrams. It seemed so simple neither could understand why it had
not been thought of before; too simple; they must have overlooked
something. Of course, as Tom pointed out, however good the idea, there
would undoubtedly be tremendous obstacles to a successfully functioning machine. And how would the energy be applied once it was
achieved? Ernest thought this no insurmountable problem; one could
place an atomic target near the perimeter of a circular electrode and
devise a method of spiraling the highest energy ions onto it—one might
even bring them entirely away from the vacuum tube itself, for use outside.

They discussed these things walking back late to the Faculty Club,
and when Ernest found Professor Donald Shane, mathematician and astronomer, still up, he told him about the idea, still bubbling over with
enthusiasm and excitement. Shane checked the mathematics and said it
sounded okay to him. "But what are you going to do with it?" he
asked.

"I'm going to bombard and break up atoms!" Ernest almost shouted.

The following morning, still excited, he told Brady, at work early in
the laboratory, about his plan, diagramming on a blackboard and writing the equations, pointing out that the symbol for the radius dropped
from one equation meant that ions would continue to accelerate with
each revolution—no matter how many there were. The excitement
lasted all day. That evening he passed Professor Brode and Henrietta
Jenkins, wife of a colleague of Ernest's, near the Life Science Building.

Mrs. Jenkins thought Ernest unusually exuberant, even for him, and remarked about it later to her husband. "I'm going to be famous!" he called as he hurried on.

There was no time to do much about the idea before leaving for Washington and the Physical Society meetings, and Ernest, with Beams, had accepted invitations to spend two months at the General Electric laboratories after the meetings. But in spite of all that had to be done for students, the idea kept intruding on his consciousness. On the journey east, via the Grand Canyon and New Orleans, he developed his sketches in more sophisticated fashion and tried to determine more exactly than he had how much energy could reasonably be expected from a small experimental apparatus, as well as what might be required in magnet size, and other necessities to reach the ultimate, which theoretically could approach the speed of light, if the Einstein equation for the increase of mass with velocity did not rule that out. At such velocities, the increase of mass might slow the outer ions sufficiently to prevent their reaching the gap between electrodes in synchronization with other particles for further boosts.

The paper, "Photoionization of Caesium and Rubidium Vapors," read at the Physical Society, was followed by one on the same subject, by Fred L. Mohler, who said the Lawrence-Edlefsen paper was superior. There was agreement between them except in a minor detail concerning cesium, and Ernest got off a letter to Edlefsen to check that. In a letter to Professor Hall, he could not refrain from commenting that he was writing across a desk from the great German physicist, Arnold Sommerfeld, at the Cosmos Club, where Swann had arranged that he stay in Washington. The previous night he had dined there with Millikan of the California Institute of Technology and Dr. Hull of General Electric and had enjoyed the opportunity to be with a host of other "interesting and distinguished gentlemen."

Ernest attended open meetings of the National Academy that followed, visited the Bureau of Standards, the Naval Research Laboratory, and Carnegie Institution where Merle, Lawrence Hafstad, and Gregory Breit were engaged in impressive work with their Tesla coil apparatus for producing high energies. Ernest discussed his own idea with Merle, pointing out that instead of trying for a single boost of energy at a voltage no known discharge tube could withstand, a more promising approach without apparent limitation was to apply a series of properly tuned smaller boosts to gain the high-energy particles desired. Merle thought so, too—*if* it could be done.

Neither Merle's nor others' doubts in any way dampened Ernest's enthusiasm as he discussed it in the coming days at Bartol with Swann, and at the Bell Laboratories and Columbia in New York. In New Haven for a few days, he spoke about it to the Physics Club, and with Don Cooksey went into the problem further than he could in the time allotted for his talk. Don believed Ernest would be able to make it work—because he was Ernest; others found various objections, all of which Ernest was certain could be overcome. Everyone had to admit that he had hardly been "buried in the hinterland" as had been prophesied when he left Yale for the Far West.

He managed to see Molly and the Blumers over a weekend, found her just as attractive, just as serious, and as casual as ever. He went to Boston for a day with his brother John before going to Schenectady and General Electric.

The two summer months in Schenectady were like a vacation, not only because it was the finest industrial laboratory of the time but also because there was the pleasure of being with Jesse again. Beams was working with Dr. Hull on a lightning arrester that depended upon a vacuum spark. Hull wanted to know how the spark originated—whether it was due to the pulling out of electrons from the cathode. (Some question existed then as to whether or not electrons are actually pulled out of metal.) By use of the rotating mirror, or the Kerr cell, the spark could be photographed just as it occurred, and it could be determined whether it started on the cathode or the anode. Dr. Hull told Ernest just to "play—snoop around," and do what he pleased.

Beams thought that a pretty high compliment for a young man, however brilliant. "He has such an instinct for things, is so capable on the fringes where there are no established rules from which we might get some solutions," said Hull. So Ernest played the "roving ambassador," looking into different problems, making, in his own words, "good or bad" suggestions. Some of the problems were of much interest to him and suggested subjects for further research in Berkeley, ". . . but I realize first I must clear the slate of projects already under way," he wrote to Professor Hall. "Good or bad," his suggestions, and Ernest himself, were greatly admired by the older men at G.E. Often the suggestions were simple enough but, as is so often the case, had not occurred to the experimenters. The problem of pulling electrons out of metal that occupied Jesse bothered Ernest somewhat because he felt it might put a limit on the potentials that could be put on a discharge tube. This could affect the acceleration of ions with his proposed method—about which he talked with everyone in general, with Jesse in particular, and the older Drs. Hull and Coolidge. The obvious simpler method, most scientists thought, would be to develop the electrostatic generator to high voltages, but Ernest was convinced that if electrons came from the electrodes, there would be too low a limit on the potential one could get. Hull and Beams were developing about 500,000 volts per centimeter before the electrons would come out and the spark go.

"There's just no use trying to build this up," Ernest insisted. "You may get a few million volts. That's limited. What we've got to do is to devise some method of accelerating through a small voltage, repeating it over and over. Multiple acceleration." He had a great idea, Beams thought, but everyone could think of some reason why it would not work. David Sloan, Hull's young research assistant whom Ernest liked and cultivated, was an exception. Ernest tried to persuade him to come to California, or go anywhere and get his Ph.D. It seemed a pity so bright and imaginative a young man should not have the opportunities the degree would give him. He advised him about other universities and about scholarships. By the time Ernest left—"with a good deal of loot in the way of photocells and vacuum tubes," including one of his own design—Sloan had promised to try to continue his formal education.

On one particularly memorable afternoon, a "fine bull session" developed with Ernest, Karl Compton, Irving Langmuir, Hull and Coolidge as participants. "Such an afternoon makes one proud to be a scientist," Ernest wrote his parents.

Ernest and Jesse drove north into Montreal and the countryside of Quebec and down the coast of Maine to Boston. In New Haven, where they had a couple of days with Dr. Swann, Ernest visited Molly and the Blumers at Haycock Point, a fine culmination of a good vacation. From New York, he entrained for Chicago, Madison, and Minneapolis and visited university laboratories in each, spreading his infectious delight in physics and "keeping in touch." His parents joined him in Minneapolis for five days of fishing in northern Minnesota before he went to Springfield for a few days at home. He then went on to Seattle, Banff, and Lake Louise in British Columbia before taking a coastal steamer to San Francisco. He had been away from Berkeley nearly four months.

There were eight graduate students under his supervision in the fall term of 1929, all working on exciting and vital problems; all requiring much time with Ernest in the laboratory. So many exciting problems surged through his mind; there were neither men nor time enough for all the experiments! How could one ever test all the considered solutions, pry into the questions nature held in such secret and dazzling array? No wonder he was impatient with students (and professors) who had difficulty selecting a problem for research, or who felt someone else to be impinging on fields they had staked out for their particular study. "There is research enough for all!" he would exclaim with impatience after any complaint of intrusion or lack of a good project.

Students with him for a second year were doing good work, finding new things, or more firmly establishing questionable theories, with his help. Many of them felt that they learned far more in the laboratory working beside Ernest than in his classrooms; he seemed to transfer to them at the bench some of his vitality and interest. "Just keep asking yourself questions," he would say. "The ideas will come of themselves, and you'll avoid a lot of useless effort." Each experiment was exciting to him, such as that of a new graduate student, Frank Dunnington, with whom he was developing an idea concerning the early stages of electric sparks that had occurred to him during the summer. He invented an alternating potential method of measuring the ratio of charge to mass which in a few months produced results at least equal to other experimental work on the subject; with Edlefsen he developed the most intense source of ultraviolet known. There were papers on these subjects ready for the December meeting of the Physical Society at Stanford, and articles to be published in the February, 1930, issue of the *Physical Review*. It is not surprising that he found no time for experimental work on accelerating ions.

Sometimes, after long hours with apparatus, he would abruptly stop work and rush off. "I've got to get some exercise," he would say. Even when he had an engagement at night, he might appear at the laboratory with an idea for the solution of a problem and run off again, or, if his engagement was concluded, take off his jacket and get to work. When exhausted, he could sit in a chair and easily and quickly go to sleep, even after great activity, an ability which one of the new professors, Robert Oppenheimer, felt was the very embodiment of health.

A quick friendship had sprung up between Ernest and Oppenheimer. As different as two men possibly could be in temperament, appearance, and general attitudes, the experimenter and the theorist found much, much in common. Nor were their interests in each other confined entirely to physics. Ernest was fascinated by Oppenheimer's quick, sensitive mind; by his deep interest and knowledge in nonscientific areas—Ernest possibly felt that the humanities, for instance, were not very important subjects—and by Robert's skillful use of language. Oppenheimer had never known a man of such "unbelievable vitality and love of life. Work all day, run off for tennis, and work half the night. His interest was so primarily active, instrumental and mine just the opposite."

Ernest knew of Oppenheimer's high reputation before his arrival in Berkeley in 1929. A New Yorker, he had been a brilliant student at Harvard, Cambridge, and Göttingen, where he had taken his degree in 1927 at the age of twenty-three. He had been a National Research Fellow at Harvard and at California Institute of Technology, and a fellow of international education in Leyden and Zurich. He had been sought by university faculties in Europe and the United States. It had been surprising to many that Berkeley had been able to obtain his services for most of the year; Caltech shared him in the spring.

"It was a challenge," Oppenheimer recalled. "Berkeley had a good chemistry department. It had no theoretical physics. Its experimental physics had been pretty old-fashioned and sleepy. I took the job at Caltech because I regarded it as so much more in touch with physics that I wouldn't get completely isolated. Now look at it! Hard to imagine. It wasn't until the early thirties that Berkeley became the center—mostly, I would say, because of Ernest's creativity."

It was Professor Williams who had presented the challenge of Berkeley—and the possibility of building a strong theoretical department—to Oppenheimer, not failing to argue also the advantages of climate and informal living for one whose health was anything but robust. He was certainly informal; appearance seemed of no importance to him, and his dress was casual—unpressed suits, unshined shoes, and old hat. There were tales about his careless driving. Professor Birge told Ernest that somewhere in the Southwest, on his way to California, Oppie had run off the road, gone down a ravine, and escaped with no more than a sprained wrist. When the car was pulled back on the road, he had continued, driving with one hand. He again had lost control in a country town, run up the steps of the courthouse, and banged the car against the door. When it was back in the street, he had casually driven off again and had arrived at Caltech looking like a tramp. Birge could not understand how the man still lived—and why he continued driving. Birge thought Ernest a good driver, perhaps by comparison, for there were others who were not too happy riding with Ernest at the wheel. If absorbed in conversation, he tended to look at his companion instead of the road.

There was nothing casual or careless about Oppenheimer's mind. On their many walks, though the principal topics concerned physics, Ernest listened with some awe to discourses on the classics, books current and old. They even enjoyed philosophical speculation, though Ernest had little knowledge of the history of philosophy. They attended concerts together and shared an appreciation of the music of Bach, particularly, and Beethoven, though it was the earlier Beethoven that Ernest most enjoyed, and the later which Oppie preferred. They shared many enriching evenings at the Gilbert Lewises', some of which were musical— Mrs. Lewis was an excellent violinist, and interest in music there was genuine. Ernest drove Oppie to Yosemite during Thanksgiving holidays, and they often rode horseback around Berkeley, sometimes with a "rather handsome, aggressive woman who liked us both." Oppenheimer thought Ernest not as fond of riding as he seemed, that his wearing of proper riding clothes and use of an English saddle served to remove the exercise as far as possible from farm associations—"he hated farming."

Oppenheimer, who had no laboratory work or particular problem, cultivated interests which Ernest did not share, and soon had other friendships of meaning with classicists and language people on the campus, where discussions of literature and philosophy were less one-sided. There seemed to be no area to which he could not contribute, except those of economics and politics. Devoid of small talk, he read no papers or magazines of general interest. Though he had considerable means from his father's investments, he learned of the stock market crash months after it occurred from Ernest, a very modest investor in stocks. The great Depression was not immediately felt at Berkeley, and Ernest, too, gave it little thought. But had there been nothing else in common, the devoted physicists, one so active and the other so reflective, found enough to share in that field alone.

Oppie always attended Ernest's Journal Club for his graduate students and considered this forum one of Ernest's great contributions. If the theorist sometimes talked over the heads of others, he found that the experimentalist often knew, in more realistic fashion, what would work. Other faculty, drawn by the excitement of the Journal Club, noted that there were times when Ernest could not follow Oppie's reasoning (often they could not either), but that in very direct discourse aided by the blackboard, Ernest came to the point, perhaps at times more successfully. Francis Jenkins, the other new professor in 1929, whom Ernest had known at Chicago, wondered at Ernest's ability to reach correct conclusions without apparent, lengthy ratiocination.

"Pan" and Henrietta Jenkins were welcome additions to the impromptu social gatherings at the homes of married professors; these—sometimes enlivened with a bit of laboratory alcohol—were great fun. There would be dancing as well as talk. Picnics were frequent among the younger faculty people; there was much social activity on a pleasant, informal plane. Ernest might bring a girl—he was once teased unmercifully for escorting a "silly-looking one with Mary Pickford curls." Oppie later took Melba Phillips, the only graduate student of his first year. He seemed little interested in girls, and one night forgot a companion, seated in the hills, and walked off without her. The worried young lady finally called the police; Oppenheimer was eventually found, sound asleep, at the Faculty Club. Ernest could be absent-minded, too, but not "under such circumstances."

Though he did not consider psychology a science, Ernest could not help wondering over the elasticity of the mind, which seemed limitless in what it could retain and recall—aside from trivial things such as remembering umbrellas, hats, packages, and whatnot when he traveled. He did not forget important things like physical problems, nor cease to think up more; these he could handle. Time was the enforcer of regrettable limits to practice. He could carry problems without apparent limit, if they were important. Even concern for his mother, who had been suffering abdominal pains with increasing frequency, did not crowd academic and laboratory problems from his mind nor prevent speculation on possible experiments for which time allowed no place.

Worry about his mother was enhanced when a Professor Kennedy, who had the next room at the Faculty Club, died of cancer. "I'm deathly afraid of cancer," he wrote John. "When you are at home next give Mother a thorough examination with a specialist. Every doctor tells her something different." John, who had been writing for advice on the best place to intern, received from Ernest almost weekly letters full of encouragement, advice, and the "pleasures and rewards of hard work." Ernest also wrote weekly to his parents and regretted that he would not see them at Christmas. He had thought of going but decided that there would be little time and that it would be more important for John to see their mother, and offered to pay his fare if he could make the journey and see about her health. He promised to stop in Springfield after the April, 1930, meetings and a month at the Fixed Nitrogen Laboratory in Washington, where he had been invited by its chief, Dr. Frederick A. Cottrell, who had once taught at California. There was work enough to do during the Christmas vacation period.

Sometime after the holidays, Ernest found the opportunity—and a hardly needed, but added, spur—to start experimentation on his idea for the multiple acceleration of ions. The spur came from visiting Professor (in physics and chemistry) Otto Stern of Hamburg. During dinner at Solari's, one evening, the German became so enthusiastic about Ernest's conception that he thought his young host should leave the restaurant and get started at once. The opportunity came the next morning when Niels Edlefsen, with whom Ernest had done beautiful experiments and published three fine articles, completed his experimental work for the doctorate he hoped to get in the spring. Edlefsen had always been interested in discussions of high voltages and methods of attaining them.

"What are you going to do for the rest of the year?" Ernest asked him.

"Since I've worked night and day in the lab, I think I need some time for theoretical work, and to brush up for exams." Edlefsen sensed that Ernest had another experiment in mind.

"Ah, there's no need to worry about that! Now about this crazy idea of mine we've discussed. So simple I can't understand why someone hasn't tried it. Can you see anything wrong with it?"

Edlefsen couldn't, but he hedged a bit. "I'm not quite well enough equipped for the exams, but I'll think about it a couple of weeks," he replied. "Okay." In two weeks Edlefsen announced that he would like to try it. "Good! Let's go to work. You line up what we need right away."

Edlefsen had to fall back on Ernest to wangle the biggest magnet in the department, with pole faces about four inches in diameter to provide the magnetic field to contain particles within the hollow semicircular electrodes. The electrodes were fashioned by silvering the interior of a flattened flask and carefully removing a narrow strip of the silver across the center of each inside face. The silvered halves then served as electrodes when wired to an oscillator so that particles crossing the narrow gap between them could be boosted, by the alternating oscillations of radio frequency, to ever-increasing velocity, all the while held within the flask by the magnetic field. The flask could be evacuated of air. There were apertures for the ion-producing filament, the introduction of proton-producing hydrogen, and a probe to determine results. These apertures were sealed with wax.

The glass cracked on the first attempt to operate it, as it did on variations of the flask approach that were tried. Finally a shallow, round, copper box was cut in half across its diameter to form two equal electrodes. These were waxed to plate glass, with a small space between the straight diameters. Radio-frequency oscillators were connected to them to produce alternating, synchronized voltage. Arrangements for the evacuation of air and the introduction of hydrogen were devised. A filament was introduced in the center to ionize the hydrogen. All joints were again sealed with wax. The completed unit was centered between the pole faces of the electromagnet. It was a sad and messy-looking affair, and there was good-natured kidding about the expected "powerful machine" that would produce potent beams of particles.

"What are you going to do with them if you get them?" was a recurring question.

"Bombard atoms!" was the recurring, enthusiastic answer.

All Edlefsen wanted, at the time, was to get particles started and circulating. He worked hard and was alone for many long hours. Dear as the project was to Ernest, there were other students and projects, six hours of lectures, grades to award, and degree committees, all of which occupied much time. He was aware of Edlefsen's concern over lack of preparation in some aspects of his degree work. However casual he had seemed when he told Edlefsen not to worry, Ernest wrote his parents that he felt like an "expectant mother" with his first Ph.D. candidacy. With Birge and Loeb, he gave Edlefsen his oral examination, and was proud of his first graduate student's conduct. He was as "jubilant as a new mother," and as his other candidates won their degrees, he concerned himself over their fates like an "old mother." Edlefsen had al-

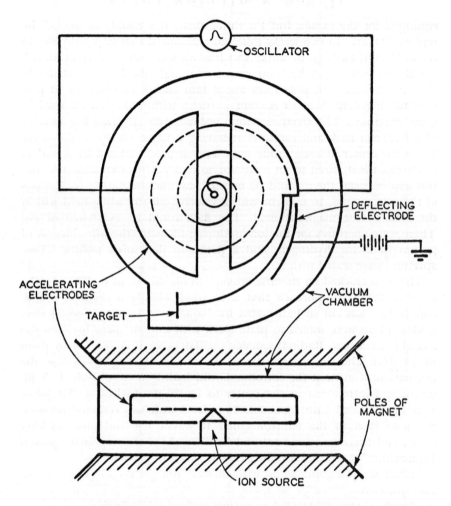

Since a magnetic field causes particles to move in circles, Lawrence used two hollow electrodes (above) to accelerate particles between the poles of an electromagnet (below). Ions introduced between the electrodes thus had to cross and recross the gap between them, each time receiving an added boost. As their velocity increased so did their orbits, so that larger circles reached the gap simultaneously, regardless of the size of the orbit, and were accelerated. The target to be bombarded, in early machines, was just inside the tank's perimeter. (*Lawrence Radiation Laboratory*)

ready accepted a position at the Davis campus of the university, but Ernest wrote letters of recommendation for other new Ph.D.'s, including some who had not been his responsibility, and interceded for them when he went East for the April, 1930, meetings in Washington. All got satisfactory positions.

After a short time at the Fixed Nitrogen Laboratory in Washington, Ernest wrote Professor Hall: "I must confess, I cannot see in what respect I am an asset to the place. I shall stay here another week and devote the remainder of the month to visiting various eastern laboratories. Already I have been around a good deal and profited very much." There had been several sessions with Merle who, with Breit, Hafstad, and Dahl, was developing tremendous energies with their Tesla coil transformer. Ernest was as skeptical of their achieving high enough sustained energies to penetrate the nucleus profitably, as Merle was of the workability of Ernest's magnetic resonance idea. Merle had produced rays capable of penetrating three inches of lead, and would later in the year win the annual $1,000 award of the American Association for the Advancement of Science for this accomplishment. In spite of his doubt about the circular accelerator, he urged Ernest to forget "spinning tops, or whatever you're on now" for the exciting nuclear field.

Beams understood the skepticism but was sure that Ernest could "lick" the problems involved in his device. He had seen Ernest flout theory and well-based opinion, experimentally. He knew that however much Ernest respected theoretical physics he would never let theory alone deter him. "There may be a way out," had been almost their motto at Yale when he had made the conclusions of more than one "great professor" seem embarrassing. "The history of science is full of examples of theory being wrong. Who did more than Faraday who was practically unschooled and never did know mathematics?" A briefer common remark of Ernest's was the old cliché: "There's more than one way to skin a cat." He liked to recall a saying of Yale's Josiah Willard Gibbs, not entirely pertinent, that "A mathematician may say anything he pleases, but a physicist must be at least partially sane."

Ernest paid a brief visit to Schenectady with Don Cooksey, to see new developments, and settled the fact that young David Sloan would go to Berkeley for graduate work with him. Ernest had arranged a job as a teaching assistant for the bright young man to make it possible for him to work toward a degree.

While Ernest was at the Fixed Nitrogen Laboratory, a wire from Edlefsen reported the achievement of resonant acceleration of hydrogen ions on the simple and crude device. Ernest's delight knew no bounds. He reported it to the still skeptical Merle, and ever-faithful Beams, and Swann. Swann was to teach during the summer session at Berkeley and would see the device. Ernest left Washington as soon as he could. In New Haven, Don Cooksey was still interested, largely, as with Beams, because Ernest had so often demonstrated the soundness of his methods.

He saw Molly briefly. She failed to become particularly excited over his new idea, and continued casual and reserved in every way, however buoyant he might be. Molly, who graduated from Vassar with honors, planned to study under famous bacteriologist Hans Zinser at Harvard. But the "whole Blumer family is wonderful," Ernest wrote John, who had begun his internship under famed brain surgeon Harvey Cushing in Boston. "I only wish that Molly were more like Elsie. Hope you marry her someday." He had a short visit with John before going to see his parents in Springfield, where his mother seemed again in good health. He had twenty-four hours in Glacier Park, and a few hours at the University of Washington in Seattle before he returned to Berkeley for the July summer session. On the train he sketched and figured toward a more sophisticated model of his acceleration device, one that would not only be more stable than the glass contraptions but also equipped with better controls for magnetic field and oscillating circuit, an accurate device for measuring results, and a satisfactory method for placing nuclear targets in the path of the highly energized protons.

There was little time for experimental work during the summer session, but there was no lack of interest. Professor Swann, whose presence on the summer faculty was a great joy, and with whom there were trips and musical evenings, seemed less skeptical than others, though he felt that a linear accelerator, in spite of the necessity to make it of unwieldy length for the usual laboratory, would be simpler and more certain to develop the energies Ernest aimed for. Cooksey visited Berkeley en route to his Trinity County, California, wilderness, and studied designs. Graduate students, in search of thesis subjects, looked at the small glass and sealing wax device and listened to Ernest's enthusiastic talk on the possibilities of the resonance principle. One of these, Stanley Livingston, who had been taking course work toward his doctorate, fell under the spell of Ernest's conviction that the idea was the soundest of proposed methods for the disintegration and study of atomic nuclei, despite the pessimistic predictions of other professors who had fairly convincing theories as to why the device could never amount to anything. It was argued, for example, that even if particles could be accelerated circularly, there was no way of focusing them for attack on the unbelievably small nucleus. Particles would wander off the circular path or strike the top and bottom of the flat tube after a few turns, and go bad. One professor warned that a graduate student might spend a couple of years fooling with the device and have nothing to show toward a degree. "Too wild an idea," was the conclusion of most student advisers. Ernest's answers for every objection were satisfactory to Stan Livingston, who went to work where Edlefsen had left off when he went to the Davis campus.

When David Sloan arrived, he, too, joined the project. Sloan was amazed at the amount of time and energy Ernest could devote to it with all the other demands on him. "It was apparent even then that about ninety percent of his interest was in the laboratory, rather than class-room teaching," Sloan remembers, "and it seemed to me, at first, that much of my time was to explore around and find necessary equipment, and Ernest would make it legal!" The efforts to make the tube of glass were soon abandoned, and Livingston set to work on a brass chamber.

Ernest then asked Sloan to construct a linear accelerator, a device in which particles could be given successive boosts along a straight, narrow path. A glass tube, somewhat complicated to permit ingress of electrical connections and withdrawal of air, was completed on a Friday, and Ernest and Sloan spent Saturday and Sunday carefully inserting eight small nickel tubes, each four millimeters in diameter and each suc-ceeding one of greater length than its predecessor, into the glass tube. The nickel tubes ranged in length from a bit more than a centimeter to almost five centimeters. These tubes were spaced between one and two centimeters apart. They were alternately connected to the two wires from an oscillator. Means of recording results were placed in the end after the longest of the nickel tubes; at the other end were provisions for introducing mercury ions. Brady's vacuum system was borrowed, as was the oscillating apparatus of the circular accelerator, to test the theory, and their work. What energy may have been developed is not recorded, but the principle was proven. It worked!

Student and teacher—who shouted "Whoopee!"—were elated. Ernest immediately suggested adding tubes to provide for thirteen more gaps, to develop 200,000-electron volts from the stepped-up 220 line current,

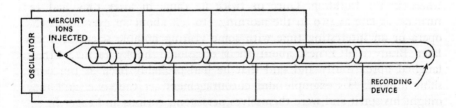

Simplified schematic diagram showing the basic principle of the linear accelerator. Within an accelerating tube is a series of electrodes of in-creasing length. Increased velocity is imparted at each gap.

which they later did successfully. Ernest and Sloan were a fine team. If Sloan had a suggestion, Ernest might say, "Oh, really?" think two or three minutes and add, "Sure." They'd check it and if it was valid, go after it. Ernest's suggestions never sounded like orders from a superior. "Let's do it this way," he'd say, making it sound like a question requiring agreement between equals. When things turned out successfully, Ernest would inevitably shout, "Whoopee!" as an error or even a slip would elicit "Oh, sugar!" or "For heaven's sake!"

With all the genuine respect in which he was held, the buoyant and optimistic young professor's words were sometimes too startling for every student to accept without proof. A new type tube that he had brought with him from G.E. had been given to Laurence Loveridge for his thesis work. Loveridge had trouble with his readings; no matter what adjustments he made, the spot of light reflected from his galvanometer would suddenly jump several centimeters from a stable position, returning in an instant. Everyone who observed it tried to determine the cause, until Ernest arrived in the laboratory and after a moment stated: "Why, that's the result of cosmic rays." After he left, Brady and Loveridge laughed. "He thinks it is due to cosmic rays!" The idea seemed ridiculous, and one of Ernest's quick judgments that for once could not be correct. But they began to consider the possibilities and decided that if his theory were correct the jumping would vary with the volume of air enclosed by the shield of the connector leading to the grid of the tube. By using smaller shield tubes they found fewer and fewer jumps, and by other tests showed that "Dr. Lawrence was right—as usual."

Sometimes those who were used to working late at night—all had studies or academic duties that took much time during the days—resorted to a ruse to get relaxation when experiments were at a critical state and Ernest might expect them to be interested in nothing else. Leaving coats and hats hung up in the lab, and the lights on, some of the boys would go off to a show, knowing that if Ernest came in, often in dinner clothes, to check the work, he would think they were elsewhere in the building. Once or twice he came in after they had returned—as late as two in the morning—to tell about an evening at the opera or an interesting time with some visiting notable scientist. Years later Brady told Ernest about their occasional hooky tactics. Ernest laughed uproariously and said that he had probably been at the same show himself. His example and encouragement set the style, and they caught his spirit and were themselves persistent, curious and eager in experimentation. "He was always the inspiring leader—the only essential was some sign in the young researcher of at least a pale reflection of his own enthusiasm for his favorite subject. Young scientists came to him eagerly and in his own words he 'found the genius of men spread rather uniformly over the entire globe,'" British scientist S. C. Curran wrote in *Nature*. If he only occasionally thought of their health, or lack of sleep, he thought as little of his own. If he noticed someone becoming weary or in apparent bad health, he was surprised, and would scold the student for negligence. He sometimes took students to his room at the Faculty Club to relax and listen to records; Milton White remembers his "pretty orthodox, classical taste."

Once, before he went East, he called Loveridge, Brady, and Milton Chaffee to his office, said they had been working too hard, and suggested they take his car and have a little vacation while he was away. They had a fine time driving down the Monterey Peninsula. In slamming a door too hard, they broke a window which, repaired, seemed unnoticeable to them. However, the day Ernest returned he said, "I see you put a new glass in the Reo's door."

If Ernest often seemed unconcerned with the physical effects of late hours and hard work on his students, he seldom forgot their mental health insofar as it might be affected by science. No problems were too tough to contemplate; any idea got a good reception, and, if worthy, support. The Journal Club, increasingly popular with students of others and with faculty, too, was never allowed to become formal. Anyone could talk off the top of his head; professors could be argued with as readily as any student; no complicated theoretical ideas were allowed to bog down a session. A student might be told that he would be called upon to discuss an idea a few hours beforehand; no one was allowed to come in with a sheaf of papers and the authority of two weeks' work— which might discourage questions. There were always excitement and stimulation.

The great German professors, Max von Laue and Rudolph Ladenburg, were appalled, when visiting the Journal Club, at the lack of discipline, and at the way youngsters spoke up to professors—even the erudite Oppenheimer was questioned, and the boyish Ernest Lawrence often took the graduate's part in elucidating the problem involved. The anything but boyish Oppenheimer was in fact younger than Lawrence. The atmosphere of Ernest's group, and even of his classes, was plainly and entirely American. Yet it was not in mockery that his students were beginning to refer to him as "Maestro"—out of his hearing, of course— even though the Germans thought he looked, and sometimes acted, more like one of the students than a professor. The *Herr Doktor* Professors, however they disagreed with the young man's methods, did find his work exciting and his company agreeable. He drove them to Yosemite ("I never tire of Yosemite") for a weekend, and, even while admiring the grandeur of the park, they listened to each other's ideas.

Whatever its past reputation for stodginess, the physics department at

Berkeley by 1930 was lively and creative. Professors Birge and Loeb had been right to insist on good young men rather than famous names in building it up. If the German theoreticians were most appreciative of Oppenheimer, who was slowly developing their branch of physics, there was no doubt that the staff had been enhanced by the addition of other young men besides Ernest and Oppie in recent years; Samuel Allison, Robert Brode, Francis Jenkins, and Harvey White would have been welcome anywhere. Astronomer Armin Leuschner, Chairman of the Board of Research, and Chemist Gilbert Lewis were proud of their parts in the development. Lewis, a member of the National Academy of Sciences, even arranged that Ernest be invited to discuss his circular accelerator in September at the first Berkeley meeting ever held by that august body, and Ernest and Edlefsen demonstrated their glass and sealing wax apparatus on a kitchen chair, with a clothes hanger for support of accessory connections. It received much attention in the press, and "South Dakota Boy Makes Good" headlines pleased Carl and Gunda Lawrence in Springfield.

Just prior to this event, however, a crisis developed in the career of Ernest Lawrence, his work at California, and for the university itself. Regents, administration, and faculty leaders became involved in rather heated discussion before it was resolved by what must be considered a most important settlement for Ernest, the university, and, perhaps, even the nation. President Walter Dill Scott of Northwestern University started it with an offer to Ernest of a full professorship and charge of research in physics at a starting salary of $6,500, a stipend high anywhere in 1930 even for full professors. Men of such rank at Berkeley started at $4,000. Ernest was elated; as he wrote John, "Naturally this offer nearly precipitated me into a state of collapse." Professor Hall, aware of the healthy ferment in the department from Ernest's work, unhesitatingly promised to seek a full professorship for him and promptly recommended it. The budget committee as promptly turned it down. Whoever heard of a twenty-nine-year-old professor! After a meeting with members of his department—Birge said Lawrence was their most valuable man—Hall appealed to the president.

Robert Gordon Sproul, who had served as secretary to the Board of Regents, comptroller and vice-president, and had just replaced President W. W. Campbell, was but ten years older than Ernest, and had not yet been officially inaugurated. As secretary, Sproul had corresponded with Ernest during negotiations to bring him to California from Yale and was thoroughly familiar with his record and growing reputation. Consultations were held with Professor Swann—who predicted that within ten years Lawrence would be one of the ten leading physicists—and a special committee under the chairmanship of Professor S. J. Holmes of zoology was appointed to consider how to keep Ernest on the California faculty.

A long letter to Sproul, signed by all the members of the committee, recommended that Lawrence be promoted to professor of physics at a salary of $5,000. Among the reasons given: "As a teacher . . . unusually satisfactory . . . well liked by his students; unusual aptitude for selecting significant and feasible problems for graduate students; and in directing and stimulating them in their research . . . this feature of [his] work has become one of great importance to the department.

"As a member of departmental staff, [he] cooperates well with his colleagues and is highly thought of by them for his ability and personality. By his good judgement and tact contributes much to smooth and efficient functioning . . . his research work extensive and exhibits an unusual degree of ingenuity, experimental skill and grasp of the field . . . earned esteem in other institutions . . . his papers regarded as real contributions of importance for development of science.

"Those . . . in position to estimate . . . agreed in pronouncing him the best experimental physicist among men his age in the country . . . realize promotion of Professor Lawrence has been uncommonly rapid and has considered . . . reactions on other members of staff . . . feel that Professor Lawrence's achievements and value to the university are such as to justify the advancement which is recommended . . . colleagues of [his] on the committee feel that it would be a very serious handicap . . . if [he] were to leave."

Meantime Ernest journeyed to Northwestern to discuss the offer and look at the department there. He was welcomed by the president and feted generally, but he thought the physics department dormant and the laboratory "punk." Northwestern's administration, which had received a new endowment of something over $8,000,000, wanted it strengthened. Ernest told the president it would take a sizable initial outlay and at least $20,000 a year to make it first-class. He returned to Berkeley hoping that circumstances would permit him to remain there. President Sproul called a joint meeting of the budget and special committees. Responses to his inquiries—all highly complimentary to Lawrence—were reported. There were harsh remarks and some bitter wrangling; naturally enough many older professors resented the young and aggressive newcomer, who had never served as an instructor, nor at California as an assistant, being granted such honor and a higher than usual salary. Sproul let them argue until Dean Lewis remarked: "We haven't met here just to decide whether or not to make a professor, but whether or not we are going to have a physics department."

Sproul, referring to Swann's opinion, announced: "If there is one chance in ten that he'll be one of the top physicists in the country, I'll take that chance." He requested Lewis to discuss salary with Ernest, who was very happy to remain at Berkeley for less than the amount promised by Northwestern. On October 21, the regents approved his promotion to full professor with an immediate increase of salary to $4,500, to be advanced to $5,000 the following term. Thus, at twenty-nine, Ernest Lawrence became the youngest full professor in the history of the university—one day before Robert Gordon Sproul was formally inaugurated as president of the University of California.

CHAPTER VI

Proton Merry-Go-Round

[OCTOBER, 1930–early 1932]

Gunda Lawrence was not surprised that her "born grown up" son had become professor of physics when barely twenty-nine years old, four years after obtaining his doctorate, and just two years after joining the faculty of a great university. Nor were any of his past associates who considered him a "young man in a hurry." And most of those at Berkeley who had opposed the unprecedented promotion and advance in salary because he was "so boyish," put aside objections, envy, and resentment with the accomplished fact—at least there was no evidence of unseemly pride or arrogance in the young professor's conduct. Open, frank, and jovial as ever, he entertained members of the physics department and their wives at the Faculty Club, of which he was steward this year. The party was successful. Ernest's jokes came off well with a little pretelling memory refreshment from a small book, easily concealed in a pocket, or beneath the linen at the table. Two days later he entertained faculty friends from other departments, this time a bit more formally.

The arrival of an invitation to apply for a Guggenheim Fellowship made Ernest realize the rapidity of his progress. He had no thought of accepting, in view of the tremendously important work under way in the laboratory, but the very ease with which he refused the invitation caused him a moment's pause; how he would have pondered such an offer a couple of years earlier, and likely have eagerly accepted it. Now, doing exactly what he wanted to do, in pleasant surroundings, and with a future he believed to be unlimited in opportunity and adventure, he had an assured salary many older men might envy. And this at a time when jobs were scarce and security seemed only a phrase.

Indeed he was aware of the financial plight of much of the nation, largely through letters from his parents—there was talk of having to close or restrict the curriculum at Carl Lawrence's college. There was little visible evidence of the Depression around Berkeley, compared to cities elsewhere, but not even a young man with his head in the clouds could fail to note its effect in the industrial East. It was hard for one who had never had trouble making money not to believe it the fault of the individual if he must sleep in a doorway wrapped in newspaper and beg his food. And it was easy to believe and echo the optimism of leaders who said the crisis was temporary. There was speculation at the Faculty Club about causes and remedies—but by men of other departments rather than by scientists concerned with *facts* of nature. All the good men working under Ernest were accomplishing worthwhile things, and if some of them had to scrimp, they were students yet; they would make their way all right, later. He did what he could to get grants or stipends for them, and more than once advanced money of his own to enable them to establish themselves in jobs. They were learning not to surrender to obstacles, catching some of the "can do" and "there's usually a way around any difficulty" spirit of the Maestro.

All the laboratory problems were interesting to Ernest, but the various experiments in the acceleration of particles to high energies, carried on in the Le Conte laboratories, occupied every moment he could spare from teaching and other work. Friends, partying with Ernest at the St. Francis Hotel across the bay, were fascinated that when he was not racing around the dance floor, he was marking up the tablecloth explaining his proton merry-go-round accelerator, one of the girls, Christine Brooke Fredericks, remembers. Ernest thought that the most intriguing device, but the linear method was progressing well; perhaps it would prove to be the most practical—the problem with it was the difficulty of nuclear exploration with heavy ions.

It was all so new; there was no experience to draw upon. Sloan found it hard to go on with it, finding himself apparently blocked after conceiving a different tube for the acceleration of lighter electrons. Ernest was in accord with Sloan's new idea but wanted the linear accelerator developed first. The circular device presented more problems. Livingston did not believe that resonance had been observed with the earlier device, or that Edlefsen's magnet had been properly calibrated, though Brady had seen that resonance came at the calculated point of the magnetic field. With Stan's neat four-and-a-half-inch brass and copper chamber, carefully calibrated four-inch magnet, and varied voltage and gas pressure—adjusting and altering as they might—they could "make them spin all right," as Ernest wrote Swann, "but we have not been able to determine how many times, and therefore at what speeds, the protons move." With persistence this was overcome and, with only 160 volts on the electrodes, energies corresponding to 1,300 volts were achieved. During the 1930 Christmas vacation Ernest and Stan borrowed vacationing student Bob Holtzer's doubly powerful magnet, and on January 2, 1931, produced 80,000-volt protons, the energies expected from Ernest's calculations. There was no doubt now of the validity of the method.

Ernest reported progress in acceleration and other experiments at the winter meetings of the Physical Society in Los Angeles. So that Brady might present his own paper, he was invited to drive to Los Angeles with Ernest. Wrapped up in speculation and discussion, they ran out of gas. After walking some distance for gasoline, they had difficulty priming the vacuum system used in those days to get gasoline from tank to carburetor. "For heaven's sake!" Ernest expressed his disgust with the system, more acidly than the expression implies. "Don't you know whose system that is, who invented it?" Brady asked. "No, it's not good anyway." "He works for you. Weinberg." Brady smiled. Lawrence could hardly believe that Weinberg, an engineer on the Berkeley staff who had asked to work in the laboratory, had made a fortune from this and other inventions. When they reached the Los Angeles restaurant where the Berkeley group met, he went at once to the table where Weinberg sat with about a dozen others. Weinberg admitted that he had invented "that darn vacuum feed," and Ernest told him what he thought of "the contraption" to the delight of everyone, including Weinberg and Ernest himself.

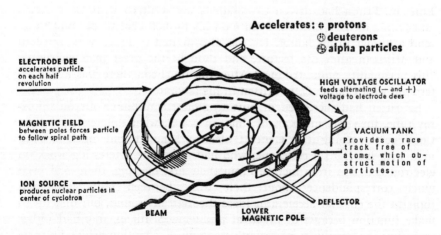

Diagram of particle acceleration in a cyclotron. (*Lawrence Radiation Laboratory*)

From Los Angeles, Ernest drove to Arizona and Navaho and Hopi country before returning to Berkeley. He had not been back for more than a week of hard work before he left with Oppie on another motor trip to Death Valley. Ernest derived rest and a sense of well being from nature, and with Oppenheimer as his companion, there was plenty of good talk. Speculation stimulated experiment, and experiment usually called for theoretical verification.

There was much delightful and informative theoretical talk, too, besides laboratory excitement, during the second term. Professor H. A. Kramers of Holland was a visiting lecturer and there were "symposia and colloquia galore, which I am enjoying," Ernest wrote to John, adding that he was not neglecting social life. He urged John to go down to New Haven and see Elsie Blumer, enclosing a $25 check for expenses. He was a weekend guest at Pebble Beach, where he was most attentive to another guest who was Australian, questioning her about her frontier land—and, of course, telling her about the realm he hoped soon to explore, beyond frontiers more difficult to penetrate than those of any continent. Pebble Beach, dancing, attendance twice at Chicago Civic Opera performances in San Francisco, theater parties, and the San Francisco Symphony—however charming and interesting his lovely young companions, these pleasures could not match his delight at receiving increasingly interesting letters from Molly at Harvard. She wrote well of her experiments in bacteriology, under the direction of Hans Zinser. Ernest could be sympathetic with her doubts and exhilarated over her successes—he could hardly wait to see her.

Nor could any social affair match the thrill of lunching with Albert Einstein. Ernest had driven to Pasadena and Caltech with Dean Lewis and Oppie to hear Einstein lecture on his unified field theory and to attend a dinner in his honor. He was also invited to lunch with Einstein and Millikan after the lecture, and thought the great man charming, "his personality most striking." After the luncheon there was a fine afternoon with Charles C. Lauritsen in his laboratory.

Lauritsen had succeeded in putting almost a million volts on his X-ray tube, for short intervals of time, in a somewhat different way than Coolidge was doing it at General Electric. Ernest found much in common with his Danish colleague, who had also done interesting work on electron emission from metals. From their first meeting, there had been much correspondence about their work between visits. Lauritsen thought the circular accelerator ideas theoretically sound, but difficult to make function because of practical problems. Millikan, too, had rather scoffed at the possibility of Ernest's resonant acceleration achieving practical results! Even if made to work, it would require apparatus too cumbersome and complicated to have a rightful place in the laboratory of a

state university, he said. Millikan rather followed the Chicago idea that
university experimenting should be done with teaching apparatus. Such
conversations, as well as the meetings with Einstein, only served as goads
to Ernest. He did not wait for Lewis and Oppenheimer to drive back to
Berkeley, but flew back "in three hours in one of those tri-motored fifteen passenger things."

He had already decided to construct a larger circular accelerator, one
that would produce at least a million volts, and calculated pretty exactly
what would be required in magnet size, semicircular electrodes—now referred to, because of their shape, as "D's"—and a more powerful radio-
frequency system. He estimated he could build it for a thousand dollars.
He got the money with little trouble from the National Research Council, and suggested to Livingston that he write his degree thesis on the
development of the present model. If, with his degree, he then wished to
work on the new model, Ernest would ask that he be made an instructor. Livingston got his degree and the instructorship. A new magnet was
designed and built, and construction of a larger "proton merry-go-
round" tube was pushed. But even before it was assembled, Ernest was
thinking of still larger machines and yet higher voltages. Though theories
of the new wave mechanics made it likely that light nuclei could be disintegrated with energies of about 500,000 volts, Ernest felt that to attack
nuclei of heavy elements much higher energies would be required, and
that protons were the most efficient "bullets." Therefore, the circular
method of multiple acceleration was the only one with which difficulties
involved in the procurement and use of high voltages could be avoided.
Meanwhile linear acceleration of heavy elements was a continuing experiment—and he would discuss this at the June meeting of the American Association for the Advancement of Science in Pasadena. In the
meantime he had commitments to lecture in the Midwest and East, and
while in New York would seek support from the Rockefeller and Carnegie foundations.

The biggest item of expense would be for a very large magnet. In discussing this with Dr. Leonard Fuller, vice-president of the Federal Telegraph Company and a member of the engineering faculty of the university, who had lent him equipment for previous experiments, Ernest
learned of an 80-ton magnet core that had been designed for a now-
obsolete arc generator of radio waves. The huge casting had been in a
warehouse for years, not only because of obsolescence but also because of
difficulties in China, for which country it had been destined. Ernest immediately started negotiations; eventually the huge magnet was given to
him by the company. That it would be costly to transport across the bay
and that he had no place to install it were minor items that in no sense
dampened his elation. There were those who thought him really unbal-

anced. He had, they thought, not thoroughly demonstrated the practicality of his idea with the four-inch instrument; the next larger was far from completed, and he spoke of 25,000,000 volts! Even some of his students, used to the optimism and high spirits of his laboratory, shook their heads. But they would not admit it to outsiders; the Maestro more than likely would come through—as usual!

Even his tennis games had new zest—the only exercise he took time for, except for another Sunday horseback ride in the Piedmont hills with Oppie and girls with whom they already had a date. Besides preparation for lectures he was committed to give at Washington University in St. Louis and the University of Iowa, and a progress report for the Washington meeting, he devoted his spare time to planning fund raising and making calculations for a huge circular multiple accelerator to fit the new magnet.

He left late in April by train through the Colorado Rockies for St. Louis and Iowa, after which he detoured a bit on his way to Chicago, to meet his parents in Sioux City for part of a day. A good report from his mother's examination at the Mayo Clinic freed his mind of that distraction, and wherever he went, Chicago, Princeton, Bartol, Yale, in New York and Boston, he preached the importance of his machine to physics as the means of "opening up the whole field of study of the atomic nucleus"—firmly convinced that the work of his laboratory would prove to be "epoch-making." He urged others to develop his device for their own studies, freely drawing plans, giving equations, withholding nothing he knew. His very eagerness to share his ideas increased the doubts of some with whom he spoke. Did one give away important ideas so easily? There was skepticism everywhere, sometimes humorously expressed, sometimes almost cynically. It bothered Ernest very little; who, with a new idea, had not been ridiculed! The foundation officials he approached listened politely, asked for references from noted scientists who would vouch for him and the soundness of his idea, and postponed answer until investigation could be made, or board members informed and assembled. He was undaunted. In Boston he discussed his accelerator in detail with John C. Slater, and enthused over it to his brother John, who was considering a move to Strong Memorial Hospital in Rochester, New York.

Ernest was in Boston for several days, and not because of John or consultations with Slater. He arrived there by train with Molly, who had been in New Haven for a weekend at his request. He had found her noticeably less casual with him; she actually appeared happy and excited over his successes, and on the train to Boston he explained his circular accelerator so clearly that she felt her resolution against falling in love slipping. "I had always known that he was brilliant, but his explanation of the concept—well, it suddenly dawned on me that I loved him." Neither declared themselves verbally, but they were together every possible moment before he had to leave—with the result that Molly later had to "cram madly" for finals. When she worried about them to Ernest he said, "I hope you'll flunk!" as though in that case she would have more time for him. She was mightily embarrassed when they were interrupted by a policeman while parked (in John's car) on a Boston parkway—and helped Ernest discover a more secluded parking place in the delivery alley behind the medical school buildings. It pleased her that Dr. Zinser thought Ernest "a smart Swede." She played hooky to see him off; he had a date in Berkeley with R. H. Fowler of Rutherford's Cavendish Laboratory. As it was he had only a day's visit in Springfield with his parents, and he left the train at Reno to fly over the High Sierra Mountains to Oakland. He arrived in Berkeley in the morning—and spent the afternoon and evening with Fowler, most of the time in the laboratory.

The first magnet constructed for the circular magnetic resonance accelerator originally had only nine-inch pole faces, and was wound with cotton-covered, number fourteen wire. Its carefully made chamber initially contained a single D electrode; a grounded slotted bar served as the other. This allowed room in half the chamber for adjustment of a deflecting plate and the placement of targets for the full impact of the high-energy beam. Dismantled parts of old radios were used in the high-frequency device. Don Cooksey, who had arrived for a visit, helped with enthusiasm, but the "merry-go-round" was not in operation, as Ernest had hoped, before the Pasadena meeting. Nevertheless, he talked about it at the meeting, though his principal remarks concerned the linear accelerator, and a new Sloan development of it for accelerating electrons. He had a stimulating time with Lauritsen, Merle, Tom Johnson, and others, discussing various methods for achieving what everyone now agreed was absolutely necessary—very high energies. Interested as he was in other methods, Ernest remained convinced that his merry-go-round would surpass them all. Only the idea of multiple resonance acceleration, with low initial voltage, he argued, could avoid the technological limitations inherent in all other methods discussed: X-ray tubes such as Lauritsen and Coolidge were developing, Merle's Tesla coil transformer, various ideas for charging capacitators in parallel, and discharging them in series, the voltage multiplier techniques John Cockcroft and Thomas Walton were developing at Cambridge with the support of Rutherford (now a peer) or the electrostatic generator being developed by Van de Graaff at Princeton. There were bound to be serious breakdown limitations with each of these methods before sufficiently high energies for thorough nuclear work—the ability to break up nuclei of all elements

—could be attained; with either his linear or circular accelerator, one could attain the necessary high energies without use of disastrously high input voltages.

Ernest found little complete agreement at the Pasadena meeting; there was chatter in his audience all during his formal address. Cooksey, sitting behind Millikan, heard him tell his neighbor: "It's a nice idea but it just won't work." Don thought that more than half the senior physicists present would agree with Millikan. "Never get enough positive ions to make it worthwhile," was frequently heard, or "Lose them before reaching high energies," and "Just not practical, at all."

Don repeated some of these remarks as they drove back to Berkeley; none of them seemed to disturb Ernest. He laughingly remarked that he might have fared better if he had stayed in the East for Beams's wedding! He was sorry to have missed that. Imagine, shy Jesse proposing marriage! And Tom Johnson had married widowed Ann Benedict. Ernest declared that it was high time he and Don embraced matrimony, and that he would if he could have the girl he wanted. "A girl out here?" Cooksey asked, innocently. "Oh, no," Ernest grinned. Don, a confirmed bachelor, thought there was much to be said for remaining single.

The discussion was cut short near Carpenteria when Ernest spotted an autogiro in a field near the road. Anxious to see it at closer range, they drove to its nearby hangar. He jumped out, examined the autogiro, and questioned a man who appeared and offered to take him up for five dollars. Don said he would "blow him to it," and Ernest went aloft for about a five-minute ride. Don, who understood that autogiros settled down rather perpendicularly, became alarmed as the machine approached to land with much forward velocity. Ernest did not mind the hard landing at all. "Marvelous!" he exclaimed, "not like another flight! You ought to try it. Like nothing you ever had before. You must go up."

Cooksey went up. After a short flight the pilot came in higher and faster than before. Don was certain the rotors would tangle with power lines, that the machine might even catch fire. He had seen planes crash in France during the war. He braced himself, put his head down, and expected the worst. Again the pilot could not slow the forward motion sufficiently; the machine hit the ground with such a thud the rotors flopped and one was sheared off by the propeller. Don jumped out; he was all right, but there was moaning from the pilot's seat. "You all right?" Don looked back at the pilot. "This is terrible!" "What's the matter? Where are you hurt?" "I'm all right—but it's my job!" the pilot cried. Ernest reached the scene, breathless from running. "You all right, Don?" "Sure." "How about the pilot?" "He's all right but his feelings are hurt," Don said, as people came running across the field. "Here they come." "Keep them back!" the pilot shouted. It was discovered that he, though an aviator, had never flown an autogiro before. Don, afraid of publicity for Ernest, got him back to the car and drove off before they could be questioned.

Ernest had been more frightened than Don; he said he thought he had sent Cooksey to his death by insisting that he take the flight. He was concerned that Don might have internal injury, but Don refused to stop in Santa Barbara for a check. His neck became stiff a little later. This experience, and the crash of a plane through the roof, floors, and into the basement of a Berkeley house, made Ernest leery of flying for several years. After some calculation, he decided that odds were not sufficiently favorable; a person's chances of being killed on a transcontinental round trip, he announced, were only one in three hundred. "But suppose that in a block three hundred feet long you knew that somewhere a foot wide steel beam would drop—would you walk it?"

Merle visited Ernest before returning to Washington from Pasadena and was impressed with his accelerators. He said there could be no question of the importance of Ernest's work. After Dean Richtmeyer of Cornell visited the laboratory, he promised that, as chairman of the National Research Council, he would do what he could to help get funds for accelerator research. And Karl Compton, who had recently left Princeton to become president of M.I.T., and had Van de Graaff building a large electrostatic generator there, spent an afternoon in the laboratory and was impressed that the nine-inch circular accelerator could produce 900,000-volt protons in quantity.

Ernest was heartened, as he had been undaunted by remarks at Pasadena. He was still certain that the machine should do better—be able to produce a million volts. Had he been less concerned with this objective, certainly a laudatory one, the history of nuclear science well might have been different, for Ernest already had, if he could have known it, more than sufficient energy with his 900,000 volts to split atoms, and could easily have been the first to do so. He would have had to develop more adequate counting and measuring instruments than were available to him—and more technical knowledge of their use. Perhaps the lack of them, and of experience in nuclear work, urged him to work toward higher voltage before taking time for nuclear experiment with energies already achieved. Even the 900,000 had not come easily, or at once; there had been many changes and adjustments and Ernest tirelessly set about making more.

Everything had to be learned as they went along, and things that now seem obvious were overlooked at first. Theory helped in some instances, but improvements were largely the result of cut-and-try. Thus a change in the shapes of the facing electrodes and adjustment of the accelerating gap between them increased currents tremendously, and electromagnetic focusing, now known as a most important factor in accelerator performance, was discovered. He decided to increase the diameter of the magnet pole faces to ten, and then to eleven inches, and still Livingston could get no more amplification than about seventy-five and concluded relativity mass was responsible. Ernest showed him that it could not be true at this velocity, that more likely the fault lay in lack of uniformity of the magnetic field. He suggested shims, small pieces of variously shaped iron, introduced between the magnet face and the evacuated "can" containing the electrodes. When it was first attempted, Ernest had to leave for a class. When he returned to the laboratory, he found his assistant downcast; he had lost rather than gained with the shims. Ernest thought a moment, then shouted: "Whoopee! If it changes it down, it can change it upward, too!"

Very soon, by changing the shapes and arrangements of shims, currents were doubled, and, with further work, doubled again. Thus another essential feature of magnetic focusing was discovered. Late in July, 1931, with improved measuring scales, it was certain that ions of 1,000,000 volts were collected at the perimeter! Ernest literally danced, after tuning the magnet through resonance, to see the galvanometer swing across the scale. He could split atoms! He wrote the figures large on the blackboard. It was an event in scientific history; never before had anyone produced million-volt particles—and with an accelerator only eleven inches in diameter.

Word quickly spread around the department; the rest of that day was spent demonstrating, explaining million-volt protons, and attempting to pass the million-volt mark. Professor Leuschner came over. Dr. Frederick Cottrell of the Research Corporation was brought in for a demonstration. Ernest convinced each of these gentlemen that the only obstacle in the way of 20,000,000 and more volts was equipment to construct a larger apparatus, with the big magnet he had been given by the telegraph company. He announced plans to go East again to raise the funds. Cottrell advised: "If you want a large sum, ask for it. It is easier to get five thousand dollars than five hundred."

Frederick Cottrell, sometime California student and member of the chemistry faculty, had initiated and promoted the Research Corporation in 1912. A sort of holding company for academic ideas and inventions, its aim was the protection of inventive rights while furthering development. Though he had refused to serve as a director or officer, Cottrell naturally remained interested in the welfare and proper functioning of the corporation. He now wrote to its president, Howard Poillon, about Ernest: "I have looked upon him as a man who should go far. He not only does good work himself, but I have been particularly impressed with how much he manages to get out of his graduate students on the research problems, of which he keeps a surprising number going full blast." Cottrell went on to discuss Ernest's work in "the production of high voltage protons for use in disintegrating the nuclei of other heavier chemical atoms . . . high voltage electrons for generation of very penetrating X rays, gamma rays (like radium etc.) and even up to artificial cosmic rays etc."

Ernest told Cottrell he needed "at least ten thousand dollars and possibly fifteen thousand" for continuation of his work. "It appears that our difficulties are no longer of a physical but of a financial nature." Appointments were made for Ernest to talk with Poillon in New York late in July.

Initially, Ernest's decision to go East again so soon had little to do with his work. He was determined that Molly become his wife, and as soon as possible. He had no more doubt of the desirability and wisdom of this than of the future of his accelerators, and saw no point in postponement. She did not need a master's degree; he certainly could not wish to wait for her to get the doctorate she had thought she wanted. He thought he could persuade her to forgo those. Her letters had become increasingly cordial, and there was real rapport between them since they had last been together. Now in Europe with her mother and Elsie, Molly had promised to let him know when she would return so that he could meet her ship. This in itself seemed encouraging. As he wrote John, he would "greet Molly on the pier, and what's more I am going to propose and try to marry her as soon as possible!!! I know that I am really in love with her and I don't want to wait for her longer than necessary. I can hardly wait till I am with her again." He suggested that John be in New York to meet the ship with him. Don Cooksey, amused by Ernest's statement, "I am beginning to realize I have two consuming loves—Molly and research," left for England before her scheduled arrival, but offered a car and guest cards for the Yale Club in New York and the Lawn and Graduate clubs in New Haven, and promised to keep Ernest's romantic intentions to himself.

In New York in late July, Ernest had immediate luck with one "consuming love." Fred Cottrell appeared personally before the Research Corporation Board to plead Ernest's case, and later personally introduced him. In the words of Joseph W. Barker of the Board, Ernest "explained . . . lucidly what he wanted to do and what equipment he needed. . . . His enthusiasm and Fred's sincere backing of him convinced the Board to make the grant even though we had to go to the bank and borrow the funds since we were in the red as the result of . . . the great depression." Five thousand dollars was pledged, to be drawn as needed. Poillon, to become one of Ernest's most respected friends and advisers, introduced Ernest to William Buffum of the Chemical Foundation, who promised another $2,500 for Ernest's work.

He chafed waiting for Molly, who cabled a later arrival date than had been planned. As he had to be in Berkeley before August 17, every day was important. He went to Washington to visit Merle—arranging for a position for his student Loveridge at Carnegie—and tried to lose himself in laboratory visits; but Molly was the consuming problem now. After her ship docked, on August 2, there was only a week to force her decision. She seemed delighted that he had waited to greet her, and he wanted to declare himself at once, but they were not alone on the drive to Connecticut.

There was little opportunity to see her alone when they reached Haycock Point, and he left late that night without having had more than a few words with her in private. It was the same the next day; there were still many relatives and friends about. In the evening he received a wire from a department secretary in Berkeley, dated August 3, 1931, addressed to him at the Blumer home: "Dr. Livingston has asked me to advise you that he has obtained 1,100,000 volt protons. He also suggested that I add 'Whoopee.'" Ernest read the telegram aloud, and, almost ignoring congratulatory comment, asked Molly to go outside with him. He guided her to the porch hammock, put an arm around her, and asked, "Molly, do you love me?" With no hesitation, she said, "I do." "Then we ought to get married right away," he said, before he kissed her.

That settled it! Though Molly did not want to rush off unceremoniously and felt they should have a proper wedding, she agreed to marry him in the coming spring—after getting her master's degree. Ernest could not even wait for her to tell her family, but announced it himself at breakfast the following morning. "Are we supposed to be surprised?" Mrs. Blumer asked. The ensuing silence made Ernest turn to Dr. Blumer. "Is there any objection?" There was none voiced; the Blumers wished their eldest's happiness. Mrs. Blumer and Elsie had noticed much evidence of Molly's feelings toward Ernest during the European trip. Molly seemed more concerned over what Dr. Zinser would think than the opinions of anyone else. Ernest left New Haven for Berkeley somewhat giddy—after promising to let Molly be the one to announce their engagement.

Molly was both "giddy" and a bit worried when she returned to Harvard and Dr. Zinser. Zinser had been reluctant to accept a girl as a student in the first place because "she'll just go off and get married when things are going well." Molly, who had gone first to see him with her well-known father, had assured him that she was never going to marry.

Now he could say, "I told you so!" He did not; when she mentioned that she was engaged, he turned to her with a terrifying stare, his bushy eyebrows seeming to jump out at her, and swore heartily in German. "You understand German?"

"Not much," Molly said.

"That's good. So you're going to get married! Is he that big Swede?"

"You're awfully close," Molly said. "His family are all Norwegian."

Zinser thought a moment. "You love this man?"

"Why, I think so." Molly was startled by the question.

"Then why the hell don't you get married!"

Ernest respected the Blumers' wishes and told no one his good news who might know the family, except Cooksey, who was in England; he asked him not to reveal it before the formal announcement by the Blumers. He saw no reason for secrecy, however, when he returned to Berkeley; had he been able to refrain from telling the news, his actions would have revealed his happiness. He placed a large picture of Molly on his desk the first morning he returned to his office. Rebekah Young, the department secretary, exclaimed: "What a lovely photograph!"

"She *is* lovely!" responded the beaming Ernest.

It was fortunate that he had returned when he did. He met Charles Gilman Hyde of the engineering faculty on the campus and, among other things about his work, said he needed space for the big magnet, which he hoped could soon be installed. Hyde pointed out an old wooden two-story building which had been used as a materials testing laboratory and which the engineers were vacating that very day for new quarters. Clapboard-sided, dating back to 1902, and resembling a house more than a university structure, it was close to Le Conte, just north of Gilman Hall, and its main room would be ideal for a new accelerator incorporating the huge magnet. Hyde said it was to be demolished and suggested,"Go see if you can get it." Ernest did not wait a minute. Enlisting the support of Leuschner, he pursued his request right to the president. Not only did Sproul approve of the use of most of the building for Ernest's accelerators—he had used as many as ten rooms in Le Conte Hall—he was so pleased by Ernest's Eastern support that he appropriated $3,000 for the necessary alterations and installation of power lines. Furthermore, he authorized Leuschner, as chairman of the Research Board, to appeal to the electric company to contribute the power. A linguistic group would retain a small room on the second floor for a time, as would a larger group from the forestry department. The new magnet, machined to form $27\frac{1}{2}$-inch tapered pole faces, and weighing 74 tons, was installed in the old building in October, and work was pushed on accessories. Pressed for a name, Ernest first suggested it be called

Penetrating Radiations Laboratory, but by the first of the year 1932 had requested that it be known simply as the Radiation Laboratory. It quickly came to be known as the Rad Lab.

Ernest's cousin, Lawrence Haugen, en route to a new assignment in the Philippines, found Ernest more buoyant than ever as he showed off his instruments and the "new" old building being prepared for the big magnet. When Haugen's wife Margaret came through later on her way to join her husband, Ernest met her at the train, drove her to visit Navy friends at Mare Island and to see some of the sights on her first visit to the West Coast. She was frightened by Ernest's driving. "He talked with his hands, trying to explain things, and never looked at the road. I really thought he was mad."

A warning from John Slater of M.I.T. that a large corporation was preparing to apply for a patent on "the idea of your proton merry-go-round, apparently entirely independent of you," elated rather than worried Ernest. That such a corporation thought it worthwhile was added confirmation of its value. Patent procedures were initiated through the Research Corporation, which found it difficult to find anyone able to make the concept "sufficiently concrete to establish claims that can be protected." Ernest did not refrain from telling anyone interested all about the machine; he had wanted it free to be copied by any university that wished to construct one, but understood that it would have to be patented to make even that possible. Newspapers had become interested, and there were annoying articles to the effect that he was trying to transmute base metal to gold.

The Sunday supplement type of notoriety of the thirties was deplored; but increasing and responsible press attention was also given to the Berkeley work, as scientists from Europe as well as America became interested. Never had an academic laboratory had so large an instrument as the proton accelerator under construction in the Rad Lab. Research fellows chose Berkeley in increasing numbers, others asked to work at the Radiation Laboratory without remuneration. Ernest had nine graduate students in early 1932; universities sought his Ph.D.'s for their faculties. When Father Macelwane, the seismologist of St. Louis University, sought a good young physicist to join his staff in the coming fall, 1932, Ernest persuaded him that he might get Brady, who had completed his work for the doctorate, if St. Louis University would grant him a research fellowship to stay on at Berkeley during the intervening months. Brady would be that much better, Ernest suggested, for the extra time spent in the laboratory. Father Macelwane agreed. Who but the Maestro could have sold such an idea! Brady stayed through the summer of 1932, working on the new accelerator after Milton White left for a summer job. Then Brady built an ionization chamber for the 11-

inch accelerator. He and White had had "just a few doubts" about the energies claimed at first, and had surreptitiously tested with various thicknesses of mica placed in the path of the beam. They were convinced. All accelerator apparatus progressed.

Sloan's tube for accelerating electrons was developing into "a helluva X-ray outfit." The original linear accelerator continued to be improved and extended. The big magnet coils, designed to be cooled in oil, were wound with $1\frac{1}{4}$-inch by $\frac{1}{16}$-inch copper strip. The bronze "can," as the proton tube (vacuum chamber containing the D's) was called, was 27 inches in diameter and, with the soft iron bottom and like cover each $1\frac{1}{2}$ inches thick, was $6\frac{1}{2}$ inches high. Around the lab this came to be called the cyclotron, by whom first, no one seems to remember. For some years the term was considered slang and the more elegant name "magnetic resonance accelerator," was used in dissertations. "Cyclotron," however, came more and more into use everywhere, until in 1936 it was made official by a footnote to a laboratory paper published in the *Physical Review*.

Ernest's affairs, laboratory and personal, progressed so well after his engagement to Molly that he sometimes felt he was tempting the gods —a most unusual idea for him—but if he tempted fate it was in overwork and lack of care for his body. By November he was very tired and unable to shake a nagging cough that much of the time seemed related to grippe. Letters from Molly, full of her work and plans for their household—her grandmother had bought her at auction some fine pieces of maple furniture for a bedroom—suddenly were full of worries about her family. Patients were not paying her father's bills; he had lost heavily in the continuing Depression; she felt she should quit Harvard at the end of the semester and get a job. Ernest felt she should quit for marriage and seized on her worries to plead for a date around Christmas, when he would be in the East to lecture at Columbia and to visit General Electric by invitation of Dr. Coolidge. Molly still wished to wait for June, and Zinser persuaded her to finish the year and write a paper on her experiment for publication. Ernest wrote John with most unaccustomed blues: "I miss Molly. I don't know what I would do if our experimental work should turn out badly. I simply wouldn't be able to stand the combination of hardships."

He left Berkeley immediately at the start of the seasonal vacation, stopping in South Dakota to see his parents and to visit Dean Akeley. In Rochester with John, he had his chest X-rayed and John was hard put to persuade the doctor that the scars revealed were old, and tuberculosis arrested. He was, however, convinced that his brother had once had the disease. Medicine and some rest improved Ernest's cough before he continued to Schenectady. In New York he invited Poillon and Buffum to attend his Columbia lecture, given in the evening before physicists from a wide area, and had conferences with those gentlemen the following day. Then he went to Boston and Molly, and while she got her work in shape to go to New Haven with him, he visited at M.I.T., and with Slater saw the work on the construction of the big Van de Graaff static generator. "They'll get fairly high potentials all right, but their trouble will really start when they try to build a tube to make use of the high potential," he warned.

He was well enough for a fine evening of dancing with Molly at the Copley Plaza before they went to New Haven. He was amazed at the preparations in progress for their wedding, still some months away—the trousseau, the guest lists, and other matters of seeming importance. Molly was distressed that, due to the crash of the stock market, one of her dearest college friends would be unable to be an attendant in her wedding party—for which Ernest learned he was expected to name six or eight ushers. He had not known that weddings involved so much; how much simpler just to get married!

He had to leave again, all too soon, for Washington, where he visited Merle, and in Charlottesville he joined Beams for the trip to New Orleans to deliver a paper on the multiple acceleration of charged particles at the Physical Society meeting. He was elected to the board of editors of the *Physical Review*, an honor, Beams thought, though Ernest suggested it might be a doubtful one if it took time from his work. He was glad to be with Beams—for the longest period since they had left Yale. His cold seemed to be on the wane, and his spirits were rising. Oppie also read a paper and in the following critique was treated rather badly—some said hostilely and without scruple—by Millikan. Ernest whispered comforting assurance to his sensitive colleague, who felt he had not done well. Ernest assured him that he had suffered worse than Oppie from the same source. Swann was reelected president and, after a joint dinner with geophysicists and meteorologists, presided at a testimonial meeting honoring the late Thomas Alva Edison.

Oppie introduced his younger brother Frank, who was planning a career in physics, and Ernest was invited to their New Mexico ranch for the next summer. Oppie assured Ernest that if he could do it without a complete rupture with Caltech, he would spend the entire academic year in Berkeley. He had been helpful with many of the problems that constantly arose in the wholly new field of multiple acceleration, as well as a good companion on walks or listening to music.

"They were together all the time," Brady remembers. "They were a great team, the experimenter and the theorist. Once I went to Lawrence with a problem, and he said it looked as though there was disparity in temperatures of the electrons in the thin film and in the bulk. 'Let's ask

Oppie,' he said. Lawrence had hardly finished his first sentence when Oppenheimer broke in—'No, no, no! Can't be. It would violate the second law of thermodynamics!' 'Okay, forget that,' Lawrence said. Oppenheimer was way over our heads, as students. I told him that, years later, and he said, 'I know. In those days I was just talking to myself. I was just trying to educate myself!' " Some students considered Oppenheimer intolerant of those without superior minds; that graduate students should be able to understand him, Oppie took for granted. He had no lower division classes. "I was regarded as so impossible I was never allowed near an undergraduate," he said much later. But Ernest's warm regard for him "was thoroughly reciprocated." Their companionship would be less constant next year, when one had a wife, but Oppie now had good friends in various disciplines. One had to forgo some advantages for the sake of others.

Back in Berkeley a week before the start of the new term, Ernest literally worked night and day in the Rad Lab with Stan Livingston and James Brady on the big magnet and its accessories. Notified that he had been elected to the famous Bohemian Club of San Francisco, and conscious of its status, he still did not take time to attend a club program until the middle of February, when the Cossack Choir performed for members. Invited members of the university faculty were excused from paying the usual high initiation fee and were billed for less than half the usual dues. When Howard Poillon visited the area to see what the Research Corporation had contributed to, and to meet President Sproul and Professor Leuschner, Ernest was glad to entertain him at the club.

Franz Simon, of the University of Berlin, was the visiting lecturer in physics that term. Though his interests were principally in Professor Giauque's low temperature laboratory, he spent many evenings with Ernest in his laboratory, at the Faculty Club, and on occasional walks. But Ernest spent parts of most evenings on his devices. He wrote a full account of the work with the 11-inch accelerator for the April issue of the *Physical Review*, stating, "It is the most important piece of work I have ever been associated with."

Molly was kept fully informed about the work, too, and shared his excitement through letters. He also tried to see that she had outings with friends of his who might be in Boston. When his good friend Joe Boyce, who had been at Princeton during Ernest's Yale days, moved to M.I.T., he was asked to look Molly up, and she was told to expect a call from him, which came soon after Joe's arrival in Boston. Rather shy and quiet, Joe was a fine companion at dinner and the symphony, and escorted her to the on-leave-from-California Brodes' for dinner, to a hotel banquet during a scientific meeting, and on Easter to the traditional afternoon-evening performance of Bach's *B Minor Mass*, with the dinner break at the Slaters'. Molly was impressed with the careful planning that made it possible for Helen Slater to serve such a good dinner to several couples in the limited time available. She hoped to be as capable, she wrote Ernest. He assured her that he had no doubts of that nature; he was convinced that with the progress at the laboratory, only her presence was needed to make life complete.

There were frustrations he did not mention to Molly but did write of to John. "I am delayed again and again through no fault of mine . . . the week with the big magnet practically wasted, coppersmiths spending the whole time trying to make an oil tight soldering job of the tanks. Thought they finally succeeded yesterday, but today I found another leak, so they'll have to go again in the morning. Time is precious for there's lots to be done between now and April! Interested to hear you have had a period of depression. I have them often—sometimes nothing seems to be OK—but I have gotten used to them now. I expect the blues and I endure them. Of course the best palliative is work, but sometimes it is hard to work under the circumstances."

And he told an associate who complained of poor treatment: "You know, you almost have to be crucified to really amount to anything in this world, but it is useless if you let criticism affect you adversely." Work! The value of what one was doing would be sufficient answer for critics and would prevent self-pity. Work, and faith in it, without getting all tied up in abstractions as to why there not always could be a happy conclusion! Few associates ever noted other than expressions of cheerful optimism from Ernest.

After the installation of the big magnet was completed and successfully tested, Ernest wrote to his family, "We had some fun, too. You should have seen the way it would take a hammer away from us when we came within three feet!" The old building became the center of his work. He had Sloan move his big tube down to the Rad Lab, and, by April, Sloan's vacuum tank was ready; he could devote full time to that project as soon as the term ended later in the month. Others worked on pumps that had to be devised to evacuate air from each accelerator properly, whatever the design; there were then no satisfactory commercially obtainable pumps. For the most part this was also true of oscillator tubes. Charles Litton, who had been responsible for tube development for the Federal Telegraph Company, was then busily attempting to construct specially designed oscillating tubes in which burned-out filaments could be replaced, saving hundreds of dollars. Economies had to be practiced. The big cyclotron and X-ray machine were expensive, each much too large and costly for the space and budget of any normal university. Even had there been no general depression, Ernest's program would have been difficult to carry so far; how fortunate that the University of California, its president and Board of Research, had faith in him and his most unusual projects—at a time when most institutions and corporations were inclined to retrench rather than support something new, heretofore unknown, and considered by many impractical even for pure research. Even the construction of the small 11-inch cyclotron had required outside financial assistance.

The Depression had finally affected the university; the budget had been cut $2,000,000, there had been a 25-percent reduction in the number of teaching assistants, and salaries were cut 10 percent. Ernest still earned more than many older men—but the economies made it difficult to keep sufficient help in the Rad Lab. Sloan had to take course work most of the year in addition to his work on the X-ray tube; Milton White felt he had to leave for a summer job to augment his small stipend. Livingston was restless and worried, since it was contrary to policy to appoint an instructor for a second year without definite intention to keep him in the future. Ernest told him not to worry, that he would somehow get $1,500, and possibly $1,800, for him. He gave Livingston pep talks when he was moody, trying to assure him of the importance of what he was doing, and the desirability of continuous work on the big machine while he himself was away.

When he left Berkeley, it was for more than his forthcoming marriage—Molly had moved that date up to May 14. It was for more than reporting to, and attending, the Washington meetings of the academy and the Physical Society. It was for more than zeal to spread the word about multiple acceleration and curiosity to see what others were doing in the high-energy field. The Rad Lab was broke. He had to find money to continue building and running his machines for experimental research. But he was optimistic; in this great country there was always money for a worthwhile project!

His buoyant spirits spread beyond the campus in Berkeley at least as far as the house on Keith Avenue to which he would bring Molly. Years later Jessie Kayser, whose house it was, wrote to Molly of the young house-hunter:

"It was a very trying time for me for we were in serious financial straits, but somehow the radiance of your future husband took a good deal of the pain out of leaving my precious home. He liked the place as a suitable one for you; he borrowed a camera from a friend and came over to take pictures. He took samples of the bedroom wallpaper to send to his beloved. It was a joyous time for him, and his joy was contagious."

Gunda Lawrence was less enthusiastic. "He has leased a house at $75.00 (a month)!" she wrote John. "6 rooms! and who will take care of all that—when Molly is attending U?" She added that she would not attend the wedding if John could visit her during the summer. It would be so expensive, there could be no vacation with Carl, whose commitments to speak at graduations in South Dakota would prevent him from being in New Haven on May 14. She asked the Blumers for a postponement of the wedding, but the invitations were already engraved and in the mail. She did attend, however, without Carl.

Ernest visited briefly with his parents in Sioux City on his way East and promised to bring his bride to Springfield on his return to California. He had a good visit with John in Rochester before going to Washington. After the meetings he went to Charlottesville for a day with Beams, visited Swann at Swarthmore, and then went to New York, where he was able to get $500 sent at once for Sloan's work and the promise of $6,000 for needed equipment from the Research Corporation and the Chemical Foundation. However, it was suggested that the money not be used for salaries; that if material costs were contributed, the university should supply the necessary men. Poillon finally agreed that if other means failed he would allow $1,500 for Livingston. Ernest wired his worried assistant that money for his keep was assured. He wrote Professor Hall to ask that he cheer up Livingston and explain Poillon's position; his benefactors would be much more generous if assured that the university was doing its part. He suggested that the alumni association be approached, if the university refused to make an exception for Livingston. The president of the alumni had told Ernest that as soon as he "really had something going" he thought he could get money to help defray the unusual expenses of the Rad Lab.

There was good news about competent help. At Princeton, Jack Livingood, who had written to ask if he could work with Ernest, agreed to spend a year at the Rad Lab without pay. Ernest was delighted: "Dr. Livingood is a very good man and I am pleased that he is so eager to come." In New Haven a research fellow, Malcolm Henderson, working on Geiger counters, also showed much interest in Ernest's work. He had returned to Yale as a Sterling Fellow after taking his Ph.D. at Cambridge the year Ernest left for California. Ernest had met him on visits to Yale, and Don Cooksey, never tired of preaching his belief that Berkeley would shortly become the center of nuclear physics, persuaded Henderson, who also could afford it, to go to the Rad Lab without pay—for his own good. His father, Dr. Yandell Henderson, was on the Yale Medical faculty, and Malcolm had gone to dancing school with Molly; the families knew each other well.

Ernest wrote Professor Hall to arrange appointments for Livingood and Henderson as research associates for one year without stipend. Furthermore Don himself and Franz Kurie, who had applied for a National Research Fellowship to work with Ernest, planned to go to California together for six weeks at the lab, beginning August 1, whether Franz got the fellowship or not. He knew a good deal about Wilson cloud expansion chambers and would design and supervise construction of one for better recording of the events of nuclear collisions. Ernest approached his wedding date satisfied that there would be ample help in his laboratory and funds enough to make progress with his plans. He wired Livingston, who had succeeded in getting 2,000,000 volts out of the big machine after much discouraging bad luck, to take a vacation until he felt entirely rested—but first to send a "letter to the editor" of the *Physical Review* announcing the successful attainment of 2,000,000 volts. That letter, he said, was to be over Livingston's name, as the "credit is yours and my name is not to go on the paper."

These matters attended to, he could relax as he awaited the big event. Relaxation, of course, meant working mornings at Sloane Laboratory with Don on Geiger tube counters—"most interesting." Afternoons when Molly was free of dress fittings, showers, or other strictly feminine events, he spent with her. Life was very good!

CHAPTER VII

Vintage Year

Life was good for Ernest Lawrence: young, healthy, extremely vigorous, and doing exactly what he wanted to do in a new, exciting field filled with adventure and the promise of discovery, he was already a leader in that field. Secure in his position, and sought elsewhere, at last engaged to the girl he wanted—what more could any man desire! Immersed in science, happy in the academic atmosphere, he had little time for concern over the state of affairs in the world at large, or even for realization of the seriousness of conditions in the nation. There had been much discussion of these topics at the Faculty Club, but then, Ernest felt, there was always speculation—even voices of impending doom—among academic people in less exact disciplines. A physical scientist need not get lost in such abstractions; even Oppie, who interested himself in the humanities, thought social scientists too vague. The Depression was discussed little in their talks; there were too many all-absorbing problems of the atom and its composition. It was more difficult to evade thoughts of the Depression in New Haven, but Ernest noticed less concern in Don and others at Sloane over the depressed market than with the problem of accurately determining the extent of radiation and energies of accelerated atomic particles. At the Blumers', the impending election was the principal topic; the affairs of the country would turn out well, the Blumers felt, if President Herbert Hoover were just given more time.

Individualistic Americans, following perhaps unconsciously the *laissez-faire* patterns by which so much had been achieved, were inclined to the belief that problems would right themselves. Some of the best business brains in the country were at work on the plight of the unemployed, restless, and often hungry millions. Riots, such as that of thousands at Ford's River Rouge plant near Detroit, in which four were killed, and the bonus march on Washington that had been suppressed with tanks and tear gas—such incidents were more often deplored as lawlessness than as symptoms of the distress and discouragement following more than three years of the most serious depression in the history of the country. Business and industry were not only plagued, but seemed stalled, in the general panic. But somehow everything would work out; this was America.

And Americans had had enough of European problems; let foreigners worry about their own; wide oceans were still barriers, even if Amelia Earhart would fly that year across the Atlantic in fifteen and a half hours. The war to save democracy had given Europe a chance to right its wrongs; we must not become involved again. That reparations would not be forthcoming from Germany was of more concern than the growth of National Socialism there. The Austrian paperhanger with the Charlie Chaplin moustache, who that year became a German citizen, was more a source of amusement than of concern; how could the intelligent Germans take Adolf Hitler seriously? It was unthinkable in early 1932 that he would become head of the German state within a year. Mussolini, who had increased his hold on Italy, had drained marshes and made Italian trains run on time; that such prerogatives of democracy as trial by jury had been abolished was of little concern to most Americans. Even mass hunger protests and marches in London, requiring police action, were far away. Japan's conquests seemed to threaten American influence in Pacific areas and were protested, but Americans without relatives or interests in Asia gave them little thought. Prosperity around the corner was of more concern than strife in another continent.

For Ernest, concerned with the infinitely tiny particles of which every physical thing is composed, such foreign and domestic problems were for others, hopefully for experts in those fields. He spent little time reading news and none studying world and domestic situations, and advised his co-workers to do likewise, "You fellows are making history, so you don't have to spend all your time reading it. It's more important to make it than to read it." Neither politician nor political economist, he worked his own garden and expected others to tend theirs as assiduously.

And indeed 1932 was a vintage year in the garden of physics. In the January issue of the *Physical Review*, Harold Urey, Ph.D., California 1923, announced the discovery at Columbia of an isotope of hydrogen —the first element in the periodic table—with a double mass. Though William Harkins at Chicago and Rutherford in England had speculated as early as 1920 about a form of hydrogen with twice the mass of ordiary hydrogen, it had not been found even by such an expert seeker as

Otto Stern. Calculations by Birge in 1931 led to an intensified search everywhere, and Urey and his co-workers found the isotope with the same single charge, but with a mass of two. A stable (nonradioactive) isotope, its importance for Ernest and nuclear physicists was not at once apparent. Urey called the isotope deuterium, and Gilbert Lewis suggested deuton for its nucleus. After much international discussion, the name deuteron was accepted for the nucleus. Ernest Rutherford, who for some time had insisted on the terms diplogen and diplon for the isotope and its nucleus, finally agreed to deuteron—because, Oppenheimer said in jest, his initials had been added in the American expression.

Rutherford thought the word deuton might be confused with neutron, the name of the second important discovery of the year; a name that had been used for years in postulating a neutral particle of the nucleus. This particle was discovered in Rutherford's Cavendish Laboratory—that laboratory of fine, simple apparatus and careful observations —by James Chadwick after years of patient search. Being neutral, it leaves no observable track in a cloud chamber. Rutherford and Chadwick had even used what are now known as Geiger counters, in 1928, in their search for the possible neutral particle, in experiments Chadwick later described as "quite wildly absurd." Though Geiger counters achieved general acceptance, former models had been regarded at Cambridge "as things which required witchcraft to work with, and they would have none of it for a long time," Malcolm Henderson remembers. While Henderson was at Cavendish, Chadwick persistently refused to allow him to use the counters. Henderson became well acquainted with Rutherford and Chadwick, sitting with them while their eyes became accustomed to a darkened room so they could personally count scintillations on a screen. The neutron had been sought in Germany, and reports by Bothe and Becker were helpful to Chadwick, and by the French Curies, who felt that if they had heard a 1920 lecture by Rutherford they would have found the neutron earlier. Important as the discovery was considered in 1932, no one then realized its significance for all of humanity, as would be so shatteringly demonstrated a dozen years later. Nor was Ernest at once fully aware of the importance neutrons would play in his own work.

Another particle of importance in the understanding of nature was found at Caltech, where Millikan's young assistant, Carl Anderson, laboriously studying cloud chamber photographs of cosmic rays, noticed the fine, broken line of an electron track that curved in the same positive direction as the more definite, unbroken proton paths. Search in thousands of other photographs confirmed his suspicions: he had proved the existence of positive electrons, of the same mass as the usual negative variety that orbit the nucleus of the atom. It was later discovered that positrons can also be created on earth from energy, and that the collision of a positron and an electron results in the disappearance of both particles—into energy! $E = mc^2$.

A fourth event of great scientific importance in this year of worldwide depression proved again the quality of Rutherford's Cavendish Laboratory. John Cockcroft and Thomas Walton had built a voltage multiplier that accelerated protons to about 300,000 volts, equivalent in number to the alpha rays that two kilograms of radium would emit had there been that much radium available in the entire world supply. Yet, like everyone else, they believed that higher energies would be needed for artificial disintegrations—though, according to Gamow's theory, protons should penetrate and transmute a nucleus more easily than alpha rays. Cockcroft and his Irish co-worker therefore reconstructed their device for higher voltages before attempting nuclear transmutation. When the attempt was made with a machine capable of 800,000 volts, they succeeded in artificially disintegrating a nucleus in a historical first; lithium had been transmuted into helium with about 125,000 volts! They could have done it almost two years before with their first machine. And Ernest could have done it in the United States with his 11-inch cyclotron had he tried it and possessed instruments sensitive enough to record it. Cockcroft and Walton had noted their results first on a scintillation screen, and later in a cloud chamber. A greater number of transmutations were recorded when the energy was raised to 250,000 volts, and ten times as many when this voltage was doubled. Data from these experiments provided further verification of Einstein's mass-energy relationship.

Ernest, who learned of this transmutation while on his honeymoon, immediately wired Brady in Berkeley to get lithium from the chemistry department and bombard it in the 11-inch cyclotron. Momentarily disturbed that with this small instrument he could have been the first in the world to artificially disintegrate a nucleus, he was soon exhilarated by the tremendous scientific importance of the event.

Congratulations to Cockcroft and Walton! To the fine Cavendish Laboratory and to Rutherford who had instilled into its personnel the spirit of careful work. Indeed, praise to the numberless predecessors upon whose findings knowledge had advanced to the point where such an event became possible; the event was always more important than the individual who, at the right time and place, brought it about. It was fun to win any race; it was ridiculous to waste time regretting another's victory. "There are discoveries enough for all—research enough for everyone," Ernest often told his students when one's problem seemed to conflict with another's. "Any research helps all research." If elements could be transmuted, atomic structure could be thoroughly studied. One could only be happy that it had been demonstrated and for those who had achieved it. He had never doubted that atoms could and would be cracked—as his accelerators progressed, all the elements became subject to meaningful shattering. With Don and Kurie helping this summer with their counting devices and with a cloud chamber, who could foretell the nuclear events that might be brought about with his higher voltages? Before the year ended, his new huge cyclotron would generate over 4,000,000 electron volts.

The event of personal significance, in that year so ominous for the world and celebrated in science, was, of course, his marriage to long-courted Mary Kimberly Blumer, on Saturday afternoon, May 14. The majority of distinguished witnesses to the ceremony in historic Trinity Church on the New Haven Green were present because of long association with the Blumers, though there were scholars in the pews behind Ernest's mother on the right side of the aisle, who had come because of him; he was particularly pleased that Franz Simon, solemn in long black winter coat and hat, in the East after his year at Berkeley, had come to the wedding. Except for John, Stewart Scott, famous Yale football player who had married Molly's cousin, and chemist Linus Pauling, the men of the wedding party were physicists: Merle Tuve, whom Ernest had known longer than anyone present except his mother, had come from Washington; Jesse Beams from Virginia; Robert Brode, like Pauling a visiting professor from California at M.I.T., who had come from Boston with Joe Boyce. Joe Morris, hand encased in a black glove to conceal radiation burns, with Ernest's graduate student, Leon Linford, now a National Research Fellow, had come up from Princeton; and Don Cooksey, who had dined the masculine contingent of the wedding party at a Lawn Club luncheon before the ceremony. Don, perhaps, was responsible more than anyone else for getting a properly dressed groom to the church on time. He had had to urge Ernest from their work at Sloane Laboratory that morning in order to be ready at the Lawn Club to greet the guests. Ernest did not seem excited or nervous until after the luncheon, when, suddenly, he became "right excited," Beams remembers. "It was my job to talk to him. Try to calm him down. He was nervous, very nervous, just before the wedding." Don discovered, none too soon, that Ernest had no fresh white shirt. That was hastily taken care of, and Don got him to the church on time.

In the sacristy of Trinity Church, Ernest thought the hurry Don had subjected him to needless since they arrived before the clergymen. Rector of the Branford Church near Haycock Point, the Reverend Clifton Brewer, of the Yale Divinity School, had been asked to assist the Reverend Charles Otis Scoville, rector of Trinity Church—causing someone to suggest that one parson was not enough to bind the ebullient Ernest in matrimony. But it was not uncommon for two clergymen to officiate at weddings when the family had associations with more than one church. The Blumers were fond of the whole Scoville family, and it was to him that Ernest and Molly had gone for the mandatory premarital counseling session that turned out to be little more than a social call. There was nervousness in the church vestibule as Miss Benson adjusted the large straw hats she had trimmed to match the yellow dresses of the bridesmaids and the aqua gown for Elsie, the maid of honor, and arranged Molly's satin gown and long tulle veil trimmed with rose point lace that had been her grandmother's. Humor relieved tension when balding Dr. Blumer asked her about his coiffure. Then one of the brides-maids checked to see that the bride wore "something old, something new, something borrowed, and something blue" —the usual garter—and Molly added what is usually forgotten in America, "a silver sixpence in her shoe," and showed that it was there. She had had the foresight to preserve the shiny coin after her return from England and Ernest's closely ensuing "we ought to get married." Actually, the strains of the wedding march pealed forth from the organ on schedule. The relativity of time was demonstrated after Ernest entered the church and waited an "eternity" for the procession to come up the aisle and permit Dr. Blumer to turn the lovely bride over to him and take his seat by Mrs. Blumer. Then it was "no time at all" before the ceremony was over, and Ernest was taking Molly back down the aisle, proud as he had ever been in his life.

The reception at the Faculty Club which followed the service was gay and festive, though Gunda Lawrence cried—from happiness, she pro-tested—and said she was happy to have a daughter. Mabel Blumer wel-comed a son at last "into this boyless family." Dr. Blumer had received special permission from club authorities to spike the punch from bottles saved for such an occasion from pre-Prohibition days. Some of the punch was lost when John upset a bowl; was it his brother's wedding or the re-splendent maid of honor that so excited him? No stimulant could add to Ernest's happiness—and relief that the ceremony was over and Molly his. Nor could any of the ensuing toasts quite match that offered by a Vassar friend of Molly's the night before: "To the offspring of Sir Ernest and Lady Mary; may they be geniuses or morons!"

Dinner, also at the club, followed the reception, before Ernest and Molly drove off in the warm spring night to Grandmother Bradley's summer cottage at Indian Neck, on the Sound. They were awakened early the next morning, Molly's twenty-second birthday, by the singing of birds. It was a leisurely drive to Vermont for a week at the Loomis Farms of Molly's maternal aunt on Lake Champlain, where thousands of apple trees in bloom made an ideal setting for a honeymoon. Ernest found time to write to Professor Hall at Berkeley about the happiness of married life—and problems of the laboratory. He was much concerned about the X-ray tube and its powerful radiations since seeing Joe Morris's burns, and wanted Dave Sloan to exercise extra caution. There had been jokes aplenty around the lab about the possibility of the powerful X rays rendering everyone sterile, and the direct beam had been scrupulously avoided, but dangerous radiation was not confined to the beam. There wasn't enough lead around the laboratory for proper shielding, and Dave had already started melting down old battery plates, taken from dumps, for this purpose. Ernest also again urged that $1,800 be found at Berkeley for Livingston's salary, or "at least $1,500."

After Vermont, Ernest and Molly stayed at Haycock Point until after the Fourth of July, "enjoying every minute, but I do not spend all the time away from physics, have in fact been working on Geiger counters at Sloane Lab. with Don Cooksey. Intend to develop some techniques along this line together . . . for our disintegration experiments which presumably will begin this fall. . . . However life is so pleasant mornings and evenings down at the shore with 'Mrs. Lawrence' that I should not complain if the rest of my time were a total loss."

Enjoy it Ernest certainly did, and not only because of his bride; he liked Dr. and Mrs. Blumer as much as in-laws as he had from their first meeting. They liked him also and were delighted to see Molly so happy. There were still shocks in store from their remarkable and less conventional son-in-law. "I'm not going to call you Mrs. Blumer," Ernest announced one day. "It's too long and I like you too much. I'm going to call you Mabel." Mrs. Blumer did not quite approve at first—"I'm a little bit on the conservative side"—but she grew to like it, and her daughters soon followed suit. "You know," Ernest told her before they left for California, "we're a remarkable pair, because you're my mother-in-law and I'm your son-in-law and we get along beautifully."

Dr. Blumer, who was now G.B. to his son-in-law, also got along well with the new member of the family, if on a more reserved basis. He was a little hurt when a bacteriology paper Molly had written with C. V. Seastone, a senior medical student, appeared in a medical journal under the name of Mary B. Lawrence. Teased about it by colleagues, he had to admit that indeed Mary Lawrence was his daughter. There was never a hint from G.B., now, of anything lacking in Ernest's education. "We liked him. I know he liked me," Mrs. Blumer remembers. "He was so friendly and cordial. He was a very remarkable person. I don't mean he was without faults, as some of his colleagues seemed to think—but he was just so full of life."

Before their departure for California, there was a memorable weekend in New York with Henry Barton, who had been unable to attend the wedding. Barton, who had been a National Research Fellow at the same time as Ernest, and was now with the American Institute of Physics, proved an excellent guide to New York night life—including speakeasies. A bachelor, he moved to his club and turned his apartment over to the newlyweds for the weekend. Ernest's pride in Molly was as evident in the big city as it had been in Connecticut, a pride also noticed by Sam Jacobsohn when he was presented to her in Chicago. Sam, and Constance Wiedeman, a classmate of Molly's, lunched with them, and Ernest and Sam had an afternoon together between trains en route to Springfield.

In South Dakota he presented his bride to family and friends with a joyous, almost boyish, "see what I have" manner. Carl Lawrence welcomed "my first daughter" in warm, reserved masculine fashion. Whatever doubts Gunda may once have entertained about Molly as the appropriate wife for her elder son were not now evident, and if she never asked her daughter-in-law, who addressed her as Mrs. Lawrence for many years, to call her "Mother," neither did Molly suggest it. To Ernest, his mother was still—and always remained—Mama, as Carl was Papa, both pronounced with strongly accented first syllables. Together they were "the folks," which at first embarrassed Molly, who considered the expressions provincial. "I got used to them later, stopped being so snobby, and even used them myself occasionally."

The only indication of possible disapproval on Gunda's part was over smoking. Molly refrained out of respect, until Ernest—who did not really approve either—insisted that she join him in smoking a cigarette after lunch, implying that not to would be hypocritical, since she smoked in her family's home. Mrs. Lawrence got up and pulled down the window shades to prevent observation by the neighbors. Perhaps to counteract that, Carl immediately went upstairs and returned with a cigar. As a college president, it was thought he should not smoke, and when he did it was usually on the upper floor of the house, Gunda hovering near the front door, as she did now, lest anyone come and smell the smoke. Ernest laughed.

"Everyone has to have some bad habit," Carl said, blowing smoke delightedly. "I'm always suspicious of anyone so perfect he has no bad habit." And to his wife's chagrin he revealed to Molly, as though it was a conspiracy, that he usually had a small chew of tobacco in his cheek. If he made Molly feel part of the family in this small intrigue, Gunda set a fine example of wifely subservience to a husband's wishes. And Molly noticed the respect and affection of Carl's faculty and the townsfolk for both the elder Lawrences. And no wonder; their concern for them was pronounced. Carl felt the plight of the farmers personally and worried about his students and their ability to afford continuing their education, almost as a father would.

Molly was a little shocked when he suggested that the recent Democratic nominee, Franklin Roosevelt, might have solutions to the Depression, if what he said could be translated to action. Still nominally Republican, he felt his party's talk of prosperity without a sound plan in such times unwise, even for the sake of votes. "The people are more intelligent than they think," he stated, "but I've always been more a La Follette man than one of the Old Guard." Molly was silent; to hear the party of stability and order questioned was a new experience, but it prepared her for Carl's later declaration that he would vote for Roosevelt, and Ernest's ensuing advocacy of the Democratic nominee. Gunda, of course, a good wife, followed her husband's opinions. As a warm human being, she shared his deep concern for the distress of farmers and townsmen, and spoke of students in motherly fashion, worrying about their comfort as much as about their finances. Indeed, the only suggestion of a wifely criticism was in regard to the latter; because of his fine generous character, Carl, she thought, might be too soft in lending money to students and too lenient about repayment.

She need not have been concerned that her daughter-in-law might not make a good wife. If her first impression had been of one "too cold and intellectual," that had been four years ago when Molly had no intention of marrying. Natural shyness and reserve might well be interpreted as coldness, and if she was intellectual, that was an asset Ernest respected. Even now that she was married, Molly was determined to continue her studies, working at Berkeley as an assistant in the bacteriology laboratory and studying with Professor Karl Meyer. It was not necessary for her to work, with Ernest's fine salary, as it had been for Gunda the only time she had left her household, for a short while in Pierre. But Ernest had agreed to Molly's plan; indeed he had arranged it for her before going East for the wedding. He certainly had had sufficient time to "think twice before taking a wife who is rich and has been used to everything," and had demonstrated that he could manage his life pretty well.

The Blumer ménage in New Haven had seemed rich by comparison with Gunda's own thrifty household, but the Blumers were not, now at least, wealthy by New England standards. There had been servants, and Molly, the "brain of the family," had been favored, perhaps, when household chores were assigned to the children. But she was as determined to be a good wife as Gunda herself had been thirty years before, and appreciated the intent behind thrifty hints dropped by the older woman. A good housekeeper and an ample cook, Gunda pressed food on her men until they protested, but no scrap was ever wasted, as she pointed out when Molly helped with meals and the cleaning up afterward.

If there was no real closeness between the two women, Molly admired the almost single-minded devotion of the gracious lady to her husband and sons. It bothered Gunda, a truly pious woman, that Ernest had not affiliated with a church in Berkeley and paid little or no attention to at least the outward forms of religion. Molly, though she had been brought up as an Episcopalian, was of no help to Gunda in that regard, having little interest in formal religious services, vaguely relating religious values to a very high sense of honesty. Gunda was active in the Springfield Episcopal Church and Carl was a stalwart supporter of Bishop Hugh Burleson, a brother of the Springfield rector, in fund raising and affairs of the diocese. Church practice was important to Gunda but she did not argue about her son's lack of it. Her gentleness, even in disagreement, was far more effective than argument. Molly sensed that her influence had been far greater than her submission to Carl's decisions might imply.

Molly was happy enough to submit to Ernest's decisions, which he sometimes made without consideration for wishes she might have had. He was nine years older, had a position of responsibility and prestige. She had noted the deference many of his colleagues showed to him. In a sense much of their early relationship was somewhat that of father-daughter; the authoritarian role of the male came naturally enough to Ernest and was not questioned by his wife. "I was a little afraid of his displeasure at first," she remembers.

Molly felt that she had not been properly trained for her role as a wife. When settled in their home in Berkeley, she leaned heavily on the woman she hired to come in part time five days a week to do the cleaning and prepare the evening dinner for them to come home to from their laboratories. Polish-German Helen Brecko taught her much about cooking and housekeeping—her department as far as Ernest was concerned. He interfered very little so long as his needs were satisfied, which meant good—usually plain American—food and a clean house. Molly was away from the house most of each day attending to her duties in the bacteriology laboratory at the university and continuing her studies.

There was neither washing machine nor vacuum cleaner in the Keith Avenue house. Helen spread torn, dampened paper on the floor to keep dust down while sweeping—when Ernest was away. He refused to be much concerned with the placement of the antiques and other furniture that arrived in Berkeley about the time they did. He was blunt and not always tactful about anything he did not like or approve of, whether a hat, a dress, or an opinion—sometimes in the presence of others, which embarrassed Molly. "I tend to resent something and say nothing about it and let it fester. I became better about this later and could discuss things on my mind, and we became much closer." Ernest was always surprised to learn when he had hurt her feelings, and in time he became more tactful and considerate. Opposed to any public display of affection, he was most affectionate when they were by themselves.

Engulfed in the problems and fast pace of his laboratory, he never thought to offer her money, or ask if she needed it. When Molly had to ask him for it, he never made any fuss—but seldom had more than change in his pocket. He never thought about carrying money with him. He wrote checks for the bills—when he got around to it—and was not too careful about making entries on the stubs. They were married almost three years before they had a joint checking account. He cared little what Molly paid for clothes or other things—if he liked them. Not that he was careless about money; he invested regularly, but he refused to worry about it. Living was cheap and there were then no income taxes for employees of the state. With an upper-bracket professor's salary, investments and insurance, there need be no concern about finances, and he was impatient with people who seemed to be preoccupied with money. "I've never been anywhere when I couldn't get money when I needed it," he once told his mother-in-law, and it was true.

Molly learned to find out if he had money with him before they went on a trip, or even to the theater; often he had given it no thought. And they took many motor trips, as he sought to delight her in California. She did not like Berkeley at first, was slow to make adjustments, but quickly came to share his love of the redwoods, where they often went, sometimes on the spur of the moment and without plans, stopping where and when they felt like it. Over Thanksgiving they drove up the Redwood Highway and beyond to Crater Lake in Oregon. Molly thought he drove rather fast, and on mountain roads had a tendency to take curves on the wrong side, but confined her backseat driving to the minimum. He always was as certain that a car would not be coming toward them as she was that one would. Sometimes an absentminded driver, even in the city, he might turn and look at her, or out the window, forgetting that he was at the wheel. On trips, they shared the driving, and Molly tried to arrange that her turn come on mountain roads. When she drove, Ernest sometimes relaxed and read a book, if the scenery was monotonous.

They skied some, at the Sierra Club Lodge, and at Cold Springs, a time or two. Otherwise recreational activities together consisted of a weekly movie, an event at the university or in San Francisco, or one of the informal parties with faculty friends where the entertainment was good talk or music, as at the Lewises', or a dance at someone's house. They tried having dances at their home, but with rugs all over the house, they were not very successful. Ernest would have liked to entertain more than they did; he was very conscious of social obligations. But with both of them away most of the day, it seemed difficult to Molly. Neither of them wanted help living in the house.

It often happened, when they started out for a movie, that Ernest would stop by the laboratory to see how the boys were getting along. And often there would be a problem—a vacuum leak, or shims needing careful adjustment—and Molly would spend the rest of the evening sitting quietly in a corner. She enjoyed that, if it didn't drag on for too many hours. She liked it that Ernest was interested in how the young men lived, some of them on what seemed to her infinitesimal amounts of money; her first entertaining was a stag party for the bachelors. She was "scared stiff" before that, but Helen Brecko helped. On some weekends they would take one or two men with them for short trips, or Lois and Stan Livingston. Occasionally Ernest would bring Oppenheimer home for dinner without warning, perhaps when there was only enough prepared for two. Oppie liked Molly at once—a few years later a physicist accused him of pining away for love of her. Molly appreciated his sensitivity and taste; she did not mind Ernest bringing him home, or his dropping in—if there were "more than two lamb chops," though his habit of wandering into the kitchen embarrassed her, especially when he wanted to help. Ernest always left her alone in this, her domain. She was warned before he brought visiting Karl Darrow to dinner with Robert Brode, soon after they were in their Berkeley home, but as notables appeared with increasing frequency at his laboratory, Ernest often invited them to their home, sometimes on the spur of the moment and without prior notice to Molly.

On evenings when they were alone they usually read, Ernest perusing scientific literature, often becoming restless and characteristically pushing his hand through his shock of hair. Often he would get up suddenly, ready to go to bed. Molly, who had always enjoyed the quiet night hours, liked to read until late. And in the morning, it was the other way around; he usually awoke promptly, alert and without sleepiness, while Molly admitted, "It always takes me about two hours to get going." Ernest usually had to urge her to get up and prepare breakfast in time for him to get to eight o'clock class. There were times, however, when she would have to go back to the bedroom for him when breakfast was ready and her calls brought no response. She might find him sitting on the bed, one sock on, the other dangling in his hand, a faraway look in his eyes, hardly more aware of her than of the hour. Usually, however, mornings found him peppy and eager to get to the laboratory, while she felt sluggish and drowsy.

Fortunately, Molly's laboratory duties started at a later hour, and she normally drove Ernest to the campus and returned to the house. They met for lunch at the Faculty Club, if he had no engagement, and usually came home together for dinner. Once, absorbed in a culture, she forgot the time and kept Ernest waiting for over an hour. She found him angry, pacing outside his laboratory. She defended herself, this time rather sharply. "When you're working in physics you can punch the buttons, stop, and go home; if you're working with living tissue you can't always do that." By the time they reached their house, each saw the humor of it and could laugh, but Molly soon understood that she could not combine marriage to Ernest and worthwhile scientific endeavor of her own. She was not very happy with her assigned experiment anyway, and soon gave it up, confining her university work to supervision of laboratory students and correction of papers.

Ernest often returned to his laboratory after dinner. Molly did not mind; she had expected that, knowing the kind of scientist he was, and had always enjoyed being by herself. If he was very late, she worried a little, at first. There was no way to reach the Radiation Laboratory after the university switchboard closed, and, since he had the car, no way to get there.

Her worries were intensified when she thought of the mysterious rays the accelerators produced. She knew the danger of X rays, and Ernest still worried about insufficient shielding around the Sloan tube. Sloan had melted about a ton of scrounged battery plate lead into thin sheets, but this was far from adequate to ensure safety as voltages were increased. Molly recalled the damage suffered by experimenters before it was known how harmful overexposure to X rays could be, and knew also that serious injury, even fatalities, still occurred. The black gloved hand of Joe Morris at her wedding haunted her at such times, late at night. The jokes the Rad Lab men bandied around about possible impotence and sterility due to the rays did not amuse her, even in daylight. And no one knew what possible deadly effects might be caused by little understood, invisible rays from machines capable of transmuting elements. Ernest himself could not explain "a strong variable background" to Geiger counter measurements of cyclotron beams, not at all certain that it was the fault of the counters, as was first believed. In fact, as more was learned, he could shudder over the realization that the reason for most counter failures was the general high level of radioactivity throughout the laboratory—actually as yet undiscovered or unidentified artificial radioactivity, which ionization chambers with linear amplifiers were not sensitive enough to detect. The radioactive atmosphere—nowhere else so intense—was also the cause of inability to construct proper Geiger counters in the laboratory. But for these handicaps of the yet unknown, artificial radioactivity could have been discovered months before the Curie and Joliot event in 1934.

Molly had seen lurid stories of "death rays" and "atom busting," many of them based on half-digested stories of her husband's work. Ernest was irritated by these sensational stories, unscientific and misleading, as he was pleased by proper accounts of responsible newsmen, but he, perhaps more than anyone else, was positive that the elements could be altered by accelerator beams. And he himself hinted that if metallic elements could be altered, so could the delicate cells of the human body, perhaps beneficially—but also, without care, tragically.

With such sinister thoughts tumbling over each other in her mind, the first time Ernest was still away at three o'clock in the morning, Molly waited desperately for her husband—or word from him that he was all right. When he finally arrived, bubbling with excitement, her worry changed to anger. She stood speechless as he talked excitedly of "intensity so great the target could not withstand it" and success "far beyond expectations," until he noticed her staring, troubled demeanor. Surprised, he stared back. "What's the matter?" he finally asked, as a boy might whose good deeds are not appreciated.

Molly could find no language to express her concern, for another moment. Then she demanded, "Are we going to have a family or are we not?" Ernest got her point and tried to reassure her that he was always careful, but it was evident that the latest achievement at the lab was uppermost in his mind. He was still talking of it as he got into bed and immediately dropped off to sleep.

The possibility of sterilization and tissue damage was beyond the jesting stage after the production of million-volt X rays on the Sloan tube. Ernest wrote of it to his supporters in the East, among whom was Dr. Francis Carter Wood of the Institute of Cancer Research; the mention was in the nature of an indication that a request might be forthcoming if he could not obtain sufficient lead otherwise for shielding. The tube was little used, while an improved model was being constructed, though Ernest demonstrated it to a group of interested alumni, showing that its rays could penetrate and reveal details in steel more than half an inch thick. No hoped-for funds were immediately forthcoming from the alumni—"the Depression, you know"—either for lead or a stipend for Livingston. Ernest felt he could not jeopardize his standing with the Research Corporation by asking for both. He solved the lead situation with his usual inspiration and boldness; through the president's office, he asked the loan of lead from the American Smelting and Refining Company in San Francisco, pointing out the merits of his work and the fact that it would cost them very little in time and expense to allow its use. The request was granted and 350 tons of quarter-inch lead sheeting arrived in time to shield the improved model. Even with the shielding, "We see X rays almost everywhere in the lab with a fluoroscope," he wrote Don, adding that they were now using Lauritsen fountain pen electroscopes to check the daily dosage of X rays. "I am sending you one for Christmas. Even though you are a bachelor, you should have a daily check."

Ernest invited Dr. Robert Stone, radiologist, and other members of the staff of the university medical school, to the laboratory for a demonstration. Stone brought dosage meters; all were impressed, not only with the performance of the tube but also with Ernest's enthusiasm as he pointed out its merits. Rays equivalent to the effects produced by a kilogram of radium—more than the available radium in the world—were generated. Ernest was quickly able to list the advantages over two or three other giant X-ray tubes: Lauritsen's at Caltech that had been pushed to over a million volts, and could be expected to operate normally in the region of 800,000 volts, as could the big Coolidge machine being built for a Detroit clinic for a reported $29,000. Each of these others required much space to house, while the Sloan tube would take little more room than a standard 200,000-volt therapy machine and could be built and installed for less than a quarter of their cost. He assured the doctors that it also surpassed the others in steadiness and reliability.

Ernest's assurance received verification when Dr. Frank Exner of the Institute of Cancer Research arrived from New York to participate in tests and remained to assist in the building of a machine for the institute. Dean Langley Porter of the medical school then promised to try to raise funds for a similar machine for the university hospital. When a regents meeting was held at the medical school, Dean Porter gave a dinner for Regent William H. Crocker, at which he invited Ernest to discuss the Sloan device. Mr. Crocker promised to go to Berkeley to look at it. Unfortunately, on the day he visited the Radiation Laboratory, the machine failed to function properly. "Oh, for heaven's sake!" Ernest exclaimed, and, lacking time to search out and rectify the trouble, had the machine disassembled and all the parts neatly laid out as if for inspection. Crocker listened as he described each part, looked for a while, and turned to Dr. Stone. "How much is needed to make it work?" he asked, not fooled for a minute. Crocker had the reputation of being a hard man to touch, but he put up the money. More than a year later, after a machine had been installed and was in use in the hospital, Crocker went to look at it again. This time the sight of some of the patients was too much for the old man. He broke down, cried, and never returned.

Pleased as Ernest was to be able to contribute toward the possible alleviation and cure of a dread disease—he never lost his early admiration for the profession of medicine—he felt that the most interesting aspect of the Sloan tube was its ability to produce intense beams of 2,000,000-volt protons. While these were not of as high velocity as those of the cy-

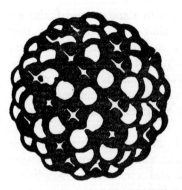

A nuclear particle of sufficient energy to penetrate a nucleus alters it by adding to it, knocking other particles from it, or, in the case of fission, splitting it into nearly equal parts. (*Lawrence Radiation Laboratory*)

clotron, much larger quantities were produced, a factor of greater importance than high-voltage X rays in the study of atomic structure. There were times when he thought it might be more profitable to concentrate on variations of the linear accelerator, of which the tube was one, to the exclusion of the cyclotron. There were many and difficult problems with each of the new and ingenious machines, but the linear approach seemed to offer fewer obstacles than the merry-go-round. He had been warned by colleagues that successful, continued operation of the cyclotron would likely be impossible, but there were fewer skeptics than there had been when he had first announced the principle. Frédéric Joliot, Madame Curie's son-in-law, had written from the famed Curie Laboratory in Paris of the interest there in Ernest's "remarkable work," stating his desire to build a similar device as soon as possible. He asked for reprints of articles on the machine, details of construction, and any special advice that might be given. Ernest went so far as to learn and inform Joliot that a magnet similar to his huge one might be obtainable in Bordeaux, where a Poulsen arc radio transmitter was being dismantled. He offered any aid he might give, in addition to descriptions he sent to the Frenchman.

The 11-inch cyclotron in Le Conte Hall soon disintegrated lithium, verifying the work of Cockcroft and Walton in Cambridge, and proving its own capability. This was the first artificial disintegration of an element in the Western Hemisphere, started by Brady after Ernest's telegraphed request and carried on by Milton White with the help of Cooksey and Kurie and their detection devices. When Malcolm Henderson got an ion counter and pulse amplifier working, so many protons were recorded they were able to extend the Cockcroft-Walton curve upward.

By increasing the proton energy from 300,000 to 1,500,000, with the 27-inch, disintegration was increased twenty times, sufficient proof that protons and other particles of even higher energies were the necessary bullets with which to attack and expose secrets of the atom. The transmutation of lithium into helium was followed quickly by the disintegration of boron, aluminum, and other elements, and Ernest confidently predicted the production of protons with energies from 10,000,000 to 25,000,000 volts.

There was some scoffing, but there had been that with his prediction of a million volts not so long before. He and his co-workers were convinced that such energies were possible and would be accomplished in the Radiation Laboratory. Those working on the cyclotron considered it the only device that would provide sufficient energy for thorough atomic study of the heavy elements; others in the department considered the linear device, of which the Sloan X-ray machine was a modification, might prove the better weapon for attack on seemingly impregnable nuclei. Ernest remained flexible, though his heart was in the cyclotron, pushing hardest on whichever at the time appeared most promising. He was receptive to any reasonable idea until it seemed to lead up a blind alley, when he could drop it without regret and look for something else. Certain physicists still considered his methods unorthodox, which bothered him not at all; results counted, and he had fine support from the university, his own department, the Research Board, and the administration. He was saddened when Professor Hall, chairman of the physics department, died in November. Hall, though ill, had stayed at his job until October when Loeb prevailed upon him to go to the infirmary where it was found he had inoperable cancer. He had supported Ernest from the beginning, regardless of criticism.

Whatever doubts were voiced elsewhere, there was recognition, too—from as far away as Russia, where Ernest was invited to spend the next summer, with all expenses within the Soviet Union taken care of by the government. Scientists came from many quarters to see the wonderful machines and talk with the director. Hitchcock Lecturer Peter Debye, of the Physical Institute at Leipzig, was fascinated, and was himself deluged with questions concerning counters. Francis W. Aston, the English physicist who had done so much with isotopes and the mass spectrograph, was in the laboratory when lithium was first disintegrated there, after which there was an almost steady stream of notables.

All marveled at the contagious enthusiasm and energy of the director, his assistants, and students who could be found experimenting or tinkering with the apparatus at almost any hour of the day or night, far beyond the call of duty. "Is he such a slave driver?" one of the young men was asked. "Hell, no," came the quick reply. "We might miss something." Few of the men were gone long even during the Christmas holidays, except Henderson, who delivered a paper on the work at the Philadelphia meeting. There was too much happening, and too much to do; commercially unobtainable pumps had to be manufactured at the lab for the unusual and necessary high vacuums, $300 oscillator tubes had somehow to be reconditioned when burned out, to save money, and countless other necessities fabricated for the practice of the hitherto unknown art.

Ernest himself worked whenever he could leave his teaching duties and wrote his parents that so many exciting things were happening, one after another, that when he went home at night, he could hardly wait until morning to go back to the lab. He managed to break away from the laboratory briefly during the year-end holidays for a bit of skiing with Molly and a drive to Pasadena where he reported to the Physical Society the latest developments in cyclotron devices and techniques—and the achievement of 4,800,000-volt protons and the certainty of going much higher. He seemed to be as certain—and accurate, as later events proved, in other matters; at dinner at the C. C. Lauritsens' the charming hostess asked how many children he and Molly planned to have. "Six," Ernest responded immediately. "I'm glad to know what I'm up against," Molly said. "How long do I have to wait for the first?"

But conversations, even at dinner, soon returned to the common interest of the men. Lauritsen was building a new X-ray tube of porcelain instead of glass to withstand high voltages, and along quite different principles than those of the linear accelerator which Sloan had converted with the use of a Tesla coil.

Shortly after his return to Berkeley in January, funds for a Sloan machine and an annex to house it at the medical school in San Francisco were made available "anonymously" by Regent Crocker. Livingston was put in charge of construction of the hospital machine—thus providing for his salary. Construction of an identical apparatus under Frank Exner of Columbia would benefit both; many improvements over the original machine that had resulted from experimentation were incorporated. Power tubes were constantly improved by Litton, Sloan, and Livingood, who also found time for atomic disintegrations with the Sloan outfit adapted as an accelerator. The Rad Lab would have been a busy place entirely aside from the "big" cyclotron, on which everyone worked at times; with the linear device, Wesley Coates, a graduate student, got exciting results bombarding elements with 2,800,000-volt mercury ions. The 11-inch cyclotron, still in Le Conte Hall, was kept at various disintegrations by Milton White, who also studied cloud chambers, for the construction of which the Research Corporation shortly gave $2,000.

With a cloud chamber, photographs of nuclear "hits" under bombardment could be studied for better understanding. Meanwhile Malcolm Henderson's counters and amplifiers clicked away on every accelerator, as one after another of the lighter elements was subjected to disintegration. In February, 1933, uranium was first bombarded in the cyclotron to check a report from Cockcroft and Walton of disintegration of this heaviest of known elements, but no alpha particles or protons resulted, "only gobs of soft X rays." Results were sometimes misinterpreted and, after having been reported, had to be corrected.

It was all so new, so exciting, and so important; there were no precedents as guides, only the certainty that at last the atom was revealing some of its secrets. Of what lasting importance was it that radiations from bombardment of aluminum as described in one issue of the *Physical Review* had to be reinterpreted the following month? "Experiments are very 'ticklish' and it's easy to make a slip in interpretation," Ernest wrote his brother after confessing faulty conclusions. But the discovery of a mistake that might have depressed most men brought no more evidence of chagrin in the Maestro than the exclamation, "Oh, sugar!" followed by the briefest of silences and, "Well, let's try it again." As little time was spent rejoicing over successes; perhaps a "Whoopee" from Ernest with a pat on the back for good work or a good idea. He shared kudos from outside; Ernest used the plural pronoun far more often than the singular when talking of the work, though it was his name that was gaining renown in laboratories all over the world.

A copy of *The Technology Review*, which had been published on the last day of January, 1933, was shown around the lab. In it Karl Compton, president of M.I.T., remarking the progress of the past two years, suggested that it would not be surprising if practical application of energy released in the transmutation of atoms were achieved within a generation. "The field is open and relatively so little explored that we cannot predict what will be discovered." Dr. Compton went on to say that the most promising methods for generating high voltages were those of two of America's youngest, yet already most distinguished physicists, Ernest Lawrence and Robert Van de Graaff. "Lawrence does not actually use very high voltage, but uses a moderate voltage to give a succession of pushes to the ions until they get going with speeds equivalent to that given by nearly 5,000,000 volts, and which may well reach a speed equivalent to 25,000,000 volts with apparatus under construction." Ernest's group considered this high praise indeed from the distinguished president of so respected an Eastern institution. Compton hoped that the Van de Graaff generator being constructed for M.I.T. would attain voltages as high as 10,000,000 volts.

Praise was implied, too, as more and more notables, not all scientists, asked to visit the laboratory and meet its director. From Arthur Brisbane, the famous Hearst columnist, Ernest adopted the idea of carrying a portable typewriter to make use of available moments for writing necessary reports, after noticing that the newsman wrote of his visit to the lab in an office while waiting to see the president. The visit Ernest most enjoyed was that of R. H. Fowler, of Cavendish Laboratory, the good friend and son-in-law of Lord Rutherford, and himself a fine theoretical physicist. Fowler had visited Berkeley two years before when the little cyclotron with a nine-inch magnet was getting into operation, and the big magnet had just been located. He marveled at the progress, how the continued enthusiasm manifested by Ernest infected his co-workers, whether graduate students, research fellows, or those attracted by the growing reputation of the laboratory as *the* exciting place to be in physics, and the "wise choice of program this might, with luck, turn out to be, and how it would appeal to Rutherford." Fowler was a fine companion outside the laboratory, too; there was an enjoyable all-day picnic one Sunday and a memorable weekend party at the Lewises' Inverness place, above San Francisco.

Dean Lewis was as interested in the Rad Lab as though it were an adjunct of his chemistry department. He promised that when he succeeded in concentrating the heavy isotope of hydrogen, Ernest could have it for use in the cyclotron. Before Ernest got the first "heavy water," however, Lewis yielded to the temptation to try it on a mouse, which showed no observable effects after drinking "the world's supply." Ernest got the next batch from Lewis, and, after it was electrolyzed to furnish gas for the ion source, injected it into the big cyclotron, and deuterons were accelerated for the first time, on March 20, 1933. With lithium as a target, alpha particles of greater range and energy then any previously noted in naturally radioactive substances were observed. Deuterons also produced neutrons of much higher intensities than had been obtained with protons. "Bewildering results! All elements when bombarded (with deuterons) yield protons of 18 cm. range and some . . . up to 40 or so cms.," Ernest wrote Cockcroft, who had asked for cyclotron details which he could incorporate in an address to be given at the famous triennial Solvay Congress in Brussels in October. Cockcroft hoped to see Ernest at the Chicago Physical Society meetings in June, and to get firsthand information at Berkeley in August. Ernest sent Cockcroft the requested information, wrote that he had been invited to speak at the Chicago meetings, looked forward to seeing his English colleague there, and that he would be most welcome at Berkeley at any time, and could then see the cyclotron in action.

It was flattering to have Cockcroft wish to discuss his work at Solvay; it was most important to Ernest that others realize the possibilities of his methods for attaining the high energies necessary to penetrate and study the resistant nuclear heart of all matter. The outstanding physicists of Europe—and usually one American—would be invited to Solvay for a week of addresses and discussions at the Institute of Physics of the University of Brussels, an exchange that could only be fruitful. Founded in 1911 by Ernest Solvay, a Belgian inventor and philanthropist who had amassed a fortune in chemicals, the notable congress in the past had honored such Americans as Michelson, Millikan, and Arthur Compton with invitations to join the distinguished Europeans. The congress this year would be devoted to nuclear physics, and Ernest wished that attacking nuclei with the potent deuterons could be discussed, but only his laboratory had both deuterium and accelerators to do this. He got Lewis to send deuterium to Lord Rutherford and suggested to Cockcroft that perhaps he, even with his lower energies, could shed light on the "bewildering results" from deuteron bombardment. His own efforts, and those of many in his laboratory, were concentrated on trying to understand the strange events. For one thing, results seemed to indicate a mass for the neutron much lower than that given to it by Chadwick, its discoverer.

With characteristic optimism, Ernest largely dismissed perplexing events in the troubled world outside the laboratory from his mind; they would be worked out by those responsible, at least in America. If the Germans permitted the expulsion of many of their finest scientists, it was their loss, not the world's. Science, thank God, was still largely international. Japanese conquests on the Asian continent were less immediate than the legalizing in the U.S. of 3.2 beer. Gold embargoes had less immediate impact than the disastrous 1933 Long Beach earthquake, particularly since the Berkeley campus, so some said, seemed dangerously astride a major fault. "The bank holiday and collapse of our financial system prove something is wrong," Ernest wrote John. "The earthquake shows the earth isn't very stable in these parts either. The bank situation can be improved; we'll have to take the earth as she is."

He was concerned over the affairs of his parents. Carl had had to go to Pierre to fight for the existence of his Springfield college, and had continued, successfully, to prevent its closing even after he had been chosen to head the larger Northern Normal and Industrial School in South Dakota's second city of Aberdeen. "Dad will enjoy the greater responsibility and prestige . . . Mother will enjoy the social life . . . will have a fine time now for a number of years," Ernest wrote John. His elation was brief. The good news was soon followed by word from Carl that he was taking his wife to the Mayo Clinic to try to discover the cause of recurring and severe abdominal pain. Ernest was so worried that Molly felt him withdrawn even from her. And when, after three weeks at the clinic, nothing had been found organically wrong, he was so relieved that he wanted to celebrate. Carl wrote that it had been decided that Gunda was suffering nervous exhaustion and must "take it easy and have plenty of rest. We have a good maid and plan to take her along to Aberdeen." Ernest attributed his mother's condition to worry about the Springfield school, the loss of positions by teachers who could not be paid, and the plight of farmers and friends—no hum of cyclotron, many hours of work, or glow of success screened out the Depression in South Dakota.

Indeed, except for his parents' problems, the Depression still had little impact on Ernest. It might have been easier to raise money for his men and the laboratory if the general financial situation had been "normal"—but he got what he needed. His own salary was higher than a young physicist could hope for even in prosperous periods. And this summer he would get $1,000 more for six weeks of lecturing at Cornell. There was plenty of opportunity for recreation; he managed a little tennis almost daily, usually with someone from the laboratory. In a letter to John about their mother, he wrote: "Molly and I are having lots of fun socially despite the fact that I am rather absorbed in laboratory activities . . . invited out frequently by many interesting people. This coming weekend we have three dinners out on our calendar—San Francisco, Martinez, and Faculty Club. Last Sunday we had three couples for supper. This was the first in a series we are planning in an attempt to repay the many social debts that have piled up. We 'owe' so much, however, that it is about hopeless to expect to catch up ever. Molly certainly has turned out to be a wonderful housekeeper. Her family won't know the girl when we come East this summer, she has changed so much. She's much more interested in her household activities than in her bacteriology."

Molly did not go with him to Pasadena in May for a Caltech symposium honoring Niels Bohr. "All agree your presence is necessary to make the discussions in any sense complete," Professor W. V. Houston, who was responsible for the symposium, had written, inviting Ernest. And, indeed, his remarks there were reported in the national news media almost to the exclusion of anyone else's, except for others' comments on his report of work at Berkeley; particularly the use of the deuteron—vastly more powerful at 2,000,000 volts than the single mass proton at 2,500,000—in the disintegration of eight elements, including aluminum, the heaviest so far. Bohr hailed this as a "marvelous advancement. The dream of yesterday has come true." Even the once skeptical Millikan pronounced Ernest's work "altogether extraordinary, and most intelligently announced."

Professor and Mrs. Bohr were house guests of the Lawrences in Berkeley for three days after the Pasadena symposium. The great man was excited by the Rad Lab, feted by others of the university community, and given the grand tour of San Francisco. To famed Berkeley anatomist Herbert Evans, Bohr remarked, of Ernest, "I've seen and heard the first person I could compare with Rutherford."

Ernest managed to test "our homemade power oscillator tubes" and find that, even with slight vacuum difficulties, more power was obtained than with commercially available tubes. He suggested that Sloan overcome vacuum difficulties by putting the tubes in separate vacuum chambers with their own pumps; the X-ray machine should then be ready for installation in the fall when its annex would be completed. With work planned for everyone for the summer months, he left with Molly for Springfield on June 10, en route to the Chicago meetings of the American Association for the Advancement of Science, then to New Haven, New York, for "my annual fund raising," and Cornell.

It was a relief to find Gunda well, though she did not think it wise to join Carl in going to Chicago with Molly and Ernest to see the World's Fair—A Century of Progress. Before they left, an intercity Rotary luncheon was arranged by proud Carl so that friends could hear his illustrious son talk about his work. The fair was much enjoyed, after which Carl departed for New Haven to visit John, and for Boston as a delegate to the Rotary convention.

The New York Times's William L. Laurence called the two-week session in Chicago the most comprehensive scientific meeting to be held anywhere, embracing as it did every subject from "stars and atoms to vitamins and archaeology." Most of Ernest's old friends were present; he met John Cockcroft, and wrote Birge—on July 1 officially to become chairman of the physics department at Berkeley—to see that Cockcroft was well taken care of in his absence and "shown around thoroughly. He is a very nice fellow." Ernest was a principal speaker at the symposium on nuclear disintegrations, presided over by Bohr, and he again received more press coverage than others—not deserved, he thought, for he had found Cockcroft excellent, the talk on neutrons by Chicago's Harkins fascinating, and Harvard's young Kenneth Bainbridge's ideas linking Einstein's theories with the atom most interesting.

Bohr again discussed the importance of Ernest's "wonderful" work. Always a poor speaker, the great man was at times too abstruse even for his sophisticated audience when he discussed complementarity, trying to explain his idea of the essential duality of all nature. *Time* reported that "the blare of the loudspeaker as Bohr fiddled with the microphone was almost a relief.

"It was much easier, and more pleasant, to understand round-faced young Professor Ernest Orlando Lawrence of the University of California tell how he transmuted elements with 'deuton' [deuteron] bullets."

The Blumers were at Haycock Point and were overjoyed to have Molly home again after the year's absence. Mrs. Blumer, who had broken her leg, loved having Molly near her. It was Molly who drove her to the hospital when the cast was replaced; old friends of her father's there greeted her warmly; one surgeon even allowed her to watch a Caesarian birth—until she nearly fainted. She had planned to spend six weeks with her family while Ernest was at Cornell, and he had agreed, but the night before his departure, when Molly was sitting on his lap, he said, "You'd better come to Ithaca with me." "I protested that Mother needed me, although it was rather obvious that there were plenty of people around to look after her," Molly remembers. "I was kind of selfish, sometimes. Mother thought it was Ernest who was being selfish, but there is no question but what I should have gone with him, and I did."

They had some difficulty finding a place to live and finally settled into a hotel cottage on Lake Cayuga. Molly, who never enjoyed freshwater swimming, had to adjust herself to unaccustomed idleness as Ernest was away all day every day. "I really caught up on my reading!" The evenings were always full, mostly through invitations from faculty people. She left Ithaca after a month to be in Berkeley when her sister Elsie arrived by ship via the Panama Canal.

There were about forty in Ernest's Cornell class on electrical discharges and in his seminar on the neutron. "In both I learned a great deal," he wrote to Professor Swann. "Likely more than my students. Had a swell time." He left immediately after his final lecture to be in Berkeley for the opening of the fall semester. There was not time to visit the new home of his parents in Aberdeen, though he had to spend an afternoon and night, between trains, in Chicago. He remembered that Luis Alvarez, brother of his secretary, Gladys Alvarez Archibald, and son of Dr. Walter Alvarez of the Mayo Clinic and the Macy Foundation Board, was in the physics department at the university. Ernest invited him to spend the afternoon and evening with him at the fair. Young Alvarez was dumbfounded and delighted, he remembers.

"It was quite a revelation to me, being a young graduate student and only knowing professors at some little distance. I was quite unprepared for Ernest's enthusiasm. He wanted to listen to the symphony for a while, and he wanted to have a drink at one of the bars, and he wanted to see the *Streets of Paris,* and just seemed to be a regular guy. My only close association with any professor was with Arthur Compton. And in those days Arthur Compton was a little on the austere side. So I had quite a different picture of what a professor of physics was like. I didn't feel any age difference at all. We had a fine time together. We walked around at a good clip, and, when we were through, we walked all the way back to the Stevens Hotel, and he said, 'Well, let's have a nightcap.' So we went into the bar to drink together. It was a wonderful experience." Luis, who Compton said was his best graduate student, came to Ernest's laboratory after getting his degree.

Ernest had sixteen men under his direction for the fall, 1933, term, including six National Research Fellows. One of the latter, Franz Kurie from Yale, who had visited the lab with Cooksey, immediately went to work building a new cloud chamber of his own design. Modifications on the large cyclotron included an outside control permitting choice from a dozen targets within the chamber. Others were planned: a means of beam withdrawal from the cyclotron and automatic magnet current control. Eager as he was to improve the machine, Ernest felt it necessary to verify or disprove his hypothesis of deuteron breakup, regardless of target, into protons of similar range and neutrons, and to establish the correct mass of the neutron. There had been a good deal of discussion on these problems at Chicago, but no one in this country was equipped to verify or dispute him. Cockcroft promised to test the theory after his return to England. Ernest naturally wished to gain more understanding of what transpired when deuterons were used as atomic projectiles.

He was at work on the problem when he was handed a letter in French from the Comité Scientifique de Solvay—a committee among whose members were Einstein, Bohr, Debye, and Leningrad's A. Joffe—inviting M. Le Professeur Ernest Lawrence to attend and participate in the congress. He could scarcely believe it, until one more familiar with French verified the invitation. Boyishly exuberant, he showed the invitation around Le Conte Hall and the Rad Lab, delighted at this "international recognition of our laboratory." He did not give a thought to going, what with all the work, his classes, and the expense until he saw Loeb.

"Leonard, look! An invitation to Solvay!"

"My God! Congratulations. What wonderful recognition!"

"Of course I can't afford to go." Ernest seemed not to mind.

"You've got to!" Loeb protested. "You must! Leave it to me. It's an honor second only to that of winning the Nobel Prize."

Loeb got in touch with Dr. Cottrell, and shortly thereafter $300 toward Ernest's expenses arrived from the Commission for Relief in Belgium Educational Foundation, a lingering entity of the Hoover war relief in which Solvay had participated. Officials were delighted with the honor reflected upon the university and the physics department; there was only encouragement to attend the congress, though it would necessitate Ernest's absence in midterm.

To have more data for Solvay, he worked more hours than ever, bombarding a variety of targets with 3,000,000-volt deuterons, by far the "most energetic atomic particles that have ever been produced artificially," he noted in an article for the *Physical Review*—and with increased beam intensity. He took Kurie off construction of the new cloud chamber to set up the old, little one near the cyclotron. With this, recoil counters, and Henderson's amplifier, results all seemed to bear out Ernest's hypothesis, no matter what element was the target. Intense beams of neutrons and recoils from neutrons as well as protons were observed; all seemed to corroborate the view that the mass of the neutron was much lower than that given by Chadwick. The powerful and penetrating neutron radiations caused some concern about possible physiological effects on the experimenters—and Ernest's feeling that they might have considerable medical importance. There was no time now for this, or for more than warnings to his boys to be careful. By the first week in October he felt that he had enough evidence to back his hypothesis and to hold his own in the distinguished company he would meet in Brussels and in Cambridge, where Cockcroft had invited him to be his house guest for as long as he wished to visit the Cavendish laboratory.

Though he had planned to fly to and from New York, he still felt it risky, and, as it would allow more time to prepare for the congress, he decided to take the train.

When Molly took him to the station on October 9, he was overwhelmed to find all his Rad Lab gang there to cheer him off.

CHAPTER VIII

Alchemists' Dream

[OCTOBER, 1933–DECEMBER, 1935]

D on Cooksey had a room for Ernest at the Yale Club when he arrived in New York Friday morning, and he sent his luggage there before rushing off to meetings at the Chemical and Macy foundations and the Research Corporation. In the afternoon Don took him to Columbia to see Exner and his Sloan X-ray tube. John came down from New Haven to join them for dinner, the last that Ernest thoroughly enjoyed until he landed in France. The *Ile de France,* one of the fastest, most luxurious ships afloat, seemed as stable as, and similar to, any of New York's great hotels when they went aboard the next morning; she seemed powerful enough to withstand the most tempestuous seas, as the tugs pulled her away at noon and Ernest waved to his brother and Don, so far below him on the pier. But Ernest had experimental proof, during the six-day crossing, that nature could uncomfortably challenge the devices of man that attempted to dominate her forces. He was glad to have a night in Paris before going on to Brussels for the opening of the congress on October 22, 1933. There, any lingering malaise was quickly forgotten in the stimulating company, "representing almost all that was known from experimental and theoretical investigation of the atomic nucleus."

He noted at once the preponderance of the British representation, with eight men from Cambridge alone, proper evidence of the predominance of the Cavendish under Rutherford. During their rather "Mark Twainish" tour of Europe in 1927, Ernest and Beams had thought Germany preeminent in physics, even after their visit to Cavendish. Now there was no one from Göttingen, already a victim of Nazi racial policies, though Erwin Schrödinger, invited for the third time, was present from Berlin, as were Peter Debye, who had lectured at Berkeley in 1932; Werner Heisenberg from Leipzig; and W. Bothe, who spoke of perplexing results from natural radiation of beryllium, from Heidelberg. Germany's single "non-Aryan"—because a native of Austria, as yet unmolested—was Lise Meitner of the Kaiser Wilhelm Institute, who, with the great Marie Curie and her daughter Irène Joliot-Curie, formed the feminine contingent. Even Einstein had left his fatherland and would move permanently to the United States. George Gamow, for whom Ernest had many questions, was present from Russia. He was himself questioned at length by Joffe of Leningrad, who told Ernest that the Russians were building a "Lawrence," as he referred to the cyclotron, a Van de Graaff as large as that at M.I.T., and a lightning generator larger than that of the General Electric Company at Pittsfield, Massachusetts. Ernest recalled to Prince de Broglie and his son the visit with Beams to their laboratory in Paris. There were exciting discussions, in corridors, with Wolfgang Pauli of Zurich and Enrico Fermi of Rome.

Ernest was genuinely humble in the presence of elders who had brought physics so far in less than half a century, even though leading scientists had proclaimed the great discoveries already made and had asserted that physics would henceforth be only a matter of refining that already known. Aware of such dogmatism even among the great, he refused to be drawn into fruitless argument. Just in the past month the press had sought him out to comment on Lord Rutherford's statement to the British Association for the Advancement of Science: "Anyone who expects a source of power from the transformation of these atoms is talking moonshine." Rutherford had been applauded—in the very hall where, a quarter of a century before, William Thompson, Lord Kelvin, had asserted that the atom was indestructible. Yet Rutherford had been the first to prove the fallacy of such a conclusion; Rutherford who had suggested the first reasonable map of the infinitesimal atom, mostly empty, with a nuclear center so infinitesimally smaller still. And it was in Rutherford's Manchester laboratory in 1912, when the term "nucleus" was first used, that young Niels Bohr started to wonder about the rest of the map, a wonder that led him to continue exploration into the unknown "indestructible" universe of the atom, and finally to fill out the map with the orbiting electrons.

No one knew more about the atom than Rutherford, and his statement that "energy produced by the breaking down of the atom is a very poor kind of thing" was considered correct, but Ernest was not alone in thinking it premature, based as it was on present knowledge. Even with such powerful beams of particles as Ernest was developing, the submicroscopic size of the nucleus and repellent electromagnetic forces within the atom made any large-scale practical nuclear breakup appear fanciful. Ernest refused to argue the matter; the purpose of disintegration was to learn atomic structure; if useful applications resulted, that was good, too. From motors to radio, how much had resulted from pure curiosity!

"We must agree that as yet the 'energy produced by the breaking down of the atom is a very poor kind of thing,' but this is purely a matter of marksmanship. At the present time it is possible to break up the atom by disintegrating its nucleus only about once in a million 'shots' . . . But the fact remains that when a 'hit' is made, the atom gives up about twenty times as much energy as was needed to break it. . . . It's a case of being able to develop a way of making a larger percentage of 'shots' reach their mark. . . . Personally, I have no opinion as to whether it can ever be done, but we are going to keep on trying to do it." He had said that at Caltech and at Chicago, and that was the position he maintained in informal corridor conversations at the Solvay Institute and in Brussels hotel rooms, and the ferment generated by those discussions only increased his optimism; the release of power accompanying atomic disintegration might well prove useful.

In formal sessions of the congress, he was prepared to defend the advantages of the cyclotron as an instrument of nuclear disintegration and to present his hypothesis of deuteron instability with evidence of a lower mass than Chadwick had postulated for the neutron. The president of the congress, Paul Langevin of the College de France, had sent copies of papers to be given to Berkeley and had asked to what extent Ernest wished to participate in discussions of them. Ernest had replied at once that he would appreciate taking part in discussions following the addresses of Chadwick, Cockcroft, Joliot, and Gamow, "particularly rather extensive remarks on Cockcroft's report." He had had a chance to study the papers thoroughly on the train to New York, had circled and underlined statements he wished to challenge, writing in the margins "Not true," or inserting question marks. Where credit had been given solely to him, he wrote in the names of Henderson, Milton White, Dave Sloan, G. N. Lewis, and Livingston—and mentioned them when he spoke at Solvay.

Lord Rutherford, in his address, acknowledged receipt of heavy hydrogen from Berkeley and told how he and his colleague, Mark Oliphant, had investigated Ernest's report of greater range particles from bombardment with it than with protons. "Our use of the magnetic field to analyse the positive ion beam precludes this possibility," the great Rutherford emphasized. Ernest defended his hypothesis, but Rutherford brushed aside any results indicated by other means than the Wilson cloud chamber, "as at present it is the final court of appeal in these matters." Ernest was insistent, and found agreement on the part of such theorists as Gamow, that the results of a 500,000-volt bombardment would be quite different from those of particles of several million volts. He regretted that only at Berkeley had voltages above 3,000,000 been used experimentally; that in fact at no other place had more than 600,000 volts been available for experiment. He urged the building of cyclotrons so that this and other hypotheses could be studied with comparable energies. Only the size of the magnet used, he argued, determined the limit of cyclotron voltage; with larger ones there was no impossible-to-overcome obstacle to voltages far above the 25,000,000 already in view. His optimistic opinions brought murmurs—even exclamations bordering on ridicule—but he defended them with vigorous assurance. If he failed to gain support for his estimates and his deuteron hypothesis from Rutherford—and no one except those at Cavendish could dispute him experimentally—he won the great man's admiration. After a particularly lively discussion, Rutherford nudged Chadwick and exclaimed, "He's just as I was at his age!"

No fault could be found with Cockcroft's discussion of the cyclotron and the work he had recently seen done with it at Berkeley, except his statement that however high the voltages, "only small currents are possible." Ernest disputed that warmly and found some support for his reasons why the high currents he strove for could and would be achieved. In most respects Cockcroft's remarks were laudatory, especially when he discussed the "art" of focusing with the cyclotron "where experiment had preceded theory." He briefly mentioned the linear accelerators and Sloan's adaption of a linear device into a powerful X-ray tube.

Cockcroft also rejected the hypothesis of deuteron instability, suggesting that indications Ernest had found in support of it were probably caused by some unrealized factor. He recalled that when he and Walton had first looked for disintegration by lithium ions, they thought they had made a great discovery, only to find, "to our sorrow, that hydrogen in the lithium had given a false interpretation." Ernest's insistence that only his hypothesis could account for the fact that deuteron breakup was indicated regardless of target failed to sway Cockcroft. There was tentative support for his theory among the theoreticians, notably Gamow, but among those present only Rutherford's people had been able to check Ernest's hypothesis experimentally with deuterons as atomic missiles.

Chadwick, supporting his mass for the neutron, was somewhat critical of the quality of work at Berkeley. Since Ernest's calculations for a lower mass were based on his disputed hypothesis, he had little to say in response to Chadwick. But even Cavendish, famous for careful measurements, and with many fine experimenters in radiation, could not hope to attain comparable voltages—and therefore the disintegration of heavy elements—with its present equipment. This fact seemed to Ernest sufficient reason for any differences. He never lost his boyish smile and graciousness. Science, he knew, was never satisfied with mere opinion; further experimentation would eventually settle the argument. Henderson had warned him that he considered the somewhat dour Chadwick quite anti-American, recalling how the Englishman had fumed over Millikan's reports of cosmic-ray work, finally announcing, in the tone of one whose honor has been impugned, "If this kind of thing goes on, the only respectable thing to do will be to exchange letters personally."

Nor were Ernest's the only ideas challenged. Chadwick himself remembered of that congress above everything else the "malicious intervention," during his address, "that Heisenberg made which was immediately quelled by Dirac." And Fräulein Meitner disputed conclusions of Irène Joliot-Curie and her husband from the bombardment of aluminum by neutrons in such a way that only consolation by Bohr and Wolfgang Pauli had revived their spirits, for Lise Meitner was also an expert on radium radiation. Ernest found the Joliot-Curie reports of alpha particle bombardment exciting; Joliot was as eager to learn more of the Berkeley work. He had been unable to raise funds for a cyclotron at the Radium Institute of Paris, though he had been the first person anywhere to wish to construct one. Boyish, brilliant Enrico Fermi could harbor no hope for large apparatus so long as Mussolini remained in control of Italy; like Rutherford and so many others, he depended on natural radiations for atomic bullets. He, too, questioned Ernest at length and expressed the hope of visiting Berkeley himself. He had been in America the past summer for the second time, having first crossed the Atlantic for an Ann Arbor symposium in 1930. As yet there were no personal problems for him because of Fascism.

The interference of governments with science was, after physics, the most frequent subject of unofficial meetings. Fine scientists were dependent on colleagues in free countries; Rutherford had done much to find positions in England for non-Aryans from Germany. It was known, if not discussed openly, that Gamow would leave Russia if he could get his wife out with him, and even Joffe, head of Leningrad's University of Physics and Mechanics, who publicly praised the support given scientists generally and his own work, was reported to have whispered that he felt as though he were living on top of a volcano that might at any time and for any reason erupt. It seemed incredible that science should be mixed up with nationalistic politics. Why, during the World War, Rutherford and others had exchanged ideas with German scientists by letters through Switzerland, with no interference. Some wondered, at the conclusion of the congress, if another with truly international representation could be held.

(*Above*) The uncovered 27½-inch cyclotron chamber, vastly improved in design, was first used with the 80-ton magnet. Projections to the right are the "D" stems connected to, and supporting the two hollow electrodes called "D's." The filament for the ion source enters the chamber on the opposite side over the gap between the "D's." Deflector and target chamber are in foreground. (*Below*) Troubleshooting. Robert Thornton listens to the directions of Ernest Lawrence while Franz Kurie, Donald Cooksey, and Edwin McMillan make mathematical calculations. (*Photos: Lawrence Radiation Laboratory*)

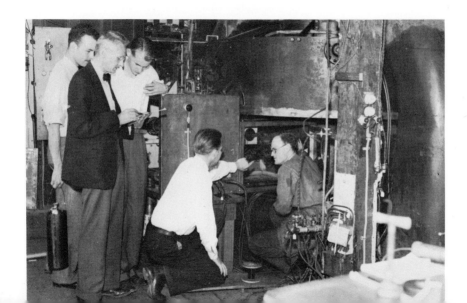

Left to right: Jack Livingood, Frank Exner, M. S. Livingston *(in front)*, David Sloan, Ernest O. Lawrence, Milton G. White, Wesley Coates, L. Jackson Laslett, and Commander T. Lucci, with 70-ton magnet with 27-inch chamber, 1933. *(Lawrence Radiation Laboratory)*

Outside the old Radiation Laboratory are Arthur Snell, Ryokichi Sagane, Lorenzo Emo, Alex Langsdorf, Dean Cowie, Franz Kurie, and J. Reginald Richardson. *(Photo by Professor Bernard Kinsey)*

Ernest and Molly Lawrence with their first child, Eric, on the balcony of
the new house in Berkeley, 1935. *(Courtesy of Dr. Donald Cooksey)*

Left to right: Carl G. Lawrence, Dr. George Blumer, Mabel Blumer, Molly Lawrence, Gunda Lawrence, and Ernest Lawrence, in Yosemite Park. *(Lawrence Radiation Laboratory)*

Ernest Lawrence examining the 37½-inch vacuum chamber with the lid removed. *(Photo by Dr. Donald Cooksey)*

Early Radiation Laboratory staff framed by the magnet for 60-inch cyclotron in 1939. *Front row, left to right:* John H. Lawrence, Robert Serber, Franz N. D. Kurie, Raymond T. Birge, Ernest O. Lawrence, Donald Cooksey, Arthur H. Snell, Luis W. Alvarez, Philip H. Abelson. *Second row:* John Backus, Wilfred B. Mann, Paul C. Aebersold, Edwin M. McMillan, Ernest Lyman, Martin D. Kamen, D. C. Kalbfell, W. W. Salisbury. *Last row:* Alex S. Langsdorf, Jr., Sam Simmons, Joseph G. Hamilton, David H. Sloan, J. Robert Oppenheimer, William Brobeck, Robert Cornog, Robert R. Wilson, Eugene Viez, J. J. Livingood. *(Lawrence Radiation Laboratory)*

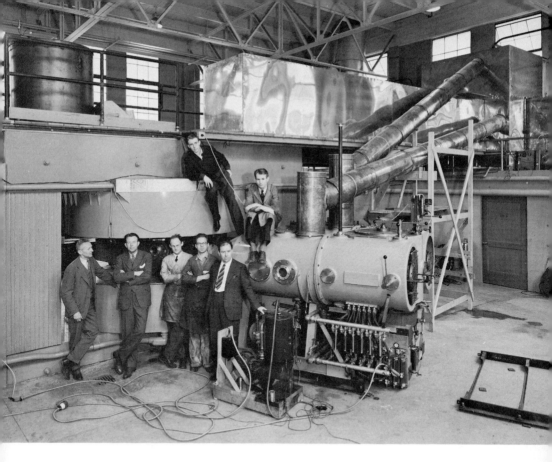

The first professional cyclotron built at Berkeley, the 60-inch, appears streamlined, from "D" stem tanks to slanting tubing covering the oscillator leads. Luis Alvarez rests on the magnet coil tank and Edwin McMillan on the "D" stem casing. Below them are *(left to right)* Donald Cooksey, Ernest Lawrence, Robert Thornton, John Backus, and Winfield Salisbury. *(Lawrence Radiation Laboratory)*

Ernest Lawrence after receiving the news of the Nobel Prize, November 9, 1939.

There will be a party! *(Photos by Dr. Donald Cooksey)*

◄ Flanked by military officers are S-1 committee and its advisers, except for Donald Cooksey, who took this picture. *Left to right:* Major Thomas Crenshaw, Robert Oppenheimer; committee members Urey, Lawrence, Conant, Briggs, Murphree, and Compton; Robert L. Thornton, and Colonel Kenneth D. Nichols. *(Photo by Dr. Donald Cooksey)*

Because of the difficulties of wartime travel in Europe, Professor Lawrence did not receive his Nobel Prize from the hands of the King in Stockholm. It was presented by the Consul General of Sweden in San Francisco, Carl E. Wallerstedt, on February 29, 1940, in the auditorium of Wheeler Hall on the Berkeley campus. University President Robert Gordon Sproul seated in the background. *(Lawrence Radiation Laboratory)*

Ernest was too occupied with physics to worry much about the state of affairs in Europe other than to regret that politics could interfere with the noble and supranational pursuit of truth. But he was reminded by others than worried Europeans that a scientist's ancestry counted more than his achievements in the eyes of irrational nationalists and racists. He had promised to call on American Ambassador Dave Hennen Morris, and, while dining at the embassy, was told of many eminent men, refugees from or declassed citizens in their own countries, who wished to emigrate to the United States. England had received almost all for whom jobs could be found; Belgium had harbored many temporarily, including Einstein, who had been received by the King himself.

Ernest was boyishly jubilant, regretting only that Molly was not with him, to be invited, "practically commanded," to dinner at the royal palace with the King and Queen, until, on the afternoon of the affair, he remembered that he had no white tie and tails. He summoned the hotel porter who threw up his hands in horror at the thought of appearing in any but the most formal evening clothes. Such disrespect for the beloved King! He assured Ernest that other guests would have ribbons and decorations, too. A hasty search failed to locate ready-made, rentable, or borrowable evening dress large enough for Ernest. He made the best of it in tuxedo and, after a moment's embarrassment when presented to the King and Queen, forgot it.

The royal couple appeared not to notice his clothes. Gracious King Albert put Ernest at ease in a rather lengthy conversation, during which he expressed his interest in and gratitude to America and his continuing interest in science.

If Solvay had been exciting and stimulating, Ernest's two days at the Cavendish Laboratory and the Cockcroft home in Cambridge were as interesting. Fowler greeted him as an old friend; C. D. Ellis, who had been at Brussels, and with whom he had previously had much correspondence, welcomed him; Rutherford himself showed Ernest around the laboratory, saying that he functioned chiefly now as a "sort of grandfather of young physicists, keeping their feet on the ground." Oliphant, engaged in experiment with Rutherford at the time, laughed at this. He had worked too long with his mentor and colleague to discount Rutherford's actual work. He told Ernest how once, after late hours in the laboratory, Rutherford had telephoned him, at three in the morning, waking him from sound, needed sleep to report a possible solution to a problem. Oliphant had asked the reason for Rutherford's conclusion.

"Reason!" the older man shouted over the phone. "You want a reason for everything! I have no reason; I feel it in my water!"

Oliphant could be excitable, too. He was more vocal against the deuteron instability hypothesis than the others, and quite an argument followed his opposition to Ernest's statement that the yield of neutrons from deuteron-bombarded lithium was "far too great to be accounted for by the reaction of lithium to form two alpha particles and a neutron." "He's a brash young man," Rutherford said of Ernest after the discussions, which eventually involved Chadwick and Cockcroft also, "but he'll learn."

Rutherford's young men were an exciting group, all doing beautiful experiments. Their comparatively simple equipment, careful observations and measurements made Ernest aware of how much time his laboratory had had to spend on construction and improvement of apparatus at the expense of pure physics; how much was needed to determine results with his larger equipment. Yet that apparatus was necessary to penetrate far into the unknown; no degree of care could define what could not be explored. However ingenious and useful within its limits, the Cockcroft and Walton device of transformers, condensers, and rectifiers could not multiply commercial power above 600,000 volts to accelerate protons. Their glass tubes were very cleverly devised to withstand these voltages and focus the accelerated beams of particles. The Radiation Laboratory could cultivate the Cavendish concern for extremely careful physics—and Cavendish ought, Ernest thought, to have the benefits of powerful apparatus. He suggested that Rutherford build a cyclotron. Rutherford replied with characteristic exaggeration: "We use only what we can make here."

"Don't you use a spectroscope?" Ernest asked innocently.

He might have challenged the remark further when Rutherford showed him Mond Laboratory with its huge apparatus which he had built for another of his young "pets," Peter Kapitza. The Russian was studying the behavior of matter in high magnetic fields at low temperatures. But only he, Cockcroft, and Oliphant had persuaded their leader to allow them big apparatus. Rutherford more than once amused Ernest by somewhat sarcastic references to "our theoretical friends"; yet it was evident that he had great respect for many theoreticians, particularly for Niels Bohr, for whom he also showed affection. And in discussing a physicist whose chief concern seemed to be the most exact measurement, he shouted, "To the last decimal point! Last decimal point! Now that's not a job for a university scientist. Give that to a bureau of standards. I've never been interested in coming closer than twenty percent in my life!" Such statements were belied by his own concern for precision and indicated why he had been called "a savage, however noble," and "a force of nature." He could not shock Ernest thus; Ernest was only uneasy with his lordship, here as he had been a time or two at Solvay, when Rutherford told one of his bawdy jokes, accompanied by his great, booming laugh. Ernest had no jokes, lewd or even off-color, with which to respond—and had to disguise his discomfort with forced laughter. It was a great two days, however, supplemented by the fine hospitality of John and Mrs. Cockcroft in their English home.

Ernest left ship at Montreal, on his return, and had time, before his train left for New York, to report on Solvay at McGill University, where Rutherford had been professor of physics in 1898. More particularly, he spoke of the importance he felt the neutron would have in nuclear work, and possibly in medicine. Professor John Stuart Foster introduced him to Arthur Snell, another of his outstanding students whom he hoped would be allowed to follow Bob Thornton and work with Ernest the following year. Ernest agreed that if Snell won a scholarship that would enable him to go to Berkeley, he would gladly have him in the laboratory. Don met Ernest at the train, found him bubbling with enthusiasm, particularly over what might be done with neutrons. "Don, I'll bet it won't be ten years before a self-sustaining reaction is achieved." That seemingly wild prophecy and his increasingly high estimates of future cyclotron voltage caused one concerned friend to consult John Lawrence about his brother's sanity. John, loyal and with unlimited trust in Ernest, dispelled the friend's worries. "He's the sanest person I know." Don took Ernest to Columbia where he again reported current European thought concerning nuclear physics, with emphasis on the neutron and his controversial deuteron hypothesis. There was a flurry of excitement when he suggested a third isotope of hydrogen, even rarer than deuterium; evidence at Berkeley before he left was not conclusive, but it had apparently been detected in Cambridge also. When he mentioned it to Otto Stern, now a refugee from Germany with a position at Carnegie Institute, Stern begged for a sample, should there be any, and Ernest promised to ask Dean Lewis.

In Washington, Ernest was impressed with the apparatus Merle Tuve was completing for nuclear work; a Van de Graaff generator with a specially designed discharge tube with which Merle hoped to get 1,500,000 volts. "I am beginning to have considerable enthusiasm for the Van de Graaff generator in conjunction with Tuve's type of tube," he wrote Cockcroft on his return to Berkeley when expressing thanks for Cockcroft's hospitality. "I persuaded Tuve to investigate the origin of the 18cm. protons and the hypothesis of the disintegration of the deuteron right away. I want to get the matter cleared up as soon as possible and it will be a great help if Tuve, with his independent setup, will investigate the problem."

There were letters to Rutherford, Fowler, and Gamow, too, reaffirming conviction in his hypothesis, and the lesser mass of the neutron. He persuaded Henderson to postpone efforts to devise—with Livingston

when he was free of the medical school X-ray tube—a means of withdrawing the proton beam from the cyclotron, and to concentrate instead
on the disputed problems. All manner of means were tried to ensure no
contamination of targets, and by mid-December Ernest wrote that "even
Chadwick will have to admit the evidence is preponderantly in favor of
the instability of the deuteron." Merle had unforeseen difficulties in getting his apparatus functioning and had as yet been unable to experiment with deuterons. Cockcroft, too, had been at work on the problem,
as had Oliphant and Rutherford himself. Cockcroft wrote on December
21 of Cavendish experiments. "We have not worked beyond 600,000
volts. . . . I feel myself, however, that the evidence so far is against
your interpretation of the breakup of H^2."

Ernest was unconvinced, even after trying Cockcroft's methods to ensure against contamination of targets. Every possible moment was devoted toward conclusive experiment, though other matters of importance demanded his personal attention. On December 4, the day before
Prohibition officially ended in the United States, the hospital X-ray tube
was turned on for the first time with the new high-power homemade oscillator tubes. And in Berkeley, automatic magnet control was installed
on the large cyclotron. The question of safety had to be considered with
neutrons recorded from every target; in the case of beryllium, they
added up to a startling near-million a second. Ernest, worried over possible harmful dosages, had everyone get a blood count. To the amusement of all, those counts indicated that only the married men were low
in white corpuscles. Relieved, Ernest took time to turn his old Reo in on
a nearly new Studebaker President convertible coupe and demonstrated
it to Molly before returning to his laboratory and making her late at
hers.

He finally declined a tempting invitation to visit Joffe's institute
(with expenses paid only within Russia). To bolster his decision, he
signed up to teach half time during the next summer session, a plan that
shortly had to be modified when he was invited to lecture at Ann Arbor
during the coming July. As a rule it was night and day at the laboratory
even into the holidays. Not until New Year's morning, 1934, when he
finished an experiment, did he pick up Molly to motor south in the new
car for a week's vacation. The first days were spent as guests of Professor
and Mrs. Richard Tolman of Caltech, though he had planned only one
day in Pasadena. A second was added to persuade Lauritsen to examine
the deuteron hypothesis with his powerful X-ray tube, and to accept
Livingston for a couple of weeks' study to learn techniques for measuring dosages, ostensibly for use with the hospital tube, though the safety
of his crew was paramount in his mind.

From Pasadena they drove to Palm Springs and to Boulder Dam, where Ernest persuaded an engineer to take him inside the dam. Molly was not allowed to accompany him, on the excuse that the men were superstitious about women on the job. Such an idea, and the refusal, irritated Molly, already so nauseated that she had been unable to face the interior of the café when Ernest had breakfast. But it was just as well she did not accompany them; she was actively sick in the gutter after they disappeared, after which she felt well enough to accompany them, when they returned from the interior, out onto a swaying catwalk, high above the gorge of the Colorado River, more exciting, she felt, than the interior could possibly be.

In Death Valley they had a day of swimming and loafing in hot sun below sea level, before driving to the Sierra snow where Ernest froze an ear—it was fourteen degrees below zero in the Mono Lake region. In spite of his "blistered ear," they continued north to Reno before returning to Berkeley. Molly could now share some of Ernest's enthusiasm for California and the West. She had a good time. She was even learning to like Berkeley, though she was not very happy about her work at the university. The experiments she was permitted to do meant little to her and seemed unimportant; she enjoyed her home far more and had made new friends. She was beginning to wonder if there would be children, as were the Blumers. Worry about radiation harm at the laboratory was laughed at—at home—however much Ernest insisted on caution and regular blood counts at the laboratory. He still insisted that they would have a large family; indeed he often looked at larger houses which he noticed were for sale.

He called her excitedly one afternoon early in the new year, telling her of a wonderful house to be had at a great bargain. He insisted that Molly join him at once to look at it. She did not like it; it was on four levels on the side of a hill. There was a wonderful view out over much of Berkeley toward the bay, but it would be a difficult house to care for. Ernest brushed that aside; Helen, the wonderful helper, could handle it. Molly thought it ugly, that her antique furniture would not fit into it well. She even wept a little as they discussed it, but Ernest had his heart set on it and talked her into agreement. Before there could be further discussion, he went out and bought the house—in an hour.

By the time they moved to it, Molly was suffering the nausea that plagued her during the early months of her first pregnancy. To Ernest, the pregnancy simply confirmed the wisdom of buying the larger house when he did. She was more unhappy about it than ever, and Helen Brecko, who helped her move, was appalled at the idea of raising babies in a house that was entered by a flight of stairs down from the street level. The entrance hall gave access to the living-dining room, which extended the length of the house, a large kitchen, and stairs up to two bedrooms, which were on the street level. There was a big, half-covered sun deck above the bedrooms, which Ernest liked, as he did the balcony off the living room, and a downstairs study and guest room below that had a brick porch, also facing west. The laundry was also on this level, and there were clothes lines down below that! "Ernest didn't realize the problems of the house any more than I realized what he went through at the lab," Molly excuses him. "But for some time I was little interested in fixing it up and secretly hoped that we would get rid of it." Ernest loved it and liked to show it to friends, particularly the top floor sun deck. As soon as Oppenheimer came up from Pasadena, he invited him to dinner with Melba Phillips, Oppie's graduate student, though there was still much to be done toward furnishing the house. Molly, who appreciated Oppie's artistic taste, asked his advice on something appropriate for the mantel. The next day he arrived with a fine copy of Breughel's "Hunters in the Snow" and hung it over the fireplace—as though it had been painted for that particular place. "I should have known better; he was too generous. If you admired something in his house up the hill, he would give it to you."

The fact that Ernest was to become a father was reassuring at the laboratory, where in mid-January neutrons had been withdrawn from the cyclotron through a thin lead window, at a rate of ten million a second. Molly was warmly congratulated the first night she came to the lab "for a few minutes" on the way to a movie with Ernest. The few minutes, as so often, became hours; the men forgot all about her and she became sicker and sicker. She was used to being forgotten, sitting quietly in a corner, when something interesting was happening at the lab, but this time was embarrassed that she might be ill in front of the men. She looked in vain for a lavatory and had to step outside to be sick under a bush—no one noticed her absence. Ernest and the gang had found new evidence favoring his deuteron hypothesis, using protons to bombard targets of calcium hydroxide, prepared with both ordinary and heavy water. Further support appeared to be coming from Caltech, where Lauritsen had observed neutrons from aluminum, carbon, and copper.

Those strange, powerful, and puzzling neutrons. He discussed the possibility of their use in medicine with Dr. Stone of the medical school whenever he went to the hospital to check the X-ray machine, now operating well at 800,000 volts, with intense radiation on the target. "Hope other hospitals install similar machines," Ernest wrote John, "for two reasons; first as help towards cancer problems, second as jobs for physicists as operators of machines. Many young Ph.D.'s are out of jobs and it would please me a great deal to find them occupations." And, as he had prophesied to Stone, he wrote John as early as January, 1934, "I think that ere long neutron rays will find their application in medicine." John had just become an instructor in the Yale Medical School and with the security it offered was contemplating marriage. "But again I would caution you," Ernest advised. "However the matter is entirely your own to work out and if you should decide to marry her *next* year you can count on me as your best man. But don't rush and get engaged now that you have good prospects for a permanent position at Yale."

On February 24, Ernest opened the latest copy of *Comptes Rendus* in his Le Conte office and read of the discovery of induced radioactivity by alpha particles on boron, by Irène and Frédéric Joliot-Curie. He raced from his office, down the stairs, and across to the Rad Lab. Livingston and Henderson were taking data on long-range alpha particles after one-minute exposures to high-energy deuteron beams. Ernest excitedly waved the magazine and announced the discovery. Everyone gathered around; within minutes slight adjustments were made, the target wheel turned to carbon, and counter circuits connected. The target was bombarded for five minutes and the cyclotron turned off, the counter turned on. There it was, the click, click, click of the counter; radioactivity was observed in less than half an hour after Ernest had read the announcement. It had been there all the time and could have been discovered in the Rad Lab months before.

"It is remarkable that we managed to avoid the discovery prior to the epoch-making announcement," Ernest said later. But Geiger counters had always seemed far more reliable for observing reactions of heavy nuclear particles. "Of course, the Geiger counters were simply being faithful to duty and recording the radiations from the artificial radioactive substances, and this became immediately apparent after the Joliot-Curie announcement." At the time Ernest was somewhat upset that, as Livingood put it, "People just never bothered to look at the Geiger counter when the cyclotron stopped running." "I always felt sorry that we didn't find it for Ernest," Henderson said. "It was in our hands. All I had to do was put the Geiger counter in and put it on target and I'd have had it. We didn't look for beta radioactivity at all; alpha radioactivity many times; turned off the machine and watched for alpha particles coming out. We know now."

Milton White felt, "Had Ernest been . . . the sort of person, in addition to being what he was, beside that been more reflective, and occasionally stopped running to take a longer look at things, he would have discovered radioactivity, artificially induced, before the Joliots, as well as the first anywhere to have discovered transmutations, ahead of Cockcroft and Walton." But this is hindsight criticism, however valid it may be. Ernest was busy with very difficult technological construction that was still ridiculed by some scientists as impractical and limited. That he had not first stumbled onto artificial radioactivity—though unknown, so prevalent in his laboratory because elements may become radioactive if bombarded by alpha, beta or gamma particles—is understandable to any scientist who has realized, when something new is pointed out, that he might have done it himself if . . .

Any regret Ernest felt that he had not first discovered induced radioactivity, so well within his reach, was short-lived; the important fact was the discovery, not who made it. He openly rejoiced over the added evidence of the "richness of the domain of the nucleus accessible to particles of several million-volt energy." Within another twenty-four hours, twelve more elements were rendered radioactive in the laboratory; elements with half-lives ranging from forty seconds for fluorine to twelve minutes for carbon. So much activity was observed with aluminum that the Geiger counter failed to register until the activity had weakened. The complexity of events, the failure to observe the unknown because it was unknown, led Ernest to his first doubt of deuteron instability. He wrote Lauritsen: "With all these new complications coming in, we must admit that we are a bit bewildered about what is going on. It is quite clear that nuclear phenomena are not at all simple!"

And to Joe Morris, "We have been kicking ourselves that we haven't had the sense to notice that the radiations given off do not stop immediately after turning off the bombarding beam. We have had these radioactive substances in our midst now for more than half a year. . . . And now I should say that were it not for the long range protons from heavy hydrogen we would not believe there was much evidence for the disintegration of the deuteron."

To complicate matters further, Fermi reported from Rome radioactivity induced by neutron bombardment. The types of radioactivity Fermi reported were confirmed in the Rad Lab, but the effects were much greater than those observed by Fermi. Silver coin, for instance, outside the vacuum chamber but in proximity to a beryllium target under bombardment by deuterons, became in a few minutes radioactive enough to register more than a thousand counts a minute.

Neutron-induced radioactivity might also have been discovered in the Rad Lab, which could produce more neutrons than Fermi could ever get from naturally radioactive substances. Here again, the very complexity of the instrument, which made so many neutrons available, occupied attention that might otherwise have considered neutrons superior to alpha particles as atomic bullets because every neutron would cause a nuclear reaction, whereas it usually took more than a million fast particles to make a single observable reaction. Fermi's classic experiments in radioactivity were made in an uncluttered laboratory, free of radiations of a cyclotron, and his attention was not distracted by the countless demands of not-yet-perfected accelerator problems. Such ratiocination was not indulged in by Ernest, as it was, privately, by some of his co-workers; Ernest had only praise for Fermi. To Poillon he wrote that a substance from which synthetic radium could be manufactured might likely be found, which would certainly be a great help to medicine in view of the scarcity and expense of radium. He would discuss the possibilities in New York between lectures he was now committed to give in the East after meetings of the National Academy.

Franz Kurie finished his new improved cloud chamber and moved it to the big cyclotron. Pictures taken with its sophisticated camera attachment showed such a wealth of nuclear "events" from cyclotron bombardment that Kurie wrote to Don Cooksey at Yale: "I'm thoroughly sold on the cyclotron as the perfect high voltage source. . . . The point is this: a cyclotron somewhat larger (than the small one) would give the same currents at say one and a half million volts, perhaps two million. Such a magnet would cost with water cooling in the neighborhood of $1,000. For another $1000. one could build the oscillator tubes, pumps etc. The expense then of a potent and usable high voltage source is around $2000. . . . With all this in mind I'd like to see my way clear, when my fellowship runs dry for me to come back to Yale and you and I to set one up . . . when completed we'd have a good nuclear lab—probably second only to Ernest's. Everyone would benefit. You and I obviously —Ernest because no one really believes his cyclotron works. . . . It could stir up enthusiasm at Yale and put it on the map in nuclear physics. Ten years from now will be too late."

The new cloud chamber showed nothing to support Ernest's deuteron hypothesis. Word from Lauritsen through Oppenheimer of his "beautifully clean" experiments seemed to clinch the arguments against it by showing that calcium deuteroxide bombarded by protons "loses hydrogen two which joins the beam and contaminates it"; that is, the disintegrated calcium deuteroxide releases deuterium gas in the cyclotron chamber, and contaminates the ion source, adding deuterons to the accelerated beam.

Merle Tuve soon got his apparatus to function and letters from him, Rutherford, and Cockcroft bore out the fact that a deuteron beam deposited hydrogen on all targets which other deuteron particles in the beam then strike, thereby causing the long-range protons and neutrons that had been interpreted as resulting from deuteron breakup. This automatically ruled out evidence for Ernest's low mass for the neutron.

Somewhat chagrined again, Ernest wrote to all concerned, apologizing for all the work he had caused in clearing up the matter and congratulating them on their results. He also wrote an explanatory letter to the editor of the *Physical Review*. To R. H. Fowler he wrote: "We humbly recognize that we are in a new field and are proceeding very cautiously before drawing any conclusions." And that was the tone of his talk when he gathered lab personnel together and urged greater care and responsibility. But there was no despondency. "Science can grow through mistakes, too. We would be eternally miserable if our errors worried us too much, because as we push forward we will no doubt make plenty more." He reminded them that Cockcroft's and Walton's first paper had mistakes that had been corrected by Rutherford and Oliphant and, "We have just found a similar error of theirs. But with it all things go forward and that's the important thing."

The error referred to involved measurements with the mass spectrograph by Francis Aston which were shown, after observation of nuclear reactions, to be less precise than had been thought. Rutherford had mentioned this in a letter to Ernest in which the great man showed that others make errors: "At first, Aston took a high line about the accuracy of his results, and the impossibility of any serious error between helium and oxygen, but when I told him that if he did not get to work, I was going to put forward the correct mass scheme, he rapidly started in, and found that he had dropped one or two bricks of reasonable magnitude."

Despite the deuteron error, Ernest's reputation had not suffered. He was honored with an invitation to address the prestigious National Academy of Sciences in late April. Because he had to be away so soon after, for the summer, he declined and refused to leave his work even after Poillon offered to pay his fare to and from Washington. Perhaps he would have accepted had he suspected the forthcoming action by the academy; on April 25, 1934, he received notice that he had been elected a member. Letters and telegrams of congratulation poured in, many of them remarking that he was the youngest ever elected to the august and limited membership.

At the same time, the cyclotron first produced 5,000,000-volt deuterons at somewhat increased beam currents, and experiment proceeded at such a pace that the university business office warned Ernest, not for the first time, about "the drain on electricity during regular days and nights" with suggestions that he "confine use of this heavy equipment to slack periods so there would be no interruption of the regular system." Ernest went to Birge about this; certainly he could not limit use of the cyclotrons, or even the linear accelerators with which Sloan, Livingood, and Bernard Kinsey were doing so well, to the "holidays and Sunday nights!" More power was provided.

Ernest was asked to give a paper on acceleration, as were Van de Graaff and Tuve, at one of the meetings of the Physical Society to be held at Berkeley in June. He was delighted over the prospect, but felt that no morning meeting allowed time enough for proper discussion—and fun.

He planned a practically continuous symposium by inviting not only Tuve and Van de Graaff, but Tom Johnson and Lauritsen to be his house guests for the week. "Hope Ann is coming," he wrote Johnson. "Hope to have the house full of physicists during the week of the meetings. We are reserving the official guest room for you and Ann. The rest will have to sleep in my study or up on the sun deck on the roof."

Fortunately Molly was no longer bothered with nausea. She had stopped working at the university, and the "house full of physicists" (Ann did not come with Johnson) proved to be no problem for her. There were lively discussions concerning their work in which experiment had to proceed without benefit of much theory, except perhaps in Johnson's work. He reminded the others once or twice that cosmic-ray work "involved high energy particles, too." It was a merry group, until after the third day of the meetings, the day on which the three accelerator men delivered their papers at a symposium in Le Conte Hall. Van de Graaff had led, followed by Tuve and Lawrence. Merle discussed "Disintegration Experiments Using Protons and Deuterons at 1200 kv," reporting his work with Hafstad and Dahl. He mentioned that they had produced a modest number of neutrons. To Ernest the production of secondary neutrons was of utmost importance, and his experiments had produced millions a second. He asked, "How many is modest?" Merle replied that he didn't know, that they hadn't measured them, but "There were neutrons there." "How many?" Ernest insisted, unable to believe that Merle did not have some idea. "One a second? One a week?" "Well," Merle said, "I don't know. We got some." It seemed actually to hurt Ernest that his old friend could not be more specific. And after his own paper, "Recent Nuclear Investigations at the University of California," Merle made what Ernest interpreted as derogatory remarks about the discredited deuteron disintegration theory.

Tempers flared. Harsh statements followed one another, perhaps particularly bitter because of the long friendship, until Professor Birge stepped in to restore calm. There was a noticeable coolness between the old friends for a while. But there was too much to do to waste time nursing ill feelings; Ernest, who had been amazed, as a student, at the too often petty feuding among scientists, felt it not only a hindrance to individual objective work but also generally an obstacle to the smooth advancement of science. And there were obstructions enough, personal and political, outside of science.

Gamow, who lingered in Berkeley after the meetings, confided that he felt it unwise to return to Russia; he hoped to get a position in the United States. Ernest was unable to persuade authorities at California to hire the Russian. He wrote letters to several other institutions praising Gamow and suggesting that he would be a valued addition to any institution. Oppie agreed that Gamow was an excellent theoretician; Ernest was glad that he, too, would be at Michigan where "I hope to learn more from him," and happier when Gamow was eventually employed by a university.

Ernest left Berkeley July 7 for Iowa. After his lecture there, he spent two days with his parents at Aberdeen before continuing eastward for other lectures, to New York to discuss finances, and to New Haven for a brief respite with the Blumers, before taking up his duties at Michigan.

Professor Harrison Randall had assembled a fine group of physicists at Ann Arbor, and, in addition to his own well-attended lectures, Ernest found much stimulation among other visitors and old friends. He found opportunities, too, to enhance the Berkeley work. Michigan Professor David Dennison drove him to Marysville where he was shown through the Beryllium Corporation plant, served cocktails, and promised the loan of whatever beryllium he needed for experiment. He was able to make a quick trip to Rochester, Minnesota, for a luncheon at the home of Dr. Alvarez to meet Mayo's Dr. Charles Sheard and further stimulate interest in the X-ray tube. Alvarez had been in Berkeley earlier on vacation with his wife and son, Luis, and had become enthusiastic about the tube. Luis was enthusiastic about the spirit of the Rad Lab; the lack of secrecy among the experimenters—the complete cooperation and excitement in each other's ideas and work seemed strange to him after the more austere atmosphere of Chicago.

Ernest went directly to Berkeley after the conclusion of the Michigan summer session in time for the opening of the fall term on August 19. As always, to get back to the Rad Lab was the greatest stimulation. Even the apparatus was viewed with affection, so much more than impersonal machines it seemed; the hum and crackle, the sparks and fluorescence, all symbols of function, hope, and promise. And the men—in almost the possessive sense with which he viewed his "folks" and in-laws—were his, too. He missed Stan Livingston, who had gone to Cornell as an instructor to build a cyclotron—the first from the Rad Lab to become a resident cyclotron missionary elsewhere. But Don was there, and would be until the later opening of the Yale term, working with Kurie on yet another and more versatile Wilson chamber; Edwin McMillan, a National Research Fellow who had started work in the lab three months before, was studying radioaluminum; Malcolm Henderson was measuring neutron energies with his coincidence linear amplifiers; Kinsey and Thornton were adding five more tubes to a linear accelerator, hoping to develope 900,000-volt lithium ions; and Livingood and Sloan were trying to get a hundred microamperes of 800,000-volt deuterons, in line with Ernest's desire for intense currents; everyone was involved in an interesting problem. Good men! One of the first things

Ernest did was to arrange with physiologist Professor H. F. Blum for help with experiments to determine the effects of neutron rays on biological organisms. It would be disastrous if inadvertently, through ignorance, they were to allow harm to come to these men.

Ernest plunged into the activity whenever other duties permitted. Birge offered to relieve him of some of his teaching duties; Ernest refused, grateful for his chairman's consideration. But teaching was important, too, and he would do his share, however much his heart was in the laboratory—where all those fortunate enough to benefit from it agreed his best teaching was done.

When he had made a dozen elements radioactive with neutrons, he tried deuterons in the same fashion and found that sodium could thus be made beneficially radioactive without many of the deleterious effects of scarce and expensive radium. He immediately thought of possible medical uses, since with a half-life of about fifteen hours, radioactive salt if administered internally would leave no dangerous residues over a long period of time and might have therapeutic value. He wrote a letter on radiosodium to the editor of the *Physical Review* and promised a paper in more detail. "It is as hard as ever, however, for us to stop experimenting long enough to write things up, but I am insisting that it be done and set the example in this instance by stopping and writing as soon as the experimental work is done," Ernest wrote.

It was, however, a month before he finished the promised article on radiosodium, on Saturday afternoon, October 20. He took the paper when he went home for supper and, when he left again for the laboratory, gave it to Molly who immediately sat down and read it. "I stuck in a comma here and there as I quite often did with his papers and speeches. Perhaps I rearranged some phrases. Then I cleaned up the kitchen, and about eleven-thirty or twelve, as he still wasn't home, I went to bed. He came home soon after and went to bed, and just about the time he turned out the light, things began to happen. I thought, Oh, Oh, sat up in bed, turned on the light, and said, 'I think the baby's coming.' "

She telephoned Dr. John Sherrick, who said she had better go to the hospital. They drove off excitedly—the baby had been expected two weeks before. Molly hoped she would have a boy; Ernest maintained he did not care "two pins" so long as the child was normal, physically and mentally. Molly was sure that with a family of girls in her background, she would never have a son. Arrival at the hospital was somewhat anticlimactic; the nurse assured them it would be hours before the baby would be born, since it was the first, and Ernest was advised to go home. Back at the house, he was still too excited to sleep. He tried to make coffee but couldn't figure out the drip device and made "a mess." About four o'clock, the hospital phoned, and he raced back there and was admitted to the delivery room where Molly was in the final throes of labor. Ernest was frightened; when she finally recognized and spoke to him, his relief left him as shaken as had his fear. He stood near her until after their son was born. "I think he too was glad it was a boy." When he got home again he was too excited to go to bed. He had forgotten to ask Molly how to make coffee. He got the newspaper and tried to read until time to go to the university, where he reported everything normal. Nevertheless, and though Henderson was expecting to become a father in a couple of months, Ernest again cautioned everyone to be wary of radiations, particularly neutrons, from the cyclotron, and checked with Professor Blum on the status of his experiments on possible biological damage in the laboratory.

Molly, "in seventh heaven to have a son," came home with John Eric on November 1, and he was ensconced in the other upstairs bedroom, next to that of his parents. If Ernest happened to be at home when Eric was awake during the day, he tried to play with him or to take his picture for the grandparents. They were as excited as the parents, the Blumers doubly so, that their first grandchild was a boy. Mrs. Blumer had written that they had about given up hope that Molly and Ernest would have any children, and "To finally have a boy in this family of girls" seemed indeed a gift of fortune. Ernest promised to bring Molly and Eric to New Haven when he went East for April meetings of the National Academy. Mama Lawrence could not wait; she came to Berkeley in February to see the baby—and the wondrous works her older son had wrought in his laboratory.

Those works were beginning to bear fruit of their kind; Livingston had progressed, against some odds, with his cyclotron at Cornell. Other institutions talked of wanting to build them, and in January, 1935, Ernest had a letter from Professor George B. Pegram of Columbia expressing more than wishes; Columbia would construct a cyclotron, provided Ernest had no objections. Objections! Ernest was overjoyed. And he wrote to Kenneth Bainbridge at Harvard, "It would give me a great deal of pleasure if many laboratories would build them." He promised Pegram every possible help.

More and more it seemed that radiosodium and other radioactive isotopes might be of value in the medical world. Ernest sent the first research quantity of radioactive phosphorus to Copenhagen, where George de Hevesy had pioneered in tracer technique with natural radioisotopes of lead. He persuaded physiologists of the university to include radiophosphorus in the daily diets of chickens. He kept at Dr. Stone about the possibility of neutron therapy administered directly from the cyclotron. It posed problems of adequate treatment quarters in the old building, and the transportation of seriously ill patients across the bay from the university hospital. Stone, however, did agree to let Ernest know when he had a suitable case of leukemia for a test of the effects of radiosodium taken internally.

Ernest's efforts to interest other disciplines to experiment with isotopes, then possible to make artificially only with the cyclotron, brought accusations from disbelievers and detractors that he stressed medical possibilities merely to raise money, and he did mention in letters to Rutherford, Cockcroft, and Bohr that the possibilities of isotopes and neutrons for biological work made fund raising easier. But he had never lost his early interest in medicine and had great faith in the medical aspects of radiation. If he was aware that mention of new weapons against such disastrous illnesses as cancer opened foundation coffers more readily than did "pure science," he was nonetheless sincere about it. And Columbia was interested enough to appoint him research consultant to the Crocker Institute of Cancer. He was delighted when, in April, Dr. Charles Sheard of the Mayo Clinic came to Berkeley for the express purpose of looking at the X-ray tube and learning more of the possibilities of radiosodium in clinical work.

Ernest refused to let such gossip as that he used cancer to raise funds bother him; had he needed the security of approval from "pure science," he need only recall his election to the National Academy, consider reports from abroad (Cockcroft, reporting to the British Institute of Physics on radiosodium, had referred to his "most startling announcement"), or note the demands on his time. Besieged with invitations to lecture wherever he went, he agreed before he left Berkeley to talk at Carnegie Tech in Pittsburgh at the request of Otto Stern, an early believer, as well as at Ohio State, Bartol, and the universities of Virginia and Rochester. He was to agree to other requests made at the meetings, and find little time for relaxation between those meetings and his efforts to get sufficient financial support for the laboratory.

Corollary to expounding the cyclotron's virtues, the potentialities of its products, and the hope that others would construct them and join in exploration of the nuclear domain was the welfare of his men. He knew that it would not be in their best interests to keep them in the minor positions he could offer, even if he could afford to pay them well. Several were highly qualified in physics and generally worthy of professorships: as a group they formed the sole reservoir of experienced cyclotron experts. He planned, wherever he lectured, to speak for them, feeling that, no matter how much he wanted any of them in the Rad Lab, other opportunities to further their careers were desirable. "Any fellowships available?" he inquired in reply to letters asking him to lecture, and he would include a list of his top men and their qualifications. The last thing he stressed to Birge before boarding the train for Washington was the necessity of securing university appointments for the lab men. The Birges were among those who came with flowers to see the Lawrences off on their first trip with the baby—including young Betty Birge who, from the time she had been crowded with her family into Ernest's flivver in New Haven, had maintained that she was going to marry Ernest when she grew up.

The journey with Eric was uneventful as far as Chicago, where Molly, going directly to New Haven, was to take a train that would avoid change of stations in New York, and Ernest another train to Washington. At the Chicago station, after leaving Molly with Eric and all the luggage in the waiting room, Ernest went off to verify reservations. He had not returned when Molly heard her train announced, and was still missing when "last call" sounded. In somewhat of a quandary, since Ernest had the tickets, and there was too much luggage for her to handle alone, she appealed to a pleasant-appearing older woman, who had been admiring Eric, to watch the luggage while she sought her husband. Taking the infant in his basket, she searched the station, finally finding Ernest engrossed in conversation with another physicist, Professor David Webster of Stanford. Though Molly thinks Mrs. Blumer has, with time, embellished the incident, her mother is certain of what followed.

"Ernest had forgotten all about her. He had forgotten he was married; forgotten he had a baby. She rushed up and said, 'Ernest, I think I've missed my train, where in the world have you been?' He said, 'Molly, where have you come from?' And she said, 'I came with you and I was to catch that train to New Haven so I wouldn't have to change in New York.' 'Oh, boy!' he said and Webster just stared at Molly. . . . Of course we were having a fit when she did not come as expected. . . . We were at the seashore. . . . George was to meet the train in New Haven and help her with the baby and all that luggage. He telephoned and said, 'No Molly, no baby, no baggage!!!' Well of course I couldn't imagine what had happened; I never thought of his absentmindedness going to that extent. She arrived decidedly late, after someone had sent a telegram for her that she was delayed. She had met a nice woman and her husband who was a physician in New York. She said she was going to meet her parents in New Haven and they were probably having a fit at the moment because she hadn't arrived. The man said he knew one New Haven man very well, Dr. George Blumer, and Molly said he was her father. Molly told them the story and they roared with laughter. . . . When they arrived in New York they put her and the luggage in their car and the chauffeur was told to see her onto a New Haven train, and this man and his wife took a taxi. She was well taken care of, but she arrived a little bit nervous and upset—and so was the baby!"

At the National Academy meeting in Washington, Ernest told of the assault on the periodic table with 3,300,000-volt deuterons and how deuteron interaction with the nuclear field becomes an abundant source of slow neutrons; "thus we find the same radioactivities that Fermi finds." Much credit was given to Oppenheimer for theoretical interpretations of experimental results, in papers which Ernest read for his men, citing results of carbon, sodium, phosphorous, chlorine, and potassium bombardment. He was elated enough to wire Birge after the announcement that two National Research Fellowships were to be granted to Berkeley men: Milton White from his laboratory and Arnold Nordsieck who had been studying with Oppenheimer. "Remarkable compliment since only four new appointments!" A third, Stanley Van Voorhis of Princeton, asked to go to the Rad Lab. Another wire to Birge, two days later, mentioned that "Even Tuve is won over, and is looking for funds to built a cyclotron."

Michigan also planned to construct one, and Professor James Cork asked to spend the summer at the Rad Lab and Professor F. A. Firestone, the fall semester. Professor P. G. Kruger, head of physics at Illinois, also wished to be at the laboratory for the summer with Kenneth Green, preparatory to construction of a cyclotron at the University of Illinois. Swann had plans for a 40-ton magnet cyclotron to be built and used in cooperation with the Cancer Research Institute of the University of Pennsylvania. Princeton wanted three Rad Lab men who would be helpful in the construction of a cyclotron. Ed McMillan, who had taken his degree there, immediately received an offer, which arrived in Berkeley the day Birge succeeded in getting an instructorship for him at California. Ernest suggested Malcolm Henderson for a Princeton appointment and that Milton White go there for his fellowship. "Idea is that with them they could make rapid strides towards another rad lab. . . . In addition to splendid support of work . . . will have contact with good men next year including Fermi and R. H. Fowler. Princeton is 'perking up' again in physics," he wrote Birge. "I have just dictated a letter to Harry White if he would be interested in a position on staff of Research Corporation . . . splendid opportunity for him. Dr. Detlev Bronk of Johnson Foundation for Medical Physics also wants one of the cyclotron men, as they too have the fever, and want Thornton." Ernest wanted Thornton to "more or less" take charge of the cyclotron, if funds to keep Thornton and Kurie at Berkeley as research associates could be raised.

Suddenly it became a problem of keeping men—when opportunities for them elsewhere were beyond what they might expect at Berkeley. Nevertheless, he recommended Kurie and Thornton for both Princeton and Michigan to "let them choose." He was soon able to telegraph Birge that he had funds to offer stipends for both Thornton and Kurie, having at the time received promises of $11,230 from the Research Corporation and the Chemical and Macy foundations. Don Cooksey who had promised to add to the amount anonymously, if necessary, to keep Kurie at the lab, himself planned to stay there a year and was appointed a research fellow without salary. There was now no worry about the laboratory becoming understaffed. Another Commonwealth Fellow wanted to come from England, and bright young men from American universities were eager to do graduate work, or apply for fellowships of one kind or another, at the Rad Lab. As for the summer: "At least half a dozen visitors will be there. Afraid too many but can hardly refuse requests from such prominent people," he wrote Birge. "You are being given credit for developing a great department of Physics."

Ernest's lectures in the East caused quite a sensation. He demonstrated the radioactivity of radiosodium with a Geiger counter, often using a weak solution as a "cocktail," if there was a willing subject for a demonstration, which added weight to his suggestions that radioactive substances might be of importance in medical work. He would not repeatedly drink one himself, however harmless a single one was considered, because of the cumulative nature of its effects. McMillan and Thornton airmailed fresh supplies, designed to reach him while the fifteen-hour half-life was effective.

The demonstration was used in his talk to the gathering of the Sigma Xi fraternity of scientists at Virginia, with the help of Jesse Beams; at Columbia before over a hundred physicists from the metropolitan area; at Swarthmore, Carnegie Tech, and Princeton; and at Yale, before a joint meeting of the departments of physics, chemistry, and the School of Medicine. Before his talk at Cambridge, he wrote McMillan: ". . . don't need another sample as this will be just to physicists . . . will not require the vaudeville, though it might be appreciated even by Bostonians." He added that McMillan, Kurie, and Thornton ought to ". . . shut down for a week or two before I return and get rested up a bit," and before the influx of summer visitors, including "Stern who is bringing a velocity selector to attempt measuring slow neutrons," F. Rassetti from Italy, and T. Yasaki from G. Nishina's laboratory in Japan.

He had hoped to be back in Berkeley before June 1, not only for his work but also to greet the many visitors, but on May 12, John, riding on the shore highway with a young medical student, had a disastrous automobile accident that delayed Ernest's departure several weeks. No one witnessed the accident; the car had apparently swerved off the road and been demolished against a tree. The student was dead when the ambulance arrived, and John, in serious condition, was rushed to the hospital. There was much concern for several weeks that his injuries might be more serious than those that could be determined at once:

slight concussion, broken nose and jaw, and the bones of his right leg fractured. He could recall nothing of the accident. Ernest, personally distraught, and concerned for his mother's reactions, stayed in New Haven until recovery was assured. After he left, the middle of June, Molly remained, visiting John frequently in the hospital and reading to him when he was well enough. Ernest stopped for a couple of days at Aberdeen to assure his parents that John was out of danger and would be all right.

He arrived in Berkeley on the twenty-first, in time for brief conferences with Birge and some of the laboratory guests, before leaving again for Physical Society meetings in Los Angeles. He took Professor Cork of Michigan, Kurie, Milton White, and graduate student Jackson Laslett with him in his car. Near a bridge, about twenty miles north of Santa Barbara, the Studebaker was struck by a Ford coupe, driving left of the center line. Kurie, who was driving, had almost stopped because he could move no farther to the right because of the bridge retaining wall. Though the driver of the Ford, which turned over, assumed the blame, and no one was injured, Ernest urged caution; science could not afford to lose so many good physicists all at once.

There was little other vacation that summer, with so many visitors, and alterations—such as the installation of water cooling around the D's—on the cyclotron. Don took men for weekends or other short periods of time to his Trinity County place, still off the roads, as much a virgin wilderness area as it had been when he was a boy. After John arrived in July, he was well enough to spend a week at Don's, and Ernest drove to Trinity County to bring his brother back to Berkeley, where John was soon busy studying the effects of neutron radiation on living tissue.

Ernest, who earlier in the year had been appointed consulting physicist to the medical school, and had suggested the possibility of direct radiation from the cyclotron for cancer treatment when the beam was drawn from the chamber, seized the opportunity to have John determine safety factors and study the possibilities for neutrons in therapy. John had had experience with X-radiation. Stone, and other people at the hospital, were interested but were too far from the lab to be of present help on neutrons, however eager Stone was to experiment with radioisotopes that could be delivered to the hospital. Ernest argued that at least a neutron beam could be much less diffused than that of X rays. "It took him some time to realize," Dr. Stone pointed out, "that his much finer neutron beam was not a factor, that cancer is not a small circular target requiring such fine pinpointing." Stone's interest was in neutron radiation, that it might be more effective, and possibly more selective, than X rays. Of more immediate value, he thought, was Ernest's idea that radioactive isotopes might "hook onto cancer cells and radiate them internally," which was to be proven effective in some types of cancer.

A young intern, Joseph Hamilton, who also had a degree in chemistry, was the person at the hospital most excited over the possibilities of neutron and isotope radiation, though his specialty had been neuropsychiatry. "That Rad Lab business is hot stuff," he told Stone, after a visit to the lab, where he had taken a radiosodium cocktail in the presence of his wife and several physicists and had noted with a Geiger counter how long it took the radioactivity to reach various parts of his body—two minutes, for example, to his fingers. But Hamilton's immediate superior wanted nothing to do with it. It was not until Hamilton became a resident physician that, with Stone's support, he received permission to use isotopic solutions on patients.

Stone phoned Ernest in October that they had a suitable leukemia patient, but at the time the cyclotron was undergoing repairs and the tests had to be postponed. It was not until March 23, 1936, that radiosodium was, for the first time, administered internally to a hospital patient for comparison with natural radium. The injection by vein was repeated in four days, and even the loss of sodium by perspiration was determined by measuring the radioactivity of bedclothes and linen. It was determined that there was no toxicity. Hamilton and Stone detailed results of the early experiments with radiosodium in *Radiology*. As Ernest wrote Cockcroft in July, 1935, "The people at California Medical School Hospital in San Francisco are interested in artificial radioactive substances, not necessarily as cheap substitutes for radium, but as substitutes having superior chemical and biological properties."

Ernest, of course, was delighted to make radioactive sodium available, and often the cyclotron ran until midnight to produce it. Then it was rushed to the ferry, across the bay, and to the hospital where Hamilton prepared the sodim solution and injected it either intravenously or intraduodenally. In the laboratory, while everyone had a hand in running the cyclotron for this purpose, Paul Aebersold was the one chiefly interested in this aspect. He also helped Dr. R. F. Zirkle, visiting from Pennsylvania during the summer, irradiate wheat seedlings with neutrons and study the effects on sprouting and growth.

Aebersold also helped John, during his sojourn at the Rad Lab, on neutron studies. They borrowed mice and rats originally intended for Professor Herbert M. Evans for hormone studies, along with a microscope and pipettes. A corner of the old building from then on housed colonies of noisome rats. They put a mouse in a small wooden block they made to fit a brass tube set in the wall of the cyclotron chamber where it would get a heavy dosage of neutrons from deuteron-bombarded beryllium. Everyone was alarmed to find the mouse dead after three minutes'

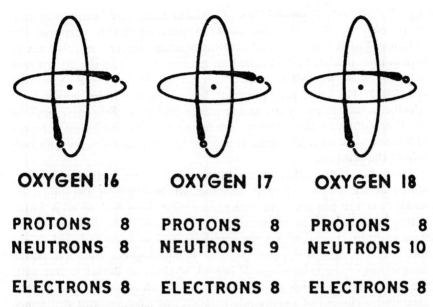

OXYGEN 16   **OXYGEN 17**   **OXYGEN 18**

| PROTONS | 8 | PROTONS | 8 | PROTONS | 8 |
| NEUTRONS | 8 | NEUTRONS | 9 | NEUTRONS | 10 |

ELECTRONS 8   **ELECTRONS 8**   **ELECTRONS 8**

Isotopes are nuclei of the same element, each with the same number of protons, but with differing numbers of neutrons. (*Lawrence Radiation Laboratory*)

exposure. The cyclotron control was moved thirty feet farther away from the apparatus, and plans were made to interpose a considerable thickness of absorbent material. Water was decided upon as the best and cheapest barrier, and a wall of square, five-gallon water-filled cans was soon erected between the controls and the cyclotron—and everyone was more careful while the machine was in operation. When the histologic report was made, some days later, it was learned that death had been caused not by neutrons but by suffocation. Someone had forgotten to open a small valve in the copper tubing of air supply. Nevertheless, the deceased-mouse episode instilled a healthy respect for cyclotrons, perhaps one of the reasons for the outstanding radiation safety record of the Rad Lab.

During the weeks that John was at the laboratory, more than fifty rats and mice were exposed to various dosages of neutrons or X rays, for comparison of effects. Indications were that, for rats, neutrons are much more lethal than X rays, but it was gradually determined that their effect varies with the substance exposed. After his return to Yale in the fall, John continued to cooperate, conducting experiments with rats exposed to X rays, in conjunction with Aebersold's neutron experiments at the Rad Lab. The rats, alas for physicists, were there to stay! The bio-

logical and medical possibilities of artifical radioactive substances produced only by the cyclotron *must* be fully exploited, whatever the
nuisance. Ernest was delighted over his brother's interest in this facet of
exploration of what he had called, in his late lectures in the East, a new
science—"Shall we call it nuclear physics or shall we call it nuclear
chemistry?" He wrote the "physical" half of an article for which John
added the "biological" part, and it was published in February, 1936, in
the *Proceedings of the National Academy*, "side by side" with a report
of Zirkle's work with seedlings. It was the first paper under joint author-
ship of the brothers.

There were many other papers from the Rad Lab, including five presented at the Physical Society meetings in Berkeley in December. So
much "nuclear physics" was being done that Don had to wait impatiently to install a new improved cyclotron chamber he finished in the
shop early in December. Larger transformers had been installed to ensure sufficient oscillator power without hampering the electrical power
for the rest of the campus—and, indeed, sections of Berkeley. But with
the old chamber, which on December 10 (at eleven o'clock at night)
produced a current of twenty microamperes of 5,000,000-volt deuterons,
the experimenters were loathe to interrupt their work.

Ernest was as happy with the improved intensity as with the achievement of the record voltage. Cooksey's new chamber, permitting an ion
spiral three inches larger in diameter than the old one, with heavier D's,
and better arrangements for water-cooling, was not placed between the
magnet poles until the afternoon of December 21, 1935. At quarter-past
six the following evening, deuterons were whirled inside it with a current of one microampere. Less than four hours later, 5,800,000 volts at
four and a half microamperes were obtained. Ernest had to leave the
next day; he was to give a series of six special lectures at Harvard immediately following the holidays, and wanted time in New York to discuss cyclotron improvements and new highs in microamperes and voltage—and to raise more money to continue the advance. He had much
else to report. Even Chadwick, who had left Rutherford and the Cavendish Laboratory to take over at Liverpool, and had just won the Nobel
Prize, now wanted a cyclotron! Ernest had written to congratulate him
on winning the prize, and offered all possible help with the accelerator.
Chadwick had replied that he was "rather lucky to get the prize" and
thanked Ernest for his offer to help build "your magnetic resonance
accelerator, which ranks with the expansion chamber as the most beautiful piece of apparatus I know."

Ernest interrupted his journey to New York to spend Christmas with
his parents in Aberdeen, South Dakota.

CHAPTER IX

Heart's Desire

[1936]

Ernest arrived in New York on January 3, 1936, in time to see Professor Joel Hildebrand, manager of the American Olympic ski team, off on the *Manhattan* for the Winter Games. Hildebrand, one of the men responsible for the excellent Berkeley chemistry department, was not only professionally interesting. The wide range of interests his family shared—within their home, at sea, or in the High Sierras—made them a stimulating and exciting group at play or at work. He had been a good friend and colleague; his student son Alexander had helped enough in the Rad Lab to be mentioned in a scientific paper. It was important enough to Ernest to wish Hildebrand *bon voyage* and luck in the forthcoming games to leave little time for seeing Poillon before he went on to New Haven for a brief visit with John and the Blumers. He arrived in Boston Sunday night, the fifth.

The week at Harvard was auspicious. From his arrival on the first Sunday of the new year to his departure the following Saturday morning, Ernest was wined and dined by President James Bryant Conant, acting Dean of the Graduate School George Birkhoff, Professor Percy Bridgman, and other dignitaries. It was apparent at once that more was involved in his visit than the scheduled lectures; President Conant asked questions beyond the requirements of courtesy about Ernest's work, his plans for the future, and his conception of the importance of the new physics concerned with the heart of the atom. Percy Bridgman discussed the state of physics at Harvard, a department Ernest considered not very important, except for the presence of Bridgman and one or two other scholars.

Dean George Birkhoff spoke of the desire to develop a graduate school of science and engineering at Harvard, second to none, and asked what it would cost to duplicate Ernest's California laboratory. Ernest enthusiastically told how reasonably it might be done; the next cyclotron he hoped to build at Berkeley, though he had not spoken of it as yet to any university authority, might cost $25,000. Much larger than his present machine, it would be capable of much deeper penetration into nuclei. When Birkhoff wondered aloud what it would take to lure Ernest away from California, Ernest was hesitant. He mentioned the fine men he had, men who could not only facilitate the construction of new and more powerful instruments but who also were aware of their uses in experiment. In addition to a cyclotron, Harvard would have to have cloud chambers and other auxiliary equipment. At California they made much from scrap found in dumps; men built their own tubes, with the help of Litton, a man of long experience in the field. There were always a number of fine physicists working hard for little or no pay, in addition to bright graduate students and fine research fellows. It had taken time to accomplish what had been developed with such help; to start fresh at Harvard and quickly duplicate the Rad Lab would involve much more than construction of a cyclotron.

Birkhoff suggested that Ernest, as dean of a new graduate division, might bring one or two of his men with him, and that undoubtedly at least as many men would come to such a laboratory in the East as in California. Harvard had previously offered a position to Oppenheimer, and if Ernest joined the faculty they would raise the offer to Oppie to $6,000. They would offer a position to McMillan, too, and possibly to others Ernest might suggest. Birkhoff felt that the support Ernest received from benefactors located in New York would be continued, perhaps enlarged, if he were at Harvard. He mentioned the close ties Harvard enjoyed with M.I.T., a cooperation which Conant also stressed. Ernest was asked to consider the Harvard position, keep it generally confidential, and withhold a decision until Conant could determine what might be done.

Ernest was, naturally enough, elated. Not one to be dazzled, he was nonetheless aware of the prestige of Harvard, generally, if not specifically in physics. It was hard to restrain himself when he visited the Blumers after leaving Boston; he knew how they would like having Molly nearer New Haven, and he was sure Molly would love to return to New England. He swore John to secrecy and in New York discussed it confidentially with Poillon, of whom Harvard had made inquiries concerning Ernest and Research Corporation support for his work if he should move to Harvard. Poillon had been asked not to discuss it with the Chemical and Macy foundations but felt that their continued support would also follow Ernest wherever he went. Poillon thought there might be advantages for Ernest's work in the East, and that many outside of Harvard would be pleased if he moved, but that he would have to decide for himself where his work would best progress. He agreed that it would be appropriate to discuss the Harvard situation, in advance of a formal offer, with Professor Leuschner of the Research Board at Berkeley; California should have a chance to counter the Harvard inducements. Ernest doubted that equivalent support could be assured at Berkeley, though he thought he would rather stay there if anything approximating what Harvard seemed ready to offer were forthcoming.

Opposed to his personal desire was the conviction that Molly would be delighted to return to New England, though she had become reconciled to Berkeley after her first homesickness and had not for some time expressed the hope that Ernest would be called to an Eastern institution. New England associations were dear to her, not only New Haven, but Harvard itself, and Boston. A move to Cambridge would be a return to the land of her roots.

Ernest, therefore, could only admire the restraint with which she greeted his enthusiastic report of the offer; she wished whatever was best for him. He must consider the climate, and his tendency toward bronchial distress, the more conventionally restricted way of life that would be expected of them, and the formal and heavy social obligations of a Harvard dean. How would it affect the children—and Molly was pretty certain another was on the way. They would have quite different lives in the urban atmosphere of Cambridge and Boston than in Berkeley. Ernest was grateful for her objectivity and her insistence that the important consideration was his work. He knew that she was as little concerned with the prestige that would come to them as he was—except as it might further his primary motivations in science. Money was important, but she was no more desirous of affluence above other goals than he was; financial security seemed assured whether he moved to Harvard or stayed in California.

Molly's calm objectivity was somewhat impaired as the days passed and it became certain that she was to have another child; she was plagued by more persistent nausea than she had been before Eric's birth. Ernest's vacillations contributed to her distress, as the pros and cons of the matter were weighed whenever he was at home. Indecision, not usually characteristic of Ernest's thinking, was not entirely of his own making; Dean Birkhoff wrote that a formal offer from Harvard must await President Conant's return from a trip to Bermuda. Leuschner, in Berkeley, had been unable to discuss the matter with President Sproul, who was at the Los Angeles branch of the university. Ernest had agreed that Leuschner discuss it with Sproul if he thought it wise and had been heartened by Leuschner's attitude that California might promise more support for his work than he was now receiving, if he stayed. But the delays in both East and West were irritating. If only he could discuss it with Cooksey and Oppie!

He again submitted a recommendation that Oppie be made a full professor, and wrote, urging the promotion, to Astronomer Donald Shane, influential on a faculty committee. Oppie might join him at Harvard; if Ernest remained at Berkeley he did not want Oppie lured away. He was sure of Cooksey in either event. Don, who was doing much to organize ideas and cyclotron data, had compiled a "Cook Book of Vacuum Chamber and Associated Parts," twenty-six copies of which had been sent to interested individuals in England, Russia, Japan, France, Denmark, and Canada as well as in the United States. Whatever California would do for it in the future, the Rad Lab undoubtedly had become the world center for nuclear investigation with high energies—a long leap in so short a time from the little glass device that had been reported to the National Academy in the fall of 1930.

Even Rutherford had been won over; Cockcroft wrote for drawings and advice for the construction of a cyclotron at Cavendish. It was not easy to consider the possibility of leaving the Rad Lab, it was so much a part of him; so much had happened, and was happening. Surely it was on the verge of even greater advances. It certainly would not be long before Cooksey and McMillan succeeded in drawing the beam outside the chamber; it was within an inch of the edge now, in February.

Everyone was busy with exciting experiments involving the cyclotron; the linear devices had been put aside, unable to compete. Already plans were being made to run it twenty-four hours a day to meet demands for experiment and to make the radioactive elements only it could provide for research anywhere. The excitement of nuclear exploration alone was enough to keep it and the men occupied; now there were the biological-medical possibilities to be tested, and Ernest insisted that time be allotted for isotope production. In February, John returned to the laboratory from Yale for a month of further investigation on the effects of neutrons on rodents. Dr. Stewart Harrison of Caltech, who had been studying cancer therapy with Lauritsen's high-voltage X-ray tube, visited Berkeley and assured Ernest that, if apparent neutron effects on malignant cells in rats proved valid, there was hope that many cancers could be retarded, perhaps eliminated. "This possibility clearly transcends anything else, and I certainly want to explore this possibility to the fullest extent," Ernest wrote to Poillon.

He was certain that Conant would realize the importance of such investigation. Rather than duplicate his Berkeley laboratory, Harvard might build a much more powerful cyclotron that could produce larger quantities of radioactive substances and neutron rays for the direct treatment of human cancer. He telegraphed Poillon about the possibility of a greater outlay by Harvard than had been discussed in the East and followed up with a lengthy letter. "What I have in mind is to build a large cyclotron immediately . . . for no matter how promising the animal experiments are, the actual efficiency of neutrons in the treatment of human cancer can only be established by actual clinical research, that is, direct irradiation of human cancer. I know that we can design and build a cyclotron powerful enough for this purpose."

Poillon wrote that Harvard could build a more powerful cyclotron and a laboratory large and complete enough to allow medical experiment, "as it is one of the few universities in the country who still have plenty of money." He suggested that Ernest draw up a comprehensive budget, "just but not extravagant," for Conant's use in arranging for funds. Confident in Harvard, Ernest again went to Leuschner, who was not optimistic about the construction of a new cyclotron and medical laboratory at the time, in Berkeley. Birge was brought into the discussions and promised to do what he could as soon as Sproul returned. But Ernest now felt that there was little hope for the kind of support at California that Harvard would give, and his hopes for a great program there often outweighed his fondness for California and his Radiation Laboratory. Molly became convinced that he had made up his mind to move.

Neither Leuschner nor Birge had conferred with Sproul when the formal offer from Harvard came on February 12. In a gracious letter, Conant asked Ernest to become Dean of the Graduate School of Engineering and Gordon McKay Professor of Applied Physics at a salary of $10,000 to $12,000 a year. He expressed his personal desire that Ernest join the Harvard faculty and build a really great school. He promised to find money outside the budget for initial equipment and annual continuance of Ernest's own research. Conant's letter was followed by one from Dean Birkhoff urging acceptance of the offer, promising to follow such acceptance with an immediate offer to Oppie of an associate professorship at $6,000, and to consider others as Ernest wished. Professor Bridgman telegraphed his hope that Ernest would join the Harvard faculty.

Ernest showed the letters to Birge, Leuschner, and Oppie. He wrote to Conant that he would soon again visit Harvard to discuss plans in greater detail. He wrote to Karl Compton and noted engineer Vannevar Bush at M.I.T. concerning the cooperation Conant had suggested existed between the institutions and asked to confer with them when he went East. Alarmed, Birge demanded to see Sproul at the earliest possible moment, stressing the fact that it was the first time since he had become chairman of the department that he had requested a private emergency meeting. Birge felt that time was running out, and though

Leuschner had expected to discuss it with the president first, and would do so later, the matter could not wait. Both men had hoped for conferences with Sproul before any formal offer arrived. Now Birge, who had known of Ernest's desire to remain at Berkeley, sensed that his attitude was one of doubt. He was the first to bring the "crisis" to Sproul's attention.

From enumerated notes, scrawled on cards, the meticulous Birge first stressed the "time available," pointing out that Leuschner had known of the offer from the day of Ernest's return and had been unable to advise the president because of his absence. Following his noted "omit myself from conversation," he dwelt on the standing of the physics department, attributing it to "Lawrence, the best experimental physicist in the country and one of the ablest in the world, and Oppenheimer, the best mathematical physicist in the country." He emphasized the fact that these two were surrounded by National Research Fellows and other very brilliant men; that because of the Rad Lab there had been a constant series of visitors to the department, including really distinguished scientists from several countries, so that, in addition to the approximately twenty men working in the Rad Lab, there had recently always been from six to twelve visiting scientists.

He stressed the magnitude of the Harvard offer and said that if Ernest left it would be the worst possible thing that could happen to the department; that Oppenheimer had twice refused positions at Harvard, but that he would follow Ernest, as would McMillan, and that the whole group would be lost to California which would drop from first to below twelfth place in physics. He outlined details of what had been offered Ernest by Harvard and Ernest's counterproposition to include medical experimentation. He told Sproul that he was sure that Harvard's distinction was of little or no interest to Ernest, and that the high salary was also secondary. He told how Professor W. L. Jepson had tried to have Ernest elected Faculty Research Lecturer, how in committee Jepson had spoken of Ernest's having the qualities of Newton, Galileo, and Pasteur combined and that he, Birge, had agreed. He reported that Poillon would support Ernest wherever he went, giving only a little to California if Ernest left, adding, "but will anyone be left here? *Only* Lawrence, in my opinion, is capable of solving experimental difficulties." He praised Ernest's character, mentioning his refusal to be relieved of his teaching load, and went on to offer further proof of the "*real* distinction of the department," comparing it to Caltech, which also wanted Oppenheimer full time, as well as McMillan, and concluding with the statement that "California is the only university at which men refuse offers from Harvard."

Birge was correct about Ernest's changing attitude. He had asked

Leuschner to discuss the situation further with Ernest while he saw Sproul. Leuschner's urging of reason and common sense in Ernest's desire for so much during a depression only antagonized Ernest. He said that he would go East within ten days to discuss the entire program with Conant. Leuschner insisted Ernest could never attain at Harvard what he could at California. Ernest consulted Oppie, who agreed it would be extremely difficult to raise money for a new cyclotron and laboratory at present in California, but was insistent that his friend could accomplish less at Harvard. He reminded him that California had already supported him far beyond reasonable expectation. Ernest maintained that he would find out how far Harvard would go; Conant had said he wanted a laboratory second to none.

Oppie said that in any case he would remain at Berkeley. He and Birge conferred the following evening. The only other department member aware of the offer, Oppenheimer thought Birge should handle the situation, since Ernest had felt antagonized after his last meeting with Leuschner. Birge said he was too good a friend to be able to do well with Ernest. Oppie insisted; all three men had told Ernest the same things, and it was a matter now of tact. Birge thought that perhaps Ernest now did not want the truth and resented their intrusion. Oppenheimer maintained that it was their duty to save their friend from himself, and to science to keep Ernest at California. The next morning Birge met with Ernest and Oppie; there was no more agreement than in the individual meetings. Ernest threatened to call Sproul himself for an appointment; Birge persuaded him to wait and to let him arrange it. Ernest left rather abruptly. Oppenheimer thought he was ashamed of his arguments, that, perhaps unconsciously, he was seeking a quarrel for justification. Birge termed it "Norwegian pigheadedness"—and wondered if Sproul might also be Norwegian.

He saw the president for the second time in three days and reported the change in Ernest's attitude. He reviewed the situation from the time of Ernest's return from Harvard more than a month before, since when, he said, it had fermented and gone to his head. "As real friends and the best friends he has, we have a duty to save Lawrence from himself," he paraphrased Oppie's statement. He told Sproul of the "remarkable sanity of Oppenheimer's views and the beauty of expression" in his arguments with Ernest. "Some think him an eccentric genius, but he's as sane as anyone on the campus. I never imagined such sane and penetrating remarks from anyone so young. One cheerful fact is that he will stay anyway, and try to keep McMillan." Birge warned that to have a quarrel would be fatal; there was already too much emotion involved and not sufficient "sane thinking," and that "he [Lawrence] will not jump at $7,000, contrary to Leuschner, and may try to insist on $8,000.

Even when offered $12,000 by Harvard, instead of immediately accepting, he began to impose additional conditions, which have now been met." Birge's notes for this meeting conclude "Is it improper to ask—when you will see Lawrence?" The president immediately phoned and asked Ernest to come to his office the following Monday, February 17.

President Sproul greeted Ernest with characteristic cordiality and in his booming voice made it clear that, personally, he wished to keep Ernest at California; that he was wholeheartedly behind the work of the Rad Lab; and that as long as he was president he would back Ernest and his work—"unless you go crazy," he said, with a great guffaw. He acknowledged that the Harvard offer was a very great honor, offered many opportunities, and that he could understand Ernest's inclination to accept it. California, however, had been generous to Ernest and his laboratory; as president that fact had been brought to his attention—not always too kindly—by less fortunate professors and department chairmen. Yet it was not impossible that further support could be found—inducements comparable to those at Harvard. "What," he concluded, "is your heart's desire?"

Ernest said that he fully appreciated all that the university and the president had done for his laboratory, but had it not been fruitful? With missionary zeal he unburdened his mind—and his heart—of the beliefs and hopes he had been turning over in his mind, beliefs and hopes that to him bore the stamp of reality. It was obvious that the work of the Radiation Laboratory was of utmost importance to physics, to science—perhaps to humanity. Recognition of this had motivated the unusual Harvard offer, nor was Harvard alone in this. Why were so many other forward-looking institutions, here and abroad, constructing cyclotrons? Why did notable scientists from everywhere journey to Berkeley and seek out the little gray house—shack, the boys called it—to see for themselves, as cyclotron men explored the unknown, the heretofore unassailable, the unseen, revealing undiscovered elements and isotopes of incalculable value to knowledge, to many disciplines, and of almost certain ultimate practical value.

No one could determine the potential of so new a field, but it seemed almost limitless; Ernest personally believed that in not too many years the energy locked in the atom might become a source of power literally as limitless as the oceans. Science, in the Radiation Laboratory, was not limited to a single discipline; chemists, biochemists, biologists, and medical men were working with physicists in an interplay unique in academic history. That laboratory must continue and grow, and he as director must have more time in it than now; he had to be too often away raising funds to keep it on the edge of the wide areas of discovery it had opened up with its power—power that existed nowhere else in the world. Furthermore, even at twenty-four hours a day, the present cyclotron could not begin to do half that which was requested. A small permanent staff was needed, particularly an assistant to supervise and coordinate laboratory activities, to guide and help students and associates, and to direct the work of men allotted from the government sponsored Works Progress Administration. Furthermore, he could not, in all conscience, neglect what seemed paramount: the medical possibilities of direct therapy with neutron beams and the production of, and experiment with, radioactive isotopes. His "heart's desire," therefore, included an entirely new laboratory with a larger cyclotron to be used chiefly in medical-biological research and experimental treatment of such scourges of mankind as cancer. Of course this called for a continuing budget to support that work and another small staff. This should include a doctor at the laboratory and a physicist for liaison with the medical school, such as was now carried on by Aebersold on a scholarship. These were his primary concerns, though he could not completely disregard salary.

Sproul betrayed no evidence that he considered these rather extravagant proposals unusual during a period of continuing depression. He asked Ernest to prepare a complete budget as soon as possible. He would then undertake to determine what could be done at California. In less than three days Ernest left an estimated budget at the president's office. Chief among the items listed was $25,000 for a new cyclotron magnet of approximately 200 tons, and $40,000 a year for the support of medical work with it. He did not suggest building costs but did estimate space requirements for animals, chemists, and direct human therapy, in addition to that required for the huge cyclotron.

He was summoned again to the president's office on the following day. Sproul boomed out that what Ernest wanted was a pretty large order. Ernest countered that he felt certain the importance of such a development would be appreciated at Harvard, and he requested permission to go East at once to discuss it with Conant. Sproul said that he, too, realized the importance of both physical and medical aspects of Ernest's program, and that there was no question that, as it had in the past, it would add prestige to the university. He asked Ernest to postpone for a week or two his trip to the East, to enable Sproul to discuss possibilities with various friends of the university. He said that he was concerned chiefly about the annual expenses involved, since the regular budget could not be expected to include so large an extra burden. Ernest agreed to delay further discussions with Conant, adding that he was very happy at California, and that any thought of leaving was motivated solely by his determination to push both the physical and medical aspects of his work to the fullest extent; neither Harvard nor any other institution would interest him unless it were clearly shown that opportunities far exceeding those at Berkeley were available. He said again that he appreciated the efforts of the administration to back his laboratory from its inception and would regret leaving it in any case.

He returned to the lab from Sproul's office, buoyed with optimism: perhaps he could remain, and under optimum conditions. Molly knew at once, when he came home for dinner, that if his indecision were not resolved, it was very nearly so. His solicitousness for her she first interpreted as evidence that he had chosen as she would not have wished. He did not stress his optimistic opinion of his discussion with Sproul, but his pleasure that his plans had not been peremptorily rejected, as he had feared. Molly continued to avoid any effort to influence his decision.

Birge and Oppie were less restrained next morning. The chairman, convinced that Ernest was unsuited to a deanship that would rob him of laboratory time even more than his fund-raising efforts had, tried to impress that fact tactfully. Actually the mere title held little interest for Ernest. Oppie, with whom Ernest again discussed pros and cons, remained convinced that Ernest could never develop his ideas as well at Harvard as at California. Ernest, who considered his friend most naïve in everything but physics, paid little heed to Oppie's comments, however eloquent, except those that pertained to science. What did Oppie know about administration, budgets, or dealing with people? Oppie who had never voted, who never read the news, and whose interests, except for science, were art, languages, philosophy, and literature! He was somewhat surprised, however, when Oppie refused to consider also going to Harvard if Ernest accepted the offer. Though he refrained from discussion of the matter with others in Berkeley, he did ask Cooksey, as if in jest, if he were too loyal to Yale, and too attached to Berkeley, to join him if he went to Harvard. Don, refusing to take it seriously, said, "Sure! I'll go." In the continuing, frequent communication with Poillon, Ernest now mentioned the "burden of added administrative duties" a deanship would entail, and the delays that would be involved in construction of a new laboratory in the East, during which his exciting research must be suspended.

Two days later he was again summoned to the president's office. Sproul announced that the Radiation Laboratory would receive official status as an independent entity within the physics department, as recommended by Professor Birge. In addition to his present title of professor of physics, Ernest would be named director of the Radiation Laboratory. Provision would be made for a full-time assistant director, a secretary, and a machinist. Twenty thousand dollars a year would be included annually in the university budget for laboratory work. As for a new laboratory and cyclotron for medical and biological research, Sproul was uncertain but optimistic. He asked for ten more days within which time Regent Crocker would return from Palm Springs to discuss the matter.

Over the weekend Ernest alternated, often vocally to poor Molly, between excitement over prospects at California and wonder whether, even with delays, his work might not progress more rapidly at Harvard. But such indecision, so foreign to him, was almost intolerable; immediately after lunch on Monday, without further word from Sproul, or discussion with anyone, he wrote to President Conant declining his generous offer. He expressed gratitude for the honor of Conant's confidence but said he felt he could best serve science and, hopefully, mankind by remaining at California, since the administration had established the Radiation Laboratory as a permanent university activity with generous and continuing support. When he showed a copy of the letter to Molly that evening, her tears of joy amazed him; an important factor of his indecision had been her love of New England and her supposed dislike of Berkeley. It was Molly's turn to be amazed; had he not known that she had overcome, long ago, that early dislike and homesickness? How could he not have perceived her consternation that he might accept the Harvard position?

Sproul boomed his delight over the phone. Oppie gently pressed his friend's hand in congratulation. Pleased, Birge divulged some of the news in a memorandum to department members (asking that it be kept confidential until announced by the university administration and that he *not* be asked for details). He gave no hint of the "crisis" now resolved and promised details as they were worked out. Even Harvard's Conant wrote that Ernest was probably correct in not delaying the rapid course of events and discoveries at his present laboratory by moving, and asked Ernest to recommend another to initiate a similar program at Harvard.

On Sunday following the decision, Don Cooksey, at work in the Rad Lab, was moved near tears when Ernest asked him to become assistant director with salary, when the new status of the Radiation Laboratory became official. Don mumbled his delight and said something about facilitating matters by continuing to serve without salary. "You'll get a salary, and you'll earn it!" said Ernest. To Don, having believed in Ernest from the day just over a decade before when he had come, wet of clothing, and with his South Dakota naïveté, into Yale's Sloane Laboratory, "it was the highlight of my life."

When the beautiful violet-colored beam streaked from the chamber for twenty-eight centimeters, a few days later, it was as much for his new position as for successful beam extraction that Don passed cigars to excited cyclotroneers and visitors. Two days later, March 28, 1936, 11,-

ooo,ooo-volt alpha particles were produced—one of the great thrills of a thrilling period. Only the rarest of known natural alpha particles approached such energy. Reported with this at the April meetings in Washington of the National Academy and the Physical Society was the first transmutation of an element into gold by Ernest and James Cork of Michigan. Though not from a base metal—the centuries old dream of alchemists—but from platinum, it was a culmination of sorts, though no one thought there was cause for concern in financial circles. It was the fact that it could be done that was exciting, as was the first artificial production of naturally radioactive nuclei from Livingood's bombardment of bismuth with deuterons, making radium E, which naturally decayed into radium F (polonium)—proving that an artificially produced nucleus could produce one that also occurs in nature. Also, this was the highest element in the periodic table thus far transmuted.

Ernest was besieged, at these meetings, by eager questioners; there was no longer a preponderance of scoffers. Requests to spend time in the laboratory were outnumbered only by requests to irradiate various items with cylotron beams, or with neutron radiation. Not all could be accepted, but the lab was so busy that summer it seemed littered with containers of various substances, cages of wasps from Pennsylvania and mice from Bar Harbor, Maine; ledges around the cyclotron were so crowded that glass containers often got knocked off and broken. There were visitors enough to hold a convention, the busy cyclotroneers thought. Indeed, a convention would have had an international flavor, with the presence of Cockcroft from Cambridge, Maurice Nahmias of the College de France, Yasaki and Ryokichi Sagane from Japan, all planning to build cyclotrons; another, Emilio Segrè of Palermo, who had worked with Fermi, was astounded that the cyclotron really worked consistently, and, when he left, not only took radioactive substances with him but also asked that more be sent to him in Italy from time to time. Ernest was pleased by the visit of Meghnad Saha of India, whose ionization equation had so impressed him as a student, and with whom he and Beams had had such enjoyable times in Copenhagen and Berlin. And there was tremendous delight in the visit of Beams, himself, and his wife, Maxine. Sagane stayed at the laboratory nearly two years, and Nahmias, Joliot's assistant, for one.

Regents, too, were more and more curious about the "phenomenon" on their campus at Berkeley. John Francis Neylan wondered about "the expensive tastes, or at least demands, of this Professor Lawrence," and decided to investigate: "I found out where his laboratory was. It was like a secondhand tin shop—a dinky little place over there on the campus, just a cul-de-sac. That's where he had his little old cyclotron, which was insulated, incidentally, with five-gallon gasoline tins filled with water—that was the insulation wall of the cyclotron. I went in there. I met him. Then I was introduced to Dr. So-and-So from Cornell, and Dr. So-and-So from Japan, and Dr. So-and-So from this place and that place—and I want to tell you I was flabbergasted. There weren't two in the place that had to shave twice a week; it was just a bunch of children! They were making something, I've forgotten what it was. A fellow was packing some tin and another fellow was packing some tubing. That day Ernest got talking, explaining to me the principle of the cyclotron. And of course, after he got started, after the first minute and a half, he was so far out beyond me I didn't know where he was going. His face lighted up—he was lost in this subject. I was tremendously impressed—attracted to him.

"I talked to Mr. [Garrett W.] McEnerney, one of the old, old-time regents, and one of the great regents, too. I was telling him about Ernest. So the next time, he and I went over to the laboratory together. McEnerney was well along in years—was the head of our bar here in the West, was quite a figure. So he had a wonderful talk with Ernest and when we walked out he said, 'How much of that did you follow?' I said, 'He lost me first time around the track.' We bumped into Gilbert Lewis, who was one of the great chemists at the time, and Mr. McEnerney said, 'Dr. Lewis, when will the work of this young man in here, this rather remarkable youngster, have any value, have any practical effect on life?' And Lewis said, 'Oh, I don't know. Maybe fifty, seventy-five years. Human beings have so many things now they don't know how to use. Why give them some more? I'd estimate, optimistically, fifty years.'

"Ernest himself thought it was John who was the greatest, who would contribute most. First time I ever met John was on Park Avenue in New York. It was evening, and I met them and he introduced me to John. Always, John was the great world figure. And Ernest was so natural about it. There was nothing forced, nothing artificial—he believed it. He believed John was greater than himself . . . the hope of the earth. It was always did I hear about John? Did I hear about John? Everything in relation to John. You know—for a fellow with his brain and his mind he was naïve, I think, in a worldly sense. . . . He would lean on me in some things because he figured I had seen the seamy side of life. And he knew I had great affection for him."

Ernest was away much of the summer. In June, with Molly and Eric, he went to South Dakota to receive an honorary degree. Dean Akeley, who had told the local Phi Beta Kappa chapter that he would disown them if they were not the first to honor Ernest, certain to become a Nobel Prize winner, was pleased that Ernest's first honorary degree was to be conferred by his alma mater. The opening words of Ernest's address formed a genuine and moving tribute to Akeley whose inspiration was initially responsible for Ernest's opportunity to explore the universe of the atom. The time would come, he prophesied, when scientists would be able to transform the mass of matter in something no larger than a piece of chalk into energy sufficient to power all the electric plants of South Dakota for a century. "The commercial transformation of matter to energy is not yet in sight, but we are sure that someday it will be possible." Incredible forecast from South Dakota's illustrious son. The return for honor would have been a happy time for all had not small Eric been ill. His dysentery worried parents and grandparents, and presented problems for Molly who felt none too well herself, with the child to come. Eric recovered completely at Haycock Point where Ernest tried to relax between trips to New York.

He left his little family with the Blumers when he departed for the Ann Arbor Symposium of Nuclear Physics, stopping en route at Rochester to find Lee DuBridge and Sid Barnes happy and excited over the initial performance of their cyclotron. Ernest was skeptical, at Michigan, about Fermi's suggestion that his group at the University of Rome had produced an element beyond uranium by neutron bombardment. Discussion of that was one of the many of interest, but the highlight of the conference was the completion and turning on of the Michigan cyclotron. There was no evidence of an effective bombarding beam, at first. Ernest pitched in to help Bob Thornton, old Radiation Laboratory colleague, and James Cork, late Rad Lab visitor. Properly placed shims, to compensate for warped D's, and slightly off parallel magnet pole faces, soon enabled it to deliver several microamperes of about 5,000,000 volts. Ernest was delighted that professors of the medical school were interested in medical-biological applications, particularly the eminent radiologist, Dr. Fred Hodges, and an equally noted cardiologist, Dr. Frank Wilson.

Hodges drove Ernest to Wilson's beautiful lake lodge for the Fourth of July weekend where he was given tattered slacks for sailing and fishing. It was a relaxed time, with good food and drink—and discourse hard to terminate even at three in the morning. Ernest took half a page in the Wilson guestbook, sketched a cyclotron on the left, an X-ray tube on the right, and between them—receiving radiation from each—an irregular lump to represent a tumor. A large question mark indicated that, as in the much discussed current presidential campaign, the winner of neutron versus X ray for therapy had yet to be decided. He asked Hodges for the most impressive name of a malignant tumor and above his lump wrote the twenty-four-letter jawbreaker "amelanoticmelanoblastoma," which Hodges said was not only impressive as a name but symbolized a particularly vicious growth. Above all, across the top of the page, Ernest printed in large letters "U.C. 1931—U.M. 1936." His signature at the bottom was preceded by a sketch of a nearly full drinking glass, and followed by the outline of a fish.

On his return to Berkeley, Ernest learned that nothing more definite had been determined toward a new cyclotron and laboratory than before he had left. Regent Crocker, still ill, would be unable to see Sproul for several more weeks. Ernest had not talked with the president since a fortuitous meeting on a transcontinental train in April when he had discovered that they were fellow passengers. He thought that he had impressed upon the president at that time the importance of phenomena to be discovered in the region above 30,000,000 volts that could in no sense be predicted from present knowledge acquired in the lower energy range, and that the projected larger cyclotron would certainly make some of this accessible. He emphasized again the likelihood of beneficial cyclotron therapy for cancer and the production of greater quantities of radioactive isotopes now so much in demand and only possible from a cyclotron. Sproul had remarked that there was criticism, in certain medical circles, of interference by medically unqualified physicists; that false hopes were raised by press reports of beneficial thereapeutic effects as yet untried. Ernest replied that he was aware of it. Sensational reports were unfortunate, but abuse must not prevent legitimate experiment; he had been disturbed before this by lurid accounts of his "atom smasher," and "death rays." There certainly would be much criticism as time went on, but legitimate criticism was a very healthy thing which he personally would always welcome. Sproul thought that the proper spirit and said he had heard nothing which in any way diminished his own faith in the project or lessened his efforts to make it a reality. Crocker, he said, had been interested enough to promise "about $60,000, possibly more" for the new laboratory. Ernest mentioned that his own fund-raising efforts in New York had so far brought a Chemical Foundation pledge of $68,000 for the cyclotron itself. He hoped, and expected, other pledges, perhaps from the Rockefeller Foundation and the National Advisory Cancer Council. The latter's board member, Dr. James Murphy, visited Ernest and suggested that the projected laboratory become a National Cancer Research Laboratory, which at first seemed advisable to Ernest. He changed his mind, however, when John pointed out that the medical field opened by the cyclotron should not be limited in scope to cancer— that the broad field of medicine and biology was more in keeping with his ideals.

He had discussed support with the foundations again during the summer, discussions based on the assumption that the new laboratory would be constructed. Yet months had passed since his conversations with Sproul on the train, without further word. Perhaps, he thought impatiently, it would have been simpler at Harvard. Though the Radiation Laboratory had become, as promised, an official entity on July 1, and experimentation had continued apace—more than a dozen papers from the laboratory were published in scientific journals in 1936, and radioactive salt had been furnished the medical school for Stone's and Hamilton's investigations—there was neither room nor equipment to proceed as planned. It was arranged with Yale that John spend two periods, totaling four months a year, at the lab, with support from the Macy and Markle foundations. He was soon to arrive, with colonies of cancerous mice for neutron radiation, at the already overtaxed laboratory. Would promising activities be slowed, or even stalled, because of the delay? At best, the new lab could not become a functioning operation in much under two years! Ernest demanded an immediate conference with Sproul.

The president had been unable, still, to see Mr. Crocker. He assuaged Ernest's impatience with positive assurance that, one way or another, the laboratory building would be provided without much more delay. He told Ernest to proceed with plans as though the building were a certainty.

Designs were already under way for enlargement of the diameter of the cyclotron magnet pole faces and chamber by ten inches, increased radio-frequency power, greater provision for cooling, and the incorporation of such improvements as Snell's vacuum-gated target chamber to permit rapid change of targets without vacuum loss; an evacuated tube, dubbed a snout, was designed to carry the beam away from and free of magnetic and other forces of the cyclotron mass. Dean Lewis facetiously said that he would have the Radiation Laboratory declared a public nuisance; that even at its present size, the cyclotron produced such potent radiation that it was impossible to carry on certain experiments in the chemistry laboratory three hundred feet away. Visiting Dr. Alvarez, whose son Luis joined the lab that summer, exclaimed, "Ernest, your baby has become a monster!" There was nothing facetious about the necessity for caution as the current was increased. Ernest asked Don to get more of Lauritsen's fountain pen electroscopes and to see that men wore them and were checked on exposures. John recalled, in warning, the many deaths and serious injuries caused by X-ray exposure in early experimentation, because its power was unknown or unheeded. Now no one knew how disastrous neutron overexposure might be for humans, but it had been proved that it was lethal for rodents, and that plants had been rendered sterile. There was a resurgence of sterilization jokes, but there was added caution, too—when the cyclotron was on. After the birth of the second Lawrence child, some wag suggested that in caution, as in everything else, the Maestro had set a good example.

Ernest had finished breakfast on September 17, 1936, and was about to rush off to the laboratory when Molly decided he had better rush her to the hospital. Ernest lost no time getting her there, discussing during the somewhat hectic drive what the baby should be named if another boy was born. Molly, certain that with her background the odds were decidedly against having two boys in succession, thought they could ignore speculation; they had already selected Margaret, in case Eric had been a girl, and they saw no reason to change, though Molly hoped she would not be called "Maggie." Arriving at the hospital, Ernest said, "Let's name her Margaret and *call* her that."

So much time elapsed between arrival at the hospital and arrival of the child that Ernest became bored; he was already irritated that he had been denied admittance to the delivery room. After a couple of hours of thinking about all he could be doing, he approached the room. "When is this going to happen anyway?" he demanded accusingly of the doctor who, according to Molly, was equally bored at the delay. The doctor shrugged and Ernest resumed his pacing. This was one thing he could do nothing to hasten. It never occurred to him that he might be worried, but he was conscious of relief when it was over and Molly and baby were pronounced "fine." The healthy infant was a girl; she *was* named Margaret Bradley.

She might have been considered a good omen; shortly after her arrival, Regent Crocker agreed to provide funds for the new laboratory building, to be named after him. Architects were appointed early in October and a site adjacent to the Radiation Laboratory approved. Ernest had a complete set of plans to show to interested parties when he crossed the country again early in December, to address the Radiological Society of America, meeting in Cincinnati. Further discussions at various foundations resulted in sufficient optimism to embolden him to increase, slightly, the size of the projected cyclotron for the Crocker Laboratory. Though Cooksey was deeply involved with the enlargement of the present cyclotron to a 37-inch diameter, Ernest asked him to begin thinking about the new 60-inch cyclotron. He suggested that construction of the 37-inch chamber and D's be hurried so that modifications could be tested before incorporation in the 60-inch, on the design of which McMillan was busy and which was sometimes referred to by cyclotroneers as the "Crocker Cracker." Don had little time for a vacation during the holidays when many of the others went off to Death Valley or to ski in the Sierras—nor did Ernest, whose parents came for Christmas and to see the new grandchild.

CHAPTER X

The Club

[1930's]

Official designation of the Radiation Laboratory as an independent activity within the physics department caused little celebration in the laboratory; the cyclotroneers had, perhaps without fully realizing it, considered themselves and the Rad Lab rather independent long before the July 1, 1936, date. Teaching duties and graduate studies were important and, hopefully, vital, but the lab was a special world, apart from all other university activities—a fraternity, club, lodge, whatever—to the few who belonged it was elite. It was a common, everyday door key each member carried, but, had anyone had time or inclination to think of such things, the key would have symbolized more than the means of entering an old, wooden building, which the founder and Grand Master had snatched from demolition—for a distinguished future of nearly thirty years. The independence and drive of the Maestro infected the "privileged" participants whether they were professors, fellows, or graduate students. Visitors permitted within the noisy, dirty sanctum came away marveling almost as much over the spirit and enthusiasm of the members as over the cyclotron. Certainly the laboratory operation and activity were unique, in the annals of academic institutions, for spirit and collaborative efforts. Director and assistants labored together toward common goals. Wilfrid Mann, a Commonwealth Fellow at the Lab, thought "friends" a better term than "assistants" for Ernest's men, and years later, in 1958, President Clark Kerr, in welcoming the National Academy to the university, said, "We use the word 'with' because it implies the kind of collaboration which Ernest Lawrence inspired and expected from his associates. They worked with him, not for him, and they were proud to work with him."

Arthur Compton thought this "unique and marvelous teamwork," and the fostering in the Rad Lab of ideas that spread throughout the country, and, indeed, throughout the world, as great and generative an achievement as the invention of the cyclotron itself. There had been scientific teams before in German chemistry laboratories, but those were wholly organized around and for one man, the Herr Professor. Ernest would permit none of the "this is my field, keep out of it" attitude, sometimes characteristic of research men. Intended for the proprietorially inclined, whether of his group or others, were his constant reminders "there is enough research for everyone," and "if one advances everyone else comes up." This attitude had been traditional with Rad Lab physicists from the first, but as men of other disciplines came in, or were associated with the work, Ernest had to warn again that people in his lab were not competing with each other, but that each was trying to learn something that would benefit all. Nor would he consider his laboratory as competing with another, except in friendliest fashion, but as a guide, helping and urging on others in the exploration of areas opened by the cyclotron. His insistence that his implements and the knowledge gained through their use be available to all was a thing of wonder. Blueprints, pictures, and information were mailed to universities from Russia to Japan and India. Requests for permission to build cyclotrons were answered with delight and the offer of all possible assistance.

If laboratory personnel revealed an air of independence, there were others on the campus, even within the physics department, to whom the attitude was somewhat overbearing. It was not uncommon to hear it said that cyclotron men thought the Rad Lab the center of the universe, and in certain areas it was just that. It is a credit to Birge that there was little open conflict in his department, though envy was certainly not unknown. Had Ernest and Birge not had respect for each other, the situation might have become impossible: salary differences; Ernest's rapid advancement against the usual, slow climb to professorship; benefits bestowed on the Rad Lab—all made comparisons inevitable.

Birge certainly was as aware as President Sproul of tensions. Indeed, he often said the situation was a case of "the tail wagging the dog," and he once told an important administrator who consulted him about a cyclotron for his southern university, "It all depends upon whether you wish a university with a cyclotron, or a cyclotron with a university attached." He often said, "I don't know what goes on in the Radiation Laboratory." In retrospect, Birge thinks that "Ernest got absolutely everything he wanted. There was always the demand for more space, more promotions for his people, and more money. But what he did was of a completely different order of magnitude from anything else, and had to be so considered." Then, remembering difficulties, Birge added,

"They kept breaking every rule in the department. Rad Lab people would clean out the stock room at night. Naturally others in the department resented this; at least they wanted to know what they took, and so on, so they could keep stock. The attitude, often, even among the students, was that what they were doing was important and the rest was not." Nevertheless the support of Raymond T. Birge, for whom research was less interesting, personally, than the teaching he loved, was an important factor in the development of the Radiation Laboratory. And he credits Sproul as a very important factor: "No other president would have put up with it—Northwestern, Harvard, all the crises—certainly not his predecessor."

The appointment of Donald Cooksey as assistant director marked the beginning of more systematic organization in the laboratory, since it provided relief from concern for Ernest when he must be absent, and perhaps for Birge, too. Don, who had respect for order and the care of tools, could appreciate the need to know the status of a supply room, and the whereabouts and condition of tools and equipment. But Don was far more to the laboratory and its people than overseer and watchdog. Much of the "haywire" accessory equipment of the cyclotron was redesigned under his supervision and with his help, as were the two last 27½-inch vacuum chambers, or "cans," and the hollow D electrodes within them that whirled protons, deuterons, or alpha particles to such incredible speeds. He redesigned all for the 37-inch enlarged magnet pole faces, D's and ton and a half cast bronze vacuum chamber, which brought the old Federal Telegraph magnet cyclotron to its maximum potential. His new yellow Packard, dubbed "The Creamliner," even served as anchor when the new chamber was block and tackled into the lab on July 8, 1937.

Don's concern for care of tools became legendary; one of the great jokes on him concerned his once leaving an automatic lathe to do something else, until the cutting tool gouged into the chuck—to the amusement of those who had known his low tolerance for carelessness. When errors are unusual, they are remembered, as is the time when Don was excused from a seminar to repair a leak in order to get the cyclotron going again quickly—a dirty job! When the seminar was over, the leak, which had been minute, had become a large hole.

Don may have been required to accept a salary, and there is no question that he earned it, but the yearly balance, had anyone checked, would have been in the laboratory's favor. "Anonymous contributions" to the research fund for needed machine shop equipment, to provide an honorarium for a deserving visitor who otherwise could not have come, or to enlarge the meager stipend of a junior fellow, somehow appeared at the right times. Only Rebekah Young, the physics department secretary, and one or two in the president's office knew that the checks were signed by Cooksey. What *was* known and appreciated by everyone were his large contributions to morale. His encouragement, help, and humor were ever present. The guestbook at the Cooksey Trinity River establishment reads like a roster of laboratory personnel and visitors through the years, and his correspondence with them attests the affection borne him.

In addition to Assistant Director Cooksey, Ernest's staff for 1936–1937 included six Fellows, eight research associates, eight junior research associates, a technical associate, a mechanic, and a secretary—in expanded offices on the third floor of Le Conte Hall. On the staff were men from England, Canada, and Italy. One Rad Lab graduate student held a scholarship for radiation studies at the university hospital and served as liaison between laboratory and medical school. The technical associate, Charles Litton, was available for help on tube problems, at the lab or at his then small company in Redwood City. Some had to attend classes as students or teachers—Ed McMillan, the first of the group to be appointed to the university faculty, managed to put in the equivalent of a working day, or more, in addition to teaching; the rest of the staff put in full and overtime. Because of the many hours and hard work, cyclotroneers might even agree at times to the slave driver accusations, but only at rare moments. But the driving force was example and expectation. Certainly Ernest appreciated hard work, extra hours. He himself spent what time he could in the laboratory and never got over the custom of dropping in at odd hours of the night to see how things were going. This was correctly interpreted, and appreciated, as interest. If for some reason he was at home, usually only because of illness and doctor's orders, guests, or personal business matters—Molly had taken over care of their checking account and bills shortly after Eric's birth—he need only tune his radio to the cyclotron frequency to know that it was running. If it were not, he would telephone and inquire, "Something wrong, having coffee, or were you out for a beer?"

It was a rare night when no one could be found at the lab. Everyone worked at night sometimes; but for several, night hours were almost as habitual as those of the day. Stan Van Voorhis, shy, uncommunicative, and solitary, whom Ernest considered an electronics shark, Philip Abelson, who had done major work in chemistry as well as physics, and Bob Wilson were among those who worked most weekends, too. Wilson found his work so interesting that he once continued to work too many extra hours—refusing to admit even to himself that he was ill until he collapsed. He was scolded by Ernest for not taking care of himself and

rushed to the hospital, where it was decided that he had been entertaining a ruptured appendix for several days. After recovery, he was as
industrious as before.

Stan Livingston tells how McMillan, who became one of the major
thinkers in planning and designing research experiments, asked to join
Ernest's group after discovering that his exploration of a molecular
beam problem had been accomplished by another, elsewhere. "Ernest
said, 'Sure, come to the lab and start work.' Ed was around for a few
days discussing things with us, not working particularly hard on any major job, but Ernest didn't seem to know he was around. I said, 'I suggest
you get here early in the morning. Try getting here at eight and get
busy doing something, if it's just sweeping the floor. Just show some activity. Ernest will like that.' Although he was not the type of person that
liked to get up, he did start coming early. This is just an example of the
situation there. Ernest was very much for, and would support strongly,
the people that showed hard work. In a very short while Ed caught on,
though his contributions were not in terms of early hours, but good
brainwork. Wasn't long before he was recognized as an important member of the team [who often worked all night]. For most of us it was the
general feeling of urgency in the lab, tremendously exciting, the whole
atmosphere made it hard to want to leave the place, and so much was
happening."

Ernest expected as much from the unsalaried who had asked to join
the lab as from everyone else. The second weekend that Livingood was
in Berkeley, Dave Sloan took him to Yosemite Park. On Monday morning Ernest told Livingood that he expected as much from him, salary or
not, as from anyone else. "Look," he recalls Ernest saying, "you came
here to work." Yet a Saturday or two later, Ernest and Molly drove him
to Carmel for the weekend, and they often took three or four men to
San Francisco for dinner. "They were very pleasant to bachelors, took
care of us," Livingood said. "It finally got to the point, after a couple of
years, where he could pay me something. He arranged some sort of title
so I could live at the Faculty Club. I asked him once if he thought it
worthwhile my staying. He said, 'Do you enjoy what you're doing?' I
said, 'Yes.' He said, 'Then stay!' " Good men worked at the lab for years
without pay, graduate students worked for degrees, and many who had
doctorates accepted bare subsistence wages. The rewards, in no case,
were measured in monetary terms, and pay, or lack of it, had no significance in status.

There was one well-liked non-physicist volunteer. Commander Telesio
Lucci, retired Italian naval officer and diplomat, had been on campus
assisting another professor for more than a year when the atmosphere
and activity of the Rad Lab became irresistible, and he asked to be al-

lowed to help as he could. Reasonably well off, he wanted no more than the opportunity to share in the excitement. He was "a most obliging pair of hands, if told what to do," and a popular member of the group. Lucci's stories of life in Italy, before his marriage to an American, were highly entertaining. Henderson actually learned a little Italian from him. Lucci had no use for the Italy of Mussolini; mention of the name made him livid with rage; his brother had been castrated by Fascists for political reasons. He was often asked to close the knife switch to start the cyclotron, which he was proud to do, and which amused others. Lucci gingerly approached and very gently closed the switch, certain that such care would prevent too sudden application of too much power, and the ensuing sparking, crash, and blowing out of lights—too often also on campus and nearby sections of Berkeley—that sometimes occurred. His willing attitude and helpfulness were rewarded by affection and acknowledged by mention of his assistance in published papers.

The first professional engineer, redheaded Berkeley native William Brobeck, quit his job with an engineering firm in Emeryville, California, in 1937, to seek a place in the Radiation Laboratory. Cooksey told him he would have to ask Ernest, who was away, but as there was no money available for salary, there was not much chance. Brobeck ignored the latter comments; could he look around? Don nodded. He was impressed by Brobeck's later questions and gave him permission to wait around the laboratory for Ernest's return. Brobeck brought thermometers with him the next day and hung them in various places around the magnet and on pipes. After a few hours of observation, he showed Cooksey sketches detailing how the magnet could be cooled very much better with certain changes in the oil flow. Before Ernest returned, Brobeck quietly and modestly pointed out other inefficiencies from an engineering point of view.

When the engineer finally accosted the professor, as he rushed from the lab, and fell in with his rapid gait, they did not stop walking; they discussed qualifications and ideas until Brobeck had permission to join the team. His suggested changes in the oil cooling system were effected, which necessitated, among other things, cutting slots in the side of the coil tank with hacksaws—and Brobeck was further impressed when Ernest sawed as much steel as anyone else. Brobeck had already decided that physicists never walked; one of his first observations was that after bombardments they ran from the cyclotron as if it might momentarily explode. The hurry, he learned, was to measure isotopes, whose half-lives might be extremely short. Even the Monday night Journal Club meetings impressed him: lab people standing around easily, anyone allowed to speak up—"even the janitor would have been listened to if he'd had something to offer." Ernest's authority was never questioned, but all relationships were very democratic, never a hint of intellectual snobbery.

Students, too, thought those Journal Club meetings one of Ernest's most important contributions. Milton White initiated the same idea at Princeton and emulated there the informality upon which Ernest insisted and which White considered its essence. A room with no fixed chairs, where people could stand or move about, encouraged to discuss any problem without previous preparation. It kept participants alert and stimulated a mental activity that was carried back to the laboratory. Philip Abelson remembers that stimulation and recalls, still with wonderment, how, in many discussions, some highly intellectual scientist, with fine reason and subtlety, would outdebate Ernest who, in spite of it, was usually correct. "Oppie could always outargue him, but logic or not, Ernest was usually right." Abelson thinks much of Ernest's strength was in his excellent intuition, though he could not always express well what he knew to be true.

When Fermi's publication on radiation by neutrons came to his attention, Ernest took it to Abelson, who had majored in chemistry. "I'm told that you know something about them. Now there is something wrong in this work of Fermi and his co-workers. You ought to have a look at it." Abelson did; Fermi's claim to have found transuranium elements (elements beyond uranium 92, long thought the heaviest) from neutron bombardment of uranium was the misinterpreted result of nuclear fission! At the time, Abelson was able only to establish that Fermi had not found element 93.

This intuition of Ernest's, so remarkable for getting at the heart of problems, and so formidable against speculation and greater erudition, in the words of Lee DuBridge, "was so good, and so often right, that finally no one wanted to go against him." In 1937 Hans Bethe, a highly respected theoretician, considered it ridiculous to build cyclotrons larger than the 27½-inch of the Rad Lab. It would be impossible, he wrote Ernest, to go above 8,000,000-volt deuterons because of the mass-speed relation of relativity, because mass increases with velocity, the heavier particles would fall out of step. Bethe also sent an article to the *Physical Review*, stating that the practical limit in cyclotrons for this reason had been reached. Ernest replied to Bethe, using a favorite old cliché, "There are various ways of skinning a cat," and asserting that relativity factors can be taken care of and that the upper limit was not yet in sight. Bethe and his colleague, M. E. Rose enlarged their limits, proving logically that increase of speed and consequent increase of mass must limit cyclotron energy. By the time the limitation was published, the cyclotron had gone beyond it. In letters to DuBridge and others, Ernest largely credited Wilson and McMillan for improved focusing conditions that, he wrote "removed any limitations on energy to some unknown point. I'm awfully glad that Bethe and Rose are working on the theory of the cyclotron, as it is not a simple problem and the more people who think about it the better." Bethe's conclusions were, of course, theoretically correct, but he failed to consider that ingenuity can devise means to offset them. Ernest's respect for theory, without acceptance of it as final, here as always was important; had he bowed to it, cyclotron progress would have been greatly retarded. He thought no theoretical idea would hold up long without experimental evidence. Biologist Hardin Jones remembers his saying, "It never does much good to find out why you can't; put the effort into what you can do." He had in this respect much in common with Lord Rutherford, who was often rather caustic in indicating the superiority of the experimental way.

Ernest and Lord Rutherford carried on a lively correspondence after Solvay, and increasingly so after Rutherford changed his mind and decided the cyclotron had merit after all. Ernest prevailed upon President Sproul to invite the great man to give a March Charter Day address and was in turn asked to determine, by informal invitation, if Rutherford could accept for 1938 or the following year. The last letter Ernest received from Rutherford regretted his inability to accept the first date as he was committed to preside over a meeting in India early in 1938, and could not at present be certain about the following year. He expressed appreciation for the invitation, said he would like the pleasure of visiting California again, "and in particular of seeing something of the work in your laboratory."

Shortly after Ernest answered Rutherford's letter, expressing disappointment that he would be unable to come in 1938 and refusing to rule out the possibility of a visit the following year, Lord Rutherford died, in October, 1937. A towering figure in science, this country boy from New Zealand long had been dominant in physics. With Niels Bohr he could be credited with initiating the fruitful exploration of the interior of the atom.

Bohr visited the laboratory for a month in March, 1937, when he gave the Hitchcock Lectures. Molly and Ernest entertained the staff and wives one Sunday to meet him and Mrs. Bohr. Fermi was there much of the summer, along with numerous other visitors. Ernest always tried to see that his people had the chance to meet such notables other than in the laboratory, and that wives could share in the experience. To a certain extent, with his almost possessive interest in his "boys," Ernest was concerned with their feminine interests. Wives in a way were part of his laboratory family, too. He was not beyond offering gratuitous advice to bachelors, as he did to Abelson, whom he saw one lunch time with a "luscious redhead." He later called Phil aside and told him he did not

think that girl quite the type for a good physicist. There seems to be little evidence behind a statement that Ernest tried to arrange matches for
his men, but Aebersold, who thought marriage a good idea for cyclotroneers, posted this advertisement in the lab:

GUARANTEED TRAINING FOR MATRIMONY

Are you lonely? Do you long for a soul-mate and a home? Room-
mates transformed into soul-mates in my special room-mate course
in matrimonial training. After a few months, (or weeks) marriage
will be the best way out.

100% success. Model husbands. No commissions asked of wives.
Testimonials—
"Paul's got da right dope, see!" Kamen.
"Marry merrily" Lovelett J. Laslett.
New Matrimonial matriculates invited.
Paul C. (for Cupid or Conjugalator) Aebersold.

The records indicate that Rad Labbers generally did well matri-
monially by themselves. Henderson met Katherine Linforth at the
Lewises'; Livingood was standing inside a big garbage can mashing down
old copper tubes when Carolyn Zipf arrived to keep a date with another,
and asked, "What in the world are you doing?" They were married after
her graduation. Milton White married Betsy Ann Higley, a physics
graduate student. As Kurie put it in a letter: "She is a swell kid and I
approve of marriage, except that it is quite absurd. Milton is broke, she
is broke, neither have prospects of jobs and both are trying to finish
Ph.D. problems. In spite of my vigorous disapproval I am to be best
man." And then Kurie married. Dottie Gede, a Berkeley girl, had
lived near the campus. Cooksey was best man at that wedding. The
wives, because of the late hours of the lab men, were often called "cyclotron widows," and McGill's John Stuart Foster, with Molly in mind,
composed and delivered a poem at a party in 1937, which was apropos
to other wives.

My husband's without a peer;
Still he *is* a cycloneer—
In the family circle this is very clear.
If he's asked to feed the cat,
Wind the clock—or this or that,
He's so full of cyclonese he doesn't hear.

Kitchen tap has dripped for seasons,
Still he musters many reasons
Why the dashed thing can't be tightened up to-day,

Vacuum cleaner squeals and sputters—
As he rushes out, he mutters
"Got to catch that cleaning job without delay."

He can scarcely keep his shirt on
If there's anything to work on—
He just worships at that little iron shrine.
Still and all I sometimes wonder,
When he's gathered in his plunder,
If he'll ever fix that toaster rack of mine."

Most lab parties were entertained by verse, jingle, or humorous story, usually by a resident cyclotroneer. The usually regular monthly stag parties, normally held at DiBiasi's Restaurant not far from the campus, were revelatory, and the topics were never far from primary concerns, such as Jackson Laslett's "Cyclotron Alphabet" written in October, 1936:

A stands for atoms, all shiny and new;
B is the beam which busts them in two.
C must be cyclotron, which keeps the lab. warm—
D suggests duants, now built on a form.
E is for Ernest, who makes the thing go.
F should be filaments, as Don ought to know.
G stands for grids, which sometimes melt thru—
H is the Hell which is caused when they do.
I means intensity—our first main objective;
J equals Joe—in no way defective.
K recalls Kinsey ("Where is my heel?")
L are the leaks (in the upper can seal?).
M must mean mice whose smell makes us moan;
N stands for neutrons, of moment unknown.
O are the oscillators, which go on the bum;
P is the pulling which then must be done.
Q is unknown (but the cyclotron has it) —
R could be Range (or Radio-static).
S now is store-room—a creation of Jack's—
T can't be tidyness, for this the lab. lacks.
U means Uranium, whose transmutation we seek.
V stands for vacuum like L stands for leak.
W is for wax, which we smear on like fools;
X hides the unknown location of tools.
Y is for you to fill in for your pleasure—
Z is the zany who put this together."

Karl Compton, writing from an eastbound train of his appreciation of a party, quoted from an old Ohio school board record, granting permission to debate the practicability of railroads, which he thought Ernest might use for its humor, and to illustrate that resistance to advanced thinking was not new.

" 'You are welcome to use the school room to debate all proper questions in, but such things as railroads and telegraphs are impossibilities and rank infidelity. There is nothing in the word of God about them. If God had designed that His intelligent creatures should travel at the frightful speed of 15 miles an hour by steam, he would have foretold it through His Holy prophets. It is a device of Satan to lead immortal souls down to Hell.' "

Now and then, after a stay at the lab of some duration, a visitor might express his appreciation to the group with a party, as did Sagane and Yasaki at a Japanese restaurant in San Francisco. The annual pic-nic at a deserted beach near Mount Tamalpais was the largest, grandest, social event—at least for invited wives and girl friends. These picnics started boisterously with the usual good fellowship. Everyone participated in games—Ernest was good at touch football. Most of the men were pretty soft from long days and nights in the lab and quickly became stiff and sore, running around like kids. Abelson recalled, laughingly, "Sometimes the games broke up—after a broken bone or two—with people mad at each other for a couple of days." Ernest, who planned to play tennis regularly, might then lecture a bit on the wisdom of scheduled exercise—without scheduling breaks in laboratory work that might more easily have permitted it. He often invited lab men for singles or doubles and was a little better than they at the game, until Carl Helmholz, who had captained a Harvard team, came to the lab. A good sport, Ernest was delighted when someone he defeated two times out of three, passed him with a good return. Some of his moves were a little awkward, and he was forever banging his shin, but he played hard. He was a good deal less proficient on skis or skates, at which some of the boys were fairly expert.

He bought a twenty-five-foot motor cruiser in April, 1937, after which there were frequent excursions around San Francisco Bay and up the river as far as Sacramento. He traded it for a thirty-foot boat a few months later, so he could accommodate more men, or visitors—and because he had repeatedly bumped his head in the cabin of the first. The newer cruiser had two cabins, higher ceilinged, and with two lower berths in each. He loved to sleep on deck even on the rare occasions when there was not a crowd aboard. A careless navigator, he was said to carry charts only to enable him to determine on what bar the boat was stuck. Sagane thought these excursions the most efficient type of recreation and referred to them as "going to a new world." And Wilfrid Mann remembered them as poetically as the Japanese, as "some far-off pleasant dream."

Cooksey later had a larger cruiser on the bay, but perhaps the most meaningful recreation afforded cyclotroneers were periods ranging from a weekend to a couple of weeks in Trinity County. Whether Cooksey was there or not, his friend and caretaker, Bob Sihlis, dubbed by grateful cyclotroneers "the doughnut king," would be on hand to welcome them with the delicacy for which he was justly named. Wives—even children—were often invited, as were girls of the men. Even farther into the wilderness lived the charming Randolph sisters, Caro and Frances—who packed protective guns. They often joined the fishing or mere general fun. Art Snell was the rhymer who celebrated them—and indicated something of the fun:

> There was a young lady named Caro
> Who swallowed a vegetable marrow.
> She said with a frown
> "It will not go down
> For the hole in my neck is too narrow."

> There was a young lady named Frances
> Who did Scandinavian dances.
> She kicked at the ceiling
> With a great deal of feeling
> And lit on the seat of her pantses.

Among Snell's limericks, the one on John Lawrence's reaction to California fleas is widely remembered:

> About his attire he's meticulous
> To think him unclean is ridiculous
> But his anguished cries
> Make us surmise
> That under his clothes he's pediculous.

Whatever transpired at the beach, DiBiasi's, or in Trinity County, there was little horseplay in the lab, except, perhaps, during periods of waiting for sufficient vacuum in the tank. Barbara Laslett, née Bridgeford, as Ernest's first secretary after the 1936 official laboratory status, remembers impromptu parties in the ratroom at such times. If the weather was good, there might then be touch football, badminton with ping-pong paddles, or baseball catch, outside the building. Rain might send waiting cyclotroneers scurrying to billiard tables at the nearby Faculty Club—Cooksey was not allowed to forget a session of bottle pool during which he put a ball through a club window. Ernest generally encouraged these brief relaxations during waiting periods, but was once upset when in deep thought on some laboratory problem, with only the sound of the vacuum pumps in the background—until Henderson stomped in with his bagpipes at full blast. Normally he would not have minded the pipes any more than he did Malcolm's penchant for knife-throwing. Henderson became fairly expert at that, practicing against an old wooden partition, until he'd hacked enough away so that, with a little sawing, the useless obstruction was completely removed.

Bernard "Where is my heel" Kinsey, a Commonwealth Fellow from Rutherford's laboratory, was so irrepressible he could scarcely sit still even for a meal. At one lunch Cooksey suggested that Henderson pay a waitress to give Kinsey an extra push as he tilted back from the table. It was unnecessary; when the poor girl, trying to serve the gesturing Kinsey, spilled soup in his lap, he fell back shouting, "God's bladders, my best bags!" He lost the heel from one shoe so often that Cooksey cast a replacement in aluminum, which Kinsey received with another expression, "By the roaring tits of the Almighty Jehovah!"—but not in Ernest's hearing. The Maestro's "Good heavens," "Oh, fudge!" or "Oh, sugar!" were tame by comparison, but in many instances almost as amusing.

It was, by and large, with all the hard work, a gay, happy, seemingly carefree group. Those inclined to be solitary or quiet and the more sociable or boisterous cooperated harmoniously. Stan Livingston was sometimes moody. The first to work on a functioning cyclotron, he sometimes felt that he was not given sufficient credit. He told Brady, when both were graduate students, that he once complained of this to Ernest, and was told, "If you're unhappy, feel free to go on any other project. There are any number of graduate students who would like to do what you're doing." Ernest had offered Livingston the choice of the cyclotron or another problem. Stan had asked Brady which he thought best. Brady unhesitatingly replied: "Oh, the accelerator, that's what Lawrence is interested in," which Brady thought was obvious.

Contemporary graduate students felt that Ernest had been unusually good to allow Stan the problem. Others comment on Ernest's insistence that his young men get proper credit. There are innumerable instances of his refusal to have his name included on a paper, or of his insistence that his name come in alphabetical order rather than first on joint papers. Henderson, prodded unjustifiably by his father asking him, "Don't you get any credit?", finally discussed it with Ernest. "He was very nice about it. He was entirely right in the way credit had been assigned. I don't know why Stan felt this way. We all got credit, and a great deal more, from Ernest. I know I got fully as much as I deserved. And this was the beginning of a whole new life for me. He picked me up and set me on a career in the right direction."

When a *Time* Magazine cover feature on Ernest appeared in November, 1937, Dr. Stone "blew his top" because John, who had just become a member of the California faculty as an assistant professor of medicine, was the only person mentioned in connection with medical-biological work. Ernest calmed Stone: Rutherford's death, his complete change of opinion in favor of the cyclotron, and his decision to build one in his laboratory had replaced much of the original article, because these facts enhanced it—and would naturally be included in that week's issue anyway. Newsmen liked the brother-brother angle. Donors such as the Research Corporation and the Chemical Foundation had not been mentioned either, though Ernest had specifically asked that their help be acknowledged. The brother team conflicted with university regulations, as had been pointed out by others, including President Sproul at the time Ernest asked that John be hired. Ernest had "good reasons" for the infraction, as he had for everything he had done from childhood, chiefly that no other doctor of John's stature was available. But he had to handle "the two members of a family" situation with tact and delicacy for a number of years.

While there was never any question of the forcefulness of Ernest's leadership, he regarded staff members as friends rather than assistants. In both letters and conversation pertaining to the laboratory and its activities, "we" was the term more often used than "I." Laboratory activity was literally cooperative in every respect. Abelson's first assignment had been to paint the cyclotron—with the caution not to obliterate the words Federal Telegraph, because that company had made this cyclotron possible. Immediately the assignment was given, Ernest pitched in and helped. "The top man and the low man," Abelson marveled. Ernest regretted that so much of his time had to be taken up with fund raising, but that endeavor was as necessary as any work within the lab, though much less fun. Without it there could have been no Radiation Laboratory as the men knew it; many of them could not even have been there. His greatest pleasure was to be in his orange lab coat, joining whoever was present at the moment, hunting trouble, repairing or replacing this or that, or engaging actively in the exciting research.

There was plenty of trouble, of course—vacuum leaks, shorts, many problems few others would have seen through to solution. Technical difficulties were gradually overcome, and experience gradually resulted in methods of procedure which became fairly standardized; as temporary expedients, through trial and error were resolved, and as the talents of

Cooksey, the skills of Win Salisbury in radio frequency, and of Bill Bro-beck in engineering, McMillan and Wilson in design and theory, were applied—everyone contributed.

Scientific search benefited from practical know-how that had to be learned on the job. Improvements in controls and tuning devices some-times resulted from accidents. Ernest's warning of the dangers of high-voltage equipment were so often repeated he once confessed to feeling like an "old crab." While so many phases were experimental and subject to change, it was impracticable to make them foolproof. The first oscil-lators were tuned by turning off the cyclotron and manipulating the coil by hand. Then someone took apart a couple of old wooden carpenter's clamps and reassembled them to form a device that stretched or com-pressed the coil by means of a wooden crank, and it could be tuned with power on. Lacking sufficient meters, a nail in the end of a wooden meter stick was used to test the sparking of an electrode or tube coil, until Liv-ingood, standing on a ladder inside the oscillator tank of the linear ac-celerator, had a spark jump down the stick to his hand. About 16,000 volts went across the right side of his body and the nails in his shoe and knocked him off the ladder.

Ernest and Henderson, running the cyclotron, heard an unusual shout and rushed to the big tank to see Snell, scared to death, bent over Liv-ingood. Henderson, cool, efficient, and experienced, checked Livingood's pulse and respiration. He was carried outside to an automobile—one that Thornton simply appropriated—taken to the hospital, and pro-nounced curable. Thornton had a difficult time returning the "stolen" car to the campus, but he and Livingood felt that it had been a "legit-imate theft." It took six months for the burns on Livingood's hands and feet to heal. He was lucky that the high voltage hadn't crossed his heart, and that in the fall he had not fractured his skull. What he did had been done many times before and was theoretically harmless. Appar-ently high voltage had been developed on the wire by a parasitic oscil-lation followed by a power arc. "Let it be a blessing in disguise," Ernest warned.

Abelson, also while on a ladder, later brushed his head against a wire charged with 10,000 volts, resulting in a hot noisy spark and a fall from the ladder. Fortunately he was not standing on metal. Another time when making an adjustment at the rear of the cyclotron, Abelson re-members, "I was two or three inches away from frying." Ernest, unaware of Abelson's presence, turned on the cyclotron. Frightened, Ernest bore down hard on the necessity for safety. Resuscitation was studied; first-aid materials were made available. Alvarez devised an interlocking switch system on the doors of the oscillator box. Cable, insulated for 20,000 volts, was used where appropriate.

The Abelson accident still on his mind a few days later, Ernest wrote Don from a train "somewhere on the Nevada desert" that all exposed hot parts *must* be enclosed with doors having automatic switches. Additional switching arrangements that would ground the oscillator when its box was open were urged. Laboratory personnel had no more serious electrical accidents than these, in which they were fortunate, as, perhaps, they also were with radiation hazards. Two fine ex-Rad Lab cyclotroneers were electrocuted after leaving Berkeley: Wesley Coates in the East, and Harold Walke in England. There were other hazards that could lead to serious injury; Franz Kurie was badly burned while applying beeswax and rosin against vacuum leaks. The messy stuff had to be heated over a Bunsen burner until hot enough to smoke. This time it caught fire, and, without thinking, Kurie stuck the can of burning wax under a water faucet. The water at once turned to steam and blew the stuff into his face. It took several hours at the hospital to remove the wax, piece by piece, and for several weeks Kurie looked as though he had run into the blast of a shotgun.

Dave Sloan never completely recovered from spinal trouble aggravated in 1934 by carrying 200-pound chunks of battery plate lead to be used for shielding. Sloan was confined to the hospital for long periods, in a cast for several years, much of the time flat on his back, or hobbling on crutches. Ernest saw that he got the best possible attention and that he remained a member of the team. Considered something of an oracle, he was often consulted while bedridden. He and Salisbury, particularly, had long discussions of oscillators, techniques of circuits, and related concerns.

The first protection against radiation from the neutron-infested target area consisted of paraffin, which was initially used to slow down neutrons for experiment. As the destructive power of neutrons became an increasing concern, more and more paraffin was used to screen the target area until it produced a fire hazard. Five-gallon cans of water were then stacked around the cyclotron until, finally, Ernest found money to have heavy tanks three feet thick, seven feet high, and ten feet long made for barriers.

Practically everything not too large was made by the men themselves in the laboratory shop. The facilities of the main physics shop were also available—if one could wait. Competent machinists there made beautiful things from crude sketches, often only half complete, on the backs of old envelopes or scraps of scratch paper. Everything was designed in the Rad Lab until ideas were fed back from laboratories where other cyclotrons were built. Salisbury suggested that three-inch instead of original one-quarter or three-eighths-inch copper tubing on the tuning coil would vastly improve the oscillator system, and it did. Van Voorhis, with technical advice from Litton, made a master oscillator power amplifier that enabled one to set and keep the frequency as desired. Wilson perfected a seal for the chamber lid, eliminating at last, and happily, the need for wax. He also discovered that probes, inserted within the D accelerating electrodes, could intercept large stray currents without appreciable effect on the external beam. These proved to be particularly useful in producing radioisotopes of material exposed on the probes and vastly increased their output.

There was much trial and error. It was thought, while trying to get the beam out of and away from the chamber, that magnetic influences might be lessened by the removal of steel near the deflector. Twenty some holes were drilled in the steel cover and, when this made no improvement, were filled again with steel plugs—and forgotten until a year or so later when a picture of a chamber built elsewhere showed how faithfully Rad Lab pictures had been studied. The plugged holes were duplicated, though Snell pointed out that they were not in exactly similar places. Inadvertently, the plugs did make a difference; they made the beam smaller.

Ideas for improvement were constantly considered and often tried. Agreement that one or another should be tried might have to wait until the cyclotron broke down, even if water was leaking from overhead cans, or cooling oil dripping from the coil tanks. Hats fashioned from newspapers were little protection at such times, but if the vacuum was good, and other things functioning well, leaking water and dripping oil would be endured until everyone agreed to, and Ernest approved, a shutdown. Someone then would immediately cut a wire or break a pipe connection before there could be a change of mind. Then everyone would get busy, cleaning, fixing, replacing leaking water cans—and mashing old ones to prevent reuse—patching oil leaks, adding this or removing that, to make it function better than before, and perhaps look a little neater—for a day or two.

Once Ernest asked Livingood to clean some of the wax off the chamber so an important, nonscientist visitor could see the brass. With a putty knife, Livingood scraped areas he considered sound, until a sudden whistle announced catastrophe; he had scraped off a penny waxed over a leak, buried beneath half an inch of wax and long forgotten. There was brass visible for the visiting notable—and an idle cyclotron.

When Rutherford decided that the cyclotron was a good thing after all and sent Cockcroft to Berkeley for information, Ernest wanted him to see every detail. The cyclotron, which could be so temperamental, had performed beautifully for days when Cockcroft arrived and continued to do so. "Something will happen pretty soon," Ernest told Cockcroft, "and then you can look inside." But the cyclotron kept purring along perfectly. Finally Ernest said to Alvarez, "We'll push it up real high and burn out a D stem insulator." He turned knobs up until meter indicators were off scale; the cyclotron continued to function. "I'll turn off the air," he told an anguished Alvarez, "and you give it the juice." "I could have died right there," remembers Alvarez. "It was running fine and he was going to ruin it. I sat there, never more miserable in my life, knowing perfectly well that when it happened Ernest would take Cockcroft out to dinner, and I would get down on my hands and knees, pull the machine apart, and open the tank. Then he would come trotting in and explain everything to Cockcroft, and I would spend the night putting it back together. And that's exactly what happened!"

Visitors presented other problems. No matter how notable, if they were there to learn or to use the cyclotron, they were requested to work along with the crews. In this they often were more trouble than help, and regulars gladly took over the visitors' tasks and shooed them off—if Ernest was away. Some medical men and biologists, increasingly interested in radioactive materials, wanted to bombard their own targets and, ignorant of cyclotron technique and functioning, had to be forbidden. Care had to be exercised to keep certain things away from the magnetic field. On John's first visit, a pair of pliers was drawn from his pocket into the cyclotron, necessitating shutdown and repair. He remembers the jaundiced view with which he was regarded for a few days afterward. The glass liquid air trap was often bumped into and broken, and the fragments sucked into the vacuum: shutdown, diassembly, cleaning, and reassembly!

Ernest was not exempt from occasional mistakes. Once while Snell changed a filament, a somewhat lengthy task, Ernest was adjusting connections on the magnet. When the cyclotron was turned on again, the filament fell over and shorted. Ernest, already irritable from the initial delay, reprimanded Snell for misconnecting the new filament. Snell, positive that he had correctly installed it, stuck to his guns. A check revealed that Ernest had inadvertently reversed the polarity of the magnet, causing the filament to short, because its current, acting in the magnetic field and thereby causing a mechanical force, made it, because of its design, able to withstand a force in one direction but not in the other. "Ernest was a real gentleman, then as always," Snell remembers. "He apologized to me for his unkind words. I remember that my estimation of him rose considerably from that day on."

Everyone found Ernest's economy of water amusing—and sometimes frustrating. He frankly stated, "I've got a phobia about wasting water from living in South Dakota where it was often extremely scarce." Recognition of the phobia did not prevent his insisting that the valves of the cooling system be turned so low that water emerged near the boiling point. He hated to see it go down the drain. Molly suffered from this at home, in the laundry, or when irrigating lawn and plants. That Berkeley had tons of water made no difference. When particularly hard up for money, Ernest searched for possible economies. He once had Livingood pick up all the solder that had dropped on the floor; Jack spent a whole morning making two or three feet of solder. It was a big day when regular clamps were available, instead of wire tightened around hoses.

Probably more time was spent in keeping the accelerating chamber properly evacuated than at any other task. Satisfactory vacuum pumps had to be homemade, and vacuum leaks were difficult to locate and keep closed. Pesky and persistent leaks became notorious, such as "Henry's hole," located by Henry Newson after a day's search by the entire staff. He poured Glyptal in exactly the right spot and closed the leak. There were loud, more than half-serious congratulations. Someone suggested that he have a reward. Ernest agreed. "Henry may have a cup of tea before seminar." Though a cup of tea before seminar was no more unusual than searching for a leak, Newson had his reward; it was the first time Ernest had ever called him Henry. Newson's somewhat diffident manner and slow speech had not impressed Ernest, who was surprised to learn that his young associate had worked as a cabdriver and on a steel-mill river gang while attending the University of Chicago. One was "in" when Ernest used his first name. A sign of further recognition was the request that one call him Ernest. There was always a period when a newcomer called him Professor Lawrence. No one in the lab ever called him Ernie—nor in his presence "Maestro" or "EOL," though the latter was pretty general all over the country.

No one long remained a member of the staff without pretty complete acceptance by Ernest, and none of the early group recalls his ever knocking another behind his back. He was strongly adverse to gossip of any kind and strongly disapproved of profanity and off-color stories, though he became more tolerant of both after World War II. Political arguments were taboo, or discussion of social issues aroused by the Depression, the Dust Bowl, migrant workers, or the pros and cons of Fascism or Communism. Oppie's sudden interest, toward the end of 1936, in these problems surprised him, though he could understand his feelings against Nazism, after Oppie told of persecuted relatives in Germany. One should deplore the European shenanigans, Ernest felt; that's why most Americans' forefathers had left Europe, but it was not our affair. One Sunday Oppie entered the lab and wrote on the blackboard, which was the general communication center: "Cocktail Party Benefit for Spanish Loyalists at Brode's, everyone at Lab invited." Half an hour later Ernest came in, alertly looked around as usual, and noticed Oppie's message. He stood for perhaps half a minute, clenching and unclenching his jaws.

Then he walked slowly to the board and erased Oppie's message, without a word. He considered Oppie, so often consulted, one of the team, though technically he was not on the Rad Lab staff.

Oppie reigned over a smoke-filled room in Le Conte, down the hall a few doors from Ernest's office, where the bright theoretical boys hung out. Out of concern and affection, Ernest advised his friend to leave social and political concerns to those hopefully expert in such matters. Oppie's protests he considered due to naïveté and emotion. "You're too good a physicist to get mixed up in politics and causes." He warned his people similarly. "If anyone wants to write letters to the editor and that sort of thing, he should get out of science and get a job on a paper." Physicists, and certainly graduate students, if at all good, had enough on their minds probing nature.

Though he preferred not to have women in the laboratory at first, a few eventually were accepted. His agreement to accept Chien-Shiung Wu for graduate work in 1937 was regretted when he saw the delicate young lady. Miss Wu had done very well in physics at Nanking's National Central University, but how could such a fragile person succeed in the Rad Lab? Yet Gee-Gee, as she was affectionately called, proved to be more than an ornament. Her work was excellent; she became the only woman to earn a Ph.D. from Ernest, and she was to achieve international fame in nuclear physics.

Contemporary with Gee-Gee in the lab was Basanti Nag, student of Meghnad Saha, who had asked Ernest to take his bright student for graduate work. Ernest saw that Nag got into the International House, had him at home for dinner—really looked out for him until he was familiar with his new environment. Nag was never made to feel a foreigner, though questioned seriously about India, Allahabad University, and Saha. The dedication of lab men to their work and the responsibility which Ernest felt for them impressed Nag. Only once, in his presence, did Ernest show irritability with no effort to conceal it and that was because one of the men had forgotten to phone a hospital about the condition of a colleague, as had been requested. The depth of Ernest's intuition—"Where others would have to guess at something many times, Lawrence would do it in one or two tries"—impressed Nag most, and he was amazed at Ernest's ability to relax at lab parties or in his home. The observant Indian did not fail to notice Ernest's appreciation of good food, which "he ate as fast as he did everything else, and he enjoyed the presence of beautiful ladies, with whom he was courteous and gay."

Two became members of the group in the formative period somewhat by happenstance. Paul Aebersold, who had been a trackman as a Stanford undergraduate, went up to Berkeley for Olympic tryouts in 1932. A physics major, he was curious about Ernest and his "gadget"—then the 11-inch model. There were few people in Le Conte Hall that Saturday. He finally found a man bending over a strange device, and, stating that he was a physics student, he asked if by chance Professor Lawrence was around—or if the accelerator could be seen. "I'm Professor Lawrence, and this is the accelerator," came the answer. "I'm trying to fix a leak. Hand me that tool over there, will you?" Aebersold was at work. Ernest learned enough that afternoon to accept Aebersold as a graduate student.

Robert Wilson, a young freshman from Wyoming, found himself repeatedly drawn from a normal path to his class by the whining generators, strangely beautiful auras, thunderous sparks, strange instruments, and intent men in the old wooden building. Fascinated, he was usually late for class. Once, staring into the strangely lighted place, unconscious of pouring rain, he was invited in from the wet. The considerate man in laboratory coat even answered his questions—Wilson was seduced by the cyclotron and the lab atmosphere. His undergraduate work was rechanneled toward the Radiation Laboratory where as a graduate student he was further infected by the Lawrence spirit.

Wilson, who developed much of the early theoretical insight of cyclotron function, tells of this experience in an excellent and understandable manner in *Accelerators,* by Wilson and Littauer. On the afternoon that Wilson was to take his oral Ph.D. examination before a committee of which Ernest was the chairman, he was asked to perform some task in the lab. Wilson hesitated, then reminded the professor that this was the afternoon of his exams. "Oh," Ernest said. "Well, good luck—and God bless you!" "Thank you, God," Wilson replied.

The spirit of the laboratory set its personnel somewhat apart in the eyes of others—on campus and in Berkeley itself. Who but a Rad Labber would leave a dance and his girl to rush over to his place of work, as Livingood did when word reached him at a Faculty Club party that cyclotron current was rising! He was pretty tardy about returning, too; the meters moved up to twenty, thirty, forty, and finally to fifty microamperes in that one night. And Snell and Cooksey once continued a serious conversation in Jake's barber shop, Don in Jake's chair calling to Art, who was waiting on a settee. After Art got his turn in another chair, Jake whispered to Cooksey, "Is he one of those genius inventors up at the university?" Cooksey said, "He sure is!" Jake nodded sagely. "Well, you can see that. He's one of those fellows that sits with his eyes shut, but his brain's awhirlin', and when he does open his mouth, he's goin' places."

Something of the spirit was carried to other laboratories when the men left, departures usually tinged with some regret. They were not likely again to be members of so unusual a group, in so exciting a place. They were missed at the laboratory, too. Ernest's determined policy was that each man should have the best possible opportunities for himself. He constantly recommended his people for suitable positions. But, while eager to spread the cyclotron gospel, it was still hard to lose good men from the laboratory. "Snell to Chicago, Van Voorhis to Rochester, Ernest Lyman to Illinois, Livingood to Harvard. All good men lost to us this spring—of course there is an influx of fine fellows, too," he wrote in 1938. There was consolation that year in the return of Bob Thornton from Michigan with a charming wife. In a brief period the year before, Laslett had gone to Copenhagen and Bohr's laboratory; Don Hurst to Cavendish to assist Cockcroft; Kinsey, shortly followed by Walke, to Liverpool and Chadwick, and Hugh Paxton to Paris to join Nahmias in Joliot's laboratory—all to construct cyclotrons! Naturally Ernest was pleased that noted European scientists wanted his cyclotron and his men. Letters back from his former students often reflected discouragement with old, habitual methods and pace, so different from the Rad Lab. Ernest always responded with suggestions and encouragement.

"As I have written Bernard [Kinsey]," he wrote to Harold Walke, "you are unjustifiably depressed with your progress. The difficulties are reasonable and natural ones, and it won't be long before you will have them cleared up. You know that in the past we have had plenty of trouble here, and everybody has them at one time or other. . . . By the way, Henry Newson has been in a similar unhappy state of mind to yours, not having a cyclotron running, and this continued to be the case after Art Snell joined him, as they still had their troubles. We have, however, just received a post card from Art to the effect that the fifteen microampere beam meter is off scale, and it is clear to Art and Henry the world is now looking a good deal brighter. I know that the same will be true with you soon, if not already by the time of arrival of this note."

The "exiles," or "alumni," found opportunities to meet with others in their areas. When Kurie, on his honeymoon, dropped in on Thornton at Ann Arbor, the Milton Whites joined them, driving from Princeton. Van Voorhis drove all night to meet the Chicago–Illinois–Indiana contingent. And in Europe "International Congresses" of cyclotroneers were held at Kinsey's "Liverpuddle," and in Paris, Copenhagen, and Stockholm, where Von Friesen, who had been at the Rad Lab, had returned to build a cyclotron. Ex-Rad Lab men derived technical benefit from each other and had great good times together. An international conference was set in northern Lapland one year, and invitations to the "Dear

Doctors and Boys" of the Rad Lab were issued. Get-togethers were reported fully to Berkeley—there was much correspondence back and forth.

In a letter to McMillan, Laslett wrote from Copenhagen about a fine article on Ernest, ". . . quite pleased with it, but his picture sitting on my table, looking at me when I got up, was making me hustle too much, and tiring me out, so I sent it on to Hugh and am now trying to recover." And Hugh Paxton, answering a letter from Abelson, wrote: "Your description of fireworks and expansion! It recalls typical Lab scenes—scenes which could happen nowhere else—pumping speed being multiplied by several, new generators, and controls unit solved, super hyper convenient oscillators being built up by another group. Honestly, Phil, the human energy concentrated there is wonderful!"

Rad Lab "human energy" was talked of elsewhere, and by nonexiles. Sometimes the methods were spoken of with disdain as "Berkeleyitis," or "Brute force." But a legend was developing that even found its way into song. Young Arthur Roberts of M.I.T. wrote words and music for a ballad of eleven verses, each followed by a refrain that had varying apropos tag lines.

THE CYCLOTRONIST'S NIGHTMARE
or
EIGHTY MILLICURIES by HALF-PAST NINE

Once upon a midnight dreary
The cyclotron crew was weak and weary;
In walked the Boss with a smile so cheery,
In walked the Boss with a very broad smile.
"Boys," he said, "Here's wonderful chance"
"Boys," he said, "It'll make you want to dance"
"Boys," he said, "We must activate some iron,
Eighty millicuries by half-past nine!"

Refrain:
Round and round and round go the deuterons
Round and round the magnet swings them
Round and round and round go the deuterons
Smack! in the target goes the ion beam.

Ernest visited the laboratories of onetime associates whenever he could. In 1937 when he was a Sigma Xi lecturer at institutions from Virginia to Oregon, Brady, at St. Louis University, wrote the national secretary of the fraternity requesting that Ernest speak at his institution. The secretary replied that Ernest's dates were filled and there would not be time between them to permit him to lecture in St. Louis. Brady mentioned it in a personal letter, and Ernest replied that he would squeeze St. Louis in somehow, and he did. And he broke into his regular lecture to mention Brady's work at California. Sensing that his old student was not too happy with the department there, he told him, as he left, that he would find another place for him. At his last lecture stop he spoke of Brady to the chairman of the department at Oregon State—Brady's father and numerous relatives lived in Oregon. Brady was soon invited to join the physics department at Oregon State.

He seldom missed Snell and Newson in the interim between the arrival of the West Coast Streamliner in Chicago in the morning, and evening departure for New York or Washington. Snell and Newson were amused over Ernest's preference for train over plane, but were happy that he had not been persuaded to change by Professor Harkins. Harkins, nearly twice Ernest's age, traveled by plane whenever possible, and urged it on Ernest. When alone with Newson, Ernest said that it was all right for Harkins, an old man who could afford to risk his few remaining years, but that it would be foolish for a man in his thirties to jeopardize so many more years, just to save a few hours on a cross country trip. (Harkins was still active in research when in his eighties.)

The bonds that united members of the group to each other and to the laboratory were too strong to be severed by separation. Men continually returned for visits or to join those carrying on, among whom were always a few from their times. Why? Perhaps Arthur Snell summed it up in a talk to physicists, meeting at U.C.L.A. in 1962: "I think that given able, strong leadership, with insight, and above all great courage; and given a worthy goal and enough success as you go along so that temporary difficulties don't set you back too far; and an insight for some suspicion of physics that remains to be seen behind the curtain that you are trying to lift—a combination like that will attract and hold young men at an age when hard work is relatively easy and they can take it in good humor and cooperation. Given also a human element that was contributed largely by Don Cooksey . . . you have just about the recipe. Fortunately the recipe still holds. And that is why it is so nice for us who spent those few years with the Rad Lab to look back on them as kind of golden years."

Mark Oliphant, who had left Cavendish to build a cyclotron at Birmingham, the year of Rutherford's death, wrote to Ernest, after a 1938 visit at Berkeley: "I find it difficult to thank you for the magnificent and instructive time which I had in Berkeley. It is truly fine of you to be so liberal of time and of thought on my behalf. I know of no laboratory in the world at the present time which has so fine a spirit or so grand a tradition of hard work. While there I seemed to feel again the spirit of the old Cavendish, and to find in you those fine qualities of a combined camaraderie and leadership which endeared Rutherford to all who worked with him. The essence of the Cavendish is now in Berkeley. I am serious in this, and for these reasons I shall return again some day, and I hope very soon."

CHAPTER XI

"Your Career Is Showing Promise"

[1937-1939]

Construction of the Crocker Radiation Laboratory building did not get under way until May of 1937. Design of its "huge" cyclotron, subject of much thought and discussion, was not determined until enlargement of the existing cyclotron was completed, and improvements which might be incorporated in the Crocker machine checked. The last 27-inch chamber was removed from the magnet on August 4. Enlarged, tapered pole tips were fitted, and the 37-inch chamber was in place two weeks later, and a few minutes after eight o'clock on the night of August 18 the first beam was obtained, with an intensity of one microampere. In two more days this had been increased to 75 microamperes, and after another two days—and nights—all the meters were off scale, with intensities of over 100 microamperes. The 37-inch was a success; the increased area of chamber and magnetic field, and the several incorporated improvements, exceeded expectations. Cooksey was now devoting his full time to coordination and supervision of the design and construction of the huge cyclotron. Overlapping committees, each responsible for specific problems, were appointed; everyone contributed to and worked on the project in addition to servicing and running the 37-inch for physical experiment and to make radioactive substances. Cyclotron time was in such demand that priorities and schedules had to be arranged.

Ernest, for whom 1937 was a year of widespread, solid recognition, regretted the necessary and frequent periods away from the laboratory. To be a 1937 Sigma Xi lecturer was an honor, but it kept him away for a month. So he did not go to Philadelphia, at the conclusion of the lecture tour, to receive the Elliott Cresson Medal of the Franklin Institute,

which was awarded to him *in absentia*. Even so, he had barely concluded checking, questioning, explaining, usually approving ideas and
suggestions for the new cyclotron and laboratory, when he had to leave
again. The first Research Corporation Scientific Award since 1931 was to
be given to him. He felt obligated to receive the plaque and $2,500 in
person, at its twenty-fifth-anniversary dinner in New York. Nor did he
return immediately after the ceremony, as planned; there had been too
many interested men of affairs present who wanted to know more about
his work, and plans, than could be explained in an evening.

He had long visits the next day with Ambassador Dave Morris, whom
he had met in Brussels, and with interested industrialists. He went to
Alfred Loomis's laboratory in Tuxedo Park, New York, which he had
visited with Karl Compton some years before. Loomis, millionaire partner in a successful Wall Street firm, lawyer, and physicist, was very much
interested in Ernest as an adventurous scientist and in his predictions of
accomplishment with the new and future cyclotrons. He admired Ernest's courage, his informed optimism, and direct frankness. He asked
his advice concerning an experiment of his own, and Ernest spent a day
with him and invited him to the Rad Lab.

Loomis, a unique figure in science, not only had converted his huge
old mansion in Tuxedo Park into a finely equipped and staffed laboratory that both promising and established scientists were invited to use
for their personal projects but had also provided living quarters, also
staffed, for them and their families. Most of the world's noted scientists
had been guests for varying periods of time at the Loomis laboratory,
experimenting as they wished, under neither pressure nor expense.
Loomis also had been the "angel" of the *Physical Review* when, without
help, it would have ceased publication. A fast friend of Karl Compton,
who had insisted as a condition to acceptance of the presidency of
M.I.T. in 1930 that Loomis be named a trustee, Loomis had first heard
of Ernest at that time. He told Ernest that he had been suggested by
Compton as his successor at Princeton, a suggestion lightly treated by
the Princeton administration—he had been "too young." Close friendship between Loomis and Ernest, from radically different backgrounds,
was natural; aside from their common interest in physics, each responded to the other's daring, imaginative insight, and resourceful-
ness.

As he was to be the 1937 commencement speaker at Stevens Institute
of Technology and receive an honorary doctor of science degree on June
12, Ernest decided it would not be worthwhile to go West for the few
days he would have in the lab. When invitations to Princeton and to
Yale for honorary degrees on the twenty-second and twenty-third caught
up with him, he telephoned Molly to join him in New Haven for all

three events. She was reluctant to leave the children, but as the faithful Helen, whom the children adored, now slept in the bedroom on the level below the living room, next to what had been the study before it became Eric's room, Molly consented. Entertaining necessitated by the multitude of visitors had made kitchen duties too burdensome for Helen, in addition to partial care of two small children, and a cook-housekeeper came during the day. Molly asked Don Cooksey to look in on Helen and the children in the evenings while she was away.

Ernest came down with a "roaring cold" in New Haven while working on the commencement address. Despite fever and much "coughing and blowing my nose," he resisted John's efforts to keep him in bed until he had prepared the address. Nervous about so important a talk, he gladly showed it to John's mentor and recent patient, Harvey Cushing, the eminent brain surgeon. Cushing made suggestions and edited it; it was his "masterful touch," Ernest wrote Don, that made the address successful. Though his cold lingered and Molly had symptoms of one, they enjoyed the Stevens events, Ernest particularly the trustees' stag dinner at the Hotel Astor in New York. An "imposing group of industrial leaders" plied him with questions as to possible practical applications of his work. He thought it early to be specific, except, perhaps about medical uses, but "tagged" isotopes would surely be useful in many ways, and he would not hesitate to predict useful power—though that might be decades in the future. Molly and Ernest had both recovered by the twenty-second, and commencement. Ernest had insisted that his parents be present for the Princeton and Yale ceremonies, and Molly that they be guests of the Blumers. Gunda was lovely in her pride of her eldest— and of John, on the faculty of Yale, who drove her and Carl to Princeton. With Carl she could share the certainty that there was no occupation so worthwhile as teaching, and for her sons there were the added opportunities found in research—Gunda was as certain that John would attain eminence as that Ernest deserved his. Molly and Ernest were entertained for lunch at the Henry Smyths'—problems of physics could not be denied for a whole day—from which they rushed off for New Haven and dinner at President J. R. Angell's.

Ernest caused concern, followed by some impatience, in the Blumer household the following morning. Requested to be at Woodbridge Hall in academic dress by 9:30, he was on the Sound in a rowboat an hour before, clad in dungarees and sneakers. He did not hold up the procession. President Angell, in conferring Ernest's degree, read: "A brilliant young general in the ranks of physical science, whose dramatic victories are everywhere recognized, your alma mater is glad to add to the honors you have already won, the degree of doctor of science." Afterward, Ernest sat, by invitation, at the high table for the alumni luncheon at which Secretary of State Cordell Hull, also a recipient of an honorary degree, was the speaker.

Thus another month had been spent away from the Rad Lab when Ernest returned on June 30. He was off again two weeks later for a series of promised lectures at Utah College of Agriculture in Logan. Leon Linford, early graduate student and member of Ernest's and Molly's wedding party, was chairman of the physics department, and his cousin Leo, more recent Rad Lab graduate student, was an instructor. Ernest and Molly were entertained in both Linford households. The Leon Linford's oldest son was named for Ernest—but Molly and both Linford women noted with amusement that Leo's charming wife got most of Ernest's attention.

There was sufficient excuse in a painful back infection to postpone commitments in the East for the latter part of July. At John's insistence, Ernest went to the hospital, where the sore was lanced, affording much relief. He was soon back at the lab and able to take visitors boating in weather rough enough for *mal de mer* among his guests. "I can't understand why Ernest is never seasick on his boat," Cooksey remarked, hearing of a wild cruise around the bay from Stuart Foster, "because he always *is* on a steamer." Someone replied that it would have been out of character for the Maestro of the Rad Lab, and world leader in nuclear fracture, to be seasick before distinguished visitors—or even associates. His sense of obligation toward visitors forced him into relaxation he might otherwise have missed—with so much to be done. As he wrote his parents, "The constant stream of visitors is very pleasant but certainly interferes with things." He was away again in mid-September, just long enough to lecture to an important audience at the International Congress of Radiology in Chicago. He returned in time to pose for color photographs and be interviewed for the *Time* Magazine cover story. He was sorry, he wrote his father and mother, that John, back at Yale after two months at the laboratory, was not present to "get in on this," for John would soon join the faculty on an all-year basis.

There were rumors again that Ernest was under consideration for the Nobel Prize; he was not fully aware of the support for his nomination voiced in scientific circles; indeed, many, including his old friend Jesse Beams, considered the distinction overdue. The Compton brothers had each consulted Birge before compiling necessary evidence of worth for the Nobel Institute. No rumors, however, prepared him for the announcement by the National Academy of Sciences that the Comstock Prize "for the most important discovery for investigation in electricity or magnetism or radiant energy within the past five years" would be awarded him at the autumn meeting in Rochester, New York. The highest honor of the National Academy, and presented not oftener than every five years, this generally was considered in the United States as second only to the Nobel award in prestige. Molly and Cooksey went East with him for that presentation. Speaking for the academy, Dr. Coolidge said, "While consideration was given to the names of other men who are doing work of a high order of merit, Dr. Lawrence's work was so outstanding as to make him unmistakably the committee's choice." At how many past meetings of the august body had there been ridicule of the cyclotron concept and, more recently, doubt of Ernest's sanity for suggesting high energies, now achieved? And to be increased!

There was no hint of "I told you so" in Ernest's response to the presentation. He always insisted, and pointedly, if he thought it necessary for another's benefit, that "an essential humility of character is just as important as brilliance of mind in the scientific world." After expressing appreciation, he paid tribute to "three splendid students" who in 1930 had "embarked with me on the voyage of experimental research that has reached the destination you have seen fit to recognize so magnificently this evening." Though the three students, Edlefsen, Livingston, and Sloan were named, as was Cooksey for later assistance, Ernest insisted that the achievement noted had resulted from the joint efforts of many, ". . . our laboratory has been blessed with a succession of fine men, and I wish there were time here to pay proper tribute to them all. . . . In thanking you . . . I am the representative of these valued associates and intimate friends . . . who share with me this great honor."

Armed with such authoritative recognition and introduced by member Arthur Compton, Ernest called on Dr. Ludvig Hektoen, executive director of the National Advisory Cancer Council, in Washington. *Science* Magazine had reported the council's intention to purchase radium for loan to hospitals throughout the country. Ernest now proposed, in the interests of economy and likely superiority of radioactive materials to radium, that the council assist in the development of cyclotrons for their manufacture. Dr. Hektoen and council members whom Ernest saw individually were receptive, if noncommittal.

Determined to explore every possible avenue of support, Ernest called on Warren Weaver, director of the Division of Natural Sciences of the Rockefeller Foundation. He had been with Dr. Weaver at his Scarsdale home for an afternoon and evening in May and had asked if the foundation might help his laboratory, should it become necessary. Weaver had said that for several years foundation members had thought that to assist the Radiation Laboratory would be an honor, but that they had not wished to intrude on another's "baby." If help was needed and no conflict with the Chemical Foundation or the Research Corporation was indicated, Ernest should not hesitate to apply to the foundation. Ernest explained that to complete the new cyclotron properly and equip the

Crocker Laboratory adequately for medical and biological work, $30,000 more than he could foresee would be needed soon after the first of the year. Weaver promised to discuss the matter with the Rockefeller board at the first opportunity.

When he reported to Arthur Compton, between trains in Chicago, on his discussions with Hektoen and members of the Cancer Council, Ernest also mentioned his conversations with Weaver. Compton approved, and said that he would sponsor an application to the Cancer Council for a Radiation Laboratory grant for the express purpose of technical research and improvements on the cyclotron. By the time he returned to Berkeley, Ernest had outlines for improvements to both cyclotrons and laboratories—which Don thought might cost more than the sum of both hoped-for grants!

The seventh high honor awarded him in 1937 came in November with the Royal Society's Hughes Medal, with £130, "for the most important instrument of physical research since the C.T.R. Wilson expansion chamber." He regretted the inadvisability of going to London to receive the honor in person, tempted though he was to take Molly for the ceremony.

Pleasure in personal honors, professional success, and the increasingly widespread recognition of the cyclotron as a major scientific instrument was clouded early in November by his mother's increasing distress. She had not been well when he and Molly had been with her, briefly, on the way to Rochester, but as usual was uncomplaining. He had, perhaps, become accustomed to her frequent periods of discomfort. He had discussed it with John, who had seen her on his way to Berkeley in October and, with her local doctor, had given her another thorough examination. Abdominal swelling had been evident, as it had before, but nothing seriously wrong was apparent except obvious fatigue. Diet, rest, and medication had been prescribed. Her distress increased after John's departure. Massive uterine hemorrhage suddenly occurred early in November, and Carl rushed her again to the Mayo Clinic. A tumor was discovered, a "frozen pelvis" impossible to remove surgically, and it was said she had no more than three months to live, Carl reported by telephone. It was decided that John should immediately go, consult the Mayo physicians, and determine the course to be taken. In Rochester, he decided to bring his mother, in spite of her condition, to California, where, under Dr. Stone's direction, Gunda received X-ray therapy from the Sloan tube. Sicker than anyone Stone had known from even small doses of X rays, she was "one of the least complaining patients." The therapy apparently was beneficial. All bleeding ceased and the tumor shrank progressively. She was able to be at Ernest's for Christmas, when Carl came for the holidays. By the end of January no tumor could be detected with certainty, though Gunda was not to feel well for a long time. She insisted on going home to Carl before the end of March, over protests that she wait until there could be some certainty of good weather in South Dakota.

Ernest had found it hard to maintain enthusiasm during his mother's critical period. Her suffering from both malady and therapy was hard on him. He could be irritable at the hospital; either the dosage was too weak to destroy the tumor, or too strong for her to bear, and at home he seemed withdrawn from Molly and the children. He finally was forced to stay in bed himself, longer than ever before, by a severe cold and streptococcal throat. He was revived considerably by a telegram from Dr. Hektoen—less than a month after meeting him. The Cancer Council executive requested information and recommendations on the most urgent needs of cyclotron projects "with special reference to cancer." Ernest did not have to leave his bed to find that out. He telegraphed at once:

"Immediate very pressing need is assurance of funds to complete equipment of our new Radiation Laboratory for medical research and cancer therapy. $12,000 for fellowships and $18,000 for materials and apparatus will assure medical cyclotron and accessory clinical equipment for effective clinical research on therapeutic uses of neutron rays and artificial radioactive substances. Apart from this immediate need it is important to provide now or later grant for express purpose of further development cyclotron for manufacture radioactive substances."

He was able to leave his bed the next day—though John would have kept him there—and dictate a detailed response to Hektoen. As his mother improved, so did his spirits, particularly after a National Advisory Council grant of $30,000 was announced. A telegram from Warren Weaver followed; the Rockefeller Foundation was prepared to grant $30,000 but was now concerned that it might conflict with the purpose of the Cancer Council grant. Ernest replied by wire and detailed letter denying conflict; when he accepted the Cancer Council's $30,000, he had no certainty that his request to the Rockefeller Foundation would be granted. Nor was there subterfuge: he had mentioned the Rockfeller application by letter and in person to Arthur Compton. The Cancer Council grant relieved the urgency of the moment; he hoped the Rockefeller grant, for the purpose of equipping the laboratory, would not be affected by it. Shortly after the first of the year the Rockefeller board voted $30,000 for a two-year period, payment to be made as needed and requested.

Meanwhile Ernest recovered his bounce; the activity of the Rad Lab was as stimulating to him as he to it. The year 1937 ended in an aura of success and optimism. The walls of the Crocker Laboratory were up; 196 tons of steel to be machined for the new magnet was at the Moore Dry

Dock in Oakland. Design of the accelerating chamber was progressing. The diameter was finally fixed at sixty inches, and it was now referred to as the "60-inch." Everyone was busy with the 37-inch, making radioactive materials and studying modifications for possible incorporation in the 60-inch. Visitors came from Japan—Sagane brought Motoo Sumitomo of the Imperial University of Kyoto; and from England—Oliphant, who hoped nearly to duplicate the 60-inch at Birmingham.

Letters from other labs expressed gratitude for help, similar to that from Harvard's Ken Bainbridge to Cooksey: "Our cyclotron design owes everything to you." The last 27-inch chamber was crated and shipped to Yale, on loan, as a former one had gone to Stanford. A piece of molybdenum which had long been subjected to bombardment in deflecting particles out from the perimeter of the old accelerator, was sent to Segrè at Palermo, Sicily. With this irradiated metal, Segrè and his colleagues discovered technetium, the first artificial element of the periodic table, created by continuous deuteron bombardment of the molybdenum.

On Christmas Eve, 1937, John had first administered radioactive phosphorus to a leukemia patient, after months of experiment by university biologists K. G. Scott, E. Tuttle, and S. F. Cook, which showed that radiophosphorus was absorbed selectively by the white blood cells of chickens, and after John's and Scott's investigations of phosphorus metabolism in leukemic mice. Professor I. L. Chaikoff, also with radiophosphorus, studied the mechanisms of phospholipid formation; biochemist D. M. Greenberg concerned himself with the role of vitamin D in phosphorus distribution in rickets. Joe Hamilton had watched the progress through the human body of radioactive sodium, chlorine, calcium, and potassium, and the rate of iodine transfer to the thyroid after oral administration. Radioiron was made in quantities for Dr. G. H. Whipple of the University of Rochester for continuing studies of iron metabolism that previously had won him a share of a Nobel Prize in medicine. Radiosulfur was sent to Caltech for biological and vitamin investigations by Doctors D. M. Yost, H. Borsook, and J. B. Koepfli. The use of many radioactive substances from the cyclotron led the distinguished English physiologist A. V. Hill to prophesy that history would show artificially radioactive substances to be as important to biology as the microscope, since, with them, the biologist could see and follow individual atoms of a biological system.

The demand for radioactive substances was so great, and so much time was consumed in making them, that physicists often felt discriminated against in the allotment of cyclotron time. Ernest, however, insisted that biomedical work was of paramount importance. Valuable as was the exploration of the nucleus, he told the physicists, it must never take precedence over anything that might lead to the alleviation of suffering and the retardation or elimination of dread diseases. Physicists should be proud to make such studies possible. With the completion of the 60-inch which, though primarily for medical purposes, would be available part of the time for nuclear exploration with far greater energy than ever known, the 37-inch could be devoted exclusively to physics.

Everyone at the lab—joined by many others—watched as the first huge, two-inch thick steel sections for the new magnet arrived, in February, 1938. And by the end of March, though it would take months to organize the laboratories completely, nonphysics appurtenances, including most of the rodent colonies, were moved from the Rad Lab to the Crocker Building—and there was a big Rad Lab celebration at Di-Biasi's!

Ernest was elected 1938 Faculty Research Lecturer, and on March 22 before an audience of two thousand he delivered a modified version of the more lengthy and technical "Atoms New and Old" address he had given at Yale in February. Demonstrations, in addition to that showing the two-minute interval between the ingestion of sodium and its presence in blood in the fingertips, now included illustration of the uptake of phosphorus in plants and cut flowers, the appearance of iodine in the thyroid, and projections on a screen of alpha tracks from a demonstration model cloud chamber.

Despite portentous events in Europe—Hitler gobbled up Austria in March—interest in cyclotrons and radioactive materials was as strong there as in the United States, though all looked to Berkeley for leadership in the field; as Karl Compton expressed it after a Rad Lab visit on the last day of March: "I believe it to be the most interesting and important scientific work now going on anywhere in the world." German scientists certainly were aware of the possibilities, though there were in all countries advocates of the superiority of stable isotopes over short-lived artificial ones. But De Hevesy, who relied on Ernest for them, found the artificial isotopes most valuable in his work. He wrote happily of the progress of cyclotron construction in Copenhagen and Stockholm. Joliot was pleased with progress in Paris, and though there were problems at Cambridge and Liverpool due to parts prefabricated outside those laboratories, Oliphant's cyclotron at Birmingham was proceeding well, just a step or two behind its model at Crocker. The Science Museum of London asked to borrow for display one of the old 10-inch cyclotron chambers, a request Ernest was proud to grant. A now-famous picture of twenty-seven men, concerned with the 60-inch, framed within its nearly 200-ton magnet, was sent to laboratory alumni and other interested parties as an indication of the size of the new cyclotron.

Ernest planned to go with Cooksey to the Washington meetings, visiting cyclotron laboratories en route, but on April 9, while skiing down a Sierra slope at some speed, he literally embraced a tree, bruising himself rather badly and injuring a knee. As he still hobbled painfully, with the aid of a cane, Cooksey went alone. Brobeck joined him later to appraise cyclotron modifications devised away from Berkeley, as well as to tell of new developments in the Rad Lab, in the growing give and take now possible.

Ernest had recovered by June 1. Leaving young Margaret with Helen, and with John's promise to sleep in the house, Molly and Eric accompanied him to Vermillion where he was commencement speaker at the University of South Dakota on the sixth. Before the ceremonies, he presided over a luncheon honoring Akeley and again publicly credited the revered dean for the inspiration to which he "owed the fact that I can labor in the wonderful field of research." Dean Akeley passed initial credit for Ernest becoming a physicist to Mrs. Akeley, whose insistence had led him, against his precedent, to urge the young student to study with him. Gunda, in better health than she had been for some time, and Carl, who met them at the train, drove them to Canton after the ceremonies for a two-hour visit with old friends at the depot, before Molly, Ernest, and Eric entrained for Chicago.

Molly and Eric went on to New Haven. Ernest visited Arthur Compton, Snell, and Newson at Chicago, and the following day went to Urbana, where Professor Kruger and Ernie Lyman were progressing with the Illinois cyclotron. Then to Rochester to see the cyclotron progress of DuBridge and Sid Barnes, and to discuss radioiron in anemia studies with Dean Whipple and colleagues at the medical school. Then conferences with Tuve in Washington, and benefactors in New York, before a few days' relaxation at Haycock Point. At Ann Arbor, on June 18, he received his fifth honorary degree, but his first doctor of laws, from the University of Michigan.

The initial $15,000 of the Rockefeller Foundation grant had arrived a few days before Ernest's return; everything had gone forward during his absence. The 37-inch had averaged just three minutes under eight hours a day, seven days a week, for the first seven months of 1938. "Exciting physics by Alvarez on slow neutrons was most interesting," Ernest wrote, but he thought everyone had a good project. The core of the 60-inch magnet was in place, and being wound with twenty-six tons of thick, wide copper strips. Visitors caught in the excitement of the 37-inch performance and construction of the unprecedentedly huge electromagnet included Rochester's DuBridge, Columbia's I. I. Rabi, Bell Lab's Karl Darrow, Bartol's Alex Allen, and Professor J. A. Gray of Queen's University, Ontario, who had joined Foster of McGill in trying to get cyclotrons in Canada.

It was much too interesting a situation to leave for a scheduled vacation cruise to Alaska with Molly, but he could not well get out of it; Elsie had come to stay with the children, and Molly looked forward to it. Though he wrote "just ideal" on a postcard to Cooksey, he was restless before a week was up. With the children in good hands, Molly thoroughly enjoyed the two restful weeks. There were still visitors when Ernest returned, and one completed core was wound on the new magnet. The pace at the Rad Lab was "humming"—all this was far more restful than calmly cruising the Inland Passage, knowing what was happening in his absence. There were also a thousand more students on campus than there had been the previous semester, a record 15,500 in all, including more than eighty graduate students in physics, a jump from the former sixty-five.

The 37-inch performed so well at 8,000,000 volts with steady 80 microampere currents that it was decided to try experimental neutron ray therapy on cancer patients before the completion of the medical 60-inch. Experiments with rodents and rabbits had been conducted since the first of the year and had been encouraging. With his usual impatience to get things done, Ernest asked the department of grounds and buildings to wall off a section of the cyclotron room in the old laboratory, immediately. Painters, carpenters, and plumbers under the competent direction of Wallace Reynolds, a university engineer who was becoming familiar with Ernest and Rad Lab ways, having supervised the placing of the Federal magnet, and been involved in frequent power problems when lights on campus and "half of Berkeley" had been blown out by Rad Lab loads, completed necessary modifications of the building in such a short time that even Ernest was surprised. He wrote congratulatory letters to those concerned, though physicists had complained of interference during the alterations—and the reduced space for physics when it was completed. The treatment room itself was pretty cramped, but on September 26, 1938, the first cancer patient was subjected to neutron rays under the supervision of Dr. Stone. It was possible to get only half a patient's body between the yokes, awkward for some exposures, but thereafter patients were brought for therapy one afternoon a week until Crocker Laboratory was ready to take them.

President Conant of Harvard happened to be at the lab on that noted day, and four days later Arthur Comptom expressed his pleasure with the activities and progress. He confidentially assured Ernest that a grant for the following year would be forthcoming from the Cancer Council. That was the day of Munich, the Chamberlain umbrella, and "Peace in our time." Compton was doubtful that it would settle the situation in Europe. Conant had been worried, too, and both were pessimistic over the fate of scientists in Germany, Austria, and Italy. Ernest had been concerned enough in July to have written Lise Meitner, inviting her to Berkeley where he could see that she would have no expenses, remarking that he had hoped since the days of the Solvay Congress to greet her at his laboratory. Professor Meitner's reply from Kungalv, Sweden, dated August 21, expressed gratitude and said she would certainly enjoy "seeing your beautiful apparatus and meeting all the people, the papers of whom I read always, with great interest and admiration," but that she had agreed to stay at Professor Siegbahn's laboratory in Stockholm, assured of a place and a stipend for several years. Closer at hand was the predicament of Professor Segrè who had written early in the year for permission to spend another three months at the Rad Lab, from the middle of July. Before Segrè could return to Italy, he received peremptory dismissal from Palermo; the first anti-Semitic laws in Italy had been promulgated in September.

Segrè's predicament was less difficult than if he or his wife and two children had been in Italy at the time; they were, in fact, without a country, but they were together—in a country free of persecution. Yet, proud of his European background, education, and traditions, it was difficult for Segrè to ask for help. Though he could not but consider Ernest friendly and exceedingly generous, privately he thought little of him as a scientist, and was somewhat disdainful of his methods. He thought well enough of the Rad Lab as the only place where he could adequately pursue his work, from which he had received the long bombarded molybdenum that had enabled him to make a celebrated discovery, and which he had depended upon for other materials nowhere else obtainable, but he was too accustomed to European ways to appreciate the Rad Lab's radical methods. He had been scornful of reports of success with the cyclotron before his first visit, certain that they were more American-style promotion than honest accounts of achievement, and his surprise that it actually worked had been evident even to graduate students. At an Ann Arbor conference he had attended with Fermi, he had expressed doubt of Ernest's statement concerning the measurement of a new isotope—until Ernest sent him a microcurie of it to measure for himself. He was one of the Fermi group that had patented the manufacture of radioactive substances by neutrons, a method which at that time could not compete with cyclotron-produced substances, patents for which had been applied for by the Research Corporation.

Nor did Segrè appreciate Ernest's sense of humor when told of Segrè's plight; Ernest said, "Fine, so we can have you for a hundred and twenty dollars a month." Then, seriously, Ernest asked Segrè if he wished to stay at Berkeley, that if he would rather be elsewhere, Ernest would use what influence he might have to get Segrè a position at the chosen place. Whatever his reservations, Segrè wanted to remain at Berkeley but was determined to safeguard the independence he feared might be jeopardized. He took a few days to announce his decision. Ernest, always short of funds for salaries, promised to find what money he could for salary, and Segrè was on the staff.

Ernest was soon called on the carpet for violation of the prohibition against employment of noncitizens by state institutions, except under very unusual conditions. Ernest was adamant; the conditions were certainly "very unusual." Early in 1939, Segrè took his family across the Mexican border and they reentered as prospective citizens. Ernest, somewhat aware that Segrè considered him less a scientist than a promoter, nevertheless was glad to have him in the group; Segrè, an outstanding scientist, is sometimes called a physicist's physicist.

Much as he deplored the expulsion of scientists on racial grounds, Ernest had little sympathy with scientists' activist roles in political problems. Oppenheimer's opposition to Nazism could be understood because of Oppie's emotional involvement. Why this understandable opposition to Nazism should cause him to attempt the conversion of others to the leftist side of Spain's political battle was never clear to Ernest. As for his late interest in American domestic issues, had not the New Deal boldly offered programs to aid the less privileged? The unemployed had been put to work—useful work, too, regardless of opposition claims. Works Progress Administration and National Youth Administration help in the laboratory could in no sense be called "boondoggling." The programs helped men and students who otherwise would have to beg. As for expense—the President, who had always had money, knew that money was for use. National debt, as Ernest argued with his New England conservative mother-in-law, was merely owing money to oneself. When it was needed, one didn't hoard it. The New Deal had attacked problems with imagination, which Ernest thought the only way to seek solutions, in whatever field.

But as a scientist, it was not his place to preach for it from stump or soapbox. Let others propagandize. A scientist's concern was science; his discoveries might develop into most important contributions to the future of humanity. As he quoted Pasteur in concluding his commencement address at South Dakota, after noting that "pioneer days and living off the fat of the land are over," one must "take interest, I implore you, in those sacred dwellings which one designates by the expressive term 'laboratories.' Demand that they be multiplied and advanced. These are the temples of the future—temples of well-being and happiness. There it is that humanity grows greater, stronger, better." And thus the scientist should contribute, instead of promoting causes, however meritorious. Ernest took a dim view of the A.F.L. teachers' union, in which Oppie had become active, and to which a few Rad Labbers had been recruited.

Though the President seemed to be turning from domestic concerns to foreign affairs, as Britain armed and treaties were scrapped, Americans, certainly in the Midwest as reflected in his father's letters, were determined not to become involved. One war for democracy was enough. Congress passed neutrality acts. And for all his disapproval of German emotionalism and conquest for "living room," Ernest considered agitation not only a waste of time but also unbecoming a scientist and wanted his laboratories free of it.

With arrival at Crocker of the big cast bronze vacuum chamber, with top and bottom cover plates of steel, interest in nuclear science was further centered on that small section of earth where his laboratories stood. Hopefully, its radiations—literally and metaphorically—might benefit humanity more than argument or ism, either of left or right. Nature knew no prejudice, science no political boundaries. Germany had no cyclotron, but Wolfgang Gentner, who had spent time at the Rad Lab, wanted to build one at Heidelberg. Cablegrams such as that from Bohr, "Copenhagen cyclotron working well, all institute wishes express thanks and admiration," or word of cyclotrons in Russia, where they were called "Lawrences," showed that physics was above politics, armies, and ideologies.

Rumors were again current in 1938 that Ernest would get the Nobel Prize. For weeks physicists had been positive that it would go either to Ernest or to Fermi, and many Americans felt Ernest the more deserving. He was aware that he was under consideration, as by all accounts he had been in 1937. The national press had no doubts; on announcement day reporters from all media were at the laboratory when Ernest arrived. Cables for radio, newsreels, and ordinary telephones were underfoot between the Rad Lab and Crocker. Ernest greeted the press good-naturedly, but, after a class, decided to go home rather than return to the labs.

The situation at home was similar; a horde of newspaper, magazine, and radio correspondents crowded his street. Wires were strung inside the house, where impatient men waited with pads and microphones. To Molly, again pregnant, it seemed a madhouse. Assured that her husband would be named, the thought of pictures, in her condition, was abhorrent; the trip to Stockholm for ceremonies at the royal palace loomed as a nightmare. She was wondering if she should fix lunch for all the strangers when the announcement came over the radio; the award had gone to Fermi. Expectation changed to deflation, audibly among the newsmen. Only Molly felt momentary joy, though disappointment for Ernest quickly dispelled personal relief. Ernest, who had been able to control his excitement when told of the tip that brought out the press, now displayed none of the disappointment he must have known. He said how pleased he was that Fermi, who he thought deserved it, had won the award. He reminded a reporter that he had told him a week before it would likely go to Fermi, and had explained the great contributions of the Italian.

When the wires had been rolled up and the last reporter and radioman had gone, he told Molly he was chiefly sorry for her; she would have enjoyed the court and the ceremonies in Stockholm; she explained why she would not at this time, and they consoled each other with such evasive aspects, until they laughed. After lunch Ernest returned to the lab to cheer his dejected associates. Later he could honestly feel the correct person had been selected, after Fermi and his wife seized the opportunity to escape Fascist Italy. After the Stockholm ceremony, they came to the United States, leaving everything but liberty behind them. Oliphant, on another visit of inquiry at the lab, thought Fermi could not otherwise have left Italy. He was pessimistic about Europe in general; England was furiously arming.

Gunda came for further therapy, and Carl joined them for the Christmas holidays, which this year were spent at home—for Ernest, at the lab. His associates took brief holidays skiing in the Sierras, or sunning in Death Valley. But from the second of January, 1939, everyone applied what time could be spared from essential tasks to the new vacuum chamber which, with its steel cover plates and related parts, weighed approximately 9,000 pounds. Work continued night and day until it was assembled, with auxiliary equipment and controls in place at the end of March. Resonance was first observed on April 17, 1939, and on the twenty-first—the day Mary Kimberly Lawrence was born in an Oakland hospital—the first voltage on the 60-inch cyclotron was obtained. The name "Mary" was chosen en route to the hospital, against Molly's initial objection that it would be abbreviated, as in her case, to Molly. Ernest said, "We won't let her be nicknamed." Smaller at birth than Eric or Margaret, she and her mother fared well. Were the cigars passed the next day for her, or the 60-inch, in which a beautiful, blue glow was visible through a chamber window?

But it was obvious that the 60-inch had not yet "arrived." Shorts in the deflector, frequency disturbances in the oscillator system—one problem after another prevented satisfactory resonance for almost a month. As Don wrote Snell in the interim: "We have been having trouble to get more than a very small amount of resonance and people's hair has been greying, trying to stretch every possible explanation to the limit to account for the situation. Last night bright boy Wilson inquired shyly into the possibility of the oscillators acting in parallel and not push-pull. . . . Salisbury, who had been wreathed in smiles for the past some days, is now sweating. Everybody else is delighted, as it is now more than ever obvious that as soon as the oscillators behave the outfit will go to town in a big way."

Locating sources of trouble had always been half the battle; a few days later, on May 17, a fine proton beam emerged and on June 7, a deuteron beam of more than 17,000,000 volts, with current of 80 micro-amperes! Larger currents were available on interior Wilson probes. Alpha particle energy reached 32,000,000 volts—the equivalent of more than a ton of radium. The huge 60-inch cyclotron, most powerful in the world, was a success. On June 30, 1939, iron was bombarded and the first radioactive isotope was produced by the 60-inch. The first cancer patient received neutron therapy from it on November 20, 1939, in the adequate treatment room of Crocker Radiation Laboratory.

Though Ernest wrote in June, "I have neglected almost everything to work on the new cyclotron, which if anything exceeds my hopes," there had been much other activity. He had been away only once—to address the American College of Physicians in New Orleans, and to see New York benefactors, in March—but there had been excitement the past January that had temporarily pushed cyclotrons and new laboratory into the background. Luis Alvarez, in a barber's chair in Stephens Union, noticed a newspaper headline about a split uranium atom. He suddenly bolted upright to read carefully what Niels Bohr had reported at a Washington conference on theoretical physics. Lise Meitner, throughout her scientific life a close associate of Otto Hahn, had been informed by him of his experiment with Fritz Strassmann, in which uranium bombarded with neutrons had split into two lighter elements, releasing the enormous energy that normally bound them together. Meitner and her nephew, Otto Frisch, concluded that fission had occurred, but had not verified it experimentally at the time of Bohr's departure for the United States. He had now received word of its verification.

Alvarez unceremoniously left chair, startled barber, and shop so quickly that the barber thought he must have cut him. He ran to the laboratory, where Phil Abelson who, trying to solve the muddle of supposed transuranium elements, had been puzzled for weeks by unexplained X-radiations from uranium after neutron bombardment. "Here's the solution to your problem," Alvarez shouted and thrust the paper before the startled Abelson. Not long thereafter they confirmed the fission; Abelson's strange X rays were not from transuranium elements at all but from those of approximately equal mass, in the middle of the periodic table. The uranium atom had split into two, with the release of enormous energy! Energy awesome to contemplate if the infinitesimal laboratory specimen were multiplied to even visible dimensions.

In the general excitement everything was forgotten but the various possibilities and the importance of fission. After it was explained at the Journal Club, Glenn Seaborg walked the streets for hours, torn between appreciation of the Germans' experiments and disgust that he had not arrived at their interpretation after so much study of "transuranium" elements. Alvarez and Ken Green observed the energetic particles with an ionization chamber and linear amplifier. Thornton and Dale Corson photographed them in a cloud chamber. Abelson identified one of the mysterious activities as iodine K X rays, one of the products of fission. McMillan studied the range of the energetic particles—it was all tremendously exciting. Alvarez, who had been doing notable work with fast and slow neutrons, searched for them in fission to determine whether neutrons were released and captured by other nuclei. "It may be the day of useful nuclear energy is not so far distant after all," Ernest, who had been considered brash for suggesting the possibility ever since Solvay in 1933, wrote to Alex Allen.

The Radiation Laboratory was not alone in rushing into confirmatory experiment after Bohr's announcement, which generated excitement everywhere. The February 15 issue of the *Physical Review* carried his report, and Abelson's "Cleavage of the Uranium Nucleus" from Berkeley. Confirmation was also reported by Carnegie Institution and by Johns Hopkins. The next issue carried verification by Fermi with J. R. Dunning at Columbia, and others. Bohr, a guest of the Institute for Advanced Studies, and John A. Wheeler, of Princeton, developed the theory in beautiful fashion, with the prediction that it was the uranium isotope 235 that was split by thermal neutrons.

The discovery of fission in Germany against the background of events there profoundly disturbed many physicists, particularly refugees personally aware of the ruthlessness of dictators. If many of several likely hypotheses were verified, the discovery so important to science might also be important for totalitarian war machines. Such release of energy, if harnessed and controlled, might be made the means of destruction on a scale hitherto undreamed of—just as it might also be used beneficially. Refugee scientists in the United States attempted to organize self-imposed secrecy in nuclear work here and abroad—without much success.

Though a few, including Harvard's Bridgman, closed their laboratories to scientists of totalitarian countries, Ernest was loath to believe that a good scientist consciously would support a Hitler or a Mussolini. Professor Bothe of Heidelberg, visiting at the Rad Lab early in the summer, had long talks with Ernest on the subject. The German, who had

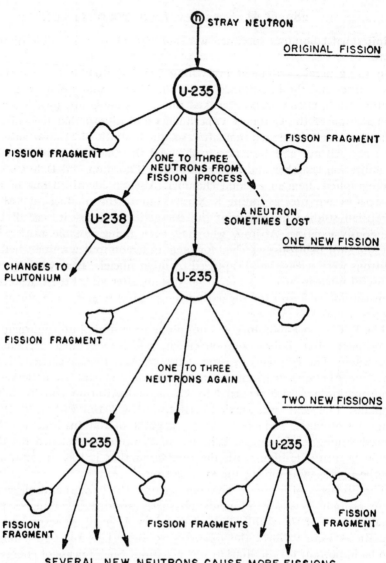

SCHEMATIC DIAGRAM OF CHAIN REACTION FROM FISSION, NEGLECTING EFFECT OF NEUTRON SPEED. IN AN EXPLOSIVE REACTION THE NUMBER OF NEUTRONS MULTIPLIES INDEFINITELY. IN A CONTROLLED REACTION THE NUMBER OF NEUTRONS BUILDS UP TO A CERTAIN LEVEL AND THEN REMAINS CONSTANT.

A nucleus of uranium 235, when split by a neutron, may release as many as three other neutrons, any of which may split other uranium 235 nuclei—thus chain reaction. (*From* Atomic Energy for Military Purposes, *by Henry De Wolf Smyth*) barely missed discovering neutrons the year before Chadwick identified them, appeared much more interested in science than in Nazi theories. Ernest continued to believe, encouraged by hope and faith in reason, that European problems would work themselves out. His laboratories would continue as energetically as possible in purely scientific pursuits and practical experimentation toward the welfare of mankind.

Normal activities were resumed after the flurry of excitement—if any work in the laboratories could be classed as "normal." John treated polycythemia patients for the first time with radioactive phosphorus. Martin Kamen searched for a long-lived isotope of carbon, exposing the element on probes inserted within the chamber, and tried to make sufficient radioactive iron for increasing demands. Requests for isotopes of various elements offset the greatly increased capacity of the 60-inch cyclotron, in which targets bombarded for as little as half an hour became intensely radioactive. Long-range handling devices had to be devised for safety of personnel, and even with five-foot thick water tank shields a third of the neutron intensities got through to the control desk, limiting safe stints there to no more than four hours a day.

Experimentation suggested by fission proceeded at a rapid and satisfactory pace. One would have thought that Ernest would be content to rest, considering the state of his laboratories and their worth, for a time. But even before the 60-inch had been proven, he had been thinking of a cyclotron "ten times greater." He spoke increasingly often, after the discovery of fission, of a truly huge cyclotron for nuclear physics. With what else could the nucleus, and fission, be fully explored? Visitors—"one of our main obligations is to entertain them"—such as Surgeon General Thomas Parran, more interested in isotopes and neutrons for medical use, wondered at it, after seeing the new huge machine in Crocker. Smyth of Princeton and Merle Tuve were urged to think about it. Merle wanted Abelson for his terrestrial magnetism department at Carnegie Institution. Abelson, who with McMillan correctly identified the first transuranium element, 93, and pointed out that 94 must follow, most certainly had been on the verge of discovering fission with his strange X rays: another week or two, Ernest told Merle, and he would have had it.

Alfred Loomis, at the lab for several months, worked on a project of his own that Ernest helped him design, as well as on the cyclotron when he was needed. He listened to and encouraged talk of a giant 100- to 200-million-volt cyclotron, which, after a few weeks at the Rad Lab, he considered justifiable. Loomis was helpful in many ways; through him Cooksey was able to help Basanti Nag get steel and copper for a Calcutta cyclotron.

Helen Griggs, who replaced Barbara Bridgeford as Ernest's secretary when the latter became Jackson Laslett's bride after his return from Copenhagen, thought there was as much excitement in the Le Conte office as in the labs. She was thrilled by the famous men who came to see Ernest. English physicist Charles Darwin, grandson of *the* Charles Darwin, whom Ernest let use his office, was an example. "I saw a lot of him. He kept inadvertently pressing the buzzer, each time wondering why I appeared." Helen had helped part time in the office before her graduation, and asked for Barbara's job. "You can have it if I like you," Ernest told her. "Just do what you can; there's hardly any trouble I can't get you out of." The first time she suggested writing a letter other than as he had dictated it, he stared at her for a moment quizzically. "Oh, well, if you like it better that way, do it your way." She wondered at his ability to choose such good people for his staff—though she sometimes thought he did not understand them very well, though he always tried. She had never seen such a group of "topflight" people. In time she worried some over his repeated colds and strep throats.

Charles Seymour, Angell's successor as president of Yale, came to see the laboratories and to discuss plans for advancing science at Yale. He even quizzed Cooksey about conditions necessary to get Ernest back at Yale. Don could not offer much hope but promised to discuss it with Ernest, whose answer was as Don had expected. Don reported to Seymour by letter: "As long as the University of California gives him the facilities for the development of his work, and adequate cooperation with the biology, chemistry, and medical departments, his love of California will keep him at Berkeley. Should it ever turn out that this cooperation were lacking or that the University did not do its utmost to help him, he would certainly leave, even though such a move would entail loss of time in building up a new laboratory." Seymour had heard predictions that California would not be able to hold Ernest, that some wealthy institution, possibly a foundation, would build him a center with facilities unparalleled anywhere.

A model cyclotron was set up at the Golden Gate International Exposition on Treasure Island, and the night before the official opening of the fair, Don Cooksey discussed it and the laboratory work over the radio. Ernest spoke on a national hookup, in which he described the new cyclotron, "the largest atom smasher built to date," and told of transmutations and the making of isotopes. He mentioned Dr. Stone and neutron ray cancer therapy, the results of which could not be determined for about five years; and of his brother's part in directing medical applications of the cyclotron. He also mentioned, for the first time publicly, his determination to build a cyclotron ten times as large as his new 60-inch, capable of energies near those of many cosmic rays. He had discussed such a powerful cyclotron for nuclear physics with Warren

Weaver during his recent visit at the laboratories, and Weaver had seemed impressed. The Rockefeller Foundation had voted the laboratories another $50,000 for a three-year period.

Germany invaded Poland on September 1, 1939, against the ultimatum of England and France, who declared war on the third. John was in Europe, having sailed from New York in July. His worried parents wired Ernest as to his whereabouts; Ernest replied that John was sailing on the *Athenia* and not to worry; that very evening, radios everywhere reported the torpedoing of the *Athenia,* said to be sinking off Scotland. Ernest was stunned, his optimism vanished, laboratories and plans were pushed to the background. Aebersold and a friend came to the house to sit with them as Ernest and Molly listened for more definite news. No one could say or do anything to help Ernest. Molly, perhaps as worried about her husband as about John, could scarcely reach him with questions or remarks; he seemed more withdrawn than he had been at the time of most concern over his mother's illness. They sat close to the radio for six hours, until it was reported that American passengers had been saved. Conflicting reports followed for nearly two days. Ernest talked with his parents several times by telephone, trying to sound optimistic, but was unable to eat or get restful sleep, until a cable from John proclaimed him "safe and sound." The relief left Ernest so distraught that he temporarily forgot John's request to bring pressure on the President to send battleships to convoy the Americans to the States.

John had indeed come close to death again. He was apparently the sole survivor from the area of the ship close to the initial explosion. The last American passenger accounted for—actually the last passenger to board a lifeboat—John had remained to the end, helping the injured, as he did for two days following on the rescuing destroyer.

Ernest had barely regained his usual buoyancy, when a letter from President H. P. Rainey of the University of Texas asked him to become his "right-hand man" as vice-president at $14,000 a year. Dr. Rainey said that the institution had an endowment of over thirty million and that he had every intention of bringing it to the first rank in the sciences. A cyclotron would be built for Ernest; the president "guaranteed that it would be a big one." He urged Ernest not to decide hastily, to visit the university, and then "take a year, if necessary," to think it over. Ernest happily showed the letter to colleagues. Professor Bolton said that Texas had great potentialities, and Professor Hildebrand thought the offer should be considered if Texas would build a greater cyclotron than could be had at California. Ernest reported offer and comments, by letter, to President Sproul.

He went to Austin on October 18, ten days after John's return, and promised to consider the proposal. From Texas he went to Providence to speak on the medical cyclotron at a National Academy meeting. Again he emphasized the feasibility of a 100,000,000-volt cyclotron with a magnet of three to five thousand tons—which brought gasps of incredulity from the audience.

A number of knowledgeable scientists, mostly chemists, thought Ernest claimed too much for artificially created isotopes. Nobelist Harold Urey thought they would be of little use; stable isotopes were so much better. A long-lived isotope of carbon, for example, had been searched for in many laboratories, without success, prompting Urey to assert that all carbon isotopes had lives too short for chemistry—to which Ernest replied, "Then chemistry will have to speed up!"

He was annoyed enough to decide himself on speed; he told Martin Kamen to drop everything else and find a long-lived carbon isotope. Kamen's search was spurred by this command—at least it was a blessing that granted priority for cyclotron time. The work of a number of associates was helpful in one way or another. Abelson explained unaccountable radiations indicated in Kamen's ionization chamber and amplifier, when he found these indications varied with Kamen's movements. He put Kamen in a corner, removed his clothes, and checked them, item by item. All the strange radiations emanated from the front of Kamen's trousers, radioactive from exposure. Kamen thereafter handled isotope production and his partner, Sam Ruben, assessed the results, never very encouraging. But they kept at it, and Ernest, too, refused to give up the search for what he felt must be, whatever a Nobel chemist might say.

There were reports from Stockholm that, because of the war, Nobel Prizes in chemistry and physics would not be awarded in 1939. So on November 9, when someone scrawled (and underlined) on the blackboard, "Assoc'd Press—E.O.L. has Nobel Prize—Unconfirmed," Ernest laughed and went to the Berkeley Tennis Club. A short time later the report was confirmed; he received the news on a court. He telephoned to Molly, who had just heard it by phone from a newsman and had shrieked, frightening the children to tears—and hurting the newsman's ear. There were no correspondents, at house or laboratory, when Ernest received official notification by telegram from Washington, and by telephone from the Swedish consul general in San Francisco. The press came later! Not only was he the first at California to win a Nobel Prize but also the first to win one while at a state-supported university. When he entered the Faculty Club dining room the following noon, everyone stood; there was a thunderous ovation. Telegrams arrived from all over the country. There were cablegrams from England, Europe, and Asia. Congratulatory letters arrived by the dozens on following days; a portion of one from Dean DuBridge of Rochester expressed the general sen-

timent: ". . . as I told you last year, most physicists in this country expected and hoped the award would be made to you in the near future. I
have heard this matter discussed on a number of occasions among physicists of my acquaintance and there seems to have been a unanimous feeling for the past two years at least that you were the outstanding candidate among American physicists for the Nobel award. Everyone will re-
joice in this tribute to the great work you have done at the Rad Lab."

The monetary prize, in excess of $35,000, was largely invested. It was
out of the question to travel to Sweden for acceptance of the diploma
and medal from the King, nor did Ernest and Molly wish to, with the
memory of John's experience fresh in their minds. Medal and diploma
were sent to the ambassador in Washington, and forwarded to the consul general in San Francisco. They were presented at a dignified ceremony in Wheeler Hall on the evening of February 29, 1940, before an
overflowing audience of faculty, visiting scientists, representatives of
other institutions, and among others, Ernest's parents. President Sproul
proudly presided. A moving recitation of Ernest's accomplishments and
a glowing accolade were delivered by Professor Birge. Swedish Consul
General Carl E. Wallerstedt made the presentation in lieu of his King.
Ernest's acceptance speech was brief, humble in tone, and generous in
ascribing his success to co-workers, past and present, the university, and
outside helpers. He had risen from a sickbed for the occasion; Molly and
John had thought the day before that he might be unable to attend the
ceremony in his honor.

Perhaps the medicine which helped most had been brought the night
night before, when Kamen and Ruben came to his bedside with the news
of their discovery of carbon 14 from neutron bombardment of nitrogen.
The new isotope had a life expectancy measurable in years, rather than
minutes or seconds, as with other isotopes of carbon found earlier. Ernest's exhilaration was so great, despite his cold and congestion, that the
young scientists left, overcome with doubt—what if, after the Maestro's
reaction, it should be found that a mistake had been made, and a long-
life carbon had not been found! They need not have worried; carbon
14, most useful of all artificial isotopes, had been discovered. It is this
carbon isotope which dates antiquities, and has become of major importance in biological studies.

There was, of course, a party at DiBiasi's for the "Noble Nobel Laureate" to which all Rad Labbers, past and present, were invited. The official announcement on the blackboard promised: "GIGANTIC JAM-
BOREE, triumphant, tremendous, tumult-unparalleled slaughter!
BROBDINGNAGIAN BRAWL AND BOOZING, Horrific, hellraising,
fabulous, fiesta! November 17th. Get your insurance renewed now."
Lorenzo Emo scrawled in a corner, "E.O.L. you owe me a case of Cham-

pagne," and when he saw it, Ernest scrawled "OK! EOL." Another added, "Thanksgiving—thankful for Laureate Lawrence, King of Atom Breakers"—and across the bottom was the reminder, "30 mikes [micro-amperes] every Thursday."

It was, as promised, a fine party, almost too large for DiBiasi's rooms. There were champagne toasts, the usual "speeches," "recitations," and, this time, a few serious observations. A ballad, "Hail Ernest Law-rence—Atom Smasher," by Aebersold, was sung to the tune of "I'm a Ramblin' Wreck from Georgia Tech." Many who could not attend be-cause of distance sent messages in limerick, prose, or telegramese. The contribution of DuBridge, from Rochester, was posted on the black-board for days afterward:

> A handsome young man with blue eyes
> Built an atom-machine of great size,
> When asked why he did it
> He blushed and admitted,
> "I was wise to the size of the prize."

The dominant culinary item was a cake shaped like the 60-inch cyclo-tron. "8 BILLION VOLTS OR BUST" was lettered in colored frosting across one side, and across the top, the words of Snell's telegram from Chicago: "DEAR ERNEST, CONGRATULATIONS, YOUR CAREER IS SHOWING PROMISE."

CHAPTER XII

"Leaping Ahead"

[1940–1941]

T he system was something like this: . . . while we were doing research with the 27-inch and the 37-inch was being designed, he was
dreaming up the 60. While we were using the 37-inch and the 60-
inch cyclotron was being designed, the 184 was being dreamed of by Ernest Lawrence."

Arthur Snell's comment brought laughter from his international audience almost a quarter of a century later, but it was no exaggeration.
When the 200-ton magnet of the "huge" 60-inch was admired, Ernest already foresaw one of 5,000 tons for a cyclotron developing 100 million to
200 million volts. His reference to such a machine had drawn gasps at
the Providence meeting in October, 1939, but "over 100 million" had
been mentioned since spring on various occasions. The figures in
a memorandum for President Sproul dated October 10, 1939, are for a
2,000-ton magnet, and energies between 100 and 200 million. In this
memorandum, after reference to the "completely successful performance
of the 60-inch," Ernest enumerates "compelling reasons for going forward without delay on a cyclotron ten times larger in the same year that
the 60-inch is put into operation," virtually the same reasons advanced
for the 60-inch and before that the 37-inch. But he could now add, "The
richness of the field opened up by the cyclotron is evidenced by the fact
that practically every laboratory of any importance in the world now
either has a cyclotron in operation or has one under construction. There
are more than 35 cyclotron projects underway . . . we at California
have a unique opportunity to pioneer a new domain . . . until we cross
the frontier of a hundred million volts, we will not know what riches lie
ahead, but that there are great riches there can be no doubt . . . evi-

dence of the cosmic rays convinces every physicist that this is so . . .
may be able to *tap the unlimited store of energy in the atom.* . . ."

Ten days later in New York, after a visit to Texas, Ernest told Warren Weaver, Alfred Loomis, and Dr. Frank B. Jewett, president of the
National Academy of Sciences, of his intention to build a new greater
cyclotron. They were interested; his ideas and abilities were not questioned, however much they were dazzled by his boldness. Poillon, of the
Research Corporation, so long a believer in Ernest and his conceptions,
promised help. Nobel recognition had established his worth in the eyes of
nonscientists. Ambassador Dave Morris asked Edsel Ford to discuss Ernest's plans with John D. Rockefeller, Jr. Dr. Weaver suggested that if a
larger one than Ernest had discussed would be *the* definitive cyclotron,
as the 200-inch was the definitive telescope, it also should be proposed.
He would submit both plans to the Rockefeller board.

Wally Reynolds and Brobeck worked on cost estimates, McMillan and
Cooksey joined Ernest on design. Student draftsmen helped. On December 13, Ernest reported to Sproul—too optimistically the president
thought. The proposed magnet at this point was 5,000 tons, in housing
120-feet in diameter. Sproul's doubts remained even after Weaver wrote
Ernest that money for one of the plans was practically assured. Ernest
then asked a budget of a hundred thousand a year which he suggested
Sproul could raise outside of the university budget! Nor was that all.

Ernest proposed enlargement of Crocker Laboratory to include a
twenty-bed medical physics hospital to be under the direction of his
brother, and to cost approximately $150,000. Sproul, when he recovered
from the shock, was not very enthusiastic. He thought it wise to proceed
one item at a time, and, he said, establishment of a hospital unit would
complicate relations with the medical school. But shock over Ernest's
daring ideas was common enough to be expected on the campus. Robert
Cornog wrote Bob Thornton: "The newest and largest cyclotron
. . . has been growing progressively and has now attained the size of
four thousand tons—correction four thousand five hundred—the four
thousand was yesterday. If it looks anything like the artist's conception,
it will be the eighth, ninth, tenth, and eleventh wonder of the world."

Weaver arrived in Berkeley early in January, 1940, to tour the laboratories. After conferences with Ernest, Cooksey, Brobeck, Reynolds, and
Alfred Loomis, he had a long luncheon meeting with Ernest and Sproul.
Weaver estimated that approximately $2,650,000 would be required to
construct the cyclotron and to ensure a proper program for ten years. He
thought the foundation would be interested in contributing $1,000,000
but he doubted that more would be available from it. However, he himself was very much interested and would be glad to recommend a larger
sum. Sproul did not think the university, or Western sources, could

finance more than the operation—$85,000 a year for ten years. He would ask the regents for this amount—even though it would mean allocating, to this one project, a sum equal to the combined research funds for all other departments. Weaver promised to present the situation to foundation president Raymond B. Fosdick and others of the board—perhaps any difference might be provided by a donor for whom the project could be named. The foundation definitely would not grant operating expenses, and, because of difficulties that had occurred in the past, would make no capital appropriation unless operating expenses for ten years were guaranteed.

On January 12, Ernest attended a regents' meeting with various pictures of the 60-inch and a complete report of activities, including treatment of cancer patients three days a week. He eloquently explained why $2,000,000 should be spent for a new cyclotron, when the medical one had just gotten into operation. He invited the regents to visit the laboratories and to see the model of the proposed great cyclotron made by Charlton Cooksey, on leave from Yale.

Alfred Loomis went East, ostensibly to discuss M.I.T. affairs with the president of that institution, Karl Compton, but in fact to get the elder Compton's opinion of the proposed cyclotron. Old friends and colleagues, bound by responsibility for another institution, they assessed Ernest's program critically; they concluded that it was worthwhile and that if difficulties with such an enormous machine arose, past history indicated that the Radiation Laboratory could overcome them. Weaver also asked that Compton's advice be confidential for officers of the foundation who wished "expert opinion from the world of science, before granting a sizable sum for what could be correctly and generally viewed as the definitive instrument for the investigation of the nucleus—the infinitesimally small—just as the two hundred inch telescope is viewed as the definitive instrument for the investigation of the universe—the infinitely great."

Karl Compton replied that the project was "one of the most interesting, the most potentially important, and the most promising projects in the whole field of natural science. . . . I should definitely place it in the number one position by a large margin among the various scientific projects of which I have knowledge. . . . No one could possibly question the selection of the University of California and Ernest Lawrence as the institution and the scientist to whom the project should be entrusted."

In February *Life* Magazine, a double-spread color photograph showed the emergence of a long purplish beam from the new 60-inch cyclotron. Ernest lectured about it at the National Academy at the request of President Jewett. He was elected an honorary member of the California

Academy of Sciences. Fermi, in Berkeley for the Hitchcock Lectures, and Oppenheimer discussed, and were inclined to agree with, Ernest's theory that mesons of cosmic rays might be developed, and their properties studied, with the projected cyclotron.

Weaver telegraphed Ernest that his division was prepared to present alternative recommendations to the Rockefeller trustees in April if he could be assured that, for either the $1,000,000, or $750,000 programs, the university would obtain not less than $250,000 from other sources, and agree in addition to supply the minimum maintenance budget for ten years after completion. Weaver cautioned Ernest that "recommendation is not acceptance." Ernest went again to Sproul—the regents' unanimous recommendation was forthcoming.

On March 25 Vannevar Bush, who had resigned as vice-president of M.I.T. to become president of the Carnegie Institution, arrived in Berkeley. He was followed a few days later by the Compton brothers and Harvard president James Conant. Somehow, these eminent scientists happened to be there at the same time; Loomis would only admit to getting them together in Cooksey's office on the second floor of the Rad Lab to discuss the huge new project. Immediately after the meeting, Karl Compton flew to New York to present personally their recommendation for the projected cyclotron to the Rockefeller board. He thereby deliberately missed a long-anticipated visit with old friends, the novelists Charles B. Nordhoff and James Norman Hall, who were due in San Francisco from Tahiti for a brief visit. Nor was this the only sign of the elder physicist-statesman's unselfishness; his recommendation postponed a grant for an M.I.T. project near to his heart. Loomis took the other conferees to Del Monte Lodge for the weekend, where Arthur Compton thought Ernest now more concerned about the Nazis than his project.

On the following Wednesday, April 3, Dr. Weaver phoned Ernest that the trustees had voted $1,150,000! The news was to be held in confidence until the university received official notification—a pretty hard thing to ask an exuberant Ernest. The official announcement was made on April 7.

Plans, already in an advanced state, were pushed. The magnet, to be made of steel plates, welded together, would weigh about 4,500 tons. Four hundred tons of copper strip four inches wide and a quarter of an inch thick would be required for the magnet coils. Pole face diameters were set at 184 inches, with a gap of approximately forty inches between them. A site in Strawberry Canyon above the stadium was first considered. Controls would be at least 150 feet from the magnet center for safety. Those neutrons! Would they turn out the blessing Ernest had hoped to prove them?

Arthur Compton had correctly sensed Ernest's concern over events in Europe—and the haunting possibilities for destruction inherent in fission, which had been discussed at Del Monte. Conant and Bush recounted concern among British scientists—Karl Darrow had written Ernest some months before of the near despair in England and France. H. Von Halban, in France, had experimented toward self-perpetuating fission for heat and power with five tons of uranium ore. If German scientists, as knowledgeable about uranium as Americans, were to succeed in making fission bombs, they would control the world. The general hope among scientists of good will was that such a weapon would prove impossible to develop. Power from nuclear splitting would inevitably be harnessed in the future. The possibility of a bomb was far less certain but should be determined—for, if possible, its force would be many thousand times stronger than any known explosive, and radiation from such a blast might prove even more disastrous. And Ernest—even against his will—"felt in his bones" that a fission bomb could be developed. If so, should not Americans do it first—before the Germans did—on behalf of humanity? The Nazi war machine would be stopped only by force. He did not then say it, nor did he like to think of the implications, but it seemed obvious that only the United States now possessed sufficient force, or the ability and resources to develop it. With nuclear bombs in their hands, the Nazis would probably be unstoppable by anyone! On April 9 they invaded Norway and Denmark.

It was known that the Kaiser Wilhelm Institute of Berlin was engaged in extensive uranium research. In the U.S., Einstein had been enlisted in an effort to inform the President of the seriousness of nuclear possibilities. A Uranium Committee, supposedly secret, had been appointed under the chairmanship of Lyman Briggs, director of the National Bureau of Standards. Ernest was unaware that anything had been accomplished beyond Alfred Nier's successful separation of uranium 235 from the much more abundant U-238! He hoped that all that could be done was being pursued by the Briggs committee.

On April 17, accompanied by Cooksey and Loomis, he went East for lectures at Purdue on the twentieth, and on the twenty-second at the National Academy—where, six months after so much doubt had greeted mention of it, he discussed the big new cyclotron. That day in Berkeley, the regents voted $250,000 for it.

On April 27, as one of the ten "Young Men of the Year," Ernest attended Governor Harold Stassen's dinner at the Waldorf. In off-the-record discussions of the war, he listened to the opinions of Stassen, Philip Reed, chairman of General Electric, and President Herman Wells of Indiana University. He did not communicate his fears of possible fission bombs; there was pessimism enough. Not all of the select ten were able to attend; baseball's Lou Gehrig was dying of cancer, and Spencer Tracy could not leave his movie set.

The following evening, Cooksey and Ernest dined with Poillon, who announced that the Research Corporation had granted $50,000 to the Rad Lab, and during the day Alfred Loomis took them to meet Edward R. Stettinius Jr. of the United States Steel Corporation. Stettinius promised to see that increasingly hard-to-get steel would be available. Loomis's entrée to Phelps Dodge Products Corporation brought assurance of sufficient copper. And he would keep after them on promises and orders after Ernest's return to Berkeley. Without his influence and help, there might have been neither promises nor orders.

Another bad cold, contracted in the East, continued to plague Ernest, and John insisted that he rest. It was hard to do, with so much activity at the laboratories, the medical program expansion, exciting nuclear physics—particularly the work of McMillan and Abelson in exploration of the mysterious transuranium elements. Surveys were underway for a road up Charter Hill. The great cyclotron would be up there where the big concrete "C" now loomed above the campus. Proposals for the new building had to be checked, magnet model tests evaluated. Paper work on Ernest's desk required attention.

Everyone on the staff had more to do than should be expected. Even when he could offer salaries, topflight men were now scarce—there was actually a demand for cyclotroneers! Many of the unanswered letters on his desk were requests for recommendations for his men. His determined policy was still that each man, however valuable, have the best possible opportunity; thus he had lost Thornton to Washington University at St. Louis about a year after getting him back from Michigan. For less skilled workers he asked more WPA help. He had found a couple of good electronics men in WPA, along with carpenters and electricians, and two that saved time for busy scientists by translating and summarizing articles from foreign scientific journals.

The flow of visitors increased, not only scientists now. Professor Herbert M. Evans brought Nobel novelist Sinclair Lewis to the lab, and both stuck dimes on the blackboard after the chalked figures of Rockefeller and other large contributions. Ernest himself brought Winthrop Aldrich, a Rockefeller Foundation trustee, from a San Francisco luncheon. On a night he entertained lab visitors at the San Francisco World's Fair on Treasure Island, he displayed more interest in the Folies Bergère building than in the girls. At a high moment of the program, he distracted those seated nearby with the announcement that its steel framing and dimensions made it admirably suited to house the new cyclotron. The following day he asked that it be obtained as a gift at the close of the fair. "Ernest came up to me in great excitement," Provost Monroe Deutsch noted for Sproul's benefit. "He had (believe it or not) attended the Folies Bergère—but in spite of it did not forget the cyclotron."

Excitement, activity, and work aggravated Ernest's lingering head cold and chronic cough. War news depressed him for longer periods than anything had before. He complained to his cousin Lawrence Haugen, now a commander, that it was hard to keep one's attention on normal problems. Nazi success, he argued, was due to "great freshness, flexibility and imagination in their military affairs, and they have taken every advantage of modern technical developments, while the Allies have gone along traditional lines. I hope that we . . . will look at the problem of warfare scientifically. . . . We need research and more research. . . . The Navy Department ought to be spending ten times as much for their research laboratory, and the Navy should somehow get the benefit of the best scientific brains in the country."

He was irritable at home and uncomfortable everywhere. Helen Brecko had finally retired, though she was available in emergencies. The devout fundamentalist who took her place refused to serve beer with Ernest's dinner. He was horrified to find her regaling a fascinated Eric and Margaret with a livid portrayal of the Judgment of Solomon. He was as irritated with her replacement, who "lived in," commenting about "fuzz on the stairs" and a "messy bathroom," though Molly might protest that all was clean before dirty children had washed up for their supper. There was no area in the house for children's play except the living room, and when Ernest was at home, he was either there or in his bedroom, having surrendered the little-used study on the lower floor to Eric. To make room for the baby, a small third room upstairs had been made by removing closets from hall and second bedroom, and a degree of quiet had to be maintained there. Consequently Ernest alternated between indulgence and irritability with the children when he was sufficiently ill to be at home. Molly finally decided that to run a house with a growing family, and with increasing entertainment demands on the kitchen, it was necessary to have more help, and a young high-school girl was hired to help with the children.

Molly drove Ernest to Yosemite for a weekend, late in April, which would have been helpful—if they had not found Margaret very ill when they returned. She had been accidentally kicked in the back by a playmate and had developed a severe infection and fever. Ernest was distraught; early the next morning he called doctors at U.C. Hospital and drove Molly and Margaret there. He stayed for hours that day and the next, until the very high fever and infection had subsided enough to permit Dr. Leon Goldman to clean up the enormous carbuncle surgically. Ernest left for the East when Margaret was out of danger, and Molly, driving herself to the hospital one day, realized that she was again pregnant.

Ernest's condition was unimproved when he returned in mid-June, and John insisted that he be seen by a nose and throat specialist in San Francisco, who said an operation would be necessary to relieve Ernest's congested sinuses. John objected to such drastic treatment and persuaded Ernest to join him on a trip through warm, dry, Southwestern deserts. They left at once by car, loitered in the sun of Arizona and Mexico, and along the Gulf of Lower California. Ernest was proud to land a 130-pound marlin off Guaymas while John, a regular fisherman, caught none. In Tucson, a nose and throat doctor they had known in Canton, South Dakota, found Ernest's sinuses improved, and after they returned to Berkeley by way of Zion and Bryce canyons, X rays at the university hospital indicated definite improvement. To keep a promise to rest for another month, Ernest took Molly, Eric, Margaret, and the high-school girl to Lake Tahoe, leaving Mary at home with the maid. He stayed less than two weeks.

During his absence, Don Cooksey and Wallie Reynolds had been to Pittsburgh and New York; steel and copper for the new cyclotron were ready for shipment. Road grading to the site was under way. Worry over the possibility of delaying shortages revived as the situation in Europe deteriorated. For all the heroism of Dunkirk, it looked black indeed for England. Norway had surrendered on June 9; Italy had declared war and invaded France the following day. On June 15, the German Army entered an undefended Paris.

President Franklin Delano Roosevelt, at the instigation of Vannevar Bush, fortunately, and perhaps designedly, in Washington now as head of the Carnegie Institution, established the National Defense Research Committee, and Bush agreed to head it. NDRC would have jurisdiction over Briggs's Uranium Committee and various subcommittees, all unpublicized. Scientists were asked to exercise discretion voluntarily in discussions of uranium or thorium fission, atomic power, separation of isotopes, and neutron studies. Scientific journals were asked to withhold publication of papers on these subjects. Ernest wrote Gregory Breit: "Heartily agree with the publication procedures . . . as recently as six months ago I should have been opposed to any such procedure, but I feel now that we are in many respects essentially on a war basis."

On June 21, the Markle Foundation granted $25,000 toward construction of the new cyclotron. The Research Corporation's $50,000 arrived. The next day France signed her surrender in the same railway car in which the Germans had signed in 1918. Adolf Hitler's little dance beside the car was pictured in all the papers. At the summer grove encamp-

With Ernest Lawrence *(left)* on the top floor of the old Rad Lab building on March 29, 1940, are Arthur H. Compton, chairman of physics and dean of physical science, University of Chicago; Vannevar Bush, president of the Carnegie Institution; James B. Conant, president of Harvard; Carl T. Compton, president of M.I.T.; and Alfred L. Loomis, physicist, financier, and trustee of both the Carnegie Institution and M.I.T. These eminent scientists had just agreed to support Ernest's proposals for the giant (184-inch) cyclotron. *(Photo by Dr. Donald Cooksey)*

Left to right: Carroll L. Wilson of the National Defense Research Committee staff; W. B. Lewis of the British Mission; Edward L. Bowles of M.I.T.; E. G. ("Taffy") Brown of the British Mission; Ernest Lawrence and Alfred Loomis, head of the NDRC radar division, on the Loomis front porch at Tuxedo Park, N. Y. John D. (now Sir John) Cockcroft, head of the British Mission, who took the picture, had explained recent British developments in radar and had appealed for American scientific, technical, and industrial help in the battle for Britain. The M.I.T. wartime radar laboratory, known for camouflage purposes as The Radiation Laboratory, was set up that afternoon. *(Courtesy of Sir John Cockcroft)*

M. L. (now Sir Mark) Oliphant's group of British scientists who worked at the University of California Radiation Laboratory on the atomic bomb project during the war. (Oliphant second from left, hands clasped on knee. At far right, back row, is T. E. Allibone.) *(Lawrence Radiation Laboratory)*

(*Above*) The first Alpha racetrack at Oak Ridge, showing the protruding ribs of the silver wound magnet coils and the covered, solid silver bus bar around the top. This racetrack contained 96 tanks for uranium isotope separation. (*Below*) One of the Alpha tanks with covers removed. On the right are the ion sources for the two beams which arc through the C-shaped tank. On the left are the two collectors for the precious U-235. (*Photos: United States Atomic Energy Commission*)

Ernest Lawrence and Margaret, Robert, Mary, and Eric on October 27, 1944, after the baptism of the children. *(Courtesy of Mrs. Ernest Lawrence)*

The world's first atomic bomb was detonated at the Trinity test site in southern New Mexico on July 16, 1945. Ernest Lawrence was among the witnesses as the fast-rising, incandescent cloud produced by the explosion turned the night into unearthly day. *(Los Alamos Scientific Laboratory)*

Hiroshima ... Smoke from the first atomic bomb dropped in warfare towering over the stricken city on August 6, 1945. *(United States Atomic Energy Commission)*

Nobel laureates Ernest Lawrence, Enrico Fermi, and I. I. Rabi relax in a lodge at the Bandolier National Monument after a Los Alamos conference in the spring of 1946. *(United States Atomic Energy Commission)*

With Professor Lawrence at the time of the presentation to him of the Medal for Merit are General Groves *(left)* and President Sproul. *(Lawrence Radiation Laboratory)*

ment of the Bohemian Club, to which Ernest had been elected an honorary member, there was much talk of affairs in Europe and possible serious involvement of the United States, but, in true Bohemian Grove fashion, emphasis was on relaxation and "the cremation of care," and though Ernest had to interrupt his stay at the grove for an important meeting at the lab, he returned to Bohemian Grove after a couple of days.

He was hopeful that European troubles could be kept away as easily; there was too much that might be accomplished at the laboratories that might be jeopardized by deeper involvement. By August 1, 1940, twenty-one cancer patients a day were being treated three times a week at Crocker Laboratory, as many as at the University Hospital, with the big X-ray machine. An increasing number of leukemia patients were receiving radioactive phosphorus. The first interest in industrial use of tracers was evidenced by the arrival of a pharmacologist, a physicist, and a biochemist, each head of a laboratory of the American Cyanamid Company, whose president William B. Bell, arrived two days later to discuss a cyclotron to manufacture commercial radioactive isotopes.

The German Air Force began its all-out attack on England August 8. Franz Simon wrote from Oxford that his children had been taken into the home of a Toronto University professor for the duration. The Blumers in New Haven contributed to a program to bring other families of academic people to America. The plight of non-German scientists in occupied countries was unenviable. Bohr was not bothered for a time; indeed Werner Heisenberg visited Copenhagen from Germany and asked that the Dane, constantly under surveillance, be less harsh in criticism of German scientists who, he claimed, resisted pressure to explore the military possibilities of fission. Bohr, like so many scientists who understood the implications, hoped that the development of a bomb would prove impossible. Joliot remained in Paris with his cyclotron, after burning papers that might be informative to the Germans. He sent his valuable supply of heavy water to Southern France, from whence it got to England. De Hevesy, in Copenhagen, sent Ernest $1,600 he had saved for a trip to the Rad Lab, to keep for him until he could make the journey.

Ernest did what he could to help find positions for refugee scientists but had troubles of his own in this respect. The matter of Segrè's employment came up again after Italy's entry into the war. Ernest had had to fight to keep him as a research associate and scratch to find funds for him. His efforts to get the Italian a teaching position were fruitless. Segrè was a valuable member of the staff, whose work at the lab had been outstanding. This year of 1940, with Dale Corson and Ken MacKenzie, he participated in the isolation of element 85 (from bismuth, bombarded in the cyclotron). Canadian MacKenzie, now a research fellow, also had to be defended against suspicion of him as an alien, as did Gee-Gee Wu. It was irritating to have to struggle to keep good people because they happened to be of different nationality—was not stressing nationality a Nazi trait?

On September 9, 1940, Vannevar Bush wrote to ask if Ernest, without hurting his important work, could head a roving committee, unattached to any division, "a sort of fire department" to call in on any problem that might arise, and suggested G. N. Lewis as a committee member. Ernest replied that he would serve in any way he could, but that it would be a little delicate for him to ask the dean of the chemistry department, so much his senior in age and service, to serve under him. Bush replied, "Forget the whole thing"; Ernest would soon be requested on short notice to attend a meeting concerning a new plan. On October 2, Bush telegraphed, "When can you come for important conference?" Ernest left for New York on the fifth.

Bush wanted Ernest on Karl Compton's committee of NDRC. Ernest immediately took the oath of office and, after conferences in New York and Washington, went to Tuxedo Park with Loomis for the weekend. On Sunday they were joined by John Cockcroft, in America with the Tizard Mission, to seek help in Britain's life-and-death struggle. Constant and destructive bombing and the threat of invasion demanded very rapid development of warning devices on which British scientists had made considerable progress. Cockcroft not only made Britain's plight clear, he eloquently pleaded for American scientific, technical, and industrial help to enable Britons to save themselves, their cities, and shores. He then spread blueprints of a new and secret "magnetron" on the floor of the Loomis living room and showed a model of the new tube vital to radar. Excitement displaced pessimism as Cockcroft explained England's scientific contribution to the battle for their Isles. Ernest could envision all sorts of possibilities with the magnetron, which could generate extremely short radio waves—"This is something you can get your teeth into!" he said. That afternoon, the foundations of a great microwave laboratory were laid. Loomis, backed by Bush and Karl Compton, wanted Ernest to oversee it; Ernest thought it more important to get ahead with the 184-inch cyclotron, but promised not only to find a good director, but also to help in every way with the organization of the laboratory and the recruitment of the best scientific minds for its staff; he would even sacrifice such men as McMillan and Alvarez from his own laboratory. After a little thought, he suggested Lee DuBridge as director and phoned him in Rochester to meet them in New York the following day. Late that night the nucleus of a fine staff and a program were on paper.

DuBridge promptly agreed to forego his plans at Rochester to devote full time and energy to the project. Initial recruiting was successful. In Boston, Karl Compton and M.I.T. administrators agreed to house and aid the laboratory. After a week, Ernest returned to Berkeley and persuaded McMillan and Alvarez to drop their experiments, important as they were, and return with him to M.I.T. to get the program under way. Larry Marshall and Win Salisbury also agreed to go. Others were persuaded by phone—insofar as secrecy permitted. "There is something interesting going on at M.I.T. that you ought to see. How about a visit there?"—was often enough, from Ernest. Rad Lab alumni everywhere were urged to take a month or two from personal work to help the project. With one or two who wanted to know when to go Ernest answered, "Why not today?" Cooksey drove him to Pasadena to recruit from Caltech. He went on to Boston and remained there a couple of weeks this time before returning to Berkeley—now shorter handed than ever. The radar laboratory at M.I.T. was officially named "Radiation Laboratory," in Ernest's honor, according to Loomis, who was responsible to Bush and the NDRC, and for disguise—let it be thought a foolhardy effort toward useful fission, rather than for something as possible and useful as radar proved to be in warning of coming raids on England, and later for planes and ships in the Pacific.

Robert Oppenheimer married Katherine Harrison in Pasadena on November 1. "We are thinking of you both today and wish you every happiness. We can hardly wait to welcome the bride Monday evening," Ernest telegraphed his friend, genuinely happy—and hopeful that perhaps Oppie would now forget his dilettante humanitarianism. They left their wives, after dinner that Monday, for the weekly session of the Journal Club. It was the eve of the presidential election, and Oppie was surprised to find Ernest undecided; Roosevelt had so strongly held his allegiance in the past. Ernest had gone with Cooksey to hear Wendell Willkie; the third term was a new argument against Roosevelt. At the Bohemian Club, he had heard responsible men of affairs back the Republican and decry the Democrat. But before the friends parted that night, Ernest had decided to vote for Roosevelt again—a fact which Poillon, his old friend and adviser, applauded.

Division of time between Berkeley and M.I.T. eventually caused Ernest to waive scruples against flying—"for this emergency." The projects required it. During one absence, foundations for the cyclotron were poured. On another return he found that steel for the magnet and copper strip for the coils had begun to arrive on the hill. After each return from a week or two at M.I.T. or an NDRC meeting in Washington, progress was evident. The first week in November, Don picked him up in Los Angeles and before taking him home in Berkeley drove him up the hill; the first huge steel plates of the giant magnet were in place and pulled together. Despite his repeated absences, everything proceeded well at Crocker. At the Rad Lab, Glenn T. Seaborg, with McMillan's permission, was continuing work on the transuranium elements and in December found what was later proven to be an isotope of element 94. Ernest strongly suspected that 94 might fission, and that it might be produced by neutrons and the plentiful uranium 238. If that was true, the construction of a pile was imperative. He discussed it with Fermi and Segrè in New York City the middle of December, with Bush in Washington, and in Cambridge with Karl Compton. Segrè would work on slow neutron fission of elements 93 and 94 with Seaborg's team of chemists. There was so much to do in the East, and as the presentation to him of the Duddell Medal of the Royal Physical Society would take place in Philadelphia on the twenty-seventh, Ernest was away from his home and family at Christmas, and for rest made his first visit to Florida. With Cooksey, who had been with him on this trip, he spent a quiet Christmas there, trying to rid himself of a cold.

The Duddell Medal was to have been presented by Lord Lothian, British Ambassador to the United States. Because of his untimely death, the first counselor to the embassy, with the help of Ernest's old friend R. H. Fowler, presented it at a dinner meeting of the Physical Society. Fowler "actually embarrassed Ernest with all the fine things he had to say." Professor Zeleny of Yale, president of the society, was chairman; Beams, Tuve, and a host of old friends were present. In London, on the same day, the Royal Physical Society celebrated the event. Ex-student Wilfrid Mann's proposal of a toast became a spontaneous recitation of Ernest's accomplishments, the spirit of his laboratory, and a tribute to his contributions to physics.

Oliphant wrote Ernest after the London affair: "It is remarkable, and a great tribute to yourself that without exception those who have visited your Laboratory, or worked within its walls, come away with a feeling of great enthusiasm for your work, inspired by the hard work of a trained team, and the pleasant companionship of yourself and all in the Laboratory. I only hope that before long this tremendous energy will be directed for a short time to helping free the world from Nazi domination. I am one of those who believes that victory will come to us in the end as much through technical superiority as through the undoubted merits and spirits of our troops in the air, on the seas, and on the land. In the tiny corner of development which we have ourselves touched we have already succeeded in making substantial steps forward, and when I compare our tiny team with your great organization, I feel that when you tackle the problem it will be solved in an extremely short interval of time."

Ernest and Don were back—this time by train—in Berkeley on New Year's Eve. They learned en route of Roosevelt's promised aid to Britain from the "Arsenal of Democracy." The hope was that it had not come too late, for England was being methodically bombed by the Luftwaffe—the winter of the long blitz.

Ernest arrived none too soon; Molly went to the hospital on New Year's Day, and their second son was born on January 2, 1941. There was great delight, particularly among the Blumers, that there was another boy. Ernest had debated staying in the East, to which he would soon have to return, feeling that Molly would have no trouble with her fourth baby, and that she and the infant might catch his cold. He had been dissuaded by her father. "There are two times," Dr. Blumer said, "when a husband should be present, at the laying of the keel, and at the launching." When Molly was asked for the baby's name, she phoned Ernest from the hospital. "Let's call him Don," he said, "and Robert." Molly told the nurse "Robert Donald." When Ernest saw the name that evening, he said, "No, not Donald. I want it to be Don," and so it is. His friends Cooksey and Oppenheimer easily won over his Norwegian ancestors. Molly did catch Ernest's cold.

Ernest's constant need to travel, his heavy schedules and responsibilities, coupled with his too-frequent colds, concerned Loomis. At a New York luncheon with Sproul, he proposed that a special university fund be set up to which he and others might contribute, and from which Ernest might draw at will, for laboratory programs and to ease his travel for national defense, without advance approval and state and Federal red tape. Such a fund would greatly facilitate his work and save valuable time. Ernest was much too valuable to be allowed to risk his health. With the university's sanction, Loomis then contributed $30,000 for this specific purpose.

Prior to this, and before the war, Regent Sidney Ehrman, who had visited the Rad Lab with a group of regents, had been concerned lest Ernest wear himself out with so much activity. "If I'd had somebody like you to talk to when I was in high school, I might have gone with science and enjoyed it," he told Ernest at one of the almost regular semimonthly luncheons they had together. Ernest and Molly were Ehrman guests at the opera once or twice a season. Mrs. Ehrman (a cousin of Governor Herbert Lehman of New York), who thought it unfortunate that Ernest had to travel on university allowances which provided only for upper berths and very reasonable hotels, had been the first to provide money for a university fund to free him of hampering restrictions. Don Cooksey contributed, to meet specific needs and, when he could, unobtrusively assumed expenses—not difficult to do; more than once Ernest boarded a train or a plane with neither ticket nor money. Molly and

Don learned to check with each other when possible to avoid such situations.

Involved though he was with the radar project, well under way early in 1941, Ernest became increasingly impatient with the pace of the Uranium Committee. No one could reasonably doubt that American involvement in the war would increase. Armament plants, barracks, and mess halls rose across the country. Millions of men had been registered for military service, yet the uranium problem, and the possibility of fission of elements 93 and 94, got scant attention—either from scientists in a position to do something or from the government.

Seaborg, Segrè, J. W. Kennedy, and graduate chemistry student Arthur Wahl chemically established the identity of an isotope of element 94 (to be called plutonium) beyond any doubt on the night of February 23, 1941—though they had worked on the element—assuming it to be 94—since December, and Ernest had reported their progress and the importance of the element to the program, to Briggs as early as the middle of January, and Seaborg had written of it to Abelson in the same month. On March 7, Seaborg had reported optimistically to Briggs on the possibility of fission: ". . . are devoting all of our available time to this and are pressing forward at as great a speed as possible." He added that, besides the four at work, only Ernest, Lewis, and McMillan were aware of the exciting results. Bohr and Wheeler had suggested that, theoretically, 94 should be fissionable with slow neutrons. Ernest continued to urge that the pile program be pushed, that 94 could be produced in quantity from regular uranium and neutrons; the tedious efforts to separate the uranium isotopes might then be unnecessary. Only at the Rad Lab was 94 produced and studied, until the St. Louis cyclotron was put to the same effort.

Ernest voiced his concern over the generally slow pace of the Uranium Committee when Warren and Mrs. Weaver visited Berkeley in February. Weaver was involved with a different section of NDRC, but he never tired of listening to Ernest's conjectures—not all of them of immediate concern to the NDRC. One night after dinner at the Lawrences', restless Ernest said, "Let's take a drive!" He took Weaver up behind the laboratory, chattering—Weaver thought unnaturally—as he drove. Weaver waited expectantly for him to get to the point, no doubt some aspect of the new cyclotron. On the hill, above the hulk of the giant magnet, with the stupendous view of the bay area and San Francisco—unmatched on a clear night—Ernest stopped chattering and came to the point—the cyclotron all right, but not the one whose magnet rose before them, much of it still in the planning stage, but about the *next* one, *much* larger, perhaps itself capable of fission! Weaver was very much irritated. This one, the great cyclotron, the definitive cyclotron, barely started, was forgotten! Ernest had slipped beyond it, was already planning the next! But Weaver's irritation vanished as quickly as it had risen.

"For half an hour or so I sat up there overlooking the marvelous Bay region listening to this marvelous person leaping ahead. I could only be tremendously inspired and lifted. He had a simply irrepressible mind. He couldn't think of anything without his imagination leaping ahead on it. A genius—perhaps the only real genius, certainly one of five or six, I've ever known. There is a distinction between a one shot and a multiple shot, and who else has done so many things? The big successes are usually one shot. After all, even Darwin has little aside from the *Origin of Species*—that and *Voyage of the Beagle is* Darwin."

Another February visitor, a onetime steel corporation president, William H. Donner, had been concerned with the state of cancer research since the disease had killed his son. Donner had been in the audience when the first paper by the Lawrence brothers, on neutron and X rays, had been read by John, who had then interested the philanthropist in visiting the Rad Lab. The brothers sensed Donner's interest in Crocker Laboratory work and discussed extension of its program and those facilities which Sproul had postponed during discussion of the 184-inch cyclotron. Donner came right to the point: how much was needed? They suggested $50,000 to $75,000. Donner said he would think it over. The following morning Ernest told Donner that a more considered estimate called for $150,000 to $175,000! Donner shortly pledged $165,000 for construction of a medical and biophysics laboratory to be named for his son, Joseph W. Donner. The regents approved a site by Founders Rock, near the Radiation and Crocker laboratories.

When Conant came for the Charter Day dinner address in March, he was urged to "light a fire under the Briggs committee. What," Ernest asked, not for the first time, "if German scientists succeed in making a nuclear bomb before we even investigate possibilities?" Briggs had communicated with Ernest, but aside from stating that as neutron intensities at Berkeley were many times greater than elsewhere, the effective areas of nuclei for a certain reaction, called cross sections, should be measured there. But Briggs's chief concern had seemed to be for secrecy. He requested that Ernest "guarantee Segrè's reliability" and warned that "Fermi has only partial clearance." On March 17, at M.I.T., Ernest told Karl Compton and Alfred Loomis that on his own initiative he was attempting to get enough U-235, the fissionable isotope, for study. He also planned to convert the 37-inch cyclotron to a large mass spectrograph. Small mass spectrographs had been used for some time to determine the mass and therefore the identity of isotopes. Why not modify and enlarge the instrument to separate them—specifically to isolate the fissionable isotope of uranium? Compton relayed Lawrence's plans to Bush and men-

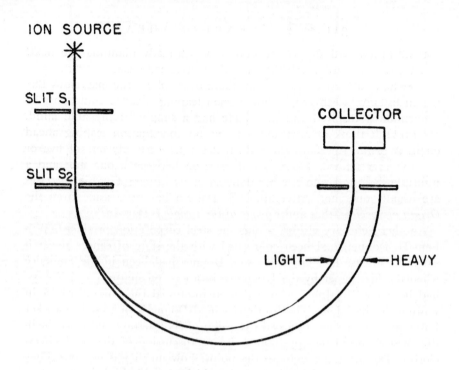

ION SOURCE

SLIT S₁

SLIT S₂

COLLECTOR

LIGHT→ ←HEAVY

MAGNETIC FIELD PERPENDICULAR
TO PLANE OF DRAWING

In the magnetic mass spectrograph ionized uranium, accelerated in a magnetic field, separates light from heavy particles, directing lighter U-235 to a collector chamber. (*From* Atomic Energy for Military Purposes, *by Henry De Wolf Smyth*)

tioned the general restlessness over lack of action by the Uranium Committee. He suggested that Lawrence be appointed Bush's deputy long enough to give the program the impetus which had started the radar program moving so well. Bush was somewhat irritated, later in the week, when Ernest confronted him directly to argue the seriousness of delay. Somewhat reluctantly (he did not wish to offend Briggs), Bush named Ernest temporary personal consultant to the Uranium Committee chairman. Funds were soon forthcoming for further work on elements 93 and 94 at Berkeley, and to enable Nier at Minnesota to separate enough U-235 with his small spectrograph for experiments here and in England. Ernest phoned the Rad Lab from New York to rush radioactive hydrogen by air to Urey at Columbia. It was because ". . . I made such a nuisance of myself generally," Ernest wrote, "that Bush requested the president of the National Academy to appoint a committee to survey the entire uranium problem and make recommendations." Ernest was a member of the Review Committee.

After the Seaborg-Segrè group demonstrated the fission of plutonium by slow neutrons, Ernest suggested that with enough plutonium a fast neutron chain reaction might be possible. He stayed in Berkeley long enough to witness the University Hospital's highest award, the Golden Cane, to his father-in-law Dr. Blumer; to show Archie Woods of the Markle Foundation the progress made at Crocker, and to have a drive in Cooksey's new Packard—to entrain again, this time for an April 18 meeting of the Review Committee, headed by Arthur Compton, and for meetings of the National Academy at which Robert Oppenheimer and Alfred Loomis were elected to membership.

The Review Committee met with those of Briggs's Uranium Committee who were in Washington for academy meetings and, later in the week, met with others in Cambridge. Ernest felt that no member of Briggs's group believed uranium fission possible for war use, although most supposed that it would sometime be important. The committee's consideration had been with uranium as a power source, possibly for submarines—though development of even that, the committee thought, would take too long. The Review Committee's report of May 17 recommended (1) intensified study of slow neutron chain reaction, (2) the possibility of radioactive materials for use over enemy territory, (3) the possibility of atomic generation of power to propel ships, and, (4) the possibility of a highly destructive nuclear bomb. Neither Bush nor Conant considered the report optimistic.

Nor was there cause for optimism elsewhere. London had its worst air raid on May 11, with more than 1,400 killed. The great British warship *Hood* was sunk three days later. President Roosevelt declared an unlimited national emergency.

Ernest phoned his sisters-in-law Elsie and Bertha Blumer from Washington to invite them to meet him and Ed McMillan for a Saturday evening in New York. As Bertha was engaged, Elsie met the train when Ernest and Ed arrived, and to Ernest's surprise and horror he watched Ed and Elsie embrace and very thoroughly kiss each other. "For heaven's sake," he protested, "you can't do that!" Ed and Elsie laughed and told Ernest they were to announce their engagement to the family the next day, Sunday. Ernest, who had been hopeful of kindling a romance, was skeptical, even after they reminded him that they had met several times at the Lawrence home in Berkeley, and had been with a group at Cooksey's in Trinity County, and that Ernest himself had asked Mrs. Blumer to invite Ed, alone in Boston, to spend the past Christmas with her family. He called the Blumers to verify the engagement. Then, joy-fully, they all talked to Molly on the telephone. To celebrate, they roller-skated, dined, and danced before going to New Haven. Ed and Elsie were married on June 7, 1941, at Haycock Point.

On June 16 Ernest became an honorary fellow of Stanford at that university's fiftieth anniversary celebration. In his address he carefully avoided mention of nuclear possibilities for war, though his subject was "The New Frontier in the Atom." On June 19 he was back in Cam-bridge for his seventh honorary degree, at Harvard, with, among others, Vannevar Bush and Viscount Halifax, Chancellor of Oxford and the new British Ambassador to the United States. After the ceremonies, Conant, Bush, and Ernest discussed nuclear power for ship propulsion, which interested Ernest far less than its explosive possibilities. There was no shortage of fuel and to convert ships from fossil fuels to fission heat seemed impractical in wartime. The sole emergency value of the pile experiments of Dunning, Fermi, and Pegram, as Ernest saw it, was as they helped determine the possibility of an explosive nuclear weapon. That question must be answered, one way or the other, without delay! Germany had no cyclotron, though Joliot's in Paris and Bohr's in Copenhagen were in Nazi hands, but there *was* strong evidence that the Germans were carrying on advanced work on atomic piles, using Czecho-slovakian uranium moderated by Norwegian heavy water. If a weapon utilizing element 94 (plutonium) were possible, and Germany devel-oped it first, the war would be decided. Germany could rule the world —or destroy it. Conant and Bush were impressed—and noncommittal. They were aware of the situation; Bush had been moving toward more effective definition of problems and coordination of efforts toward their solution. On June 28, by Executive order, President Roosevelt estab-lished the Office of Scientific Research and Development (OSRD), re-sponsible to him, and within which the NDRC would operate. Bush was named its chairman. The Uranium Committee became the S-1 section on which Conant would represent Bush; Ernest was appointed to it.

He again had to argue to keep Segrè, Gee-Gee Wu and Ken MacKen-zie. He told the administration that he could not reveal the vital work relative to national defense that Segrè, in the process of becoming a citi-zen, was doing, but that it was imperative that he not be disturbed. Miss Wu was a valued member of the Crocker team, which, in addition to bi-ophysics, was producing an important ingredient for OSRD; and MacKenzie was a very important member of the Rad Lab team, working overtime on another vital project for national defense. Ernest won fur-ther delay, and eventually held on to Segrè and MacKenzie; Miss Wu accepted a position at Smith College. Ernest showed the regents the progress on Charter Hill, where the steel-ribbed skeleton of a circular building, 160 feet in diameter and 90 feet high, surrounded the largest magnet in the world. A few regents were on hand at ground-breaking ceremonies for the Donner Laboratory, after which Cooksey put Ernest on a train for San Diego.

The successful organization and functioning of the radar program at M.I.T. prompted an NDRC request for Ernest's help in stimulating the Anti-Submarine Warfare Program at San Diego. After his first San Diego visit, he summoned Ed McMillan from M.I.T. to help at San Diego—to the concern of Loomis and DuBridge. In a July 10 letter to Bush he wrote: "Alfred and Karl, I'm afraid, have a little feeling I'm walking out on them in being so concerned with the submarine program . . . [it] seems so clear the microwave committee is well along . . . on the other hand the submarine program has not gelled and there is urgent need for the best scientific talent." He was delayed a couple of days on the next visit to San Diego by another emergency with Margaret, whose crying awakened him and Molly in the night. It was obvious that she was pretty sick but, as a doctor's daughter, Molly was loath to call one in the middle of the night. Ernest put Margaret in bed with Molly and tried to be helpful. She had to have her appendix removed the following morning. Ernest was worried until assured that she would be all right. The U.C. Hospital surgeon refused payment; Dr. Glen Bell wrote: ". . . Even though he does not have an M.D., I consider him part of the profession . . . and never know when I may have to come over and have him turn his Big Bertha loose on me!" From San Diego Ernest flew to Washington. Though he still had scruples, backed by statistical odds, on the safety of transcontinental flight, he requested general air travel authorization from OSRD to prevent airport delays!

He had asked that samples of "material," as the precious uranium 235 was called, for experimentation in Britain be sent through Fowler. Cockcroft, whose cyclotron at Cavendish was now functioning well, used U-235 thus obtained to convince the British uranium committee of its merit in a "super-explosive bomb." That committee, known as Maud, now urged on their American colleagues immediate attention to the separation of uranium isotopes. The experiments of an old friend of Ernest's, the refugee Franz Simon, favored for that purpose a diffusion process in which gaseous uranium hexafluoride was forced through porous diaphragms. The magnitude of that operation and the estimated $50,000,000 cost of constructing and operating the necessary plant practically prohibited the undertaking in England, and the British pressed their American colleagues to take it up. To get thorough firsthand information on the activities of the Maud committee, Ernest wired Oliphant, briefly in America, to meet him. "I'll even fly from Washington to meet at convenient time at Berkeley."

Oliphant was as impressed with Ernest's convictions and efforts as Ernest was by what had been accomplished in England. The British were convinced that a bomb could be made. They had measured new cross sections to determine the probabilities that bombarding particles would produce reactions, an essential preliminary. That investigation had proceeded so well under bombings, and in war, seemed remarkable and, by comparison, progress in America too leisurely. Ernest asked Oliphant to outline English work and ideas at an S-1 meeting; the Briton needed no urging. In fact he had intended to see Ernest; the British felt, he said, that if Ernest took hold of the uranium problem, results would be forthcoming. He was doubly sure of this after listening to Ernest's ideas on the possibilities of element 94, at this time called "copper" for secrecy, until the expression "real" or "honest-to-God copper" threatened to give the code word away.

In March, 1942, Seaborg chose the name plutonium for the new element, following McMillan's choice of neptunium for element 93, beyond Uranus, for which 92 had been named. Its symbol, Pu, was picked over Pl as much from a sense of humor as for any other reason. British scientists agreed that a pile for the development of heat for power would serve no useful war purpose; plutonium production from the controlled fission of uranium alone gave meaning to the pile experimentation at Columbia. Ernest thought every effort should be made to achieve proper pile construction and plutonium production. Conversion on his own initiative of the 37-inch cyclotron to a huge mass spectrograph, in which vaporized uranium chloride was ionized and accelerated across the modified cyclotron chamber in an 180-degree arc, would test the magnetic approach. The heavier isotope ions, under the influence of a strong magnetic pull, should enter a collector slit a fraction of an inch away from the lighter ones which would fall aside.

The activity of the Rad Lab was evidence enough for Oliphant of Ernest's interest in the overall endeavor. Before he left Berkeley, Oliphant planned similar conversion of his Birmingham cyclotron.

The idea of magnetic separation of isotopes on a large scale had been dismissed rather lightly in both countries because of space-charge problems. Experience with cyclotron vacuum chambers led Ernest to consider this random distribution of excess electrons not an unsolvable problem. That blue glow, visible in cyclotron chambers, was evidence of space-charge neutralization. Oliphant and Ernest, both bold experimenters, agreed that separation problems could be solved by one method or another. Ernest assured his British colleague that he would do everything possible to push every hopeful means. Oliphant, for his part, left Berkeley with renewed hope. ". . . how much I still admire the way in which things are done in your laboratory," he wrote after he left, "I feel quite sure that in your hands the uranium question will receive proper and complete consideration, and I do hope that you are able to do something in the matter.''

It did not take Ernest long to do something. Early in September he telephoned Arthur Compton in Chicago and told him that he could no longer entertain doubt that an atomic bomb could be made; that the Germans, with a head start, must be as certain; there was little time to lose if we were to catch up, let alone win the race for a bomb. Compton was used to Ernest's optimism, but Ernest's insistence that a weapon could be made with either plutonium or U-235 was convincing; he had a reasonable plan for building an atomic bomb, Compton reported. No other scientist had such assurance—would stake his reputation and his laboratory on such an unproved assumption. "What he was most certain of," Compton later wrote, was "that plutonium 239 could be made in a chain reacting pile and then separated by chemical methods from its parent, uranium 238. His evidence was good, that the necessary amount of plutonium would not be too much to produce and extract by this method. . . . The whole wartime atomic program was greatly indebted to the initiative and drive imparted by Lawrence. . . . His confidence in the success and his intent to let no barriers prevent the progress of the program gave heart to the entire atomic research team."

Ernest was committed to give an address on "The Cyclotron in Medicine" at the Museum of Science and Industry in Chicago on September 25, as part of the University of Chicago's fiftieth anniversary celebration. Compton suggested that Ernest come to his home after the ceremonies; he would also invite Conant, who, with Ernest, was to receive an honorary degree.

Ernest, who, in a letter, had written that he was involved in "at least a three ring circus," did not forget his laboratories on the campus—he was present when the foundations for Donner were poured—or the growing one on Charter Hill. Indeed, it was already in his mind that the huge 184-inch magnet might be used for an almost unbelievably large mass spectrograph before it ever became a cyclotron. For all his off-campus activity, he was able to push and inspire the medical programs of Crocker, nor did his zeal for interesting others abate. He planned the usual demonstrations for the Chicago lecture and wrote Newson asking that a Geiger counter be available. Newson asked in reply. "Are you going to be the guinea pig for both the iodine and sodium demonstrations?" "I was hoping to locate a couple of guinea pigs around the U of Chicago radiation laboratory," Ernest wrote. "How about you and Art?" A few days later Ernest received a post card from Newson, "Dear Ernest, Oink! Oink!"

In *Atomic Quest,* Arthur Compton tells of the meeting with Ernest and Conant by the fireplace of his home. Ernest spoke first of the results of English experiments, which, with those in the United States, had convinced him that a bomb could be made with only a few kilograms of fissionable material. He told of the Berkeley experiments that indicated that such a weapon could use either uranium 235 or plutonium. He proposed making element 94 in sufficient quantity, by pile controlled chain reaction, from plentiful uranium 238. Fissionable plutonium, a different element, could then be extracted by straightforward chemical methods. Uranium isotope separation meanwhile should be pushed along several lines because it was so complicated, since isotopes of the same element could not be chemically distinguished. The process of Dunning and Urey at Columbia seemed most reasonable, but Beams's centrifuge method should not be overlooked. Perhaps most expensive, but more certain, would be magnetic separation which Ernest would continue to develop at Berkeley. He concluded with the impassioned insistence that many able German scientists must have been at work on separation, and that it had to be supposed that they had made progress. The Nazis must certainly be aware of the possibilities of an atomic bomb; imagine the consequences if such a weapon were first available to them! He then vented his dissatisfaction with American efforts.

Compton thought Conant had seemed reluctant to proceed, and was in fact on the point of withdrawing support for nuclear research as a wartime study. Conant spoke of the need for scientists to work on problems *certain* to be helpful, said the country could ill afford to waste resources on anything of questionable military value. Perhaps his reluctance was a pose; he knew what the British were doing as well as what had been done in America. Compton supported Ernest, validating his interpretation of experimental results, and the reasoning that led to the certainty that a bomb could be made. Compton produced evidence of Nazi efforts, and agreed that the free nations could not "afford to let the Nazis beat us . . . this would be inviting disaster." Conant agreed that, if it was as important as Ernest and Compton maintained, there was certainly no time to lose. He admitted that he had argued that the uranium project be postponed for the war period, but if a weapon was to be made the U.S. must certainly do it first. He asked Ernest if he were prepared to devote the next several years of his life to the problem.

The question, Compton remembers, "brought up Lawrence with a start. I can still recall the expression in his eyes as he sat there with his mouth half open. This was a serious personal decision. He hesitated only a moment. 'If you tell me this is my job, I'll do it.'" Conant then told Compton to assemble his committee, examine the evidence, and get a report to Bush as quickly as possible. Procedure was outlined. Ernest would study the preparation of plutonium and the separation of U-235.

Chemists and engineers would be added to Compton's committee. Conant would discuss new developments with Bush and call a meeting of those most actively concerned, in Washington. Secrecy must be observed—it might be disastrous if the Germans knew they were in a race with American science and industry. As Compton wrote: "The fight had now begun, . . . the full strength of the nation must be rallied, nothing less would be enough."

Ernest asked Compton, in the interest of immediate action, to go at once to Washington and present Oliphant's report and other information to Compton's friend Vice President Henry Wallace, who could enlist White House support. This Compton did, to the annoyance of Bush, who had kept Wallace informed, and who was now constantly prodded by Conant. Ernest's enthusiasm and penchant for taking matters into his own hands could be annoying, but it accomplished objectives. He was constantly warned against consulting unauthorized people. Conant had rebuked him at Compton's house for having discussed his calculations with Oppenheimer; not that Oppenheimer was suspect, but because he was not officially involved in the program. Ernest thought the subject too important to forgo the calculated opinions of such a brilliant man as Oppie.

He had scolded Oppie again about his "leftwandering activities," particularly after Oppie tried to recruit him and other Rad Lab people for the American Association of Scientific Workers, an organization meeting at his house, attended by some Rad Labbers, junior faculty members, and student assistants. Oppie had been eloquent about the importance of scientists' taking an interest in political affairs. Ernest called those from the laboratories who had attended to a meeting in his office. "I don't think it is a good idea," Ed Lofgren remembers his saying. "I don't want you to join it. I know nothing wrong with it, but we're planning big things in connection with the war effort, and it wouldn't be right. I want no occasion for somebody in Washington to find fault with us." Lofgren thought his point reasonable; Rad Lab and Crocker people did not join the organization.

With Oppie, Ernest was more emphatic; there was no place in a wartime lab for questionable organizations. He warned him again against lending his name to "causes and concerns" not compatible with science. Oppie protested that humanity was everyone's concern and that "underdogs" should be helped by the more fortunate. Ernest countered that forestalling the Nazi threat was the most important consideration now; if Oppie wanted to help, he had best leave unions alone. He told him how he was responsible for having consulted him; that it had been disapproved in some quarters, and that he, Ernest, had insisted on Oppie's reliability. Bush, Conant, and Briggs were forever cautioning secrecy; a union in the laboratory could only reduce its value to science and the nation. When Oppie brought his brother Frank to Ernest, he again spoke of questionable activities. Frank promised that, if given a job, he would forgo the associations that had plagued him before and not get the laboratory involved in publicity concerning "causes," labor difficulties, and the like. Frank, too, was a first-rate physicist—why could they not stick to science! Scientists were being used, Ernest maintained—he had just replied sharply to Harold Urey's request that his name be used in connection with an organization purporting to unite the democracies of the world.

Oppie did not agree on the danger of a union in the lab until after he had attended a secret meeting in the East with Ernest, and had become sufficiently involved in the war program to see Ernest's point. Oppenheimer's decision that it might not be wise under present circumstances came at a time when Ernest had been called East. Oppie wrote to him in New York on November 12, 1941. ". . . had hoped to see you . . . write to assure you that there will be no further difficulties at any time with the A.A.S.W. I think that your own feeling about the men working directly with you will have a good deal of weight also with those scientists whose defense efforts are not in the Radiation Laboratory, and I doubt very much whether anyone will want to start at this time an organization which could in any way embarrass, divide or interfere with the work we have in hand. I have not yet spoken to everyone involved, but all of those to whom I have spoken agree with us; so you can forget it."

Bush had a conference on October 9 with both Roosevelt and Wallace and was instructed to determine definitely whether a bomb could be made and what it would cost. The President, too, emphasized secrecy. Certainly the need for haste could not be doubted. The sinking of ships carrying food and supplies to beleaguered Britain was increasing; now even U.S. destroyers were being attacked and sunk. The Navy had been ordered to shoot first at submarines found in waters considered vital to the U.S.

After receiving another honorary degree from Rutgers University on October 10, with a group that included Karl Compton, Queen Wilhelmina of the Netherlands, and Wendell Willkie, Ernest happened to meet Henry Smyth of Princeton. In a long discussion of the magnetic separation of isotopes, in which Smyth too believed, they reviewed the objections to it, chiefly the space-charge problem, and the difficulty of producing ions. Both agreed that all possibilities for large-scale separation should be investigated. Smyth and Bob Wilson were doing promising work at Princeton with a magnetic method different from that used at Berkeley.

In spite of the fact that Oppie had been involved with "unions" and "organizations" at the lab, Ernest had persuaded Arthur Compton to allow Oppie to accompany him to the October 21 committee meeting in Cambridge: "I have a great deal of confidence in Oppie," he wrote, "and I'm anxious to have the benefit of his judgment in our deliberation." His presence was authorized. But the pessimistic tone of the meeting alarmed Ernest. Engineers from the Bell Telephone, General Electric, and Westinghouse laboratories were unable to estimate either the cost of the commercial help that would be necessary, to build an atomic bomb, or the time involved. Oppie thought approximately a hundred kilograms of U-235 would be needed for a weapon. The committee was timid, but Ernest was insistent. He wrote Compton after the meeting: "It seems to me so clear now that in the light of recent developments everything must be done to expedite the uranium program. The stakes envisaged are fantastically high, and I should certainly not want to be one who impeded in any way an all-out effort to get the answers to the uranium problems as quickly as possible.

"In our meeting yesterday, there was a tendency to emphasize the uncertainties, and accordingly the possibility that uranium will not be a factor in the war. This, to my mind, was very dangerous. We should have fastened our attention on the fact that the evidence now is that there is a substantial prospect that the chain reaction will be achieved in the near future, one way or another, and that military applications of transcendental importance may follow.

"It will not be a calamity if, when we get the answers to the uranium problem, they turn out negative from the military point of view, but if the answers are fantastically positive and we fail to get them first, the results for our country may well be tragic disaster. I feel strongly, therefore, that anyone who hesitates on a vigorous, all-out effort on uranium assumes a grave responsibility."

"His unique contribution," Compton said of Ernest, "was a feasible proposal for making a bomb. No one else ever proposed the possibility. He came forward with what he felt could be carried through, and had something tangible to take hold of."

Ernest urged on his ex-student Robert Wilson, now at Princeton, and his old friend Jesse Beams, with his centrifuge experiments at Virginia, and supported the gaseous and thermal-diffusion separation methods of Urey and Dunning at Columbia. In Berkeley, uranium and plutonium had priority over everything else. The conversion of the 37-inch cyclotron was nearing completion; Ernest got $5,000 from Poillon to finance the effort. Chemists were studying plutonium by 60-inch cyclotron bombardment. Carl Helmholz was investigating the possibilities of fission in other heavy elements.

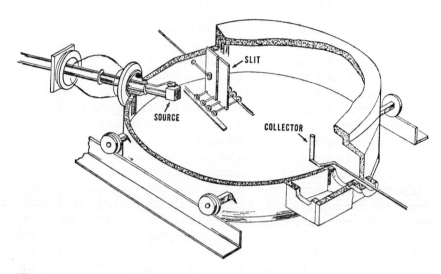

"D's" and other cyclotron parts were removed from the 37-inch vacuum chamber and replaced by devices to make it act as a mass spectrograph. (*Diagram by Helen Anderson from* The New World, *by Richard G. Hewlett and Oscar E. Anderson, Jr.*)

Laboratory buildings and available space in Le Conte were overcrowded. "We number ninety to a hundred, counting wives, biologists, and other necessities or oddities," Aebersold wrote in his invitation letter for the 1941 Christmas "annual sanctimonious cyclotron supper," which was sent to sixty-seven Rad Labbers fanned out over the country. Sproul made space available in the "New Classroom Building," later called Durant. The forms were almost all in place, preparatory to pouring concrete for the third floor of Donner Laboratory, when Ernest went east again. At the end of November, 1941, the 37-inch mass spectrograph was ready. Alfred Nier, an expert in this field, who came from Minnesota to help Seaborg's team, had found further positive factors pointing to the feasibility of plutonium fission. Ernest had cause for optimism! Certainly things were going well in his laboratories; radar work at M.I.T. was excellent—he had discussed this thoroughly with Win Salisbury and their host over dinner at the Alfred Loomis penthouse in New York—and a recent visit to San Diego and the Anti-Submarine project had been encouraging. On December 1, Seaborg brought the hopeful report of Kennedy and Wahl that spontaneous fission in 94 "is certainly no greater than in 235, and presumably less." For that reason, Ernest immediately wrote Briggs, "push should be given the pile work going on at Columbia to get a chain reaction going with a natural isotope mixture as soon as possible."

There had been less cause for celebration in the halls of government. Secretary of State Cordell Hull had presented Japanese envoys with what amounted to an ultimatum on November 26, but tension with Japan increased. On December 6, the 37-inch spectrograph actually separated a small amount of U-235 from U-238. That same day President Roosevelt appealed directly to the Emperor of Japan, urging peace, and Briggs told his committee the President would support a full research program in every way.

Early in the morning of December 7, the planes and submarines of a Japanese carrier task force struck at Pearl Harbor. On the eighth, Congress declared war on Japan by a vote of 470 to 1. On the tenth, Japan landed troops on northern Luzon in the Philippines, and sank the great British battleships *Prince of Wales* and *Repulse* off Malaya. Until now, concern and activity in American scientific circles had been directed almost entirely against Germany—a nation that now, having attacked Russia, was at war on two fronts. Concentration on the possibility of a German bomb had perhaps lessened awareness among scientists of the growing tensions in the Pacific. But there was little hesitation because of the new danger from Japan. Damage to American naval strength and prestige could only encourage the Nazis. More than ever it was necessary to "beat them to the bomb." The added drain on American industrial and material resources and brains, because another country had attacked the nation, must not be allowed to detract from concern with the danger that German science might succeed in fashioning a fission bomb. Anyway, there was little danger of such lessening of concern after December 11, when Germany and Italy declared war on the United States. The President was quick to act in the atomic matter. After conferences with his most trusted advisers, he approved the recommendations Bush had presented.

On December 18 the S-1 section met in Washington. Its first appropriation, $400,000, was for large scale electromagnetic separation work at Berkeley. No longer was there talk of nuclear power plants. The single justification for the pile was plutonium—for a bomb. The manufacture of conventional weapons was speeded up everywhere; science, already involved with war projects, now also must produce the ultimate, as quickly and secretly as possible, and in any way it could. The question that Conant had asked Ernest some months before, now confronted many scientists all across the country: the willingness to put personal concerns and projects aside for several years, and devote full time to the development and production of an unproven weapon so secret that most men were not completely aware of how their own efforts related to the whole program.

CHAPTER XIII

The Race

[1942–JULY 16, 1945]

Germany might well have a lead in any race for nuclear weapons; calculated guesses so indicated on the basis of what little was known. The Nazis' interest in uranium was known to be high, and their war plans were demonstrably efficient and unrestricted by old-fashioned strategy. Physicists, chemists, and engineers of high order were numerous in Germany. To the most optimistic scientist it was inconceivable that nuclear weapons had not been considered seriously in the country where fission had been discovered. Certainly a *Führer* would marshal scientists behind the war machine no less zealously than he had engineers and others able in any way to contribute to German might. Perhaps unity of effort, long established under dictatorial rule, could be offset by the spontaneous unity of a free people after attack, but organization for war takes time: planning, mobilization of resources and troops, transport, supply. In all the endless details of war carried to foreign soil, Germany was clearly ahead. Fortunately, the United States had made beginnings in the basics of armament as "the Arsenal of Democracy." As for an atomic weapon, the great topic of conjecture was—had Germany fully used her two-year advantage? Some thought so; no one knew definitely. But Ernest believed the United States had used that time too leisurely, in study and development of equipment. Only the day before the Pearl Harbor disaster, President Roosevelt had promised full support for the uranium problem—none too soon for so crucial a race against German science and technique, aided by the advantage in time. The destruction of ships and planes at Pearl Harbor had at least eliminated apathy, isolationism, and optimistic speculations about German nuclear possibilities. One must surely now assume that a nuclear bomb could be made, and that the first to achieve that goal would win all the prizes.

The Radiation Laboratory had had advantages over others in America; it was the "big lab"; it had, despite depletion of personnel for other projects, a highly competent and inspired staff; for months the nuclear problem had been its principal concern. Much of the operation of the 60-inch cyclotron had been for plutonium, then made only in Crocker. Seaborg, Segrè, and their assistants were deep in study of the new element. Since 1940, when Ernest had first suggested that plutonium might be as satisfactory as uranium, or more so, in a fission bomb, and might also be free of costly separation problems, he had insisted on full exploration of the possibility. Only six months ago, in July, 1941, he had detailed the advantages of plutonium in a special memorandum attached to a committee report: it behaved like uranium 235, it could be manufactured in quantity if controlled chain reaction with unseparated uranium was achieved and allowed to continue for a long enough period, it could then be separated from other fission products by straightforward chemical means, and it should make a very powerful bomb.

Experiment with the 37-inch had demonstrated that large magnetic spectrographs could separate fissionable U-235 from the very much more abundant U-238, in relatively large amounts—measured in micrograms. Separation of isotopes of any element in quantity is particularly difficult. Gaseous diffusion appeared to be the best means, but was yet unproven. Magnetic separation, long believed impossible on a large scale, might be quickest; Ernest, almost alone, was positive of it. He was determined that it and all other potential methods should be explored fully—no possibility in such a race should be eliminated without trial. He obtained Sproul's permission to stop work on the 184-inch cyclotron as such, and to finish its huge magnet for use as a gigantic mass spectrograph. Perhaps as many as ten separators would fit into the six-foot gap between the pole faces! But the magnet was not scheduled for completion until November!

He decided not to wait; time was more expensive now than money. Three construction shifts should complete the magnet by spring. He quickly estimated that $60,000 would permit the employment of extra laborers and technicians for work around the clock. When the OSRD refused to contribute toward what must remain university property, Ernest telephoned Weaver and urged a meeting in Washington on a very secret and important matter that could not be mentioned over the phone. In order to discuss it at all, he would have Weaver cleared. Weaver wanted no clearance; in any case he knew there could be but one thing Ernest wanted from him—money. When they met, Ernest asked for $60,000 additional funds to expedite work on the giant cyclotron —for a very important and secret project. "You've got to get it for me without any discussion about what it's for, with anyone." Weaver would do what he could. As soon as possible, he told President Fosdick of the Rockefeller board of Ernest's request. The money was granted "for unnamed purposes"—the only time the Rockefeller Foundation ever voted money without explanation. Crews then worked around the clock to complete the magnet.

It was less easy to implement the technical staff for design and construction of huge separation units for the 184-inch spectrograph, continue experimentation and production with the 37-inch, man the 60-inch for plutonium production, study possible fission in other heavy elements, and oversee all the necessary expansion concomitant with building and developing a huge new laboratory on a hitherto vacant hill. Ernest turned first to campus and friends: Professor M. P. O'Brien of the engineering faculty became executive engineer; and Wally Reynolds, already familiar with Crocker and the Rad Lab, was lent by the department of grounds and buildings for full-time service as managing engineer. Kenneth Priestley, of Associated Students, moved to the laboratory as business manager. Rex Barton, longtime friend of Don Cooksey's, and collaborator with Lowell Thomas, became an administrative assistant concerned with security, safety, and allocation of space. Cooksey and Reynolds recruited Wilfred S. Bigelow, who had hired and trained students as Realsilk Hosiery salesmen on many campuses, to handle nonscientific personnel matters.

Physicists were everywhere in demand. Ernest was unwilling to ask for men needed on other important projects. No further help could be expected from the Berkeley physics faculty, already depleted for war projects; Leonard Loeb was on active duty with the Navy, Harvey White had an NDRC project, and Robert Brode had a Navy program. Ernest unexpectedly acquired Professor Pan Jenkins. He had recruited Jenkins for the San Diego Naval Laboratory; Pan had left early in December on a two-week secret mission. On Christmas Day, Henrietta Jenkins, who had not heard from her husband since his departure, learned that he had been at Pearl Harbor during the attack. Ernest tried to allay her fears; Pan would come back. When he did, after the New Year, he joined Ernest's staff.

Former students and associates were called back; among them Bob Thornton from Washington University, St. Louis, and Reg Richardson from Illinois. Ernest persuaded Don Loughridge to leave his professorship at the University of Washington, and Clarence Larson his at College of the Pacific. Sid Barnes, early cyclotroneer, came from Rochester. Ernest wired, telephoned, and visited across the country. Those far from his routes to and from Washington, New York, and Boston were given travel pay for interviews; little explanation could be given through public communications. He persuaded L. P. Smith and his Cornell group to move to Berkeley where they could more fully explore their possible method of separation. To explore various other hopeful methods, Ed Condon and J. J. Slepian of Westinghouse spent varying periods at Berkeley, as did Irving Langmuir and Kenneth Kingdon of General Electric. Current staffers did yeoman work throughout: Segrè, Brobeck, Sloan, MacKenzie, Aebersold, John Backus, Helmholz, Bob Livingston, Byron Wright, Wilson Powell, Oppie's younger brother Frank; graduate students Ed Lofgren, Fred Schmidt, Hubert Yockey—so many! There was little thought given to hours. The first 37-inch separator, in a modified cyclotron chamber, produced eighteen micrograms of 25 percent U-235 by the middle of January, 1942, and seventy-five microgram samples of 30-percent U-235 a month later, for Chicago, Berkeley and British scientists.

Meanwhile, as the spectrograph called for a semicircular beam across the magnetic field, a C-shaped chamber, requiring less vacuum and offering less chance for leakage than the circular cyclotron can, was constructed. In one end of the C an improved ion source was installed to initiate a beam of uranium particles which arced 180 degrees and under influence of the magnet drew the heavier uranium isotopes away from lighter ones. These were deposited in collectors at the other end of the C chamber. Refinements were continuous, but this first C, by the end of February, already had produced more U-235 than had been expected, though the amount was actually very small. There was sufficient reason to believe that enough C's could produce the pounds necessary for a bomb—in time. Though gaseous diffusion and centrifuge experimentation had been started a year earlier, neither appeared to be as promising as the spectrograph method for early production of the precious U-235.

But more help would be needed to bring in the 184-inch with its huge separators, each perhaps with several beams and collectors. As it developed with its accessory buildings and shops, responsible plant supervision had to be found. Ernest turned to Edward Strong, philosophy professor and frequent tennis partner. He had borrowed from his Nobel Prize money to enable Strong to build his own house. After a dinner for the Lawrences in the completed dwelling, Ernest had taken Strong to see the new, developing laboratory and asked Strong, as a service to his country, to join the enterprise as manager of facilities on the hill. The philosopher soon found himself pitching scrap, working a thirty-ton crane, inspecting a water treatment plant, and checking shifts on and off the job. He worked 365 days the first year, including Christmas. Ernest

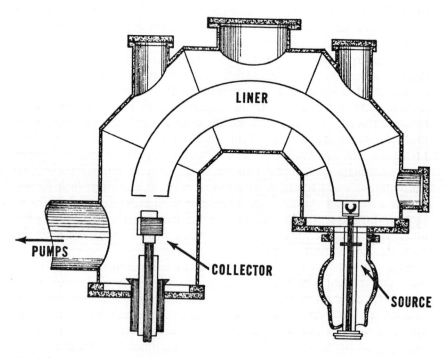

The first Calutron, the C-shaped vacuum tank built to operate between the poles of the 37-inch cyclotron magnet. (*Diagram by Helen Anderson from* The New World, *by Richard G. Hewlett and Oscar E. Anderson, Jr.*)

loved to tell visitors, "This was a philosopher, before I brought him up here."

Later in the year, during lunch at the Faculty Club, Ernest asked astronomy professor C. D. Shane to become director of scientific personnel for the laboratories. On an eastbound train, he met George Everson, who had been associated with the Farnsworth radio enterprises, and hired him as an administrative assistant to Shane. Jim Norton, electronics expert from Hollywood's Paramount studios, was brought in to supervise electrical maintenance; the electronics shop was under old-timer Bill Baker, who had once been fired for refusing to stop one thing to do another at Ernest's request and, when bawled out, had consigned the Maestro to hell. McMillan and Alvarez had tried to persuade him to apologize and come back. Baker had refused; he thought Ernest owed the apology. He had remained away until one day when Ernest asked Alvarez to camouflage a Geiger counter in a book. "Get someone to help you at once. NDRC wants it." Alvarez replied, "Best person I can think of for this is Bill Baker." "Fine!" Ernest said, "you get Bill. I haven't seen him around lately. What's happened to him?" Baker was rehired. Later Alvarez spoke of the time Bill was fired. "What do you mean I fired Bill Baker?" Ernest said. "I couldn't do without him. He's the most valuable guy in the laboratory." Alvarez refreshed his memory; Ernest thought it very funny.

He had never been dependent on name and fame as qualifications. He would try a bright student as readily and fairly as a man already established. Professor Joel Hildebrand's nineteen-year-old son, Roger, was surprised coming from a final examination. "Had any experience in electronics?" Ernest asked. "No." "You've built a radio set, haven't you?" "No." "Fine!" said Ernest. "Come with me." Young Roger was introduced to Fred Schmidt at the controls of the 60-inch. "You stand here and learn what's going on," Ernest said and departed. "I was absolutely floored," Roger remembers. "Of course I'd heard about the cyclotrons and the Rad Lab excitement, and here I was watching the control panel and admiring Schmidt. After ten minutes he turned to me and said, 'You.' I sat down and for a couple of hours he told me what to do. Then he left the room and I was on my own. Ernest dropped in now and then. Though I just barely kept my head above water, Ernest always said, 'Fine! Fine!' He might sit down a couple of minutes and explain things. I'd feel I really had the picture—and a great boost.

"On New Year's Eve he came in and said, 'I've been talking with Aebersold. Come on, you're too good just to be running the cyclotron.' He took me across the street to the old Rad Lab and the 37-inch. That was the most thrilling experience of my life! I had no notion of what was going on. Frank Oppenheimer, Carl Helmholz, Bob Livingston, Fred Schmidt, and one or two others all working so intensely—a little before midnight on New Year's Eve! They were working so furiously— and had been for hours—it really looked as though the war was being won right in that room! Horrible pile of haywire. The whole group seemed to have caught the spirit of Ernest; no time to wait for orders. No patch panels, and for insulators, bits of glass tubing. Common everyday light cord—an impossible mass of wires. Frank Oppenheimer was on his back screwing a switch on the bottom of a kitchen table.

"For a moment, Ernest surveyed the scene with obvious delight, then said, 'Here you are, go to work.' Frank asked me to heat a soldering iron. I got it cherry red and Frank lost time making it right. They said they were separating metals, tubealloy, magnesium, and aluminum. Those were all code words; if I didn't figure it out, I'd go back across the street. They were working on a mass spectrograph—had nothing to do with magnesium and aluminum. Something about uranium; the British had coined tubealloy for that. After I tumbled, I never had such intense instruction in anything. Again, Ernest would sit with me two or three minutes at a time and give a little elementary lecture—tunneling effect, mean free path—it all stuck in my mind. I caught the spirit. My first real job was to make a power supply for the filament [the source of the ions]. I rushed around and got a bunch of storage batteries. I really felt we had to have this *right now*. l burned a number of screwdrivers, dropping them across the power supply. Of all the war experience, that early work was the most thrilling; getting Ernest's instructions and so on—the relationship with Ernest at that time. And the way he'd operate!"

After the move up the hill to the 184-inch, Roger got the idea of using tantalum instead of tungsten for the filament. Ernest's interest in this gave Roger a "terrific boost," but he could be frightening, too. Once he asked, "How much AC power necessary for these?" (They were DC filaments.) Roger answered at once, as best he could. "Fine," Ernest said. He picked up the phone, called someone in Washington, and repeated the figures Roger had given so glibly. "Flabbergasted, I spent the night checking the figures. Ernest knew I would, and that if it was the wrong answer I'd get it right in a hurry and come crawling into his office with the right one."

Ernest liked direct answers. Later during a difficult period, when asked, "What are you doing?" Roger answered generally. "No! No! No! What are you doing *right now?*" Before Roger could respond, Ernest saw a man with his feet on a table, reading a sports page. "Get out!" he shouted. "You're fired! There's no room in this laboratory for anyone who isn't more interested in the outcome of the war than that." The man looked over the top of his paper without moving. "Mister, I don't give a damn who you are, but you can't fire me. I work for the telephone company, and I have to wait here for that phone to ring." Ernest stomped out of the room. He simply could not tolerate laziness, and, as pressures mounted, became more and more impatient with stupid mistakes. When a big tank that had been worked on night and day failed to hold a vacuum and had to be opened up to seek the cause, a cigaret butt and a pencil, which prevented a tight seal, were found inside. Someone on the welding crew cracked, "There must have been gremlins in there taking notes and smoking cigarettes." Everyone laughed except Ernest—he glowered and was furious. A whole day lost when every hour counted, with crews working around the clock!

When he realized that he would never get enough competent people through normal channels, he called the men together and gave a pep talk, as a coach might before a game. He was not very expert with jokes, but he tried one to illustrate the scientific approach: "One night a fellow got very drunk on Scotch and soda. So the next night he drank bourbon and soda, and got very drunk. So it must be the soda!" It was that easy to misinterpret results. "You can't see what you are doing here, but it's important"—and so on. After a truly inspiring talk, those who were learning technical procedures could become as efficient as the experienced. They were not to be discouraged by failures, Ernest told them; he had had many. The thing to do was get the job done; even economy was no excuse for delay—"We can't wait a week to save a hundred dollars because in this every day may be worth a million." He then asked everyone to recruit people they knew who could do *anything well,* whether truck drivers, first-aid people, or scientists.

In the first months of 1942 the expanding roster listed about a hundred people; more room in Durant Hall was made available. The old wooden Rad Lab was overcrowded. John's group, investigating high-altitude effects on fliers for the OSRD, occupied part of Crocker Laboratory until completion of the Donner building—already being enlarged to accommodate a low-pressure chamber large enough for fifteen people, to simulate various altitudes. Joe Hamilton, also in Crocker, was studying medical and biological effects of new elements and fission products, under another OSRD contract. Crocker was crowded, indeed. Direct cyclotron therapy had ceased. Dr. Stone, picked to establish an atomic health section, had headquarters in Chicago. Conant had been opposed to a big medical program as were some in Berkeley, including Oppie—if the boys at the front were taking chances, the boys in the lab could, too. Ernest and Compton thought otherwise; more was involved than protection of personnel. There were military questions to be answered; the aftereffects of nuclear bombing—radioactive material spread over a countryside, an exposed army, biological effects over long periods, and the effects of inhalation of radioactive dust.

Ernest had little time for his family even when in Berkeley, though in February of that first year of actual war his thirteen-month-old son, Robert, very ill with pneumonia and a middle ear abscess, drew him to Children's Hospital of the East Bay several times in two days. Robert was ill a long time and, after release from the hospital, developed an abscess in his other ear. Later that spring there was a five-week siege of children's measles and chicken pox, but Ernest was away most of that time. Fortunately, Molly had good help in Anna Olson, who had won Ernest's admiration on the night of the first air-raid alert and blackout. He and Molly, who had started out for a movie, and gotten sidetracked at the lab and caught there by the blackout, had inched their way up the angular, curving road to their house without lights. Anna had kept the children calm and remained so herself. Numerous guests never disturbed her pleasant efficiency—the Kenneth Meeses of Eastman Kodak were dinner guests at the height of the crisis with Robert's illness—and Ernest was glad to have her there when he was away.

S-1 Committee responsibilities and activities demanded more time than the Berkeley laboratories, whose competent crews were used to group effort on new and unproven projects. The Princeton magnetic program seemed hopeful for several months, as did Beams's centrifuge separation efforts at Virginia. Urey was discouraged with gaseous diffusion; though theoretically the best separation method, it had met with little experimental success. The pile at Columbia—about which Conant had had early doubts—Ernest considered as important as the other projects. Fermi's estimate of the toxic effects of plutonium was frightening, but that too could be overcome. If the acquisition of sufficient uranium ore loomed as a problem at least the turning of it into metal of sufficient purity and the right size and shape for a pile was in the capable hands of Frank Spedding, rare earth specialist at Ames, Iowa. Proper graphite to moderate it was the concern of National Carbon Company.

There was not time enough to wait for solutions before future steps were undertaken. Conant suggested, perhaps only for debate, concentration on one method of separation, but Ernest was insistent that all methods be urgently pursued. His magnetic method had proved it could separate the precious 235, but the quantities, though sufficient for experiment, were small; it would take a great many separators to produce enough for weapons. Conant thought it might pay to eliminate experimentally unproven methods and, expensive though it would be, to concentrate on as many spectrographs as necessary to produce the desired quantity. Ernest strongly opposed that plan; in this race, no white horse with any possibility of defeating the dark, unknown German entry should be eliminated. Plutonium, he thought, if produced in a pile, might prove the best solution, particularly if several weapons were necessary, but, until it was assured, separation programs must be pursued. Gaseous diffusion presented problems, but, as the British had suggested, it offered the most straightforward method; difficulties could be overcome with inventive ingenuity.

Consolidation of projects scattered from coast to coast would be beneficial, but there was as much disagreement as to location as there was on the merits of various programs. Berkeley was the logical place for complete centralization, if for no other reason than the impossibility of moving the huge cyclotrons and magnets, but objections from other laboratories prevented decisions. It was decided to center all pile, plutonium, and bomb studies in a "Metallurgical Laboratory" in Chicago where Sam Allison was constructing a pile. Fermi's project would move there from Columbia, eventually, as would Seaborg's plutonium chemistry team, from Berkeley. Diffusion separation work and heavy water production would continue at Columbia, as would centrifuge experiments at Virginia, and large-scale magnetic spectrographic separation would be accelerated at Berkeley. Compton agreed with Conant that magnetic separation surpassed other methods, if sufficient U-235 were to be available in time. Other methods might eventually prove cheaper; Ernest's at least, however expensive, seemed the shortcut to victory. Bush found the atmosphere of the Berkeley laboratories so refreshing and stimulating that he feared other efforts suffered merely by comparison. Nevertheless his report to the President was optimistic; he, too, thought the Berkeley program might provide the key to victory in the race for the bomb.

Ernest's association with the Anti-Submarine Program lessened as that effort got under way. But even at one of the last meetings he attended, his influence was decisive. As R. S. Shankland, of Case Institute, remembers: ". . . Ted Hunt of Harvard asked for support for his work on the acoustic torpedo . . . was very severely criticized . . . not enough supporting documentation . . . Hunt's request would have been killed except for support of E.O.L. After all others had said their pieces, he made a very thoughtful and persuasive and forceful statement pointing out the urgency of the problem and finished by saying that he would be willing to support with his own money a program of this type, if those working on it showed the *enthusiasm* that Hunt and his colleagues had demonstrated. This carried the day . . . [the acoustic torpedo] was decisive, along with radar, in the destruction of U-boats in May and June 1943 in the Bay of Biscay."

Conant, to lessen the disruptive effects of free-for-all argument in S-1 meetings, on March 13 limited future attendance to fourteen listed American scientists and four authorized British representatives. Yet argument continued to delay conclusions, and the substance of discussions leaked to nonmembers to such an extent that Conant asked Ernest to withhold his reports from the full committee. Unannounced meetings, limited to the few program leaders, became the practice. While Conant tried to reduce the number of divergent voices, Ernest remained convinced that much would be gained by the inclusion of Oppenheimer. On March 26, he reported that the 184-inch magnet coils would be completed by April 1, and added, "Want to bring to your attention the advisability of asking Oppie [to our meeting] . . . could serve as member of S-1. Would be tremendous asset in every way . . . combines penetrating insight of theoretical aspects of whole program with solid common sense . . . sure you and Bush would find him a useful advisor."

Oppenheimer, working with Gregory Breit—who had been dubbed "Coordinator of the Rapid Rupture"—calculated that three times the first suggested energy would be released in a nuclear explosion. He, too, was confident that a nuclear bomb could be made and that the chain reaction in a bomb could be withheld until a desired moment. The possibility of a more compact and manageable bomb seemed reasonable. Oppenheimer thought, with Ernest, that plutonium would more readily fission than uranium, and that it could be more easily produced in a pile than U-235 could be separated by any method.

Conant's early optimism over Ernest's electromagnetic separation did not remove his recurring doubts of the worth of the uranium investigation, considering how much it took from work that might be of more value toward winning the war. He favored elimination of the gaseous diffusion and centrifuge projects. He also questioned the wisdom of allocating another $1,500,000 dollars to a doubtful plutonium project, when so much remained to be done, even if pile production proved successful, and plutonium could be separated from other fission products. He sometimes wondered if the enthusiasm and optimism which Compton shared with Ernest were based on anything more than hope. The very insistence that all methods be explored implied doubt. Yet Ernest was as confident of the success of the plutonium project as of his own.

At a May 23 meeting with his leaders and, at Bush's request, to represent the Army, General W. D. Styer, Conant asked for individual recommendations as to which programs should be expanded, and which eliminated. Ernest refused to give assurance that a possible full-scale electromagnetic plant could produce sufficient quantities of U-235. He would know the answer in June or July after the first 184-inch separator was in operation. He thought a 100-gram-a-day plant would be justified. He also favored 100-gram-a-day centrifuge and gaseous diffusion pilot plants. At least one huge pile for plutonium production should be started. Recommendations of other leaders were similar. Total cost of all was estimated at $80,000,000 for construction and an annual $34,000,000 for operation. All leaders were opposed to any delay. Conant and Bush had foreseen such a vast construction program and had decided that only the Army, in wartime, could accomplish it. In March, General Styer had appeared in Ernest's office with an introductory letter from Bush: ". . . designated by General [George C.] Marshall as liaison officer. I wish him to have full information on all aspects. He will wish to consult you personally." The Army became part of the team—for plant construction.

On May 26, the giant magnet was turned on for the first time. Initially, the C tanks in its field were used for experiment on such questions as how many beams might be used in a single tank, problems of arc source, focusing, collection, magnetic field, current, and a variety of adjustments and relationships between all of these. Most of the work was on the basis of cut-and-try; theory alone would have stalled the operation. The Rad Lab system, "Start out and invent around the difficulties,"of which there were many, applied. Cyclotroneers on the job, old hands at overcoming variations in magnetic fields, used shims and tried cyclotron techniques to control the area, but it was September before beams successfully deposited isotopes into proper collectors—a continuing problem throughout the fall. Successful operation was maintained during the last quarter of 1942. At the suggestion of George Everson, the huge spectrograph was dubbed "Calutron," the University of California.

Army responsibilities for large-scale planning relieved Conant and Bush of many problems, but responsibility for supervision and evaluation of laboratory work remained with OSRD. With Bush's approval, Conant had formed the S-1 Executive Committee and limited membership to Briggs, Compton, Ernest, Urey, and Eger Murphree of Standard Oil Development Company. Colonel J. C. Marshall, Corps of Engineers, was assigned the tasks of handling contracts for construction, preparing for procurement of materials, and selecting sites for manufacture; because his offices were in New York, he called it the Manhattan District. Stone and Webster Engineering Corporation was appointed chief contractor for the project. A site originally intended for all the industrial plants was picked in the Clinch River Valley, west of Knoxville, Tennessee, where abundance of cooling water for piles, ample electricity from TVA for separation devices, easy railroad access, and as much privacy as could be expected of so huge an operation were prime assets.

Differences between OSRD officials and generals they were unable to convince of the project's importance stalled the plant programs until Leslie R. Groves, made brigadier general for the job, assumed control in September. Groves took over in positive, military fashion; priority obstacles crumbled, decisions were promptly made and followed through. Security under military responsibility further relieved Bush and Conant, but fears of many scientists over military interference were not lessened by the general's autocratic manner; only the presence of Bush, with Conant as alternate, on the newly formed Military Policy Committee somewhat appeased them. Rumors that Manhattan scientists would have to accept commissions came to naught—though Groves considered lack of discipline among scientists a prime fault. He disapproved of informal relationships between leaders and others on the project. "Ernest," he often said impatiently, "you should make these men address you as 'Professor' or 'Doctor' if you want their respect, and it would be better for you to call them by their last names."

Meanwhile, late in August, the S-1 Executive Committee again considered exclusive concentration on electromagnetic separation; even Chief Engineer A. C. Klein of Stone and Webster, infected with Berkeley drive and enthusiasm, considered the Calutron well enough developed to urge freezing of design and construction of a pilot plant. In September the Executive Committee, meeting in Berkeley, observed the activities there with optimistic enthusiasm. On the thirteenth, Ernest entertained the group—with Cooksey, Oppenheimer, and Thornton as consultants, and Colonel Kenneth Nichols and Major Thomas T. Crenshaw as Army observers—at the Bohemian Grove Lodge, north of San Francisco. Conant again demanded definite plans and recommendations. Ernest was still the most vocal opponent of concentration on the magnetic program: ". . . if such a decision implies that we are now picking a horse for a long pull, for it seems to me quite likely that other methods will ultimately prove to be better. The only reason for going ahead now with the mass spectrograph is that it appears likely to produce some useful materials sooner than otherwise, and almost regardless of cost we should endeavor to get, as soon as possible, enough materials for full-scale experiment." The committee recommended construction of a Calutron pilot plant, simultaneously with the start of a full-scale 200-tank system in Tennessee.

The Executive Committee first met with General Groves two weeks later. Already he had personally moved through channels to obtain unquestioned priorities. He had cleared confusion over the Tennessee site by ordering its acquisition. Groves might be blunt and shy of tact, but it was obvious that he would brook no delays, and that more decisive conclusions by the committee were necessary. But decisions came hard; the ups and downs of projects continued to pose doubts; new factors appeared.

Oppenheimer, whom Compton had asked to concern himself with nuclear bomb mechanics and design after frustrated Gregory Breit had resigned for other war work, had conducted theoretical discussions at Berkeley during the summer. He had been startled by the suggestion of theoreticians Edward Teller and Emil J. Konopinski that thermonuclear fusion of hydrogen might produce a far more powerful explosion than uranium or plutonium fission—and that it might be more easily attainable. Certainly the supply of hydrogen was abundant, and separation of its isotopes was a proven possibility. Production of heavy water (deuterium) had been neglected with the selection of graphite as moderator for the pile. The committee now made plans to resume its manufacture, though fission still seemed more feasible.

General Groves first visited Berkeley on October 8. A second type of C tank had been between the magnet's poles for three days, and Ernest explained its advantages over C-1. Groves was no more immune than anyone else to stimulation by laboratory spirit and energy and, like Conant, steeled his objectivity against the infectious enthusiasm. He noted the problems but was impressed by the manner in which research, development, and operation were carried on simultaneously. As he wrote in *Now It Can Be Told,* "We would never have attempted it if it had not been for the great confidence that we, particularly Bush, Conant and I, had in the ability and drive of Dr. Ernest O. Lawrence of the University of California."

Groves and Oppenheimer discussed conclusions of the summer theoretical study group. In appearance, the very casually clothed, wild-haired Oppenheimer was hardly one to impress a West Point general, but Groves appreciated the quick and penetrating intelligence beneath the surface. Compton had first briefed him on Oppie's ability. He listened to Ernest's extravagant recommendations for his friend with reservations; he knew that Ernest had been Oppie's chief advocate for participation in the program. Now Oppenheimer was concerned with bomb techniques and the coordination of data on controlled fission, much of it conflicting. Groves agreed that too little thought had been given to the actual mechanics and design of a nuclear bomb. Certainly it must have explosive material, but quality and quantity requirements would be determined by the weapon. He thought it unlikely that a nuclear bomb could be put together quickly and easily even when sufficient material was available, an attitude that had frustrated Breit.

Groves half formulated the idea of a military laboratory, independent of the others, to cope properly with the problems and complexities foreseen by Oppenheimer. He realized that design and manufacture of controllable nuclear bombs would not be easy and had come to Berkeley expecting to request Ernest to undertake the job. "I had no doubt that Ernest Lawrence could handle it. . . . However he could not be spared from his work on the electromagnetic process; in fact without him we would have had to drop it for it was far too difficult and complex for anyone else." Groves at first dismissed Ernest's and Compton's recommendation of Oppie; he was a theoretician, and Groves considered this a job for an experimentalist. Oppenheimer had no administrative experience, and—for Groves a major consideration—he was not a Nobel laureate as were other laboratory chiefs. The Military Policy Committee opposed his selection. The project took on increased importance in Groves' eyes; he gave the new laboratory the symbol Y before either its location or its leader was selected. He vetoed the Tennessee site and both the Metallurgical and Radiation Laboratories—there would be too much gossip among the scientists if all projects were bunched. Y must be remote, and military.

Nevertheless it was now assumed that Oppenheimer would head it. Ernest and Compton assured Groves that, if Oppie failed, Ernest would take over. Utmost secrecy would have to be maintained; the possibility of a hydrogen fusion bomb, treated so secretly that Oppie had crossed the country to report it personally to Compton, had been discussed in Berkeley and Chicago before it was reported to Conant and Bush. At Groves' suggestion, Oppie applied for an Army commission, and set about recruiting key personnel. He found much opposition to the release of desired physicists from critical war projects for something that could be described only as "important." Oppie also found resistance from scientists themselves. Join the Army! Work directly under the military! If Groves complained that scientists failed to understand discipline, most scientists considered military rigidity dangerous. Science must be open to question, not subject to command; nor could military ideas of security be coupled with scientific practices. Groves finally agreed that laboratory organization be civilian and persuaded the University of California to take it under its wing. A military post would, however, be established at Y, and, in the final stages of the work, special conditions would likely require that scientists and engineers be commissioned.

Ed McMillan, one of the first recruits, obtained his release from the San Diego Anti-Submarine Project, and in November joined Oppie and Colonel Dudley in the search for a suitable site. Army surveys eliminated all but two areas, each within a fifty-mile radius of Albuquerque, New Mexico. Los Alamos, high on a mesa twenty miles from Santa Fe was chosen. Groves soon had contractors at work preparing the site. Oppenheimer intensified recruitment. John Manley, who had served the summer committee experimentally, Robert Serber, one of Oppie's bright Berkeley students, theoretician Edward Teller, and Ed McMillan planned laboratory organization. Groves was pleased with the progress until security authorities protested Oppie's inclusion in the project and denied him clearance for Manhattan District work! Though every S-1 leader endorsed his appointment, and opposition on the Military Policy Committee had evaporated, military counterintelligence considered him too great a risk.

On January 15, 1943, Ernest again vouched for his colleague, this time in writing. "To whom it may concern: I have known J. Robert Oppenheimer for fourteen years as a faculty colleague and close personal friend. I am glad to recommend him in the highest terms as a man of great intellectual caliber and of fine character and personality. There can be no question as to his integrity." The issue was not settled for another six months, when Groves, tired of the annoyance, issued a fiat: "In accordance with my verbal directions of July 15, it is desired that clearance be issued for the employment of Julius Robert Oppenheimer without delay, irrespective of the information which you have concerning Mr. Oppenheimer. He is absolutely essential to the project."

Oppenheimer's letter of appointment, signed by Conant and Groves, followed. Shane, with Oppie shortly afterward on a recruiting trip, noted some bitterness over it on Oppie's part, in which the university was also an object. Shane assured Oppie that there had been only support for him from laboratory and university. That Ernest, whom Shane called "one of the three most admired men of my career," could be considered other than as a supporter seemed ridiculous, however he felt about Oppie's "causes."

Ernest's Calutron project proved an up-and-down affair requiring continuous experiment. Problems were overcome by "inventing around them." By the end of 1942 a variety of separators, each with its code name and each with a variety of collectors and sources, had been tried at Berkeley. At a late December, 1942, meeting, at which the Army and Stone and Webster were represented, design was frozen and construction of a 500-tank electromagnetic plant authorized. Design and experiment for future Calutrons continued. A most favorable feature was the fact that units could produce while adjoining ones were under experiment or repair, whereas the other methods required continuous flow. Thus, with the electromagnetic batch process, continued production was expected even during partial breakdown.

Stone and Webster representatives remained at Berkeley. A large group from the Tennessee Eastman Company, headed by Fred Conklin, arrived February 1, 1943, to learn operational procedures. Ernest's people occupied part of Donner Laboratory when it was finished, John and his aeromedical group the rest. Shops and small offices on the hill were crowded; several rooms in Le Conte were occupied by Manhattan District people. Plutonium was still manufactured and shipped from Crocker Laboratory, in charge of Joe Hamilton, and special problems of radioactivity were studied there. Though Seaborg's group had moved to Chicago, much project chemistry was carried on at Berkeley under Dean Wendell Latimer. Personnel were trained for Los Alamos plutonium work. Cleared technicians were sent to New Mexico and replaced with new recruits. All of Durant Hall was finally turned over to the project, at Groves' request.

Ernest made repeated trips all through 1942, for meetings, investigations of research, and plant equipment conferences with General Electric, Westinghouse, and Allis Chalmers. The plutonium project constantly needed support even after Groves took over. Not only was there slow progress with pile construction but there were also unknown factors concerning the reactions of element 94—among other problems. In the fall, reports of James Chadwick's fears of spontaneous fission, if seemingly impossible levels of purity were not maintained, had alarmed and annoyed Conant. Why had neither Ernest nor Compton mentioned it? Groves appointed Ernest, Oppie, Compton, and McMillan to investigate the situation thoroughly. New purity standards were established that would add to the difficulties of extraction and manufacture, but which Ernest and Compton assured Groves were safe and not impossible to meet. Fortunately the Chicago pile was completed and began functioning on December 2, the very day a review committee was present to decide its fate! Apprised of the historic achievement by Compton, Ernest wired back: "Congratulations to the parents. Can hardly wait to see the new arrival."

Ernest was able to receive another honorary degree in person, at the University of Pennsylvania—and take the opportunity to recruit good men. He had to postpone personal acceptance of the Holley Medal of the American Society of Mechanical Engineers. Alone in New York, he sometimes telephoned Mrs. Blumer and begged her to come down from New Haven for dinner and the theater. Dr. Blumer disapproved, somewhat, because of the late hour at which she would have to return alone. But aware that he was involved in the war effort, they were glad to provide needed relaxation. Mabel Blumer and Ernest enjoyed each other's company, however exasperating she thought his politics. At other times he might dine alone where someone entertained at the piano. A room for him was always available at the Loomis town residence, as also at the Loomis quarters in the Wardman Park Hotel in Washington. Once he asked Margaret Haugen to meet him there between afternoon appointments. He pointed out a suspicious man sitting nearby in the bar who had been following him; when they left so did the man.

The outstanding extracurricular events of early summer, 1942, were occasioned by weddings, including those of the Rad Lab's three most eligible—or incorrigible—bachelors. The first, and most social, was John's marriage to lovely Amy Bowles, on June 20, at Trinity Church, San Francisco—and the gala reception that followed. Ernest was his brother's best man, and five ushers were from the Rad Lab and Crocker. Six days later Don Cooksey, most incorrigible of the incorrigibles, married charming and popular Milicent Sperry, who had been lower division secretary in the physics department. The younger, but most vocal advocate of single bliss, Paul Aebersold, succumbed to Florence Martinson of the purchasing department. Chemist Melvin Calvin, youngest and perhaps a less-determined bachelor, married Genevieve Jemtegaard. Even Ernest's secretary, Helen Griggs, asked him whom she should train to take her place. Startled, he looked up, and promised a raise. "Don't you think I should get married?" Helen asked. "Oh, yes! You should get married. Who is the lucky fellow?" "Glenn Seaborg." Ernest jumped up then, beamed, and shook hands, as pleased as he was surprised. "Well, if you know anyone who wants to get married, just train her for my secretary." After Priscilla Greene, who did not leave for marriage, but to go to Los Alamos with Oppie—with Ernest's reluctant blessing—Beatrice Bishop held the position until the end of the war.

Calutron experiments indicated that approximately 2,000 individual sources and collectors would be necessary to produce 100 grams of U-235 per day! To economize on steel for such a number of separators, huge oval magnets, each with 96 separator tanks, were built at what Groves designated as the Y-12 site, at Oak Ridge, Tennessee, and a one-sixteenth scale model was constructed on the hill at Berkeley. Because of the oval shape, they were referred to as racetracks; officially they were called Alpha I tracks. Cyclotron experience proved invaluable, but there were problems aplenty; never before had such vacuums been demanded, and in such large tanks. The 184-inch magnet had been the world's largest for a short while; when all the Y-12 racetracks were in, their magnets, combined, were a hundred times larger. Special tools had to be made to enable men to hold onto them against the magnetic pull, which was great enough to pull on shoe nails when walked over. When sufficient copper was unobtainable, 14,000 tons of coin silver, worth $400,-000,000 were borrowed from the United States Treasury and rolled into strips for magnet coils. All this to produce infinitesimal amounts of U-235 in each tank, each day—until there was sufficient for a bomb!

Ernest knew that plant erection and particularly operation would present difficulties for Stone and Webster and Tennessee Eastman Corporation. There was not in the entire world as much evacuated space as would be required in the racetrack Calutrons, and each tank would have to be opened after each run, and reevacuated before another. Men were trained at Berkeley for maintenance of all aspects of the huge devices—hundreds were sent to Oak Ridge. Technique should improve from operation; as Groves later said, he was betting on Ernest Lawrence to find ways to settle the many difficulties.

Groves, authoritarian believer in chain of command and channels, understood Ernest's methods, for all his impatience with his camaraderie, first-name relationships, and lack of formal organization. There was a table of organization at Berkeley, chiefly concerned with administration—the so-called "housekeeping" activities necessary to so large an operation—but there was no hard-and-fast organization for the heart of the project, that for which the rest existed. Everything was flexible: Ernest could move personnel from project to project without causing injured feelings or any sense of demotion. Programs were decided day by day. Everyone expected at the eight A.M. policy meeting took pains to be present and seated before Ernest arrived. Some thought his arrival a sort of grand entrance, as he appeared and rather majestically strode the length of the room, to its only comfortable chair. Seated, he beamed at everyone and asked, "What's new?" Each was expected to have some-

thing worthwhile to contribute, which may have kept him up and thinking half the night. All ideas were discussed, none laughed down, however apparently ridiculous. Everyone had a feeling of deep participation.
After perhaps an hour of free discussion, Ernest, who assimilated and
evaluated quickly, would define the course to be followed. It was said
that if a janitor made the best suggestion, it would be adopted, and the
most senior physicists would be asked to help him. Thus the most
promising methods, whether of focusing, collecting, or dealing with any
of the perplexities, would be emphasized, and personnel shifted from
less likely efforts. If several ideas seemed hopeful, all would be pushed
equally; when one appeared to be less fruitful, it could be dropped as
quickly. There were no pet projects; completion of the job was all that
counted. For example, William Parkins, interested in a particular approach, seemed always assigned to another. When excellent results had
been attained on one of these, he thought he could leave it and remarked, "Now I can get back to something important." Ernest said
nothing at the time, but after the meeting detained Parkins. "He gave
me hell; I gave in. He was right; he needed follow-up on the same problem and didn't want me going off on this other thing, which wouldn't
work in the long run—he felt it in his bones and he was right."

Men accustomed to usual academic or highly organized industrial laboratory procedures found the system strange, but there were undeniable
advantages. Excellent teamwork was developed, personal participation
and responsibility were deeply felt, and, perhaps most important, everyone remained alert and well informed. There was criticism that a great
deal more action—doing—than theorizing took place, and it was very
empirical; if one of ten different ways might work, ten would be tried.
One good idea justified a hundred failures, over which no sense of guilt
was permitted. Chauncey Starr called it "profligate empiricism—like nature's seeds—a maelstrom of scientific effort." Perhaps the job could not
have been accomplished otherwise; as in early cyclotron days, there was
little preknowledge or theory to rely on. Ernest's very paternalism—one
could always go to him directly—created a protective atmosphere that
would have been stifled elsewhere. Personal competitiveness was discouraged for the success of the team, the result. Starr said that at times
it was as though Ernest were a shepherd herding his charges toward the
best pastures, but that Ernest's overall methods reminded him more than
anything else of a great general of ancient times, spurring, inspiring,
leading his men to the objective.

For whatever reasons, Ernest had the confidence of Groves, who told
contractors on January 3, 1943, that he expected the Alpha I racetrack,
Oak Ridge's first, to be in operation by July 1. Stone and Webster representatives said that would be impossible; Berkeley was still experi-

menting with design. Groves was adamant; if they tried, they might actually finish it earlier! He, too, was intolerant of indecision, delay, and fear of risk. He savored the idea of an eventual five racetracks, each 15 feet high, 122 feet long, and 77 feet wide; each enclosing 96 separator tanks, in two-story reinforced masonry buildings. On the lower floor would be huge vacuum pumps and massive cooling equipment. Each cubicle, with control panels for two tanks, would require an operator. These were to be recruited largely from young women of the surrounding area in Tennessee, and fully trained by the time the racetracks were completed. Ernest was to hold regular coordination meetings with contractors' representatives; when Groves could not attend, he would be represented by Captain Harold Fidler. Fidler, the area engineer, would settle technical and administrative details and keep Groves informed. Starr thought Fidler's job must have been uncomfortable, "adjusting the government to suit Ernest Lawrence." TEC would supply the material, perform necessary chemical processes, and coordinate the manufacture and procurement of equipment at Y-12. Wally Reynolds established offices in Oak Ridge and near Stone and Webster Co. in Boston for administrative coordination. Starr performed liaison duties with TEC on technical matters in Berkeley.

Continued experiment and alteration delayed final tank and collector designs until early spring. In the meantime Ernest considered tanks enlarged from twelve to fifteen feet, in which as many as sixteen sources might launch sixteen beams, arcing through the evacuated magnetic field to sixteen collectors. Ed Lofgren, with help from other staffers, designed and proposed a second or "Beta" stage, designed further to enrich material from the first Alpha tracks. Ernest liked the idea and Groves approved. A second stage might also improve the product of the hoped-for gaseous diffusion plant; Betas required smaller racetracks; other items need be only half the size of Alpha counterparts.

Stone and Webster broke ground for the first Y-12 building on February 18, 1943—with no more than foundation plans. Their problems were multiple, from modifications and shattered limestone in foundation excavations to labor recruitment. Oak Ridge grew to a city, where formerly a sleepy valley had held a few scattered farm buildings. Already dwellings, schools, a church, and shopping centers were rising. Ernest, at the end of April, was thrilled at the progress. Miles of new road, trainloads of material and equipment on miles of new tracks, homes, barracks, warehouses were framed by the rolling hills. As he said on his return to Berkeley, May 6, "When you see the magnitude of that operation there, it sobers you up and makes you realize that whether we want to or not, we've got to make things go. . . . You can see that a thousand people would just be lost in this place, and we've got to make a definite attempt to just hire everybody in sight and somehow use them, because it's going to be an awful job to get those racetracks into operation on schedule. We must do it!"

A small section of an Alpha racetrack in Berkeley, used for training TEC personnel and for experiment, seemed to indicate successful operation for the Y-12 plant. Berkeley scientists continued experimentation toward source improvement and more efficient collectors—Sid Barnes developed a new and better collector in 1943. The first experimental Alpha unit at Y-12 operated successfully August 1, 1943—just as Oppenheimer's theoretical group decided that three times as much U-235 as had been estimated would be required for a bomb. At the same time new problems encountered in the gaseous diffusion process were discouraging. Perhaps the only chance to win lay in building more racetracks. Groves spoke of cutting out final diffusion stages at Oak Ridge and feeding partially enriched material from early stages to Y-12 Calutrons.

In September a new Alpha plant to cost $150,000,000 was authorized, before the first main plant had been tested. When that, Alpha I, was tried out in November, it seemed to be a complete failure: magnet coils shorted out, vacuum tanks leaked badly, and the powerful magnets pulled tanks out of line. Novice operators were confused and helpless. Operation stopped entirely in December. It was found that rust and sediment in cooling oil had shorted the magnets; all the coils had to be returned to Allis Chalmers for cleaning and repair. In the future, filters would be used, and piping carefully cleaned before installation. The second Alpha track, after precautionary cleaning and filtering, encountered electrical failures; to repair the damage caused by even small mistakes required hours, with further time lost in regaining vacuums. Lack of spare parts and chemical equipment breakdowns slowed Alpha-2 almost to a stop. But a few tanks held up, and operation on these improved somewhat.

Though most of the summer and fall had been devoted to testing and the training of TEC personnel, many more operators had been hired when the number of racetracks was increased. Even Berkeley-trained girls seemed unable to operate efficiently. If the second Alpha track had suffered no major equipment failures, operating difficulties, electrical failures, minor breakdowns, and lack of spare parts were still the despair of all at Y-12—except Ernest. He went to Berkeley and hastily recruited a train car full of his men. "Would you like to go to Tennessee?" he beamed as though it were for a holiday. Any indication of agreement brought an almost impossible "Good, you leave day after tomorrow, by train." Hesitation or unwillingness, because of family ties, or whatever, brought the reminder that Tennessee was a good deal better place to be than a training camp, or a South Pacific jungle.

Eventually more than a hundred Berkeley physicists, engineers, and technicians were assigned to Oak Ridge for periods of three months to a year or more. The first Berkeley contingent found utter confusion, lack of organization, garbled information, insufficiency of equipment, and, worst of all, extremely poor morale at Y-12. Both TEC and the Army seemed to have given up any expectation of successful operation of the racetracks. Nor was confusion limited to operation. Ignoring poor quarters, mud, and bad weather, Ernest, who had preceded their arrival, greeted his men with assurances that they could right all failures and remove any impediment: "You go down there tomorrow morning and start running the first block of cubicles on the racetracks. Two of you to a cubicle until it's operating properly; then split up, one to another cubicle and one remaining with a learning operator, until the whole track is operating. Others stand by to chase and correct trouble."

Passes had not been obtained for these Rad Lab men who knew that no excuse would be acceptable. A guard was bluffed with official-looking paper to gain entry to the plant the first day. Passes were unavailable for two days; various expedients were used. Berkeley crews left at odd times during the night; often there was more difficulty getting out of the plant than gaining entrance. Guards required the signature of each departing man, followed by the name of his supervisor. Ernest was the only superior the scientists knew, and his name was classified. One ruse was at first successful. After his signature, each named as his supervisor the man in line behind him. Once, last in line, Herb York wrote, for supervisor, "J. C. Almighty." The guard called "Wait!" as the bus started. "Drive!" York shouted authoritatively, and they got away.

Three weeks after they received passes, a new system was inaugurated; the Berkeley men were again locked out. In the plant itself, "everything happened—silly mistakes of one kind or another." Roger Hildebrand suddenly lost vacuum after his spectrograph finally worked; it was discovered that a painter on the lower floor had pulled a chain, opening a valve. Non-Berkeley people stood around helplessly, for the most part. Even Groves was pessimistic but seemed to be "under Ernest's thumb," Hildebrand thought. Ernest cheerfully bustled around with the general as though nothing had been amiss. He assured Groves, during those most hopeless days, that it would work. Groves realized that Ernest himself was the difference. Everything moved better when he was at the site. He considered him one scientist who could understand a really big operation, who was not afraid of the big effort. Groves believed him so valuable to the program that he forbade Ernest to fly, just when Ernest had accepted plane travel—and was in more of a hurry than ever. After his first drive with Ernest at the wheel—and attention elsewhere— Groves also forbade him to drive! John Hecker, TEC production manager, was amused when Groves challenged Ernest at the time things were darkest: "Dr. Lawrence, you know your reputation's at stake."

"No, General," Ernest replied. "My reputation is made. Yours is at stake."

While Ernest could not infuse all of Y-12 with the "Berkeley spirit" —TEC had nearly five thousand employees there early in 1944—enough tanks operated all the time in February of that year to produce enriched materials for Los Alamos. More and more problems were solved, and many difficult operations became routine. Ernest straightened out other than technical problems, too, as when Bill Parkins found hindrance after hindrance holding up a job and reported to Ernest. "Come on, let's go," Ernest said. He took Parkins in his chauffered car to the plant manager and, without sitting down, cleared matters there. Parkins recalls, "After three or four such stops, everything was straightened out. Wouldn't tolerate any waste of time by TEC people, and was pretty rough on the Army too. Of course, in the end Groves had the final say, but though they didn't always agree they got along very well. Ernest never stubbornly held out when he was wrong, and even with the general was just like a little boy, pleased and enthusiastic when the results were good, regardless of who was responsible. He went out of his way to show his appreciation of those whose efforts were responsible."

Ernest was open and frank with Groves. When heated sources were tried for quicker starting, Groves confused the calrods (elements like those of any electric range) with cooling pipes and told young Hildebrand they were not large enough for proper circulation. Hildebrand looked imploringly at Ernest for rescue from embarrassment. Ernest smiled, shrugged, and indicated that Roger should explain the heating elements. Ernest refused to adopt the military idea of distance between men and leaders. When he spotted Private Cecil Leith at work, he insisted on introducing him to General Groves as one of his old laboratory boys. His recognition of men in lower echelons was a strong factor in morale. One elderly man became a confirmed hero worshipper after Ernest greeted him one morning, "Well, George, how are you?" "Imagine! Lawrence *knew* me!" "He talked of nothing else for weeks," Jimmy Vale, longtime lab employee, reported. "You can't picture how pleased these guys were that he knew their names. That's why they all liked him."

Groves and Ernest once toured the plant with an unofficial-looking person who obviously had Ernest's respect. He pointedly introduced the stranger to young Hildebrand as Dr. Baker and asked Roger to explain things, repeating "Dr. Baker," or "Nicholas Baker." When he had a chance, he nudged Roger and whispered, "It's Bohr!" Even then Roger didn't realize at once that he had talked with the famous Niels Bohr.

"He would bring in an important man like that, introduce him, and ask the lowest man what it was all about."

With all his respect and affection for the Dane, Ernest thought Bohr impossibly naïve, fretting about future consequences of the bomb. "How will it be used?" "To end the war! What else?" Bohr himself had reported that Heisenberg now headed the German atomic program, and rumor from Switzerland indicated that controlled chain reaction had been achieved. Ernest had no quarrel with Bohr's hope that possession of the bomb might ensure world peace—he believed that himself, if the holder was the United States. Bohr and Oppie, though such fine scientists, by fussing with philosophical and political problems, distracted from science—and these two had such influence on adoring young followers. Groves, amusingly enough, complained about Bohr as he did about Ernest—that he talked too much! It made no difference that those they talked to were on the project; no one should know more than was necessary for his particular and immediate job.

The general worried most about possible security violations when British scientists came to help at Berkeley and Los Alamos. The half-dozen under Oliphant who first went to Berkeley soon numbered twenty-nine, and were of tremendous assistance, particularly as American brains and manpower, first tapped for radar, underwater sound, and Chicago's Metallurgical Laboratory, had been further depleted for Oak Ridge and Los Alamos. Groves felt that Ernest and Oliphant were too friendly and showed little discretion. He later testified that immediately after he had requested him not to reveal something, Ernest went to a blackboard and told a small group, "I know General Groves doesn't want me to say this, but," and proceeded to discuss the forbidden topic. Groves never understood the value to scientific progress of free discussion; scientists, generally, failed to appreciate Groves's rigid notions of security. Ernest's name was not supposed to be used. Telegrams, mail, and phone calls from Berkeley reached him at Oak Ridge as "Junior, care of W. B. Reynolds." His official Manhattan code name was "E. Lawson." Groves often called him "Oscar Wilde," which he thought any learned person should understand because of Wilde's play, *The Importance of Being Earnest*.

"He got on very well with all his own men, of course, but he also got on very well with all my men," said Kenneth Mees, vice-president of Eastman Kodak Company, the parent of TEC. "We were very fond of him at Oak Ridge. I think he was genuinely fond of many of the people. . . . I sat several times at conference meetings with Ernest in the chair . . . going over the work, planning the next move. . . . That is the thing I have been doing all my life, and I appreciated immediately that Ernest had the whole thing in his hands and yet didn't take over much of the meetings. He let other fellows do the talking. He got the results he wanted out of the meeting; that is the art of directing research. Of course he was primarily a physicist but secondly he was a research director of the first rank. . . . You wouldn't expect a man to be a first-class mathematician and also an experimental physicist; he would be a phenomenon. There are very few great experimental physicists. Ernest was one of these. I used to tell my English friends that he ranked with Rutherford. It annoyed them, who regarded Rutherford as a god, but I still think that Ernest ranks with Rutherford. . . . He was definitely in the Genius class. He was the greatest experimental physicist that the United States has ever had, I should say."

Mees, who was in Berkeley for three weeks to give the Hitchcock Lectures in 1943, was fascinated by the Calutron, "Aston's mass spectrograph multiplied by a million! I happened to have seen the first mass spectrograph and had it explained to me by [Francis] Aston and J. J. Thomson at Cambridge, in 1919, I think. . . . I realized that Ernest was a great leader of men."

William Douglass, not overly enamored of Ernest because, as an early night guard on the hill, while a law student by day, he had been reprimanded for refusal to admit Ernest without pass or badge, pondered this "leadership" after he had moved up to Rad Lab purchasing agent. "He had this personal force and it didn't make any difference, when he said, 'We're going to do it,' we did it. That was all there was to it. Nobody minded. There was grumbling outside, but never at the lab. He was 'It.' Just the way when nothing would go at Oak Ridge, he took half the lab, key people, back there and got it running. Nobody who ever knew him ever doubted that he could make it run. Tremendously respected— unusually respected for the top man. I've often heard people outside remark, 'What in heaven's name has this man got?' "

For all his buoyancy, and at times now it was feigned in order to support morale in others, the strain of many problems in several places and the need to rush from one to another took its toll. Colds, bronchial trouble, and an increasingly persistent backache were too often concurrent afflictions; the need to get the job done prevented sufficient rest for alleviation—generally. In late 1943, in Chicago, he just managed to get himself to a meeting. Back at his hotel he tried in desperation to reach John by long distance, without any luck. Finally he got to the hospital on the Chicago campus and was put to bed. He phoned Alvarez, recently moved from M.I.T. for a six-months' stint at the Chicago Metallurgical Laboratory, en route to Los Alamos.

"He was just exhausted," Alvarez remembers. "I have never seen him so completely beaten in my life. Just depressed, in very poor spirits.

They had built these huge magnets, and when they turned them on, one by one they had shorted out and they had to tear the whole damn thing down. It was costing a lot of delay and a lot of money. There were a lot of people, of course, who felt that the whole thing was a boondoggle in the first place, and here was Ernest responsible for this whole thing and something had happened that he couldn't personally check on. He had assumed the commercial engineers were experienced and would do a proper job. There was nothing he could do but sweat it out, and wait for these things to be pulled apart, fixed, and put back together again. I sort of held his hand for several days while he was in the hospital there in Chicago. He had a backache. While I was there an orthopedic corset man came in and tied the damn thing on, and he was pretty unhappy with it. Something was really hurting him and on top of that other business—why, I've never seen Ernest so completely beaten and depressed."

Repair and replacement of equipment on the first racetrack were not completed until March, 1944, when repeated breakdowns continued to keep its production low. Beta Calutrons did not operate successfully for a time because of ion source failure. Nevertheless, the difficulties that still held up the gaseous diffusion project left the Calutron tracks the best hope in the race. Though the pilot plutonium pile at Oak Ridge operated successfully at the end of 1943, construction of the production plant at Hanford, Washington, had not then started. Six months later, in May, 1944, Ernest wrote to Conant optimistically: ". . . in spite of difficulties of operating procedures, shortage of spare parts, etc. . . . there is no longer an element of gamble, since the electromagnetic plant is successful, and developments at Los Alamos . . . leave no doubt that the production can be used as an overwhelmingly powerful explosive. It is only a question of time, and indeed it is the time schedule that indicates need of at least two more Alpha-2 buildings." And on July 4, at a meeting with Groves and Y-12 contractors, it was decided to convert Alpha-2 tracks to receive partially enriched material from first-stage gaseous diffusion units, hopefully to be successfully completed soon, or from Abelson's thermal diffusion plant, construction of which had been started near the steam plant of the gaseous diffusion works at Oak Ridge.

One of the more glaring examples of the faults of a security program that demanded rigid compartmentalization was the ignorance of the S-1 Committee and, initially, of General Groves, of Abelson's thermal diffusion development at the Naval Research Laboratory—though President Roosevelt's directive had insisted that the Navy be kept completely out of the bomb project. Groves, in desperation over slow progress in gaseous diffusion plants and the Y-12 difficulties, almost doubted, for a time, that a bomb really could be produced for this war—the Allies had successfully invaded Normandy on June 6. He had learned of the Abelson project early in 1943, but an agreement with the Navy failed to materialize. It was not until the middle of June, 1944, that Groves could order hurried construction of an Abelson-type thermal diffusion plant at Oak Ridge—to supply slightly enriched uranium for Y-12 Calutrons until the gaseous diffusion plant could be partially completed. In midsummer 1944, this appeared the only hope for a weapon within a year.

By the end of June, 1944, five Alpha tracks and two Beta tracks were in operation, but misfortunes still prevented peak performances. Insulators failed, leaks developed, operators made costly mistakes, and chemical operations were inefficient. It was estimated that the tracks were operating at 83-percent efficiency. With other woes, physicists had paid less attention than necessary to chemistry, though Ernest had insisted on Beta chemical research early in 1943. Precious U-235, hard to recover and purify, tended to become lost on electrodes and liners. Tanks had to be scoured after each run to retrieve the precious material. Noticeable and valuable amounts were embedded in parts, left behind in cleaned tanks, trapped in glass-lined tubing, in filters, centrifuges, and even on rubber gloves. All had to be carefully recovered. Clarence Larson, who had been head of the chemistry department at the College of the Pacific, suggested copper liners that could be dissolved for chemical separation in solution. Ernest asked when it could be tried. Larson suggested two weeks. "Well," Ernest said, with a great deal of charm, "we need it tomorrow." Larson worked all night; the system worked. Chemistry problems were gradually solved, insulators finally were made to stand up, and operators became more efficient. In November, 1944, as much enriched uranium was separated as the total of all previous months. All nine Alpha tracks and three Betas were processing satisfactorily. One Beta track was used to train operators properly. By the first of March, 1945, starting with partially enriched material from the thermal diffusion plant, racetrack production again surpassed that of all previous months combined. Armed couriers, in civilian clothing, now left regularly for Los Alamos with the precious U-235 in specially adapted, but normal appearing, suitcases. Groves decided on a fourth Beta track. He estimated that, in May, Los Alamos would also have received sufficient quantities of plutonium for a bomb from the Hanford, Washington plant.

No great problems were involved in manufacture of the uranium bomb, once sufficient proper material was available. A specially designed gun barrel would shoot half of the critical amount—that necessary for self-induced explosion—to the other half. The united halves would spontaneously fission, and, properly encased, explode with tremendous force. A recent disappointment at Los Alamos had been the discovery that it was not practical to use plutonium in this way and that implosion of a less than critical amount must be used. Plutonium must be encased in conventional explosive in such a way that detonation of the latter would exert sufficient pressure to squeeze the plutonium core into a critical state. This involved problems that leading explosive expert George B. Kistiakowsky at first thought impossible to solve. But those problems were now thought to be overcome; Luis Alvarez and Ed Lofgren groups devised the detonator.

Los Alamos had procurement and administrative problems nearly as thorny as the technical ones.

In July, Don Shane went from Berkeley to Los Alamos to help with personnel matters and to attempt to improve relationships in the scientific staff, university, and Army triangle. Groves did his best to keep differences between scientists and soldiers from erupting. He told his officers that this was one place where the Army served science. "I've combed the world to bring this bunch of scientists together and by gosh you've got to get along with them." But friction between the laboratory and the Los Angeles procurement office could not be solved by Army fiat. "Ernest's leadership at Berkeley made things go—and smoothly," Shane said and Cooksey's notes indicate how procurement was handled there. "Top University men want the Lab to move fast, but handling of details for the University is in the hands of older men who have gained positions through moving slowly and patiently as befits peacetime operation of a great state university. In order to break this down Lab operates on blanket orders, getting all bids over the phone, confirming by wire, and later backtracking with the paper. These duties are performed by young men and their decisions are backed. Rather make mistakes and move fast. We will not brook being slowed down by an accounting department or any other because they don't like troubles of backtracking."

Perhaps only Ernest, with his reputation for getting what he wanted, could prevail over the natural dislike of such methods by accountants and officials accustomed to normal routines. Ernest had met with Comptroller Olaf Lundberg and the secretary-treasurer of the regents, Robert Underhill, early in the war, had locked the door behind him, and told them how very important the project was and asked to have all laboratory concerns pushed. Underhill was also the responsible university financial officer for Los Alamos and handled all negotiations with the Government. Everyone at Los Alamos blamed the university, Shane found, "the lab group, particularly, always considered the University at fault, in problems from insurance arrangements to patent procedures."

With discord among laboratory personnel, Shane requested a copy of an old Benedictine Monastery print that hung in the lounge of the Faculty Club at Berkeley:

Bene Dictum, Benedicte! If any pilgrim monk come from distant parts, if with wish as a guest to dwell in the monastery, and will be content with the customs which he finds in the place, & do not perchance by his lavishness disturb the monastery, but is simply content with what he finds, he shall be received, for as long a time as he desires. If, indeed, he find fault with anything, or expose it, reasonably, and with the humility of charity, the Abbot shall discuss it prudently, lest perchance God had sent him for this very thing. But, if he have been found gossipy and contumacious in the time of his sojourn as guest, not only ought he not to be joined to the body of the monastery, but also it shall be said to him, honestly, that he must depart. If he does not go, let two stout monks, in the name of God, explain the matter to him. Saint Benedict.

"Oh, we had a continual bicker with the university," Oppenheimer recalled. "And that was because we were running a fantastic operation. Quite unusual, quite complicated, and loused up for security reasons, and with an impatience which was in our directive. . . . People just didn't want to be delayed on the risk that we would be the cause of not having done a job on time, and no university comptroller, no matter how many wings he had, could have done it right for us."

Conant and Groves summoned the S-1 Executive Committee to Los Alamos in January, 1944. (Oppie told Ernest that he had been able to persuade Conant and the general to invite them only by suggesting that, if the project failed, committee members would blame them for not taking the committee into their confidence.) Conclusions were optimistic in spite of lingering problems. After the meeting Ernest told Sproul, in Berkeley, that the war would be over by July, 1945, and that consideration of the postwar laboratories should not be postponed. At a four-day Los Alamos meeting with Urey, Compton, and R. C. Tolman, a scientific advisor to Groves, beginning July 31, Ernest realized that, with the overall program functioning at last, his laboratories would have progressively less to do with it.

The 60-inch cyclotron in Crocker Laboratory ceased wartime operation in July, 1944, after nearly eight months of bombardment of tiny graphite rods to determine the stability of graphite in the Hanford piles, in which fast neutron bombardment would be of much greater intensity than in the Oak Ridge pile—which, since its completion in November, 1943, had released the cyclotron of plutonium production. (A pile could produce thousands of times more neutrons than any cyclotron.) Thus, after 20,000 hours of almost continuous operaton, overhaul of the 60-inch was commenced in July, 1944. Ernest, even when burdened with war problems, often thought of his 184-inch peacetime cyclotron. Interest in linear accelerators, put aside in the thirties for the cyclotron, had been revived by radar development. Late in 1943, when hospitalized in Chicago, he and Alvarez had discussed the application of microwave frequencies to a large linear accelerator. Knowledge and experience gained through wartime projects should more than make up for time lost from peacetime pursuits.

Oak Ridge people should be free soon to return; some had already left Tennessee for Los Alamos. McMillan, Alvarez, and most Los Alamos scientists would have to remain until the end but when they were free Ernest could count on them. Segrè and Chaim Richman, late recruits for New Mexico, had further depleted the physics personnel at Berkeley, and Professor Birge was understandably concerned about the teaching staff of his physics department. Rumors of enticement of good men to other universities were rife. Compton was accused of attempting to lure Fermi from Columbia to Chicago. Bush directed that no advantage be taken of government projects to build up postwar faculties. Ernest was pretty sure of his Rad Lab people.

There had been discontent at Chicago's Metallurgical Laboratory since Du Pont's assumption of responsibility for plutonium. Compton repeatedly had to assure his scientists that their interests would be protected. Ernest had no personnel problems comparable to those elsewhere. He had started with advantages; the nucleus of a big laboratory, men accustomed to large operations, and his unquestioned authority and influence. Problems at Berkeley primarily concerned security and minor irritations caused by the Federation of Architects, Engineers, Chemists and Technicians. Oppie's teachers' union had collapsed as he had promised Ernest, but union efforts had not disappeared; Bernard Peters of the FAECT was persistent in trying to formulate policies concerning transfers of men to and from Oak Ridge. Ernest had no patience with that, but he thought security people were too concerned with past associations; they had done their best, for instance, to deprive the program of such competence as Oppie's. Ernest had fought to retain several considered of doubtful loyalty. Security Chief Colonel John Lansdale later testified that Ernest resented having good scientists removed from the projects, commenting, "We had more trouble with Ernest Lawrence about personnel than any four other people put together." A few suspected scientists were "eased out" of the laboratory, some inducted into the Army. Ernest recognized the need for security in general—it never bothered him to have to show a badge, if he had not forgotten to carry it—but he thought the Army overly suspicious and narrow in its appraisal.

He knew that some of the young scientists were considered "leftists"; if they were good scientists, they would get over it. He could not believe they were dangerous. On a train to Oak Ridge, Ernest had a long talk with Frank Oppenheimer about rumors that he was still an active "Red": "Why do you fool around with these things? Good scientists aren't like people who just want to eat, sleep, and make love. You're not like people who can't get anywhere. You don't need that!" Frank remembers Ernest telling him: "Physicists involved in politics might make for inhomogeneity in the laboratory. You're too good a physicist to be mixed up in these things." He warned Frank, as he had so often warned Robert before the war, not to let his concern for the oppressed—the underdog—take his attention from the main objective, science. Science could best help humanity by doing its job—anything that interfered with that should be shunned.

He was particularly distressed to learn upon a return to Berkeley that Martin Kamen, responsible for finding carbon 14, had "resigned"—by request. Kamen had attended a small party given by the Soviet vice consul in a San Francisco restaurant, to meet violinist Isaac Stern. Kamen's father had befriended the virtuoso's family. Kamen had been brought to the United States from his native Canada when three months old, but his father was born in Russia. Though Russia was an ally of the United States, the brief association with its consular officials—like Kamen, musically inclined—had been noted by intelligence agents. They apparently imagined that he might have revealed classified information, though a joint Congressional committee later concluded that any possible revelation was not deliberate, and Kamen won a libel suit against a metropolitan paper in which the charges were repeated.

Ernest, like others of key importance, was almost constantly guarded —for protection and to intervene in the event of careless discussion of sensitive topics. A rifle bullet had passed near enough for him to hear it sing, one dark night on the hill, before the Army took over. Army personnel, usually Robert Traver or Joe O'Malley, drove, or followed, Ernest around the bay area. He often did not know his guards on long trips; he once discovered that a man he had eaten with in a diner was his security. At a restaurant with Lowell Thomas, Ernest eventually realized that security people were at the adjoining table. He told Thomas, deliberately in their hearing, how he had ducked out a kitchen door at the Waldorf in New York and caught a train for Florida—for much-needed rest. At the Everglades Hotel, he asked for a tennis partner and got one—the guard trailing him. Wally Reynolds tells how Ernest left one train in Cincinnati, stepped onto another on an adjoining

track, and arrived in Chicago an hour ahead of schedule. Security people reported him missing when he failed to arrive on the original, later,
train. The appearance of guards at the house always excited the Lawrence children; Eric discovered a service revolver in the car. Molly did
not always appreciate the presence of the third party on the rare occasions when they could get away together. For one Carmel weekend, Ernest arranged to have his guard follow in a separate car. "We spent the
weekend giving him the slip," Molly remembers. "Once we stopped in
the only parking space at a restaurant, and while he looked for a space
we departed. Then I worried that he would be worried. I knew that his
job was to protect Ernest and to keep his ears open, to prevent slips."

There was little opportunity for home life when Ernest was in Berkeley. The children missed the Sunday rides and trips to the zoo. When
Ernest did come home—often announced by a phone call from the laboratory—he tired after a few minutes of hugging and tossing them
around. Tensions then often developed between him and the youngsters.
Neighborhood children, used to congregating noisily at the house, frayed
his taut nerves and might be abruptly ordered out, which once infuri-
ated five-year-old Mary. Molly sensed Ernest's exhaustion, though she
did not realize what he was doing, or how heavy were his responsibilities, even after going with him to Oak Ridge for a couple of weeks. He
could be amused by the children, too—when Molly was not. They once
drove a nice college girl who helped regular maid Dixie Venable—maids
were scarce during the war years—almost frantic when Molly was out.
Carried away with mob psychology, they and their friends threw everything movable, from crib mattress to a large box of dusting powder,
down the laundry chute. Ernest and Molly arrived home to a frightened
and tearful girl—which Ernest thought very funny! The girl left at the
end of the college year, in June, 1944. Dixie came more often after that,
though she never lived in the house except when Molly was away.

Ernest may have worried Groves by his conversations with scientists,
but there were no grounds for complaint at home. Molly sometimes had
an itinerary when he left Berkeley; she never asked why he went after
being told it was none of her business. When he was at home, groups of
men, military and industrial, frequently including General Groves,
often came for cocktails before dinner. Groves was stiff and formal the
first time. Molly heard him ask Cooksey about her reliability; she might
have overheard something. When most of the other men had gone, he
poked his head into the kitchen. "Come out of there and go to dinner
with us," he ordered. Molly demurred. "Go on, change your clothes and
come." She had a delightful evening with Ernest and the general. It
amused Ernest that on other occasions Groves frightened her; Ernest
himself was not in awe of any of the high brass and other Government

people. He enjoyed Groves. They often played tennis and, when they could, went to football games together. Ernest defended Groves when other scientists were critical of him; it took such a man to do the job.

Though the Allies appeared to be winning—Paris was liberated in August, 1944, and the German borders were penetrated the following month—much desperate fighting continued in Europe. In the Pacific, where American troops invaded the Philippines in October, ultimate victory seemed equally certain, if more distant. Whatever causes for optimism existed, American voters refused to risk a change in administration and elected Franklin Roosevelt to an unprecedented fourth term —and a handful of knowledgeable people feared that nuclear materials might be the basis of Hitler's frequently boasted secret weapon. Enraged by the destructive bombing of Germany, he had shouted that "one drastic stroke" would end the war, and that "mankind is not far from the point where it can at will blow up half the globe."

The Military Policy Committee, with Conant, Compton, and Urey, studied the use of radioactive poisons, based on conclusions of Dr. Robert Stone's health physics group; in the event of inability to make a bomb in time, Hitler might order the employment of radioactive substances to deny terrain to, or destroy, invading troops. General Marshall secretly had warned Allied Headquarters of such a possibility. Portable Geiger counters were made in quantity and soldiers trained to use them. Medical units were advised how to detect and treat a "disease of unknown etiology." Military Intelligence, with the help of Bush, organized a special mission under Colonel Boris Pash of Manhattan District's intelligence and Dutch-born physicist Samuel Goudsmit to join forward Allied units. Under the code name "Alsos," those scientists and officers were to ferret out and search German laboratories, to disrupt atomic work, and to capture nuclear scientists. In Paris, Alsos people learned that Germans had used Joliot's cyclotron for nuclear work, but those scientists had already skipped. Little was learned of atomic weapon progress in Germany; possible atomic plants had been prime bomber targets, but there was ample evidence of work with uranium. The whereabouts of top scientists was not immediately discovered. The search continued; in any event the Army wanted to find German nuclear physicists before the Russians did.

Thus, however the war progressed in favor of the Allies, the laboratories must not slacken the pace, though Groves enjoyed needling top Berkeley laboratory people about closing out their activities. Oppie phoned that progress was good at Los Alamos. Ernest's presence at Oak Ridge was less necessary as racetracks improved and operators became more proficient. But his value to morale remained. During the Christmas season of 1944, he organized a big dinner meeting at which he gave an inspiring talk. "I can't tell you anything about it, what's going on, or how, but don't get discouraged. You'll have some good news in the not far distant future. It is very important," Jimmy Vale remembers Ernest saying, adding, "That speech did a lot of good. He convinced us we weren't wasting our time. Everybody respected him so highly, when he said something, they'd think, 'Ernest is usually right.' This happened time and time again, that, whenever he spoke, everybody listened."

When James Ellis, in charge of engineering for TEC, finished his Y-12 duties at Oak Ridge, he wrote Ernest, on February 2, 1945: "I cannot help but write you that progress in the Y-12 job has been largely due to your energy and inspiration to many of us."

Secretary of War Henry Stimson visited Y-12 on the morning of April 12, 1945, and was "immensely cheered and braced up. The Tennessee complex was," he said, "the largest and most extraordinary scientific experiment in history." That afternoon President Roosevelt died at not-far-distant Warm Springs, Georgia. Less than a month later, on May 7, 1945, Germany surrendered to the Allies.

The racetracks, in operation a full year ahead of both the gaseous diffusion plant at Oak Ridge and the plutonium works at Hanford, produced well throughout the winter. Slightly enriched material from the thermal and gaseous diffusion plants was fed through the Calutrons. By the middle of June, as the first gaseous diffusion stages improved, more heavily enriched material went to the Beta tracks. Lest the surrender of Germany cause a letdown just as sufficiently rich quantities became available, Ernest again appealed to the patriotism of TEC workmen. "You may not realize what you're doing, but in a hundred or a thousand years, people will know it. They may not even remember that there was a war, but they will know what you have done." He strongly implied that many Americans desperately engaged with Japanese forces would be saved if the Beta tracks functioned at capacity.

The uranium bomb, relatively safe and certain of performance, required no final testing. Solutions for the technical problems of the plutonium implosion weapon had now been found—theoretically. No one, however, could be certain without a full-scale test. A remote site near Alamogordo, New Mexico, called Trinity, had been selected for this early in 1945, and preparations for the test, in charge of Kenneth Bainbridge, lately at the radar lab, were under way. Tons of high explosives scattered radioactive wastes for the calibration of instruments and gauging of radioactivity. A steel tower to hold the bomb aboveground was erected. Shelters for observation were built ten thousand yards north, south, and west from it. Other observation posts were ten and twenty miles distant. Arrangements were made for emergency evacuation of small communities, beyond the outlying posts and theoretically safe; no one actually knew to what distances radioactive danger might extend. Final preliminary tests were successfully completed on July 10; Oppie wired Ernest, "Anytime after the fifteenth would be good for our fishing trip. Because we are not certain of the weather, we may be delayed several days. As we do not have enough sleeping bags to go around, we ask you please not to bring any friends with you. Let us know where in Albuquerque you can be reached."

General Groves, with Bush and Conant, visited the Berkeley laboratories a few days before the fifteenth, and Ernest joined them in the general's plane for the trip to Albuquerque, where Groves was horrified at the telltale numbers of distinguished scientists in groups at both airport and hotel. He dispersed them into rooms or onto side streets. Ernest saw Ed McMillan with Chadwick, now knighted, and William Laurence of *The New York Times*, the single newsman permitted knowledge of the secret. He talked with Luis Alvarez, who would observe the test from a B-29 bomber. It was true, as the general feared, that anyone who could recognize these men would realize their gathering to be very important.

A Los Alamos sedan picked up Ernest, Charles A. Thomas, Monsanto Chemical executive, metallurgical co-ordinator among Berkeley, Los Alamos, and Ames, and reporter Laurence near midnight for the journey to Compania Hill, twenty miles northwest of the tower-supported bomb. The weather was not propitious; rain and scudding clouds contributed to the tension. It was a bumpy, uncomfortable ride; on rocky Compania Hill, it was chilly when the caravan arrived about three o'clock on the morning of the sixteenth. Chadwick was there, Teller, others deep in the problem. Ernest thought of men at base camp, ten miles closer and at the tower itself. Oppie, Robert Bacher, Bainbridge—so many whose efforts hung in the balance—were at shelters only 10,000 yards from the tower. On Compania Hill there were bets made on the outcome as the hours passed. Ernest and Thomas wagered modestly on complete success, but the definite assurance Ernest usually displayed seemed missing. Thomas thought; he could not force success here. The countdown was postponed a couple of times. Sleep was attempted without much success.

When the countdown actually began, Ernest nervously got in and out of the car. "I'll watch it from outside. No, I'll watch it from in here," he said a number of times. A few seconds before five-thirty, zero arrived; a brilliant light grew from a point, to a huge, molten column that spewed over and engulfed the desert in light as no noon sun had ever done. "Jesus Christ! It's got away from the long hairs," a security guard exclaimed. Awestruck, no one else broke the strange ensuing silence for seconds. Then excited babble broke out. "It works! It works!" Ernest shouted, jumping from Thomas to Laurence to Chadwick—whom he slapped heartily on the back. Almost two minutes after the great light, the thunder and blast wave of the explosion reached the hill, as sharp as the detonation of a five-inch gun at a hundred yards. Awed and excited, the spectators of "something new in the world" returned to Albuquerque. There, news of concern about an "overwhelming explosion" poured in from as far as El Paso, Texas, and Silver City, 180 miles away in New Mexico. Such reports were solemnly countered; an ammunition magazine "containing a considerable amount of high explosives and pyrotechnics" had exploded.

No evacuations had been necessary. Dr. Stafford Warren's radiation effects detail determined the extent of fallout. Alvarez had made rapid sketches as the fireball turned into an ugly cloud, until the winds dissipated it into sections that drifted away in various directions. One of those cloud portions distributed radioactive fallout over an area approximately one hundred miles long and thirty miles wide. Late in the afternoon Groves started back to Washington with Ernest, Conant, Bush, and Tolman in his plane. The general observed that the scientists were still upset and could talk of nothing but the morning's event—and why not? Never had anything similar been caused by man. It was estimated that the center of the fireball had been four times as hot as the sun's center, more than ten thousand times as hot as its surface. After four-fifths of a second, it had sent a column higher than the Empire State Building and had depressed the ground with more than a hundred billion atmospheres! Yes, the scientists were somewhat disturbed. Their technical victory had been greater than expected, though the enemy against whom the technological race had been run was already defeated. How the victory might be used, for good or evil, was sufficient cause for wonderment and concern. Groves noted that the awesome explosion's effects upon the scientists "were quite profound for a number of days. As for me, my thoughts were now completely wrapped up with the preparation for the coming climax in Japan."

CHAPTER XIV

Crossroads

The brilliantly successful demonstration at Trinity was a triumph—who that knew of it could doubt it?—but General Groves was right about its effect on the scientists; many who witnessed it were staggered by the awesome implications. The theoretically tremendous energy of nuclear fission had been realized beyond expectation, had been controlled and released at man's bidding. Could his use of so awesome a force also be controlled? Would the triumph prove a Pyrrhic victory? The tremendous effort and dedication that had made it all possible had been initially generated, despite natural hesitation, not just to prove by this elaborate experiment the theoretically possible conclusions of the elegant idea of mass-energy relationships. It had been to forestall a competent but ruthless enemy and had developed into a race with the freedom of the world at stake. The fact that victory had come after the elimination of that opponent could not be evaded. Scientific leaders—certainly Ernest—had given possible use of the bomb against Japan little, if any, thought until the collapse of Germany. "Now we've got it, what shall we do with it?" may well have been the question back of the "profound" effects Groves noticed among his scientists, after Trinity. He alone had no doubts; having set machinery in motion for the bomb's delivery, he was as determined that it be used as he was convinced that it would terminate the war.

But should it be used against Japan, without question already near collapse? B-29 raids regularly carried devastation to Japanese home islands; a huge double raid, late in May, had burned out more than eighteen square miles of Tokyo. The remains of the Japanese fleet, huddled in the Inland Sea, could no longer be considered of much consequence, but sizable and competent land forces certainly would make invasion costly in lives and matériel. Kamikaze suicide planes, indicative of desperation, were demonstrating the will to resist—a Kamikaze attack on the carrier *Bunker Hill* had killed 373 Navy personnel off Okinawa in May. Tarawa, Iwo Jima—every campaign had frighteningly demonstrated Japanese tenacity. Scientists were no better informed than other laymen as to actual Japanese capability to resist the invasion of her ancestral islands that her rulers surely must expect. But even among scientists who were unaware of Trinity, there had been doubts about the use of nuclear force in war, ever since the surrender of Germany. If no one else had it, should we initiate it?

Some of the scientists at the Metallurgical Laboratory, long unhappy that Du Pont had taken the plutonium project from their hands, and denied a research plan Groves had turned down because he saw nothing in it for the war, and moreover concerned about the future of academic research, protested the use of the bomb on moral grounds, protested also leaving so important a decision to military minds. They favored a technical demonstration rather than military use. Arthur Compton had taken one of their leaders, James Franck, to Washington for a discussion of the Chicago scientists' concern with the Vice-President, before the death of the President, and a memorandum had been left for the Secretary of War. The memorandum enumerated moral objections and expressed concern over the likelihood of continuing military control of fission and imposed secrecy. It argued the conflict between loyalty and conscience which they faced as scientists.

Later, impatient that they were not being heard, Leo Szilard, ironically one of the first to urge all-out effort to develop the bomb, circulated a petition among the scientists at Chicago that asked the new president, Harry Truman, to forbid the use of the bomb except under stated conditions and after consideration of the terrible responsibility of initiating "devastation on an unimaginable scale." The protests were less than unanimous; there were counter petitions. Polled in July at Compton's request, 15 percent of the Metallurgical scientists favored outright military use, only 2 percent no use at all, and the rest military use if other means failed to bring surrender. "Other means" included the previously suggested witnessed demonstration on an unoccupied island, coupled with a warning of the terrible consequences of the use of the bomb against an enemy.

Bush and Conant had concerned themselves about the role of science in the postwar era as early as August, 1944. They had advocated, to Secretary Stimson, that basic scientific information on fission be released with the cessation of war, and that legislation to control nuclear power be initiated as soon as possible. To consider it, Stimson had, on May 4,

1945, appointed an Interim Committee, composed of his special consultant, life insurance executive George L. Harrison, Bush, Conant, Karl Compton, Under Secretary of the Navy Ralph A. Bard, Assistant Secretary of State William L. Clayton, and, as Presidential representative, James Byrnes. To advise the committee, Stimson asked Ernest, Arthur Compton, Oppenheimer, and Fermi to form the Scientific Panel.

Generals Marshall and Groves attended the first meeting of the Interim Committee and the Scientific Panel at the Pentagon, on May 31. Stimson personally asked recommendations on all atomic energy matters: controls for the remainder of the war, public announcements, postwar organization, and legislation. The possibility of a many times more powerful hydrogen super bomb was discussed; Oppie thought development of this "super" would take three years. Compton suggested encouragement of industrial use and maintenance of uranium stockpiles. Ernest stressed maintenance of the United States' lead in nuclear energy; for this, research must be fostered and investigation of new possibilities and materials pursued. He suggested that the Government vigorously encourage exploitation in every way. The accumulation of reserves was imperative; the search for the ore in the United States should be made profitable. Oppenheimer thought it unwise to continue wartime measures after the termination of hostilities; research thrived best in an open, normal atmosphere. He suggested free and voluntary exchange of information, before the bomb was dropped, to preserve the country's moral position. Russia? Oppie thought Russia friendly to science. He had suggested to General Marshall that a couple of prominent Russians be invited to witness the Trinity test. Groves was horrified, and Byrnes adamant against any information being given the Russians. Oppie agreed that the United States must keep its lead.

As to use of the bomb against Japan, Roosevelt and Churchill had approved an *aide-memoire* in September, 1944, which read: "When a bomb is finally available, it might, perhaps, after mature consideration, be used against the Japanese." Ernest, who had not seen the Chicago petition before the May 31 meeting, suggested a witnessed, innocuous but striking demonstration, with a warning that failure of Japan to surrender would mean immediate use of the bomb. Compton tended toward demonstration but warned that its failure might prolong the war and pass up the chance to show the world the necessity for peace, though it might induce surrender. Oppie argued that no demonstration, however spectacular, would persuade the Japanese militarists of the futility of further resistance. If warned, they might move captured Americans to the target area, or even destroy the delivery plane. What if the dropped bomb happened to be a dud? The Japanese might then have the precious explosive and the bomb mechanism! As for moral grounds, would a nuclear bomb be any worse than the fire bombs that had burned out Tokyo and Yokohama? Marshall wondered aloud if the secret could be kept if the bomb was neither demonstrated nor used against the enemy. The consensus of the scientists was that it would be impossible to keep it a secret.

Panel members then were asked to consider the future, with atomic energy a fact, and to submit suggestions. Ernest, hopeful that use of the bomb against a populated city could be avoided, in spite of the reasons marshaled for it, left the meeting convinced that the country was in good hands with Secretary Stimson and General Marshall as top advisers. He spoke particularly of General Marshall when Don Cooksey met him on his return to California.

Ernest submitted his suggestions for a postwar world in which atomic power would be a new force, with stress on peaceful uses—as important as its use as a military weapon, which never should have to be employed. In the hands of the United States, Ernest felt it would be a preventative against future war, its energy turned to medical, biological, and industrial uses, under control of a commission. Research should be fostered, and industrial application encouraged.

The Scientific Panel met again on June 16 at Los Alamos. Deliberations were interrupted by a telephone call from Harrison—the Interim Committee wished opinions as to the immediate use of the bomb. The Chicago group, determined that the Interim Committee—and the President—understand their views, had demanded consideration of their report. They insisted upon no more than a technical demonstration of the weapon. Compton observed that the men of his laboratory failed to consider possible alternatives to a successful demonstration—continuation of the war and the tremendous cost in casualties which invasion of the Japanese home islands must entail. Certainly no one could wish repeated Tarawas, Iwo Jimas, and Okinawas! Compton now believed the bomb should be used as soon as possible to save American lives and to demonstrate a force that would prevent future war. Ernest held out to the last for some method of successful demonstration and warning, before bombing a city. Compton suggested that Ernest's concern was due to his fondness for Japanese students in the prewar Rad Lab. Oppie was convinced that only use on a real target, with existing structures, would be effective. He could not envision any means of prior demonstration likely to be successful. He thought the number killed would not be greater in order of magnitude than the number already killed in fire raids and would undoubtedly be less than those destroyed in an invasion.

The panel recommended direct military use—but only after the Allies had been advised of American technical progress in atomic weapons and asked to cooperate in use of the new force toward international peace. The threat of the bomb in good hands must be the enforcer of peace. The United Nations parley at San Francisco, the latter part of April, held promise for continuing international discussions. The U.N. was scheduled to meet soon again to consider a charter. Scientific information should be revealed; only technical aspects of bomb construction and mechanics need remain secret. Industrial advisers to the Interim Committee also advised use over a military target, in a city that included urban buildings. It was generally agreed that President Truman should inform the Russians of the bomb and its expected use at the scheduled Big Three meeting. Byrnes remained adamant against any specific knowledge being made available to the Russians.

The Trinity test did not alter the conclusions. Surely no nation, however fanatical its militarists, would hold out against such a weapon. Ernest was convinced that it not only would quickly end the war but also that, properly handled, it would make future war unthinkable. He envisioned a "new era in the pursuit of the useful arts of peace . . . with lasting benefit to all the peoples of the world, which is the goal of all science and all scientists."

On August 6, a single uranium bomb, with an explosive force equivalent to nearly twenty thousand tons of TNT, almost obliterated a city whose population had numbered a quarter of a million. Three days after Hiroshima, a plutonium bomb destroyed the industrial center of the great port of Nagasaki. Russia declared war on Japan the same day, after invading Manchuria. The following day Japan submitted an offer of surrender, asking that the sovereignty of her emperor be retained.

Suddenly the secret was out: the story of the bomb, culminating in Trinity, Hiroshima, and Nagasaki. "Secret Weapon" headlines appeared in West Coast afternoon papers the day Hiroshima was bombed—with pictures of Ernest and Oppie. Molly was overcome with surprise, Ernest surprised that she was. Morning papers of the seventh had larger headlines and more pictures. Not only the bomb but also a new world was heralded. On the eighth, photographs of the 184-inch cyclotron complex above the U.C. campus appeared with stories of Ernest's part in the bomb project—it was his forty-fourth birthday. The children brought the paper to him; the mystery of the guards and guns in cars was cleared. The Nagasaki bombing caused more of the same; on the tenth, Ernest was glad to escape reporters and telephones and fly to Los Alamos. He returned to Berkeley on the fourteenth—the day of surrender.

With all the celebrations, joy, and relief, for some of those who had witnessed the Trinity demonstration, the actual victory over Japan was somewhat anticlimactic. Others went so far as to worry aloud that what appeared to be a happy conclusion to war might in fact be the beginning of an era in which peace at best would be precarious. Among those for whom Hiroshima and Nagasaki answered the riddle their compartmentalized efforts had posed, reactions ranged from satisfaction to wonderment; from hope in the dawn of an era of greater understanding of nature's forces to horror at what their efforts had done to two centers of humanity, however hostile. Somehow, the fact that a single plane and a single bomb could wreak such devastation and death—70,000 killed at Hiroshima alone, and who could count the injured?—seemed far more evil than the suffering and destruction caused by many super fortresses, each unleashing tons of fire and explosive bombs.

For Ernest, though he had hoped other means than that employed could be found to demonstrate the bomb's power to the world, there was less soul-searching and moral concern over its use than for many of his colleagues. As a dedicated scientist he resented the idea that scientific efforts to halt aggressive conquest and bypass costly invasion were evil. What of the lives and suffering of Americans—and Japanese, too—had invasion been necessary? The bomb had brought the war to an end. All evidence pointed to far greater maiming and killing had invasion been necessary. War was evil, however conducted; the shorter its duration, the better, if only by months or weeks. He felt none of the guilt Oppie proclaimed scientists now had on their consciences. On the contrary, he was proud of the scientific achievement; the war had been ended by it; its very horror should prevent future war. What ruthless dictator would risk the destruction of cities and a radiation-laden atmosphere! If one wished to invoke symbols with religious connotations, suddenly so prevalent in speeches and the press, he preferred such a one as "the terrible swift sword" of righteousness to those of sin and guilt. As he wrote to Dean Akeley: "We have accomplished the first objective of ending the war and I think the second, that of ending all wars, will be achieved. Atomic bombs of the future will be much more devastating. For a few years we will have supremacy, though we cannot count on dominating the situation indefinitely." The thing to do was to stop whining and maintain that supremacy until all countries realized that peace is the only climate for progress. For scientists, the proper course was to get back to work in science, which is neither good nor evil.

A Presidential commission empowered to oversee all aspects of atomic energy, and to subsidize research and development, could assume control without objectionable wartime features or military restraints. Technical details, Ernest felt—the mechanics of the bomb—should not be disclosed; the scientific aspects it would be impossible to keep secret for any length of time. Thus restriction of scientific intercourse could be discarded; in a peaceful world, science could again become international.

Even concern over Russia, which Groves had confessed clouded his thoughts on postwar plans, should not deter the "free interchange of scientific information," Ernest wrote in 1945. With such freedom, "We have the greater assurance of international cooperation and collaboration, and the best source of knowledge that something is not going on in a foreign country inimical to us. . . . There is no doubt in my mind that the best channel of information about what is going on in Russia would be developed by encouraging free interchange of science and scientists. In fact it is the only avenue I can think of that has a reasonable chance of working at the present time. . . . I, therefore, hope very much that this first step advocated by the President of exchange of scientific information and scientists, with all countries, will be welcomed by all countries, especially Russia, as the first step in a broad international understanding." The United Nations, its charter signed in San Francisco before the war's conclusion, appeared a hopeful avenue for initiating scientific cooperation.

Ernest had spent the weekend following the Nagasaki bombing in Los Alamos, discussing postwar plans. Weary Oppenheimer, suffering an understandable letdown and harassed by demands of many at Los Alamos for immediate release to go home, was anything but optimistic. Moral scruples—after the fact—disturbed him. Perhaps those killed in Hiroshima and Nagasaki were the lucky ones; one could not estimate the damage to survivors—perhaps to those yet unborn. Ernest was as patient as Ernest could be with his friend; every qualm that bothered Oppie could be interpreted as a reason to ensure that the bomb need never be used again. Oppie drafted a letter to Secretary Stimson, with the Scientific Panel's recommendations that all developments of atomic energy be placed under international control and the warning that a thermonuclear fusion super bomb, far more terrible than the demonstrated fission bombs, could probably be developed within three years.

Oppie intended to deliver the letter to the Interim Committee personally, but only Bush and George L. Harrison were in Washington when he arrived. He discussed with them, in more detail than the letter conveyed, the panel's concern for the future, in the nation and internationally. He explained the reluctance of many scientists to continue bomb work, "just like poison gases after the last war," and, as he reported later to Ernest, told them that, "all of us are willing to wait for a bit and help with any plan that looks reasonable, but in the end this will have to be based on a national policy which is intelligible in its broad outlines to the men who are doing the work." Oppie sensed from conversations with Bush and Harrison that little had been done at Potsdam to interest Stalin in collaboration and control. "I don't know how seriously an effort was made; apparently neither Churchill, nor Attlee, nor Stalin was any help at all, but this is only my conjecture. While I was in Washington two things happened, both rather gloomy: The President issued an absolute ukase, forbidding any disclosures on the atomic bomb . . . without his personal approval. The other was that Harrison took our letter to Byrnes, who sent back word, just as I was leaving, that 'in the present critical international situation' there was no alternative to pushing the Manhattan program full steam ahead."

Bush was as anxious as anyone that freedom of research and protection of scientists from military domination be assured in any postwar legislation. Harrison, familiar with the draft of an atomic energy bill he had asked Kenneth Royall and William Marbery (civilian attorneys with the War Department) to write, said nothing could be done until policies toward Russia and international control had been decided. With Stimson, Harrison favored prevention of an "armament race of a rather desperate character," by offering confidence and partnership in atomic matters to Russia. But they were in a minority. Stimson left long national service on his seventy-eighth birthday. At a ceremony at which Truman awarded him the Distinguished Service Medal, Stimson pleaded eloquently for open research and development. His replacement, Robert Patterson, seemed inclined to follow the Stimson philosophy. However, publicized resistance to the idea by Byrnes and Secretary of the Navy James Forrestal aroused already impatient groups of scientists, particularly at Chicago, who felt that they should have been consulted.

Groves became concerned over actual and threatened departures of scientists from wartime laboratories to academic institutions. Sam Allison said that security restrictions might reduce scientists to study of the color of butterfly wings; Fermi explained that it was not that scientists would not work for the government but that they could not, until research was free and beyond military control, and that continued restrictions could deprive the country of its supremacy in science. Groves endeavored to quiet Chicago scientists on the grounds that their protests would upset the "legislative applecart." They were not appeased. Various bills were introduced in both Congressional bodies, none of which won general approval. The President-blessed Stimson-Royall-Marbery bill was introduced in October, under the sponsorship of Senator Edwin C. Johnson of Colorado and Congressman Andrew J. May of the Military Affairs Committee. Such sponsorship only lent credence to accusations that the bill would preserve military control of atomic energy. At the same time, President Truman, in a message to Congress, proposed that the nations of the world ban the bomb, under an administrative and control commission. The May-Johnson Bill was pushed through committees—"railroaded through," its opponents said—and, though supported by Bush, Conant, Ernest and Oppie, aroused the dissident groups of scientists. All sorts of bugaboos were seen in this bill, from military interference to security provisions that threatened jail terms for involuntary and innocuous classroom mistakes. The faith of other scientists in the Advisory Panel was shaken after Oppie secured the signatures of Ernest and Fermi to a telegram to Patterson supporting the bill. When Ernest later saw the bill in its final draft, at a Washington meeting of the panel, he was shocked to find included provisions of which he had been unaware when he authorized his signature on the supporting telegram. Arthur Compton wisely had refused his signature until he could read the bill as submitted.

Under the same date as that of the telegram, Ernest's personal message stressed the need for pure science, the fact that valuable practical applications usually stemmed from it, and the necessity for freedom of inquiry and information, "the keystone of any structure designed to promote scientific progress. . . . I am firmly convinced that . . . even considerations of national security demand that we maintain complete openness and freedom in our work in the basic sciences . . . our greatest safety therefore is not a static defense but a dynamic progression forward in unravelling nature's secrets. . . . I should like to point out a very realistic policy of insurance. It goes without saying that other countries are not going to be asleep in pursuing the paths of the new knowledge and if we practice secrecy control in the fundamental sciences, we can be sure other countries will do likewise. . . . We shall always have the specter before us of the possibility . . . of fundamental discoveries far outreaching our progress, and to our disaster. . . . In certain realms of the applied sciences, in technical knowhow and in the development of weapons I quite agree on the desirability and necessity of secrecy . . . in conclusion may I say that if this climate of free science is maintained by our government we may look forward with optimism to the future."

Amendments were drafted to rectify "misinterpretations" of the bill's provisions. Oppenheimer tried to assuage the flood of scientists' objections without much success. His single objection to the bill before the committee was the lack of explicit definition of the proposed atomic control commission's powers. Others found nothing favorable—fearing the likelihood of too much military control. Physicists Szilard and Herbert Anderson antagonized Congressional committee members with their testimony; the wrangling continued.

Meanwhile Senator Brien McMahon of Connecticut introduced a resolution in the Senate for the establishment of a committee to study the matter and evaluate all bills and resolutions concerned with atomic energy. It was established, with McMahon as its chairman, on October 23. On December 20, a bill bearing his name was introduced, a bill drafted after consultation with scientist groups and with their support. Indeed, groups of scientists had descended upon Washington, where they min-gled with ambassadors, Cabinet officers, members of Congress and so-cialites—who welcomed them at their cocktail parties. Several groups joined to organize the Federation of Atomic Scientists, and, for the dis-semination of information, the National Committee on Atomic Informa-tion. They not only would be heard, they would propagandize, inspire, and recruit lobby assistance from nonscientific organizations. Liaison be-tween the McMahon Committee and the FAS was good. The committee had studied the Smyth Report, which told all that was permitted of the bomb project, and visited the vast Oak Ridge complex; the resulting bill quickly assumed a leading position. The final blow to military control, and the May-Johnson Bill, was inadvertently delivered by the Army it-self: General Douglas MacArthur's forces in Japan destroyed the Japa-nese cyclotrons and dropped the refuse into the Pacific Ocean. Patter-son's justification of this demolition aroused greater fear than ever of military control and was seized upon by the FAS to stimulate opposition to the May-Johnson Bill. McMahon's bill, with its civilian commission, took on new luster.

Ernest was deeply distressed and incensed over the destruction of the Japanese cyclotrons, nor was he appeased by reports that Secretary of War Patterson had exonerated the occupation forces and placed the blame on an office error. That seemed as lame as a previous excuse that cyclotrons could be used for military purposes and were "of special value in atomic research." He wrote to Bush: "I hope very much something will be done to rectify this error. . . . The right thing to do would be at least to re-equip Nishina's laboratory." Ernest had expressed concern over those Japanese scientists whom he knew, particularly those who had spent much time at the Rad Lab, and continued to send dried fruit, condensed milk, and candy to Sagane's children, and cigarettes and sci-entific periodicals to Sagane and Nishina by officers going to Japan, un-til shortages there were eased.

The scientists' rumpus in Washington also distressed Ernest. Necessary as it might be to call attention to a possible scientific contribution to national defense, or to advise on the proper handling of the new atomic force and facts of which scientists were more aware than others, the noisy lobbying conducted by scientists demeaned science. It was not science they were concerned with but that their opinions on the conduct of affairs be followed. What superiority endowed them with such compe-tence over other citizens? Their great contribution? Others had con-tributed without demanding the right to dictate. What arrogance! How undemocratic! The scientist agitators would be the first to resent such assumptions by any other single element of society: the military, for in-stance, the clergy, or any certain class, each as sincerely convinced that a program tailored to its ideas would be best in the long run. Why didn't they get to work? The decline of Los Alamos might then be checked, morale at Oak Ridge lifted. He disliked the necessity of going to Washington more than ever, but he regarded appearances before committees or conferences with officialdom as a necessary, patriotic duty.

Liked or not, with or without cooperation, the Manhattan District had to retain control until relieved by some other agency, acting more or less as a holding operation. Groves could shut down certain facilities but must maintain production of uranium U-235 and plutonium. The newest Beta track at Oak Ridge was not completed until two months after the war's conclusion, when, with more enriched feed from the now flourishing gaseous diffusion plant, production was greatly increased; indeed the danger of accumulating enriched material beyond safe amounts now had to be avoided. But uncertainty of the future, among other things, kept morale low and people leaving. At Los Alamos, efforts were made to keep sufficient personnel to stockpile and improve weapons. That those weapons were technically in the custody of the University of California bothered Ernest, until Groves appropriated an Army facility at Sandia, the old Albuquerque airport, and moved assembly operations there, from the New Mexico hill.

Oppie resigned in October and Norris Bradbury, Stanford physicist and Navy officer who had been in charge of implosion field-tests assumed what he expected to be temporary charge, an unenviable job. Personnel, tired of confinement, plagued by water shortage, and lured by better jobs, or academic prospects, continued to leave. Hanford's problems were largely technical, and that of changing operating companies. The Rad Lab, voluntarily cut back from a May total of 1,086 personnel to 853, ended the year with a roster of 454—a reduction of some 800 from the high of midsummer 1944. There alone, it seemed to Ernest, was there no discontent, rebellion, or what too often appeared as whining complaint. As project work tapered off, investigation into long-neglected problems was resumed whenever possible. Only the 60-inch, now capable of producing deuterons of 20 million volts and alpha particles of twice that energy, was available for cyclotron work. Soon after this voltage was achieved, two new transuranium elements, 95 and 96, were produced.

Ernest had not waited for the war's end to plan the laboratory's future, and he had the great and unique advantage of having entered the emergency with an established, big laboratory. His aim now was resumption of prewar pursuits. First on the agenda, in charge of Thornton, was completion of the 184-inch cyclotron, incorporating the principles of McMillan's phase stability, an idea he had developed during his last year at Los Alamos, and Reg Richardson's frequency modulation.

McMillan's idea, equally applicable to electrons, stimulated interest in design of the Rad Lab's first circular electron accelerator, or synchrotron, which it was hoped would produce 300 million volts. The Russians were known to be constructing a synchrotron; the new principle had been discovered independently—and previously announced—by Vladimir Veksler of Russia, unknown to McMillan. Revival of interest in linear accelerators, abandoned in the midthirties for the cyclotron, resulted from Alvarez's ideas for use of microwave power to accelerate protons to high energies. The availability of surplus radar materials made construction economically attractive. With the engineering skills of Brobeck, recently appointed assistant director, and the overall help of Associate Director Cooksey, the Rad Lab lost no time in the transition to peacetime pursuits. By the end of 1945, Groves had allocated $170,000 toward completion of the 184-inch synchrocyclotron and had authorized construction of the electron synchrotron, under the wartime contract.

A division of medical physics, in conjunction with the medical school, was instituted and initially staffed by John, Crocker Laboratory head Joe Hamilton, and Donner staffers Cornelius Tobias and Hardin Jones. Robert Stone was expected to continue neutron therapy after his return from Chicago, and Ernest hoped that Earl Miller, also of the University Hospital, would continue to devote part of his time to health physics at the laboratory. Dean Wendell Latimer, whose chemistry group had continued to make and study plutonium after Seaborg's departure for Chicago, would oversee the chemistry program. Seaborg eventually would have charge of inorganic chemistry, as it pertained to transuranium elements; until his return from Chicago, Isadore Perlman, among the first to return from the Metallurgical Laboratory, would be in charge. Melvin Calvin would supervise organic chemistry and biological research. Oppie was included in Ernest's plans for a greater than ever Radiation Laboratory, "a paradise of physics"; until Oppie's return, his onetime student, Robert Serber, was chief theoretician.

Oppie was being a little difficult. Birge's letters about his returning to the faculty had long been unanswered; Ernest knew there had been attractive offers from other universities. In fact, early in the year, when Ernest was asked by Conant for recommendations on major Harvard appointments, he had felt honor-bound to put Oppie and Alvarez at the top of two lists, "though it would be no less than a calamity if either Oppie or Alvarez should not return here, but as committee-man am not letting that awful possibility prejudice my judgment." Ernest had discussed Rad Lab and physics department plans with Oppie at Los Alamos in August after a Scientific Panel meeting. The discussion had become heated; Oppie brought up administrative difficulties Los Alamos had had with the university as one reason a return to Berkeley lacked luster. Finally differences of temperament and values between the two men were expressed. Ernest defended his aversion to mixing politics and science. Oppie asserted the obligation for active concern with humanity, whether Loyalist resistance to mercenary rebels, Nazi genocide, or the plight of migrant workers in rich California valleys. They might agree on the advisability of international accord on nuclear energy, but Ernest could not concur that use of the bomb was morally reprehensible, however much he had regretted the necessity of its use. Oppie was reminded that he had been chief advocate for bombing a Japanese city and Ernest the last to go along. This was no time to whine over error but to ensure that further nuclear bombing would be unthinkable—in terms immoral leaders could understand. That, for a scientist, involved dedication to his own discipline, where he understood the terms. Competence in physics—even the ability to organize and supervise a bomb laboratory—did not imply the ability, or confer the right, to order the affairs of men of other, perhaps more applicable, capabilities. Oppie hinted at Ernest's respect for generals—because they were generals, and for successful men of affairs—because they were successful. Ernest thought Oppie quick enough to take personal advantage of his success at Los Alamos. Did he not enjoy being generally credited with the bomb? Oppie thought that Ernest, used to being important, resented the new stature of a colleague heretofore in his shadow.

A couple of weeks later Oppie wrote from New Mexico: "We have been at the ranch some days now, and I'm beginning to recover a little of the sanity that had all but vanished by the weekend you visited Y. I have very mixed and sad feelings about our discussions on Berkeley. I meant them in a far more friendly, tentative and considerate spirit than they appeared to you; and was aware and tried to make you aware at the time that fatigue and confusion gave them a false emphasis and color. It may seem odd and wrong to you that the lack of sympathy between us at Y and the California administration over the operation of the project could make me consider not coming back: I think it would not have seemed so odd if you had lived through the history as we did, nor so hard to understand if you remembered how much more of an underdogger I have always been than you. That is a part of me that is unlikely to change, for I am not ashamed of it; it is responsible for such differences as we have had in the past, I think; I should have thought that after the long years it would not be new to you. In any case it seemed little more than honorable to tell you of the misgivings, however unfortunate the timing. My own thought and plans have not come clear, though they no doubt will. But it must be apparent that your own very strong, very negative reactions would, if confirmed and quite apart from the views of others involved, tend to carry a considerable weight with me, since any fruitful future in Berkeley would have to depend, not on identity certainly, but on a certain mutual respect for non-identical points of view." The letter was signed "affectionately, Robert."

Ernest spoke only briefly about the university with Oppenheimer in the next month and not again with such personal and emotional depth. In any case, Ernest was in no sense responsible for Los Alamos-university problems, consequences of a high-rolling and secret operation. They were together a good deal in Washington, at panel meetings and during hearings on the May-Johnson Bill. Their relationship had much of the old camaraderie. There was unity in their dedication to a proper and not-long-postponed atomic energy program. If Ernest thought Oppie naïve and not too sensible outside of physics, he was glad that his unusual persuasive powers, enhanced by his sudden fame, were directed toward a worthy objective—as they had been when so skillfully exercised in recruitment for Los Alamos. In a report to the regents, a few days after the Los Alamos arguments, he had singled out Oppie with high praise for his contribution. Some regents felt that Ernest was overly modest about his own contributions. Sproul knew that in 1941, when the decision to proceed with the uranium project hung in the balance, it had been Ernest, with the only hopeful plan, who had tipped the scales. He also knew that, without the electromagnetic process, another year would have passed without a bomb, and that it had been Ernest who had first suggested and pushed the plutonium program, without which even Fermi's pile would have been useless in the war. Ernest insisted that there would have been no plutonium without a pile, and probably no bomb without Oppie.

Ernest was not concerned with personal recognition; that had continued to come even during the war. He had been elected Honorary Fellow of the National Institute of Sciences of India and been given an honorary fellowship in Chicago's Institute of Medicine. He had been elected to the Russian Academy of Sciences and had received the credentials at the Soviet Embassy from the hands of Andrei Gromyko, then coming into prominence. He had to decline the invitation to visit Russia at the end of the war. He had been unable personally to accept the citation on the four hundredth anniversary of the death of Copernicus; Karl Darrow had received that for him in Carnegie Hall. In 1944 he had been elected to the Board of Trustees of the Carnegie Institution of Washington. Praise had come from officials of Stone and Webster, Eastman Kodak, and its subsidiary, TEC—perhaps best summed up in the letter of P. S. Wilcox: "You deserve much more credit than you received for making it possible to have U-235 available at the early date it was used. If it had not been for your great ability, your energy, and your enthusiasm, all of which enabled you to obtain the wholehearted cooperation of the fine organization you had, it would not have been possible to solve the manufacturing difficulties as soon as we did.

"While you have been given little public acknowledgment for what you have done—I understand it does not bother you. You are too big to be concerned about what is said today because your name will go down in history as one of the most important individuals who had to do with the project. Be sure TEC and Kodak realize it."

Ernest was particularly pleased to receive the biennial Wheeler Award, in October, 1945, as "Berkeley's most useful citizen." Introduced by Sproul, Ernest said it was fortunate that a speech was not expected from him. "I don't believe you can appreciate what a comfort that is, because the War Department went to great pains to seal my lips all through the war years, and now I find I've just about forgotten how to talk. Of course, under ordinary circumstances I would be constrained to question some of the overwhelmingly kind things President Sproul said about me, but I'm not sure it would be sound policy in this instance. If he had any illusions along this line, rather than debating his views it would seem to be the part of prudence to give him every encouragement for, after all, he is President and he is my Boss! . . . May I say that there is nothing nicer than to be well spoken of in one's home town and for this reason above all I thank you from the bottom of my heart."

At a special academic convocation held in the Greek Theater, the university was awarded the E for excellence in recognition of its contribution to the war effort. At the same time an honorary doctorate was conferred on General Groves—his first.

Recognition in a very practical sense were requests for Ernest's advice that culminated in consultant contracts with the General Electric and Eastman Kodak companies. Shortly thereafter, in 1946, he was also retained as consultant to the American Cyanamid Company, with, in addition to personal remuneration, a $10,000 annual contribution to a special fund for aiding research.

The Presidential Citation and Medal for Merit were presented to Ernest in March, 1946, with his family, laboratory personnel, and faculty members present. "We started a hundred million dollar project with nothing but confidence in Lawrence," said General Groves. "We bet a hundred million on him and won." Sproul said, "Ernest, I congratulate you. This is by no means personal for me; it is in behalf of thirty thousand students and many thousands of alumni." John Francis Neylan, chairman of the regents' committee on atomic energy projects, was concerned lest Ernest's modesty, in view of the publicity received in other quarters, might harm the laboratory. The Rad Lab had been Neylan's pet project for a decade, and, though considered a crank on the expenditure of public money since his Sacramento days with Hiram Johnson, he never questioned Ernest:

"We took him on faith, just one thousand percent, and he's the only human being we ever did. All I ever did was ask him what he wanted. Oh yes, and our committee was the dumbest committee in the world. Our chief function was to know nothing . . . but we could short-stop things for him. . . . One thing I was able to do and I did it conscientiously. Everybody wanted to know what was going on, and I ultimately became the most ignorant man in America on what was going on. I wouldn't look into anything and I kept myself in a position where members of the board—My God, they would drive you crazy. They wanted to go see this and go see that, and I'd always say, 'How can I do that? I'm chairman of the committee and I've never even seen it.' I rendered him one service: I kept the curious off his back, from the low-grade to the high and mighty curious. And the funny thing about it, he was just as naïve about it. I'd say, 'Now, you go fry your own fish, I'll just back-stop things.' Remember the flood of publicity after the atom bomb? . . . I called a meeting of the committee for lunch at the Pacific Union Club. I said, 'I'm sick and tired of this thing. All these people taking credit that belongs to Ernest and fixing this thing up to make Chicago the focal point of pure science. It's about time it's properly placed.' Everyone at the table was with me except Ernest. He said, 'Now, Jack, you're all wrong. I hope you don't think I'm taking too much liberty here, but in the first place it would be dishonest for any one man or any one group to gather to himself the credit for this, because we've all had the benefit of so much research by so many fine people you couldn't possibly appraise it. We happened to be at a junction where a lot of ideas met.' He said that he was just lucky to be there.

"I didn't get anywhere arguing with him, but I knew from some very prominent Chicago alumni what was on the ticket there. Urey and Fermi were in Chicago; they'd invited Oppenheimer. They were trying to get Seaborg for ten thousand dollars and a full professorship. Ernest just stood there stiff legged. He just said, 'Jack, take it easy and don't worry.' Sometime later he asked me to lunch with him. He was very mysterious. Afterwards we went up on the hill. Just like a big kid, you know, with something hidden under his coat. When he got up there, he showed me some apparatus. 'See that,' he said, and there was millions of dollars worth of excess radar equipment. 'Now quit worrying about Chicago.' 'What does it mean?' I asked. He said, 'Groves ordered it sent to us!'

"He was still determined to have Oppenheimer. Finally he called Oppenheimer on the phone and said, 'Robert, when you get through wandering around, come on back home. Your old office is waiting, your old hat is on the rack, your desk hasn't been cleaned out.' He just rolled out the red carpet for Oppenheimer. After all that publicity! Mr. Atomic Bomb and all that! Oh, I think they mentioned Ernest occasionally in some of the stuff. . . . Robert Oppenheimer is a great scientist, no question about that, but Ernest was one who by his very modesty incited the greatest admiration."

Perhaps Regent Neylan's comments are indicative of part of Oppie's reluctance to return to Berkeley. Shane had noted Oppie's dissatisfaction even before Los Alamos was well under way, and there is other prewar evidence, such as that of a physics department budget meeting when Oppie, following Ernest, had been sarcastic: "Now I suppose I may order a gross of pencils." In any event, though Oppie had accepted a full-time professorship at Caltech—before requesting a year's extension of his wartime leave of absence from California—he ultimately returned to Berkeley in 1946, and became, for the first time, officially, a member of the Rad Lab staff. He was not amused with Ernest's congratulations upon return: "Good, and I can clip your wings a little."

Neylan also worried about Ernest's health. "Thought he was wearing himself out. At the end of 1945 I persuaded him to refuse the Secretary of War's request to serve on an important committee. He was kind of boyish about it. Came over to see me. I told him, 'They are looking for somebody to be the fall guy and you're nominated.' He said, 'Oh, do you think they'd do that?' I got him to refuse that one." There was reason for Neylan's concern. Bronchial trouble lingered after head colds from which Ernest recovered insufficiently before plunging again into his affairs. Molly tried to keep him in bed or at home. "He knew he had to watch out for respiratory infections. He just wouldn't stay home and take care of himself when he had a cold. Always promising to, but he wouldn't. He'd listen to John lay down the law, and might stay in bed part of a day, but I'd return from the market and find the car gone. He was at the Lab."

He moved his office from Durant Hall to Donner Laboratory a few months after the end of the war, but it was still not close to activities on the hill, and he felt he must at least appear in all four areas each day. The old Rad Lab and Crocker were handy to Donner, but most of the excitement was up near the big machine and in buildings near it where the other new accelerators were being designed and built. He had a new secretary in October; Bea Bishop had followed the examples of her predecessors and married. Eleanor Irvine had been one of the secretaries in the offices of Cooksey, Reynolds, Shane and Chaney, so, when she became Ernest's secretary, the transition was smooth enough. Eleanor remained single for nine more years—and when she did change her last name to Davisson, she did not quit.

In late November Ernest returned to Berkeley from Pasadena and a long session of Tolman's Declassification Committee, with a cold which he endured with his usual lack of care. Early in December virus pneumonia developed; he was very sick. The virus left him weak and John said it was imperative that he "take it easy until April." Ernest promised Molly that he would take a couple of weeks off! He disliked the idea of more time away from the laboratory with such interesting things happening, especially the application of frequency modulation to the 37-inch, converted again by Richardson, MacKenzie, Lofgren, Wright, and Fred Schmidt, as a pilot model for the 184-inch as a synchrocyclotron, on which Thornton and Brobeck were busy. McMillan was designing his synchrotron. Alvarez and Wolfgang K. H. Panofsky, with the help of Chaim Richman, Frank Oppenheimer, and Larry Marshall, were having so much luck with their radar equipment that, after construction of a proper tube, it was hoped protons would be accelerated to energies between a hundred million and a billion volts! But just wandering around looking into things with Cooksey tired Ernest, though he always insisted that he was all right. John was as insistent that he get away from the labs and from Berkeley, a goal finally realized in order to keep a date in Pasadena, December 27, 1945—the day the United States, Britain, and Russia agreed to set up a U.N. atomic energy commission.

The first night was spent with the Blumers, now living in San Marino, and the following day Ernest and Molly drove to Palm Springs, where Ernest's health improved enough to make him restless; they returned to San Marino after a week. The Blumers were surprised; G.B. tried to persuade his son-in-law that rest and relaxation were as important to body and mind as the second law of thermodynamics is to physics. Longer, or more frequent vacations were essential if he was to keep his health. Ernest agreed heartily—while it was being discussed—and promised a long vacation—next summer, perhaps at Balboa, where the Blumers had rented a house on the island the previous summer; there was a larger one nearby, on the waterfront. With little further discussion, Ernest asked Molly to phone and engage it for the coming summer. She reported that the owner was not interested; he had a tenant and was thinking of selling the place. "Fine," Ernest said. "Call him up again and tell him we'll buy it." Molly, with some reluctance, phoned again. When she could not persuade the owner, Ernest took the phone and wangled an agreement to show the house later that day.

Ernest liked the house at once: lots of room and an apartment over the garage. To Molly it was "an old wreck, actually one of the oldest around, and built without benefit of architect. Ernest insisted we could fix it up. We went to a motel and the next day examined it again, and others nearby, for by that time Ernest was determined to buy a place at Balboa Island. All from the hazy notion of renting for the summer that had occurred to him the day before. The old house was the one he set his heart on because it fronted on the bay. If he had it, he said he would really spend time there. A price was set and we bought it. When he got back to Berkeley he sold some stock and paid the full amount."

Progress at the laboratory early in 1946 was such that he wired Warren Weaver, "so you will hear before word reaches you via the grape vine," of the likelihood of the 184-inch producing as high as 400-million-volt protons and alphas and 200-million-volt deuterons. He asked that foundation president Fosdick be informed that his offered help for completion of the accelerator would not be needed, as necessary funds were available from the Manhattan Project. Weaver wired back his congratulations and followed with a letter asking Ernest's opinion of various scientists' organizations, particularly the Federation of American Scientists. Ernest responded: "I am one of those evidently showing signs of senility because I see no need for a new organization along the lines of the proposed Federation of American Scientists, for there are plenty of organizations already such as the A.A.A.S. to represent the views of science and scientists. In fact, my own feeling is that this political activity of many of our atomic scientists is unfortunate in many ways.

"It is particularly a great pity that they are frittering away so much time and energy on political problems, when they could be devoting themselves to scientific pursuits."

Since the war he had been besieged by letters asking his support for various causes, or for his signature on petitions or protests, most of which he ignored. There were requests to speak before various civilian groups—"this Rotary club, that women's auxiliary," as Alfred Loomis put it. Nor were they all from clubs—Senator McMahon requested personal comment on his atomic energy bill. As Ernest had initially supported the May-Johnson Bill, he consulted Neylan, who saw merit in still a third bill. Ernest answered the Senator noncommittally: "The three bills are basically sound in that they have essentially declared the same purposes and objectives . . . inappropriate, if not presumptuous, for me to undertake critical analysis of the detailed differences involving legal, political, government and organizational considerations, a field in which I have no special qualification . . . can only reaffirm the urgency of early passage of one of these bills, or a suitable compromise, as it is indeed important for our national security and welfare that we get on with a vigorous national program . . . it is perhaps natural that I should be concerned for the freedom of science and the encouragement of unfettered fundamental research. I also favor the encouragement of private industrial enterprise in the atomic energy program."

Loomis, in California for a month, happened to be at the laboratory when Ernest received a request from a top rank colleague of the Manhattan Project, asking him to speak at a meeting of a radical group. When Loomis suggested that Ernest toss the telegram in the wastebasket, Ernest protested; that would be discourteous to an important scientist. Loomis asked to see Ernest's reply. He read it aloud: "I regret exceedingly that I will be unable to attend your meeting." Loomis asked, "Would you really like to have that read at such a meeting, that you wish you could be there, and regret that you can't?" Ernest sheepishly crumpled his answer and threw it in a wastebasket. Loomis had been friend and confidant to Ernest throughout the war. His Manhattan and Washington residences had always been available, whether the Loomises were present or not; at the Wardman Park suite one might have found any of the OSRD top command, or people in Loomis's radar program—such as Rowan Gaither, who had proved to be such a fine administrator for Loomis at M.I.T. Ernest's affection for Loomis was bolstered by great respect. He knew of his successful enterprises by hearsay; he knew firsthand of his regard for and ability in physics. He had observed the deference of corporation heads to Loomis when material for the 184-inch was procured. Ernest seldom argued with his friend on political, social, or economic matters; Loomis's good judgment was proven. For his part, Loomis had such admiration and regard for Ernest that, prior to the war, he had planned to move to California to participate actively in the Rad Lab. Since the war, as Neylan had repeatedly done, Loomis cautioned against any feeling of obligation to accept invitations to speak, join, or sign.

Concerned lest advantage be taken of Ernest—"so goodhearted and helpful"—Loomis asked H. Rowan Gaither, Jr., a San Francisco resident, to advise him and help keep him free of pressure groups and circulators of protests and petitions. Rowan indicated willingness—if Ernest requested it. The matter was settled over a long weekend at Del Monte, when the Gaithers and Lawrences were guests. Ernest would consult Rowan on all such matters. It was the beginning of a growing and happy relationship between the men. The young San Francisco attorney-financier soon became a consultant to the Radiation Laboratory. And a year later, when Gaither was asked to organize the Rand Corporation, a nonprofit organization to ensure the military, particularly the Air Force, the continued benefits of science, it was Rowan's turn to consult Ernest on trustees for Rand. Ernest was finally persuaded to become a trustee of Rand himself.

Initially, Ernest was advised against accepting positions on either the

Secretary of State's Committee, or the Board of Consultants for the formulation and recommendation of atomic energy policies, since both were politically involved and would require much time in Washington. In March, 1946, he was advised, again to his own satisfaction, to decline regretfully Bernard Baruch's request to join his advisory staff. Baruch, the American representative on the United Nations Atomic Energy Commission, asked his old friend Neylan to intercede for him and urge Ernest to accept. Neylan explained his sanction of Ernest's refusal, ". . . listing five reasons: the heavy load of directing the Rad Lab, itself far beyond a normal job, his fatigue after the war which culminated in pneumonia, the wear and tear of outside demands upon him because of his eminence in the field, his dislike of publicity and distress by controversies among scientists, and his enormous program in the field of nuclear physics." Neylan concluded his letter to Baruch with a promise that Ernest would "make his knowledge and advice in his field available [to him] personally at all times, and that [he thought] Ernest would be most useful on this individual basis."

It was fortunate that Ernest was free of committees and advisory duties in Washington, for he was again confined with a severe cold early in 1946. Forced inactivity could not suppress impatience at politicking in Washington, the slow progress in setting up peacetime handling of atomic power in the United States, and the recalcitrance of Russia in international efforts. Foreign missions in Moscow reported that Soviet scientists had split the atom. In announcing a new five-year plan, Joseph Stalin predicted that they would catch up and surpass scientists abroad. James Byrnes countered with assurance of exclusive U.S. possession of the bomb secrets, though twenty-two espionage suspects had been arrested in Canada. The Russians admitted receiving data from Canadian spies; this information, they said, could not jeopardize American security, since what they had learned from espionage had been made public in the Smyth Report.

The second illness forced Ernest to miss the inauguration of Arthur Compton as chancellor of Washington University, St. Louis. He mailed a recording of the address he had prepared which was read at the St. Louis ceremony. Recalling their early association at Chicago in 1923, and the inspiration Compton had been, Ernest spoke of the thrill of witnessing Compton's famous discovery. Of the war years he told of the "friendly race between three white horses, three hopeful methods of producing the bomb, and a sinister dark horse, for we knew that the enemy was also working on the problem. . . . This dreadful possibility constituted perhaps the greatest stimulus to pushing our white horses to the final goal. . . . You will be interested to know that your distinguished chancellor made a bet with Dr. Conant at a very early state . . . that a certain quantity of plutonium would be produced by January 1, 1945, more than two years later. . . . The bet was for a champagne dinner with all the trimmings and, as a sort of witness and umpire, I was to be in on the feast regardless of who won. Well, Dr. Compton lost out by some ten days. You may think I came to this inaugural but I really came for the pay off, including the champagne!" But Ernest was in bed. He got up a few days later for the funeral of Dean Gilbert Lewis, who had died while at work in his laboratory.

When he was better, Ernest took Molly and the Loomises to Balboa for a weekend. For all its decrepit appearance, the large old house was comfortable enough, with old wicker furniture and gray paint on all the walls. He was sufficiently recovered after their return to go to Washington for a board meeting of Carnegie Institution, where he had the pleasure of participating in the appointment of Merle Tuve as director of its Department of Terrestrial Magnetism. Ernest wondered aloud, to Bush and Tuve, why anyone should choose to participate in the Washington hotbed of discussion and dissension. He congratulated himself that Neylan had persuaded him that it was not his patriotic duty to accept appointments that would have required more continuous presence in the Capital and possibly forced participation in public argument. The merits of various atomic energy bills before Congress, and possible U.N. and international controls were debated by scientists everywhere—usually with considerable heat.

Ernest thought much of the concern over secrecy was silly; such Russians as Kapitza, who had worked at Cambridge until detained from returning there after a Russian vacation, could unravel scientific aspects of controlled fission, knowing it has been accomplished. Perhaps, in light of the exposed Canadian espionage ring, technical secrets were already known by the Russians. Winston Churchill's Fulton, Missouri, speech, Ernest felt, while stressing the need for Anglo-American friendship, could certainly be regarded as incitement of enmity toward Russia. American altruism, in its plan for international authority over all exploitation of nuclear fission, seemed, to many, offset by scheduled atomic demonstrations at Bikini atoll in the South Pacific; "atom diplomacy" was charged, not only by the Russians, but also by some American scientists.

"Crossroads," as the scheduled May 15 Bikini tests were named, sprang from the Navy's desire to determine the effect of atomic bombs on ships of war, with Japanese ships and obsolete American vessels as targets. Foreign observers, journalists, and Congressmen had been invited as witnesses. So many Senators and Representatives wanted to witness the events that President Truman postponed Crossroads, keeping Congress in session to consider legislation, particularly the now favored

McMahon bill, under which Federal monopoly of all United States atomic energy activities would be exercised by a civilian commission, advised by a panel of scientists. The exclusion of the military appeased most of the scientific groups but aroused opposition elsewhere.

Admiral Blandy, Crossroads task force commander, visited the Radiation Laboratory prior to the operation. Dr. Shields Warren, who had been in charge of the Navy survey team at Hiroshima and Nagasaki, found Ernest and John helpful in preliminary arrangements for biological studies, in which Joe Hamilton and a Berkeley team would participate at Bikini. The number of visitors at the Rad Lab was reminiscent of prewar days, nor were all concerned with South Pacific tests. Bob Wilson and Case Institute's Bob Shankland were there for the summer, studying the scattering of 14.5-million-volt protons. John A. Wheeler of Princeton and Irving Langmuir of General Electric, 1946 Hitchcock Lecturer, were around for weeks. Hugo Atterling and two colleagues from the Nobel Institute in Sweden worked at Crocker for a while; the summer meeting of the Physical Society at Berkeley, at which Ernest spoke, brought a flood of visitors for a few days.

He took his family to Balboa when the children were freed from school, with a college girl who had been helping care for them. Though he was not there himself very much of the summer, Ernest congratulated himself on acquiring it for his family.

He did not attend the Crossroads tests. In the first, a plutonium bomb, dropped from an altitude of 30,000 feet, was exploded over 73 ships, causing greater damage over a wider area than had ever been suffered by ships from a single explosion. Radiation lowered blood counts in 90 percent of the exposed animals. In another test, a plutonium bomb was exploded underwater, sending a spectacular and tremendous column of water skyward. Ten ships, including the battleship *Arkansas* and the carrier *Saratoga,* were sunk immediately. Reports to the President were awesome—there was no doubt that atomic war could destroy whole nations and change standards of civilization itself.

On June 14, at the first meeting of the U.N. Atomic Energy Commission, Bernard Baruch offered a hopeful and generous American proposal: the United States would surrender its store of bombs and relinquish its secrets to a world atomic authority, over which no nation could exercise a veto. The American plan was countered five days later by the Soviets, with a proposal to outlaw all A-bombs by international agreement but to retain the right of veto by the five major powers of the Security Council. Andrei Gromyko, Soviet delegate to the Atomic Energy Commission of the United Nations, flatly rejected the United States plan. His government understood and agreed with the United States' original intent to keep its atomic secrets; there was no quarrel there. Soviet Foreign Minister Vyacheslav Molotov later urged the U.N. to reduce all armaments and ban atomic weapons entirely, which was agreeable to the Americans—if effective measures to insure compliance were provided. The United States would not destroy atomic weapons until an inspection and control plan was in effective operation. The Soviets opposed inspection of any nature, within Russia.

The McMahon Bill, amended to include military participation in the development of atomic energy and the manufacture of weapons, by means of a liaison committee, finally passed both houses of Congress. The Atomic Energy Act of 1946 was signed by the President on August 1. Ernest, who had never shared the distrust in which the military establishment was held by many scientists, was pleased that it had not been completely excluded; cooperation was essential in a world where victory seemed not to have included peace. He hoped for a strong commission, and a General Advisory Committee of highly qualified and independent scientists, both free of politics.

Ernest's determination to keep free of political involvement in atomic affairs was not always easy to practice. Presentation to him of the Holley Medal of the American Society of Mechanical Engineers, postponed since 1942, was scheduled for a joint meeting of several engineering groups in Los Angeles on July 26. When notified that a formal banquet, with political figures sharing the rostrum, was planned "to make a proper presentation," he was tempted to avoid the banquet, and wrote: "I endeavor to remain completely non-political in my activities and the dinner you have so graciously outlined with the leading politicians would not be in accord with this policy . . . might I suggest the medal be awarded at a regular meeting of the Los Angeles Engineering Council. . . . I am more at home before a group of engineers than before a wider audience." The banquet was not cancelled, but the political figures were not listed on the program, which included two generals—and Caltech's Millikan, who, near eighty, but rosy-cheeked and peppy, sat next to Cooksey and burbled over information he had just received from cosmic-ray films taken at the highest altitude ever by means of rocket flights.

After the presentation, Ernest and Cooksey left Los Angeles and, after a brief stop at their respective homes, drove north of San Francisco to the Bohemian Grove, a redwood forest where the annual summer encampment of that select and famous San Francisco club was in progress. Both were members of the comparatively modest "Sons of Toil" camp, where they slept and usually ate with intimate friends of common interests, but there was much mingling of Bohemians from the many camps, each of whose members were banded together by common social or professional interests. Rowan Gaither belonged to "Friends of the Forest"

—and members of all participated in the initial "Cremation of Care" festivities, such programs as the annual "Highjinks" and "Lowjinks," and the usually more serious "Lakeside Talks." Upon arrival at the grove, Ernest found an invitation to breakfast with former President Herbert Hoover the next day—a high honor for any of the grove's campers. In the morning he walked up the road past the lake and behind the seats of the outdoor stage, to the camp called "Cave Man's," where he was met by Mr. Hoover. There was much hullabaloo at "Cave Man's" over a telegram from President Truman's secretary, which requested Hoover's guest, Lewis Strauss, to call the White House. Mr. Strauss thought the telegram a joke, in keeping with the general levity normal to grove encampments. This opinion was reinforced by the fact that Strauss, a decided Republican, had received the telegram in care of Herbert Hoover. Others at Cave Man's agreed, and the telegram was ignored. The breakfast was a thoroughly enjoyable occasion for Ernest, who had great respect for Hoover. He had met Strauss in 1938 through Poillon and knew him to be one of the few civilians to attain the rank of admiral in the Navy; Strauss, long concerned with applications of radiation to cancer, naturally respected Ernest, who found much of interest at the Hoover breakfast besides the political jesting caused by the Strauss telegram. Very late that day, a Western Union messenger located Strauss.

The telegram had not been a prank, and, on the advice of Mr. Hoover, Strauss left the grove and flew to Washington. At the White House, the President asked him to become a member of the newly created Atomic Energy Commission. Other members of the five-man commission, not announced until October 28, 1946, were David Lilienthal, Chairman of the Tennessee Valley Authority; William Waymack, a Des Moines newspaper editor and a director of the Federal Reserve Bank of Chicago; Sumner Pike, once of the Securities Exchange Commission; and, the only scientist, Robert Bacher, who had been prominent in Los Alamos plutonium work and bomb design.

In New York, toward the end of August, Ernest chanced to meet Regent Neylan, who insisted that Ernest meet Bernard Baruch. When Neylan phoned Baruch, he was asked to bring Ernest to Baruch's Empire State Building offices as soon as possible; Baruch would cancel his afternoon appointments. Herbert Swope joined them, and, after the usual amenities, Neylan asked if Baruch were getting anywhere with the Russians. "No," Baruch answered, as Neylan later recalled his comments, "We don't speak the same language . . . entirely different values. We think of human life as important. As far as they are concerned, if the three fellows on the other side of the table drop dead . . . they just come in and pull them out, and in would come three others who'd start saying 'No' where they left off. You talk about human rights, they just don't know what you're talking about. They think you're kind of silly." They sat and talked all afternoon, and Ernest "captivated them."

After both were back in California, Neylan also took Ernest to San Simeon, to meet William Randolph Hearst in his baroque castle overlooking the Pacific Ocean, and scarcely a notable visited San Francisco but he asked Ernest to meet him—often at a luncheon at the Pacific Union Club. He was interested in Carl and Gunda when Ernest confided to him his father's predicament after the elder Lawrence's move to Berkeley. Carl, accustomed to an active, useful life, found retirement and removal from a community to which he had been an important contributor almost intolerable. The situation was alleviated after Carl, on the advice of Neylan, acquired an office, where he looked after his mail and worked on an autobiography. He joined Rotary and other civic associations, served on the Berkeley Library Board, and became generally active in the community—and an ardent fan of the Oakland baseball team. In October, 1946, during the World Series, Neylan had a "Lawrence Day" at his Menlo Park estate for Carl and Gunda, their sons, and Molly and Amy. The scheduled two o'clock dinner was delayed so that Carl could hear the World Series game without interruption.

Ernest had expected the 184-inch cyclotron to be completed by October 1, and, characteristically, had been thinking of bigger things throughout the summer. At the Princeton bicentennial, in September, he said, in his address, "We are already considering construction of an atom smasher that could generate atomic particles of the unheard-of energy of ten billion volts." When asked how serious he was about it, he admitted that "Brobeck has been making daydreaming studies." He also mentioned it to Sweden's Manne Siegbahn, who, after a recent visit, called the Radiation Laboratory "the mecca of the nuclear physicists." Ernest had invited Dean and Mrs. Akeley to be his guests "for the 184-inch inauguration, or if it is not ready, a sort of housewarming. I want to have you and Mrs. Akeley for the occasion, as in a very real sense if it had not been for you there probably would not have been any cyclotron. Also invited are Dr. Fosdick and Dr. Warren Weaver of the Rockefeller Foundation, Dr. Conant of Harvard, Dr. Bush, Karl Compton, General Groves, the Regents, and some others." The 184-inch was not ready when the Akeleys came for their visit, but they had a wonderful week anyway. A car and chauffeur were at their disposal, so they could go where they wished when not being entertained by one of the Lawrences. Ernest was as delighted to enable them to do this, as the Akeleys enjoyed doing it.

Before his new giant was completed, Ernest helped old friend Stewart Foster inaugurate a cyclotron at McGill University in Montreal—where he received an honorary degree, as did Niels Bohr, who was worried over the world's lack of preparedness to cope with the new atomic knowledge. Ernest recalled how at a joint meeting of the Physical Society and the Optical Society of America at McGill in February, 1926, when he was a National Research Fellow, he had given one of his first papers. Foster barely remembered the abstract but laughingly recalled Ernest's "shame and embarrassment" over the conduct of certain notable American scientists. Sir Arthur Currie, principal of McGill, on learning that it was a very distinguished body the university would be entertaining, had ordered a banquet—"nothing like it since"—at the Mount Royal Hotel. Dozens of chefs prepared the feast which was accompanied by wines, to which some prohibition-accustomed gentlemen at the head table paid too much attention. "Ernest was a regular puritan about it, he was so chagrined."

The first actual operation of the 184-inch synchrocyclotron on November 1, 1946, produced a beam of 200-million-volt deuterons, "beautifully, with hardly a hitch." No dignitaries were present; it was fifteen minutes past midnight. Ernest and the hardworking crew—"half the lab" on this expectant night—needed no other celebration than the performance and the marvelous beam—most powerful in the world. It was six years and three months after foundation excavations had been started. Then 100-million-volt particles had been the goal—ridiculed in many quarters—if necessary by "brute force" application of tremendous power to the D's. For Ernest, successful initial operation at twice the voltage originally hoped for was further justification of his methods: forget obstacles, build a basic part of what is desired, and proceed, inventing around difficulties as they arise. Time had elapsed after the erection of the huge magnet—which fortunately had been available for another purpose—and ideas and techniques unknown at the start had contributed; thus science progresses: by interchange between pure and applied science contributions from seemingly unrelated fields—the thought and work of many men, some of them long dead. A continually growing edifice.

The evolution of the cyclotron, in just a decade and a half, from an idea generated in a young American mind by a Norwegian's illustration of a Swede's suggestion in a German magazine, to the powerful instrument on Charter Hill, was spectacular. From the 4-inch glass and wax model of 1930, to the many thousand ton 184-inch, numerous "discoveries" and ideas had contributed, only the last of which were the phase stability suggestions of Ed McMillan and frequency modulation developments of Reg Richardson, applied by a Rad Lab team under the supervision of experimentalist Bob Thornton and engineer Bill Brobeck

—each machine along the way conceived, initiated, and pushed to completion by Ernest.

But reflection on past accomplishment was neither a Lawrence trait nor a Rad Lab habit; leader and staff shared a "what next?" attitude. In two years, protons would be acclerated to 350 million volts, and alpha particles to 400 million, and, within another decade, the 184-inch would generate beams of 735-million-volt protons, 460-million-volt deuterons, 915-million-volt alphas, and one billion, 140-million-volt helium-3 atoms—a far cry from the low, theoretically absolute limits published in the thirties. Even with the initial 200-million-volt deuterons, it was hoped that cosmic rays could be produced artificially. Certainly more knowledge of forces involved in the release of nuclear energy would be revealed. The biomedical program, too, must benefit from experiment with the new energy available.

Congratulatory telegrams and letters followed public announcement of the spectacular 184-inch debut on November 13, 1946. From the Rockefeller Foundation, Warren Weaver wired: "We are jubilant but not surprised for we have had complete confidence in your success. Warmest congratulations to yourself and the entire group." From Merle Tuve and the Carnegie group: "Magnificent achievement of imagination, courage, and teamwork. Niels Bohr joins us in warmest personal congratulations." Alfred Loomis's celebration of the event, from November 15 to November 17, was planned to be reminiscent of the Del Monte weekend of March 30, 1940, which had immediately preceded the Rockefeller grant for the huge cyclotron. Bush, Conant, and the Comptons were invited. Most of the guests arrived at Del Monte from Pasadena and the induction ceremonies of Lee DuBridge as president of Caltech; it was a festive weekend. The party left Del Monte for Berkeley on Sunday afternoon to be on hand for Monday's ceremonies.

Ernest and Oppie met the newly nominated members of the Atomic Energy Commission—not yet confirmed by the Senate—at the airport that evening. If the commissioners had previously had ideas of the enormity and complexity of their jobs, Los Alamos had enhanced them; the New Mexico town was out of water, the exodus of scientists continued, morale was understandably very low. They had heard little except complaints. Bradbury and his loyal scientists could not be held liable for the poor morale in a town where toilets could not be flushed, nor even infants' laundry cared for. The Army got the blame, but in a few weeks everything concerning the place, including the laboratory for which it existed, would be the commissioners' responsibility. To be greeted after a somewhat solemn flight from New Mexico by one who reflected only buoyant enthusiasm and cheerful optimism was a pleasant relief.

Ernest took them to Trader Vic's for what Lewis Strauss remembers as a hilariously relaxing evening. The commissioners were introduced to the famous rum Zombies, with the descriptive term, "lethal." With exotic food and pleasant talk, their task seemed less enormous. But Ernest could not let the evening pass without a reference to the serious problems confronting the commissioners, not as a complaint, but as something constructive, to be taken hold of as an adventure. According to Strauss he said, "Look, fellows, you gotta get away from concentration on this weapons business. It's perfectly possible right now to build reactors to light bulbs." He drew reactor designs on menus, with modifications and possible improvements thought up on the moment. "You've got to get your feet wet on something, even if it's only a Model T. If you wait for the perfect model you never will." Strauss thinks at that moment the commissioners thought that was the most important thing to do.

They were further impressed with what they saw at the Radiation Laboratory the next day, November 18, and by far more than the pleasant 184-inch inaugural ceremonies and the glowing comments of such guests as Bush and the Comptons. They saw the 184-inch in operation, had the synchrotron explained by McMillan, and the linear accelerator, by Alvarez. Crocker Laboratory was a hum of activity around the improved 60-inch, explained by Hamilton, and in the old Rad Lab building they saw the famous 37, with which so much had been accomplished even before its use as a pilot spectrograph for uranium separation, and the more recent modification to test ideas incorporated into the 184-inch. They were impressed that rather than let the 37-inch be relegated to the background by later, greater machines, it was to be sent to U.C.L.A., for further service to science and education. John did the honors at Donner, in the presence of its donor, William H. Donner, who promised a new wing for the building. At a cocktail party, concluding inaugural festivities, it was apparent that the Loomis guests and the commissioners felt they had witnessed a wonderfully dynamic, functioning enterprise.

Publicity was successfully avoided as far as the inauguration festivities and famous names were concerned, but news and pictures of the 184-inch appeared in major newspapers, with stories of the men involved. Dick Pearce of the *San Francisco Examiner*, who had written of the lab before the war, noted a slight difference in the appearance of the director. In "Genius Turns Atom Smasher" he wrote ". . . the heavy responsibility of the world atom bomb race, which he shared with perhaps four other men at the very top of the scientific high command, has left its mark upon him, but he still has the quick boyish smile and the six foot plus of athletic frame that makes him least like the public conception of a great scientist."

John, concerned to keep Ernest healthy, succeeded in getting him away for a Texas hunting expedition with Drs. Jim and Jack Maxwell, of Dallas. However successful the shooting may have been, Ernest afterward talked most of a visit to the huge King Ranch and its operation by Richard and Robert Kleberg. He was made an honorary Texas Ranger. It wasn't as long a change of scene, nor as much of a rest, as John had hoped; four days after their arrival in Texas, Ernest was busy with Merle Tuve in Washington. The capital was still deep in the pros and cons of atomic matters. Senate delay in confirmation of appointments to the Atomic Energy Commission was evidence of the general confusion. Lilienthal, particularly, long a target as administrator of the Tennessee Valley Authority, suffered heavy criticism. On the international level, a plan for world control, compatible with Baruch's original proposals, was approved by a ten to nothing vote of the U.N. Atomic Energy Commission. It meant little; Russia and Poland abstained, and any meaningful international control was given small chance. On December 31, 1946, in the late afternoon, the new, still unconfirmed commissioners, with the exception of Bacher, who was busy in Los Alamos, went to the White House. With Patterson, Groves, and Nichols, they witnessed the signing of the Executive order transferring all atomic energy concerns to the new commission. The Manhattan District was a thing of the past.

CHAPTER XV

Berkeley Is Mecca—
Ernest the Prophet

[1947–1949]

Ernest was impressed with the commissioners. Perhaps with atomic control in their civilian hands, suspicious scientists would settle down to science, the more-than-ever promising study of the nucleus. Perhaps dissolution of the national laboratories could be checked, and they could become again the thriving, exciting places confrontation with emergency had made them. It might even be that some scientists who had left would return to Los Alamos and Oak Ridge, as Groves had prophesied. The importance of work to be done could not, Ernest thought, be evaded, and much of it now could be done on a proper scale only in those specifically designed establishments. Few universities—in 1947 perhaps only California with its Rad Lab—could offer the opportunities of the wartime laboratories. Yet the exodus of scientists and technicians had continued since the war's end, in no way stemmed by Groves's efforts, or his complaint that "my first and second teams have left, my third and fourth are leaving." The remark was neither very accurate nor very tactful. Good men had remained, resisting the temptation to return to academic life, in spite of drought and inconvenience. Certainly teaching had suffered during the war and must be stepped up; the exploitation of nuclear energy would demand an increasing number of physicists, chemists, and engineers. Education in those areas seemed to Ernest as vital an element in maintenance of America's advantage as possession of the bomb. Perhaps the commission could arrange to staff adequately both laboratories and classrooms. At Berkeley, the Rad Lab and physical science department staffs often divided their time between classroom and lab.

The commissioners' interest in biomedical activities also pleased Ernest. Those were particularly important peaceful applications of nuclear energy; who knew what health-giving aspects of atomic energy might be forthcoming, what understanding of life processes might be gained? Already, in the new bio-organic division of the Rad Lab, guided by Melvin Calvin, exciting things were happening in photosynthesis: Industrial applications must be studied. As for pure physics, the prospect could not be more exciting. Eugene Gardner already thought his group had evidence of mesons, hitherto found only in cosmic rays, from 184-inch bombardments, and, if they were mistaken, it was pretty certain someone soon would. The Alvarez team had a 40-foot section of the linear acclerator oscillating with just one radar set. Oppie thought this linear approach might prove most productive. Construction of McMillan's synchrotron was well under way.

Everyone was busy with an important project—yet there were so many others begging attention. Fusion, theoretically the source of the sun's energy, and far more powerful than fission, must be fully explored, hopefully at Los Alamos where it had been a secondary problem during the war. Ernest hoped too that the commission would push vigorously reactor programs at Oak Ridge and at Argonne, the national laboratory near Chicago. What a field to explore, for knowledge of nuclear reaction products, and for the generation of power to turn wheels, for which the pile had first been considered. Perhaps more direct generation of electricity than by reactor-heated water, steam, and turbine was possible.

Happily, the commissioners, under the Atomic Energy Act, could organize and support all possibilities for exploitation; scientists, their ranks augmented by dedicated new recruits from universities, could embark on programs undreamed of heretofore. The commission should have excellent scientific direction with such competence as the President had made available on the General Advisory Committee. This GAC, at its first meeting, elected Oppenheimer its chairman. Ernest hoped that his old friend, whom he suspected rather enjoyed being lionized, would quit speechmaking and moralizing, and apply his tremendous talents to physics—and at Berkeley, in spite of a new and appealing offer.

When they had met the commissioners at the airport, Lewis Strauss had taken Oppie aside and asked him to consider becoming director of the Institute for Advanced Studies at Princeton, New Jersey, of which Strauss was a trustee. Oppie had discussed it at length with Ernest, who argued that Oppie would not be happy in the position. Had he not had enough of administration, supervising a brood of highly intellectual but often temperamental individuals? He did not need the

$25,000 yearly salary; he would be most content and productive at the university, where he could restore the outstanding theoretical school of the country—which meant the world. Everyone knew how his bright students had respected him, even emulated him down to gestures and mannerisms. At the institute, his charges would be established scholars of stature, with patterns long set. He would miss the excitement of molding young minds; he would be most unhappy after the thrill of being director had worn off. It would become just a job, a bore, without sufficient challenge for his talents.

Oppie was still undecided when they drove to Davis, the U.C. campus near Sacramento, in February to speak, at Sproul's request, at the All-University Conference. In their addresses, though in different ways, each spoke of the interrelationships of various disciplines, Ernest stressing the value to each of the long-standing Berkeley cooperation between chemistry, physics, medicine, and biology at the Rad Lab. Oppie spoke of the dangers of overspecialization in any general education program. The new national laboratories of the Atomic Energy Commission generally were following this Rad Lab pattern, established before the war and augmented since. Both Argonne, in the Midwest, and Brookhaven, on Long Island, had participating universities. Neither would limit activities to physics and chemistry. At Oak Ridge, too, scholars from several universities and disciplines would participate. The Radiation Laboratory's advantage lay in its tradition of cooperation. It, alone, had evolved to its size and eminence; the national laboratories had been created by fiat. Ernest, by far the most experienced administrator of such a program, had created his laboratory and position; other directors had been appointed. According to a Brobeck story, when the commission formulated rules for laboratory administration, they reserved the right to replace any director. Someone asked how they would go about replacing Ernest Lawrence; the only solution anyone could think of would be "to replace the commission."

The commission had a rough start. Organizational work, efforts to establish morale in neglected laboratories, whatever it attempted was criticized. Senator Kenneth McKellar, long a Lilienthal-TVA foe, branded the chairman a Communist. The charge was refuted by the President, but his nomination received Senate confirmation fifty to thirty-one only after a ten-week fight. The U.N. Atomic Energy Commission fared worse; it had no authority, and its suggestions were doomed by Russian intransigence. Gromyko accused the Americans of trying to retain a monopoly. To Ernest, such obstructionism left superior United States strength the only assurance of international peace and order. More and more he considered unrealistic the insistence of some colleagues that United States renunciation of atomic weapons would be followed by

Russia. Gromyko, he felt, seized upon this to proclaim that **Russia** would accept international inspection—if the bomb was first outlawed and considered with conventional weapons in disarmament talks.

If Oppie really believed that failure to solve the problem of international control would result in "the death of our society," he could not explain to Ernest's understanding how agreement could be reached without abdication to the Russians. Oppie finally accepted the position as director of the Institute for Advanced Studies in April—at least that is when Ernest learned of it, by radio. He was still of the opinion that Oppie could contribute most by remaining at a university. The glamour of his sudden fame and the distinction of his new position would erode with time; he would realize that a good scientist's place is outside the political arena, except as a consultant in those fields in which he has special competence.

Ernest was willing to give such advice as might be requested, in areas of which he had knowledge, without fanfare. He might call attention to some factor, also within his competence, that might be of value, but he would do it quietly. Thus, he was irritated by disclosures that experiments had been conducted with radioactive materials dispersed over the ground by planes. He had suggested this as a means to deny terrain to an enemy or by advance warning to cause the evacuation of large urban centers to prevent harm to populations. To commissioners and others, he continually urged the importance of pushing the still-too-dormant reactor program—for peaceful as well as military purposes. He taunted the commissioners good-naturedly for stalling on decisions to construct them; delay and indecision would lose them the handful of scientists with reactor experience they had. Except for a low power reactor at Los Alamos, which had commenced operation before the commission's tenure, nothing had been done in that field. He was encouraged by a visit to the laboratory of Captain Hyman C. Rickover, eager for atomic power for submarine propulsion. He had a chance to urge cooperation with Rickover's small group when the commission, laboratory heads, and members of the GAC visited the Rad Lab in August and were entertained over a long weekend at the Bohemian Grove. Construction of the first peacetime pile finally began at Brookhaven.

As a consultant to the General Electric Company, Ernest advised industrial exploration and development of reactors. Dr. Harvey Brooks, then with G.E., stated at a Lawrence Award ceremony much later: "The discussions and arguments I used to have with Ernest Lawrence during those early exciting days formed a very important part of my education in nuclear energy. The number of people interested in reactors was small . . . [there was] a good deal of coming and going to information meetings and other more informal gatherings. A well remembered feature of these . . . was the heated argument with Ernest in hotel rooms and meeting halls about fantastic reactor schemes. He would throw out a seemingly outrageous idea and challenge you to explain what was wrong with it. He was never at a loss for a good answer to your objections, but in the process of give and take the idea evolved or new ideas emerged and you suddenly realized that you had been goaded into inventing. It was the catalytic idea of Lawrence's that was the secret of his greatness. He could always make others accomplish more than they thought possible themselves. My memory of these early days is bound up in the intellectual excitement of these arguments with Ernest, and I feel that many of us in our later contributions have continued to draw on the knowledgeable capital which we developed under Lawrence's stimulation."

Ernest's consultant duties for Eastman, G.E., and American Cyanamid usually could be handled in conjunction with other necessary trips, or if it was necessary to go to Rochester or Schenectady, he managed to attend to other matters during the same stay. He tried to avoid Washington, except for Carnegie meetings, but it was seldom possible with so much laboratory work sponsored by the AEC. McMillan, chemist Ken Pitzer, and Latimer had accompanied him to Washington in January for discussions with commissioners and AEC General Manager Carroll Wilson pertaining to Rad Lab work; new buildings on the hill were authorized. He was in the Capital again in February to receive the Trasenster Medal of the University of Liège at the Belgium Embassy. His appointment by President Truman in July to the Board of Foreign Scholarship, charged with the general supervision of the educational exchange program authorized by the Fulbright Act, necessitated his attendance at meetings at the State Department; Ernest felt one could not refuse a Presidential request except for very good reasons. He thought the Fulbright scholarships an excellent means of exchange of ideas and information, as well as inspiration toward academic excellence. As far back as 1945, he had advocated free interchange of scientists between countries, "especially Russia, as the first step in a broad international understanding." He had, however, little hesitation in refusing appointments requiring long periods in the Capital—or those of a political or controversial nature. When the Secretary of the Navy asked him to serve a two-year term on the Naval Research Advisory Committee, he wrote, ". . . regretfully beg to be excused . . . trying to keep as free as possible of outside commitments, in order to devote my energies to experimental work in progress here in the lab.

"I need hardly say . . . if [there is] any special service I could render to you at any time for which conceivably I might have special qualifications I hope you will feel free to call upon me."

In May, Cooksey drove Ernest to Seattle, where Ernest represented the University of California at the inauguration of R. B. Allen as president of the University of Washington, and Cooksey represented the Physical Society, then meeting in Seattle. They also visited the University of Vancouver. It was a busy week; Don was too tired to join Ernest at the inaugural banquet. Ernest had as much rest and relaxation as he could patiently endure for a week when he took his family to Balboa for the summer, this time with dependable Dixie for help.

At Berkeley there were the usual number and variety of visitors, from Governor Earl Warren—afterward entertained at dinner—to the exotic arrival of H.R.H. Prince Saud al-Saud of Arabia, complete with retinue, flowing robes, and jeweled scimitars. Stanislau Winter of the College de France, Kai Seigbahn of the Nobel Institute, and Gerald Pickavance of the British Atomic Energy Research Establishment were among the Europeans at the lab. Pickavance stayed for several months preparatory to the construction of a 110-inch cyclotron at Harwell, the British national laboratory that Cockcroft had organized after the war. Conant, while Sproul's guest, spent a day at the Rad Lab—amazed at development on the hill since the war—and was entertained at a Lawrence dinner that included the Sprouls and the Neylans. It was true, Neylan thought, what one of the regents had said recently, that Berkeley had become the mecca of physics, and Ernest its prophet. Neylan was more excited than Ernest when Michigan State requested permission to make a semirelief sculpture of Ernest to share with Einstein one of several panels depicting the last hundred years of physics.

Molly left the children with Dixie at Balboa and returned to Berkeley on August 1, to await the arrival of another child, who was born on Ernest's own birthday, August 8, 1947. Barbara seemed to Ernest and Molly the start of a second family, which pleased them. Ernest had had more time to enjoy his children in the past year, and they had again looked forward to Sunday drives with Father. These excursions usually started with no announced destination. They might end in Muir Woods, a "true lark" for the children, or at Belvedere. Any trip that involved crossing the bay on one of the old ferries was also a lark; all but Molly would scramble out of the car, the children to race around while Ernest paced contentedly along the deck, perhaps in a favorite maroon, V-necked, long-sleeved sweater. Molly was glad to relax after making and packing a large and complete lunch and getting the children ready. Ernest was rather expansive on these trips and permitted eager hands to search his pockets for candy money. In the countryside, there were frequent stops at roadside stands for ice cream or to purchase small trinkets. Sometimes the drive would be postponed until after Sunday school, after Ernest had decided, with a good deal of encouragement from his mother, that his children should attend. Back in 1944, there had been a mass baptism of the four then in the family in the Episcopal Church.

Ernest was no help whatever in getting the children dressed and fed, and, after a few pleading requests resulted in such assistance as sweaters on inside out, he was not asked. If Carl and Gunda did not come for Sunday dinner, the family usually went to their apartment, where there was always too much food. The children learned to be as fond of *lefsa* —those large, very thin Norwegian potato flour pancakes—as their father was. The older children decided that Ernest "sort of ran his parents." As Margaret remembers: "They didn't tell him things; it was just the opposite. Grandma was a little doubtful at times, but believed anything Dad said was gospel, and never tired of telling us that he was born grown up."

Occasionally John's family would be there at the same time. Young John, born in 1943, was called Mark, to avoid the "junior," and Shelley, born in 1946, also bore the name Amy, after her mother. Gunda loved having the families, however it crowded the apartment. She was fond of Molly and Amy, and, though they were extravagant by her standards, never criticized except, perhaps, by indirection. She might exclaim: "Another new dress! How pretty! Was it expensive?" Molly, slightly embarrassed, always told the truth; Amy would give an outrageously extravagant figure such as, "Oh, only five hundred dollars!" Gunda sometimes helped with baby-sitting if the college girl could not be present —and she enjoyed it.

Dixie brought the older children back to Berkeley for school in September, shortly before Ernest left for Washington. When he went East in October, he persuaded Molly to join him. They spent a few days at Oak Ridge—"it's still a big boost for morale here when you come!" Aebersold wrote. In Washington they were guests of the Bushes for three days, during which Ernest conferred with AEC officials and twice met with the Fulbright Scholarship Committee at the State Department. On the tenth they went to Princeton for an afternoon and night with Robert and Kitty Oppenheimer—after which Ernest wrote Oppie: "The brief glimpse of your Princeton activities provides pretty convincing evidence that I was way off in my dire prognostications . . . looking forward to your being out here next summer. It ought to be a good summer." The weekend was spent with the Loomises in New York, after which there was a full week in New Haven, where Ernest gave the Silliman Lecture, and participated in the centennial of the Sheffield Scientific School—an event which Cooksey had looked forward to but was prevented from attending by the birth of his second child, a daughter, Helen, on October 12.

Ernest and Molly were back in Berkeley only a short time when he left for Vancouver, where, on the twenty-ninth, he received an honorary degree from the University of British Columbia. In mid-November he was again in Washington when Merle Tuve was presented the Research Corporation Award, for contributions in the development of the proximity fuse and in bringing physics and biology closer together.

The linear accelerator began operation in November, 1947. Experimental physics with the 184-inch was exciting; for the first time fission was observed in elements of atomic number less than 90; bismuth, lead, thallium, mercury, gold, platinum, and tantalum nuclei were split into nearly equal halves. Radioactive isotopes were provided for the International Health Division of the Rockefeller Foundation, though isotope production was simpler and more efficient in reactors. Early in September, President Truman had removed the ban on export of radioactive isotopes to foreign scientists. Within three days, thirty countries. including Russia, had filed applications with the AEC for various radioactive substances produced in Oak Ridge reactors built during the war.

Disclosure of the preparation of an atomic weapons proving ground, on Eniwetok Atoll in the South Pacific, again aroused protests against "provocation" by the United States. Ernest saw no cause for criticism; the critics never considered Russian intransigence except as the fault of the United States. Surely there was no intention to use our weapons except for defense. The AEC had warned that the twelve largest cities in the United States could be destroyed in a single atomic attack. Testing was necessary to keep weapons advanced. President Truman recommended compulsory military training for all males reaching eighteen years of age, as indispensable to the nation's security in the atomic age. It seemed certain that the Russians were at work on a bomb; no one could know their progress. Two Oak Ridge scientists had been suspended, pending loyalty hearings, two ex-Army photographers were charged with the theft of secret photographs, and in November Russian Foreign Minister Vyacheslav Molotov boasted on the thirtieth anniversary of the Bolshevik Revolution that the atom bomb secret "has long ceased to exist." Clearly, Ernest thought, we must look out for our own security.

Progress with atomic energy could not be expected at the wartime pace, but Ernest thought it could be more rapid than it was; Brookhaven was not finished at the end of the year. The exodus of scientists from Los Alamos and Oak Ridge had been checked in 1947, and morale improved. But insufficient efforts had been made to engage industry in the development of nuclear power. There were problems in any government-industry relationship involving secrecy, government controls, and other restrictions inconsistent with free enterprise, but they had been surmounted in the General Electric Company atomic program—the shining example of AEC-industry cooperative effort.

Strangely enough, it seemed to Ernest at times, scientists themselves formed the most vocal obstruction to atomic progress—certainly their postwar associations seemed overly concerned with moral and political problems that were beyond their special competence. How did they know what Russia would or would not do? How and when had she shown even an effort to foster goodwill? Regent Edwin Pauley, who had been the President's reparations ambassador, had reported Russia's greed in conquered areas—even in Manchuria where she had fought but a few days. Those demanding agreement with Russia seemed to overlook the simple fact that it takes two to cooperate. Ernest never doubted the sincerity of American efforts toward international amity and accord in atomic matters, and was convinced that there were no actual reservations on the part of the English, however Churchill might fulminate against the Soviets. Perhaps the old wartime leader had been correct in earlier statements about Russia, which many had considered excessive. Cooperation in the field of atomic energy with England, still the subject of diplomatic discussion, was as smooth and pleasant with the Rad Lab as it had always been. In December a telegram from H. W. Skinner and Pickavance reported, "Harwell cyclotron started working at about 160 million volts. Many thanks for all your help." Pickavance had earlier written of his gratitude for help received at Berkeley.

Professor Leonard Loeb, who in August had delivered the Kelvin Lecture to the Institution of Electrical Engineers in London, thought England was recovering from her wartime battering as fast as could be expected. Ernest, who had been unable to accept invitations to give the Kelvin Lecture during the war, had discovered that the expense of the trip might prevent Loeb's journey to England. He had insisted that Loeb give the lecture and had arranged that all expenses be paid from the special fund. Fourteen years before, Loeb had enabled Ernest to attend the Solvay Conference by interceding with Cottrell for funds. Ernest also, through the fund, made it possible for Chairman Birge to be of great assistance as a consultant.

Ernest became a director of the Yosemite Park and Curry Company early in 1948. He had had a deep love for Yosemite since his first visit the year he came to California. Donald Tresidder, president of Stanford and Yosemite director, had nominted Ernest for the board just prior to his death in January. Tresidder had married Mary Curry, whose father had first visited Yosemite in 1894 and had founded the company in 1899. At least twice a year, directors' meetings were held at the famous Ahwahnee Hotel in Yosemite Valley; meetings that were more like house parties than business affairs. The association was a thoroughly enjoyable one in every way for both Ernest and Molly. Particularly for a winter meeting, they would arrive at the park on Friday afternoon, for predinner cocktails in Mary Tresidder's apartment atop the Ahwahnee. Molly remembers several Saturday mornings when she got up to discover the beautiful valley covered with fresh snow, untouched except for deer or rabbit tracks trailing across smooth white patches beneath the trees. Meetings might also be held at the Conejo Ranch of Director Ed Janss, Jr., where the weekend might entail plane or horseback rides and a fine barbecue. There were delightful times—sometimes with the children—at the ranch of Director Walter Starr, north of San Jose Mission, of which the ranch had been a part before the earthquake of 1864.

Starr remembers a Yosemite summer meeting which was followed by a trip around High Sierra camps, with overnight stays at May Lake, Glen Alen, Tuolumne Meadows, Vogelsang, and Merced Lake. Ernest was excited by, and liked best, the journey over 10,400-foot Vogelsang Pass, of which Director Preston Hotchkis wrote—"an emerald lake hidden in trees, or Mt. Lyell with a glacier hanging just under the peak—in fact the whole trek—weather, company, camps, and frequent hilarity was complete perfection and enjoyment." They had slept that night in three-bed tents, and Starr had awakened in the night to hear Ernest talking with a stranger from Chicago who had started out in daylight for Mammoth Lakes, gone as far as Mount Lyell, and returned. Ernest was asked if his title was medical and had answered, "Oh, no, I just got it from a college." Starr, who had seen Ernest in Washington occasionally during the war, had been interested in discussing, at one of the camps, why Ernest had then been so secretive. But, of that conversation, he remembers chiefly Ernest's remark that at the final showdown on the Tennessee plant, he had become so tense that he had to be carried into the meeting. Director H. Oehlmann remembers Ernest once getting off his horse "at the side of Sunrise Creek, lying down on the grass, and promptly falling asleep from sheer accumulation of fatigue while the rest of us prepared lunch," and the "lively discussion of the country's atomic research program as we were having cocktails alongside Fletcher Creek, at Vogelsang Camp." Ernest also started to ski again, at Yosemite.

Neither skiing, regular tennis, nor habitual rapid pace prevented a tendency on Ernest's part toward overweight after the war. He enjoyed good food too much, ate rather too rapidly, and, often with best intentions, had too many calories—always the case at his mother's. Gunda pushed extra servings toward him as though he were still a skinny boy. In periods of weight consciousness he often told Molly, "I don't want to go to Mother's; she's going to get me too fat." He was, in Molly's words, "a periodic dieter." After one illness, an allergy specialist prescribed an elimination diet, but "he was like a kid about dieting." Molly could scold, tell him it would not mean anything if he destroyed evidence by eating what the curriculum proscribed. He meekly agreed, always. "I guess Dr. Rowe would say the same thing. I'll be good." And, like a small boy, he would try. He gave up cigarettes and for a time enjoyed only an occasional cigar. Then he gave up tobacco entirely. When John Gofman, one of the bright young doctors in medical physics, undertook a program centered on factors that control the level of fatty substances in the blood—the relation of lipoproteins to heart risk—Ernest volunteered as a guinea pig. Gofman's diet was quite restrictive and very low in fat. All test subjects on the campus ate their noon meal at a special dietary table in Cowell Hospital on the campus, near Donner, and were provided with lists of suitable foods that might be eaten at other meals. Periodic samples of each subject's blood were examined, the results compared with former tests. It might have worked, had Ernest eaten only at home or Cowell Hospital. Molly had urged participation in the program to provide an excuse for less dining out, but there were still visitors to entertain, and many invitations—which Ernest often accepted even though he would have preferred to stay at home. Molly remembers: "When someone would call up and ask us to dinner, I'd ask him if I should explain that he was on a very limited diet and was not dining out these days, or say that he could have a lamb chop, if they didn't mind. He'd say 'Oh, don't say anything, for heaven's sake. I'll just eat what they have.' I'd tell him he shouldn't, but he would. He'd bring home one of Gofman's menus to be strictly followed, and then we'd go to dinner where the hostess liked lots of whipped cream. He'd eat it."

For all his failure to conform, Ernest was an ardent advocate of Gofman's program. With missionary zeal he recruited subjects among scientific associates, businessmen, Yosemite directors, and regents. Neylan remembered: "Ernest came over one day and we had lunch in the Alley. He was telling me about this kid over there in the laboratory, Gofman. He'd gone through medicine, won the Gold Cane out on Parnassus Heights, and went over there and took up atherosclerosis. He said he needed guinea pigs, would I be willing, so we walked up the Alley by number one Montgomery Street, and I said good-bye to Ernest right there. I got up to my office and barely in my chair when the girl telephoned in and said, 'Dr. Gofman waits to see you,' and this kid walks in with his bag. I think he was sitting across the street on the Wells Fargo Bank steps, and that Ernest tipped him off to come ahead. Anyway he took a pint of blood out of me; at least it felt like a pint. Three days later, Ernest called up and congratulated me. 'You're just a young man, you tested out beautifully.' So I asked how he came out. 'Oh, I'm an old man.' He tested badly, poor fellow—except as a human."

Positive identification of artificially produced mesons, strange particles of cosmic radiation, which constantly bombard the earth, and which H. Yukawa had postulated in 1935 as the force binding nuclear particles together, was finally achieved. The elusive mesons had been sought for more than a year. Cesare Lattes, a talented Brazilian with much experience in the identification of natural mesons, had joined Gardner in the search for this artificially produced cosmic-ray particle which culminated on February 21, 1948. These first man-made mesons were produced with 380-million-volt alpha particles of the 184-inch synchrocyclotron. It was a tremendous event that posed more questions than it solved and opened a whole new area. Since heretofore mesons had been found only in cosmic ray photographs taken at high altitudes, the discovery that they could be artificially produced was considered by some scientists to be as noteworthy as the discovery of uranium fission. "Isn't physics wonderful?" said Rabi's telegram of congratulation—one of many received.

The 184-inch synchrocyclotron was the first and, at this time, only instrument in the world capable of such production. Speculation as to what might be found if greater energies could be attained was not limited to Berkeley. The production of the meson marked the birth of a new era in science—that of high-energy physics. Work proceeded at the lab to develop higher energies, and, by the end of the year 1948, 350-million-volt proton beams were available with the 184-inch. The synchrotron, also operative in December, 1948, added powerful electron beams to those of the 184-inch protons, deuterons, and alpha particles.

It was not surprising to old associates of the Rad Lab that plans for a bigger—even a multibillion volt—machine had been under way at Berkeley. There were as compelling reasons as there had been for each former step up to a bigger accelerator; if 380 million volts could produce artificial mesons, perhaps billions of volts could lead to understanding laws as valid for the infinitely small as those known for the macrocosm. No physicist could doubt that such an accelerator would be useful; cosmic-ray students thought a billion volts would produce other particles. Ernest lost no opportunity to impress the importance of a new, greater giant on visitors, whether Secretary of the Army Kenneth Royall, whom Regent Pauley brought to the Rad Lab, Senators, Congressmen, or atomic energy commissioners. Brobeck had been doing more about it than the "daydreaming" Ernest had mentioned as long ago as 1946. Lloyd Smith had been studying theoretical problems for a year. Design was officially begun early in 1948, before cyclotron production of the meson. Because the size of a conventional cyclotron magnet for such a machine would be beyond possibility—far more steel than required for the greatest battleship—Brobeck's magnet was shaped like a huge doughnut, 110 feet in diameter, the field of which would control protons on what would be the equivalent of the perimeter of a huge cyclotron chamber, with its center cut away. Even so, 10,000 tons of steel would be required. It was estimated that the billion-volt giant would cost $9,000,-000. When James Fisk, director of AEC research, was in Berkeley for conferences, construction of a quarter scale pilot model of a six-billion-volt machine was authorized. A similar accelerator of half the energy for Brookhaven was designed at the same time, and physicists from the New York laboratory were frequently at the Rad Lab—as they were on March 28 when, after a morning press release on negative mesons, positive mesons were observed at noon!

There was much discussion as to what the billion-volt giants should be called. One suggestion was cyclodrome—which inspired I. I. Rabi to start a poem—a parody of Coleridge's "Kubla Khan"—of which Ed McMillan remembers the following:

> In Berkeley did Lawrence Khan
> A stately cyclodrome decree
> Where Alph, the sacred particle, ran
> Through vacuums measureless to man
> Down to a single dee.

Berkeley and Brookhaven failed to agree on a name; the Rad Lab's billion-volt accelerator would be called a Bevatron from the symbol Bev (billion electron volts) and the Brookhaven machine, a Cosmotron. Public announcement that the Bevatron would be constructed was made in April while Lilienthal was at the Rad Lab for his second visit of 1948.

Lilienthal had been out earlier to sign contracts for the continued operation of Los Alamos by the university. The regents had thought this extension of the university in another state should be terminated after the war. Indeed Bob Underhill, who had handled government contracts, had been sent to Washington to give the six months' required notice, but Ernest pleaded for continuation, and the notice was rescinded. "My God, you couldn't refuse him!" Neylan explained. There were improved types of weapons in the stockpile, Lilienthal announced, and development of new types would continue at Los Alamos.

Lilienthal also said that the likelihood of international agreement, at least within three years, was remote. That same month Secretary of Defense James Forrestal told a Senate committee the Russians knew how to make atomic bombs but lacked the industrial facilities for manufacture. Concern with United States security began to manifest itself in many quarters, and in various ways, as hope for Russian-American accord faded. Retired Supreme Court Justice Owen J. Roberts, whom the AEC had chosen to head a loyalty review board for commission employees, advocated universal military training. He wired Ernest: "Important at this time that prominent atomic scientist controvert recently published views that atom bomb makes UMT unnecessary. Would you wire me statement and endorsement. . . ." Ernest replied that he had not given the subject sufficient study to warrant a statement. At a later date he regretted Senator Chandler Gurney's invitation to testify on Universal Military Training for the Committee on Armed Services, but he mightily approved the growing concern over the country's safety. AEC tests of improved atomic weapons at Eniwetok, in the spring of 1948, also successfully demonstrated the system for detection of atomic explosions elsewhere, perhaps of equal importance to weapon improvement. Commissioner Strauss had advocated this against strong opposition. Strauss credited "the prestige of Ernest's backing" for success in establishment of the monitoring system, "though in many quarters it was considered folly."

Carnegie Institution trustees visited the Rad Lab after dedication of the 200-inch Hale telescope, at Palomar, in Southern California. Ernest compared the telescope and the cyclotron—both probed the unknown, one the infinite distance of space, the other the infinitely small of which all else is composed. Merle and Winnie Tuve were guests of the Lawrence's after others of the Carnegie group left. There were the usual excursions, but for the men whose friendship and association spanned more than forty years, the exciting frontier of physical science held the great interest. Winifred Tuve, who had worked beside her husband in his laboratory, studying biological effects of radiation, was interested in the work at Crocker and Donner laboratories. Perhaps the most interesting event was a stimulating evening with Fermi and Oppenheimer, both of whom were at Berkeley for the summer. Another of Ernest's visitors, Professor Swann, stayed at the Faculty Club. Swann had fallen into disrepute in some quarters—Oppie thought him almost a charlatan— but Ernest loyally upheld the old teacher who had done so much for him and from whom he had learned electromagnetism so well that it was the core of his technical knowledge. Swann had once been in the forefront of physics, his present tendency toward metaphysics notwithstanding. Swann marveled at the evidence of his foremost pupil's contributions, the great machines he had conceived and built, and the honors which had come to him.

Honors continued to come. In march, Ernest had been elected a member of the Newcomen Society of England and North America, and an honorary member of the Royal Irish Academy. Highest recognition of the year was his election as an Honorary Fellow of The Physical Society of London. No more than six Honorary Fellows were permitted at any one time, and in 1948 only Bohr and Einstein shared the select group with Ernest. In November, the Cross of *Officier de la Legion d'Honneur* was presented to Ernest in San Francisco by the French consul general. The Phi Delta Epsilon Service Award—for contributions to the advancement of medical science in the fields of research, diagnosis, and treatment, was accepted for him by Bob Thornton, in San Francisco, since Ernest was at Balboa Island with his family for the Christmas holidays.

His intention to spend long summer vacations at Balboa had yet to materialize; even intervals so apportioned during the summer were interrupted; the past August by a trip to Oak Ridge to see Clarence Larson, and later by one to General Electric concerning its atomic laboratory. He had promised Molly to spend the entire holiday period with the family if she would go with him earlier in December to St. Louis and Washington. They had been entertained at the chancellor's residence in St. Louis, by the Comptons, and the physics department of Washington University entertained Ernest at a luncheon to which Charles Thomas and representatives of St. Louis industry had been invited. Thomas, executive vice president of the Monsanto Chemical Company, had been wartime coordinator between Los Alamos and other laboratories, including the Rad Lab, and had helped prepare the Acheson-Lilienthal Report on international control of atomic energy, on the achievement of which he was now pessimistic. In Washington, besides conferences with AEC people, there was a day at Merle's laboratory, followed by cocktails at the Tuve home. At the annual Carnegie trustees dinner, Ernest and Molly and the Seeley Mudds made plans to fly later to Mexico and Guatemala, ostensibly to look at Carnegie work with Indian ruins—which had been discussed at the day's meeting.

Washington was still agog over the unexpected reelection of President Truman a month earlier, the increasing impasse with Russia, including the Berlin airlift, and the proliferation of accusations of disloyalty. Atomic scientists seemed singled out as targets of the Un-American Activities Committee, which promised revelations of espionage throughout the Manhattan Project. The removal of physicist Edward U. Condon as director of the National Bureau of Standards was demanded, even after his clearance had been reviewed with the declaration that his loyalty was unquestionable. Lilienthal reported that unjustified attacks were driving scientists from government service. President Truman had denounced the attacks on scientists at a meeting of the American Association for the Advancement of Science and had shaken hands with Condon on the platform.

Five of those the Un-American Activities Committee accused of wartime, Soviet-directed atomic espionage had been at the Rad Lab. Ernest, naturally enough, was distressed at charges involving the laboratory; he also thought science was discredited, perhaps a reaction following public acclaim for its wartime work. He thought Oppie had not helped the general public stature of scientists with his statement in a *Fortune* Magazine article that pictured him, Ernest, and others, as morally wrong by saying, "In some sort of crude sense which no vulgarity, no humor, no overstatement can quite extinguish the physicists have known sin; and this is a knowledge which they cannot lose." Ernest protested: "I am a physicist and I have no knowledge to lose in which physics has caused me to know sin."

Nevertheless, there were problems at the Rad Lab. Ernest had helped Frank Oppenheimer get a job at Minnesota rather than fire him, when Frank persisted in lecturing to "left-wing" organizations after having promised not to. Ernest had gone to bat for Frank, tried to advise him in confidence—and felt he had been betrayed. He was a little bitter about that—the betrayal more than the politics. Some of Frank's speeches had been reported in the press—the kind of publicity Ernest thoroughly disliked. He once read that Frank had told reporters a certain talk had been given in a small hall because Negroes would not have been allowed in a larger one. He summoned Frank. "Now look what you've done! You've brought race relations into the lab!" The bitterness remained, and, when Frank asked permission to work at the Rad Lab for a few weeks the following summer, he was refused. He came to Berkeley anyway, and Oppie was told that Ernest had requested one of his staff to rescind an invitation to Frank for dinner at his home. Oppie was a little bitter about that; Frank had worked very hard during the war, "and the testimony is that he did a good job." Oppie remembers meeting Ernest later that summer, "at one of those big parties somebody else was giving. I said something about it. I don't think Ernest minded that, but, as often was the case, my wife said something sharper, and I think maybe he minded that."

Differences between the two were growing, however, on other issues; Oppie opposed the development of reactors on a large scale. "Nuclear power for planes and battleships is so much hogwash," he told an interviewer from the *Oakland Tribune*. Oppie had testified before the Un-American Activities Committee on Communist activities in Berkeley before and during the war; it seemed, even to such friends of his as Bethe and Condon, that he had been unjust to certain physicists, some of whom had been his pupils. Oppie had tried to appease the outrage with a letter to a newspaper editor, the contents of which seemed inconsistent with his testimony. When Ernest tried to question him about it, and about Communists in the Rad Lab during the war, Oppie was impatient with him, as with one who could not understand what he was talking about.

There were a few scientists currently at the Rad Lab who had appeared before a local loyalty board composed of Regent Neylan, Admiral Chester Nimitz, and Marine General K. A. Joyce. It was kept from the press at the time but was very distressing to Ernest. It also had bothered Neylan, who, however conservative he might be considered, had once been a Hiram Johnson liberal and had even defended Communist agitators. As a lawyer, he disliked a situation in which a man could neither be faced by his accuser, nor see the evidence that was furnished by the FBI. In every case, Neylan carefully advised the subject of his right to counsel and to object to any member of the board. "Some of the cockier ones took a look at our white hairs and thought, These three nice old goats, telling me about my rights and all that. I tried patiently with those kids but several of them were fired." One of the accused, of whose guilt there could be no doubt, Neylan found had been immediately rehired by Dean Latimer, who had testified at the man's hearing. He was fired again. There were several for whom Ernest fought valiantly, who were not evasive, and for whom there was considerable doubt of conscious intent to betray; they were cleared. "Ernest backed his life on some of them and proved to be right. He helped some by getting them not to fight it; but there were some devils, too. Two or three of them appealed to the regents, in open meeting. They were bounced," Neylan said.

If local hearings were conducted quietly, Washington investigations made up for it; Berkeley and the Rad Lab had their share of resulting headlines. All unfortunate and unnecessary, Ernest thought. Security measures were undoubtedly necessary, even in peacetime, but what secrecy was there in blaring forth every accusation! He still believed that science could not flourish in a secretive atmosphere, but the glare of publicity was also unhealthy, particularly the kind that disturbed the equanimity proper to scientific pursuits, a prime reason why scientists, particularly those in positions considered "sensitive," should avoid politics. The barbed wire, guarded gates, and badges—he seldom wore his —did not disturb him. It was part of the price, certainly a small one, for opportunities impossible to have without Federal sponsorship. He could never understand why such minor annoyances bothered so many of his colleagues, who developed them into intellectual problems. Warren Weaver once teased him when passing guards and gates to get on the hill.

"It was the only thing that troubled me in my relationship with Ernest," Weaver said. "I never understood, and disagreed emphatically, on this aspect of security, or maybe secrecy. Many share his views, but there was no one so great who accommodated himself so to the views on control and security and secrecy. He seemed to think all this not only tolerable, but proper. . . . The intellectual climate shouldn't be secret —so fenced!"

Fences, even if ten feet high, seemed a petty issue one way or the other, but in mid-1949 the AEC confirmed reports that a small amount of uranium had disappeared from the Argonne Laboratory. The denial that it was either stolen or lost seemed incongruous. This, and charges that AEC fellowships were granted to Communist students, and the general tension with Russia, brought the demand by Senator Bourke Hickenlooper for Lilienthal's resignation on May 22, 1949, the day former Secretary of Defense James Forrestal "in a sudden fit of despondency" plunged to his death from the sixteenth floor of Bethesda Naval Hospital. Perhaps no one was more disturbed with the depressing news than Ernest, in Washington at the time. He had considered Forrestal a true patriot, had lauded his efforts at coordination of the Army, Navy, and Air Force into a cohesive force, and had regretted his resignation. Doctors described his illness as "severe depression of the type seen in operational fatigue during the war." Ernest thought it might indeed have been depression from operational fatigue, in Washington.

He was glad that his return to Berkeley had been planned to take him through South Dakota, reminiscent of a less complicated time. It was good to talk again with Dean Akeley in Vermillion, old friends in Springfield, and relatives in Canton. He also spent a night in Sioux Falls and went on to Pierre and Aberdeen.

On his return to Berkeley he found a different loyalty-security furor, precipitated by an administrative notice that all letters of acceptance for appointments in the coming year would contain a non-Communist oath, which must be signed before any salary would be paid. This seemed harmless enough, if redundant—every state employee already took an annual oath to uphold the constitution of the state. There had long been an anti-Communist policy at the university, but a few of the faculty resented the fact that the new oath had been announced through newspapers and felt that it was calculated to catch faculty members off guard, just as vacations commenced. Various other objections were made, none of which had anything to do with the content of the oath, which had not yet been revealed. Ernest thought both oath and objections somewhat ridiculous; a Communist would sign and shut up, but neither could he see any of the evils conjured up by early protesters against the oath.

He had been unaware of growing criticism of the university from the State (so called "little") Un-American Activities Committee. As if vying with Washington, this group's accusations of Red influence were hurled at institutions, unions, organizations, and books. University representatives in Sacramento, aware of the committee mood, advised Sproul that some sort of legislation restricting the university surely would be introduced, unless assurances of non-Communist tendencies were dramatically evident. The university's independence from political pressure—and of the legislature itself except for appropriations—was a highly prized factor in its stature. Sproul sought convincing means of demonstrating its patriotism and loyalty, to forestall legislative interference. After consultation with a handful of professors, but not the Academic Senate— jealous of its prerogatives—Sproul proposed the oath as a means of forestalling tampering with the university's autonomy. Neylan and a few other regents doubted both the efficacy of Sproul's plan and his assurance that the faculty would approve the oath; they were quickly proved correct as far as the faculty was concerned. Many reasons were given for resistance to being singled out for a special oath, and, before the issue was resolved, a year later, all were more or less condensed to a single objection: the threat to academic freedom. A three-cornered tug-of-war evolved among Academic Senate, university administration, and the Board of Regents—with none of the parties wholly right, or entirely wrong. The great university was badly damaged by the rumpus, particularly in the departments of psychology and English, and very nearly lost, for a time, its position as an outstanding institution.

It was a very uncomfortable time for Ernest. He agreed that the oath was silly business, but what difference did it make, and how did it affect academic freedom? At the Rad Lab, now almost entirely supported by the Federal Government, it seemed actually unpatriotic to quit over such a trifle, as a few did.

"He was intensely patriotic, with a relatively simple approach to matters of politics . . . couldn't be bothered with complicated arguments concerning politics or patriotism . . . always claimed he was a Democrat, and he was in some ways, but he was also fairly far to the right in many of his views—apparently leaned a little farther right as he grew older. When it came to government spending, welfare state, Socialism, and all that, he was a New Dealer; when it came to security, Communists, and so on, he was off on the right—because of this simple approach; I mean, there were people who had right politics and people who had wrong politics, and that's how it was," Herbert York remembers. "But he was also a complicated man. It was the disappointment involved with some of the people he had believed in that really turned him the other way. He went to bat for some of these people, talked to them in confidence, and when it turned out they had lied to him, he became very bitter about it. When he had strong opinions outside of science and technology, they were so strong that people around him who had such admiration for him . . . didn't argue with him on these things. . . .

It is a fact, but it is also part of Ernest's personality, we never argued with him. . . . You see, all of us that were close to Ernest were also very great admirers of him. He was a person who got a great degree of loyalty from the people who worked with him. . . . We didn't want to argue with Ernest, because there was a big load on his shoulders and it was a difficult thing for him, and I didn't want it to be any harder. . . . Because I was very fond of him . . . also I think most of us just didn't have enough guts to argue about some things either—he was an awesome person in these things, too."

Not all of the postwar newcomers to the Rad Lab were as close to Ernest; there were violent scenes; one eminent theoretician was fired by Ernest, despite the intercession of McMillan and Alvarez, who thought it unjust. The Rad Lab suffered, though not to the extent of the university as a whole. Of greatest personal sorrow was the effect of the conflict on his good friend Neylan who, he felt, unjustly emerged from the controversy as the villain. The faculty did not realize that he had been the first to protest the oath and to argue that it would be unacceptable. To prevent further dissension, Neylan let blame be ascribed to him that should have been directed elsewhere.

There were plenty of exciting happenings without running off to crusade for a freedom already possessed. One might understand how European refugees could worry lest that freedom be lost, but there were others who had known persecution who supported the oath for the identical reason. It was unthinkable, to Ernest, that anyone could doubt freedom in America; to agitate for it in California seemed to him agitation for the sake of agitation. The first man-made meson would be remembered long after the ridiculous squabble had been forgotten.

The quarter-scale model of the Bevatron performed so beautifully there could be no doubt that the six-billion volt machine would make history; construction of the big one was initiated in September, 1949. The synchrotron continued to perform as expected; with this machine the first observation of photo-production of mesons was made by Ed McMillan, J. M. Peterson, and R. S. White in 1949, and later, final convincing evidence for the existence of the neutral pi-meson was produced by J. Steinberger, W. H. K. Panofsky, and J. S. Stellar. Rabi's expressive, "Isn't physics wonderful?" could be so true when physicists tended to physics!

John insisted that Ernest get away from the disturbing, argumentative atmosphere, somehow more taxing than his work. Why not spend a few weeks with his family at Balboa? Ernest protested that departure from the scene did not automatically sever concerns. Nevertheless he went to Balboa, with every intention of swimming, boating, and generally relaxing with his family. But it was never easy to relax. After so many excursions in a speedboat, even reckless ones that frightened the children, and some to Catalina Island with unorthodox returns after dark, there wasn't much to occupy the mind, or dispel worries about things one could not confront at a beach vacation spot. He became restless. Perhaps a vacation, however attractive relaxation at a beach appeared in anticipation, could be effective only in unusual surroundings, such as the Mexican trip he and Molly had had earlier in the year with the Seeley Mudds.

When they had planned it and set the date at the Carnegie annual dinner, Molly had little hope that it would materialize. As it was, Ernest had returned from the East just in time for the scheduled takeoff in Mudd's private plane, a most comfortable craft in the capable hands of two professional pilots. They had stopped in Acapulco for a couple of days (enough) of loafing and some fishing. In Mexico City, where Mudd had business interests, the four were entertained by various American executives. There had been a big party at the fine Mexican home of M. S. Vallarta, the prominent university physicist. Except for Molly's collapse on a side trip to Taxco, it had been a fine, excitingly restful three weeks. Ernest had been sure that Molly's malaise could be charged to the winding road and the poor chauffeur, until, after the return to Mexico City, she confessed to him that she was pregnant. She had not previously mentioned it for fear of "spoiling the fun." Though they had decided to have another child, closer to Barbara's age than their older children, Ernest was surprised, but with Mudd, a physician, present saw no harm in continuing the trip. Perhaps because of Mudd no one was afflicted with the usual tourist ailments.

At least in retrospect, that had been a real vacation. Now, in Balboa, after the first few days of fun, he wondered if he were understanding for the first time in his life what boredom is—until his children asked him to explain television. It was much in the news because the rapid expansion of stations had caused interference problems and because of the rising interest in color. For several days Ernest spent happy hours on the beach with no boredom. He traced circuits in the sand, and when they were too complex for that medium, it was only a few steps to the house and paper, or to the garage, where he could tinker. His "rest" was shortly concluded. With several ideas—even systems—which he thought superior to those on the market, there could be no rest until they were tested. He flew back to San Francisco where he called at Color Television Incorporated, possesser of one of the three systems under consideration by the Federal Communications Commission. "Had a most interesting day," he wrote in a notebook acquired to log his TV activities. At the Rad Lab he talked with Jimmy Vale, for whose electronic competence he had much respect. Four days later, after a conference with a patent attorney who considered Ernest's ideas "hot," he arranged with technicians Ross Aiken and Richard Mack for translation of ideas to apparatus; a third of any remuneration resulting from his concepts and their work would go to them. He then left with Cooksey for the Bohemian Grove—certainly relaxing—and in mid-August participated in another delightful High Sierra camp trip with Yosemite directors.

He did not return to Balboa after the Yosemite expedition. In Berkeley, alterations on the house needed speeding up if they were to be finished before the family's return. A new, more convenient laundry adjoining the kitchen, in space excavated under the garage, was partially completed, as was the glass wall to enclose the covered portion of the top deck. With the new small bathroom, that would permit private quarters for teen-age Margaret. There were good excuses for remaining on the job at the laboratory, too; Cooksey was ailing, and vacations left fewer than normal administrative personnel in the offices, now all in new buildings on the hill. Ken Priestley, business manager since the early forties, had died, and Wally Reynolds had added those duties to his own as managing engineer. Ernest perhaps had taken Don somewhat for granted of late; his value to the laboratory loomed large in his absence. Ernest was concerned not only for his friend but also for the Rad Lab without him.

A large delegation of admirals and other Navy officers arrived on August 25 for consultation on the use of atomic energy for their concerns. Ernest had advocated reactor power for propulsion; Rickover, after a three-year struggle, had finally won permission to build and was at work on a reactor to power a submarine. Most naval officials wanted to await the outcome of that before going farther, but were concerned with weapons for Navy planes. Belief that an atom bomb must be huge and heavy prevailed. Ernest maintained that "the new bombs don't have to be that big . . . a big carrier-based plane is a sitting duck . . . from the overall view, smaller planes make sense." John T. "Chick" Hayward, later an Admiral, remembers his argument. Hayward thinks Ernest was ". . . always practical. He understood the problem better than anyone else—the *one* top scientist who understood it from our point of view . . . a staunch supporter in those days and he's been proven right. We could go to him and present our case. . . . There was false military thinking, too, and he'd tell us in no uncertain terms."

The Navy people left, but, since Don was no better, Ernest stayed in Berkeley. On September 1, Don had abdominal surgery, followed by four days of transfusions. A second operation was necessary on the seventh, after which he improved rapidly, but Ernest had been worried.

He was finally able to answer Groves's query: "He came through wonderfully and will almost certainly be in better health than he has been for a long time."

Groves's interest in atomic matters had continued; he followed progress as best he could and was interested in Ernest's advocacy of a stronger reactor program, as was General Mark Clark. Ernest had talked with Clark when both had received honorary degrees at the University of San Francisco—Ernest's second of 1949, having received one in April from the University of Southern California. He had found cause for hope in the reactor program in conferences with Lawrence Hafstad, then AEC director of the Reactor Division, Don Loughridge, and Tom Johnson earlier in the year.

Johnson and Ernest always met as though there had been no lapse after previous conversation, no matter how long the interval. Now chairman of the Physics Division at Brookhaven, where a reactor for research was under construction, Tom also advocated more effort behind the program. Loughridge had served well in two critical periods at the Rad Lab during the war. Larry Hafstad, who had been on the early Tuve high-voltage team, was also an old friend. He had provided technical assistance to Strauss in the development of the early detection program insisted upon by the commissioner—America's only protection against ignorance of possible nuclear explosions within the great land mass of Asia. Hafstad was as aware as anyone of the problems involved but also felt that industry and science could quickly solve them; the bomb problems had been overcome by concerted effort.

Cockcroft, now Sir John, had built two reactors at Harwell and was experimenting with different types; he believed in their future as substitutes for coal, as well as for isotope production and physical experiment. So did Oliphant, now Sir Mark, shortly to leave Birmingham for the Australian National University at Canberra. The French claimed to have developed a self-sufficient pile, and at Chalk River, in Canada, a heavy water reactor produced neutrons far in excess of any pile in the United States. On any comparative basis—size, wealth, industrial capacity—Americans were far behind, Ernest thought. On a week-long joint orientation conference, to which Forrestal had invited him before his retirement, Ernest preached the necessity and wisdom of reactor development to military officials and industrialists alike. Let moral arguments against development toward defense be offset by the enormous benefits that would accrue for humanity in medical knowledge, therapy, research, and in the promise of a great new source of energy—the very basis of industry. Eager listeners nicknamed him "the flying particle." California alumnus J. J. Hopkins, head of General Dynamics Corporation, became a convert. He questioned Ernest throughout the conference, which had started at the Pentagon, been continued in military air-craft en route to Norfolk, Virginia, to observe naval activities, and on to Fort Benning, Georgia, for Army demonstrations. Ernest hoped Hopkins was the type of adventurous businessman willing to take chances—as he thought the successful earlier industrialists who made American enter-prise preeminent had been.

As a member of the Barnard Prize Committee of the National Acad-emy, Ernest advocated the selection of Fermi for the medal—for his work with the pile.

On September 23, 1949, Ernest, stopping for a signal in Merced, while en route to Yosemite, saw the headlines. Russia had achieved an atomic explosion, probably on August 29. How fortunate that the monitoring system had been in use! Joe 1, as the Soviet explosion became known, ought to be proof enough for the most naïve of Russian intention to proceed with atomic development; it also should, Ernest felt, be all that was necessary to rally scientists for the nation's security. What scientist could now doubt that, if the Russians had developed a fission bomb in two years' less time than anyone had calculated possible, they would at-tempt thermonuclear fusion—might beat us to it if we continued our present pace? Perhaps even Oppie would now see the light and put the weight of his great influence behind it. But Ernest was doomed to disap-pointment; at an Armed Forces Special Weapons project meeting, which Ernest attended with Bradbury, he learned from General Nichols that there was still strong opposition to an urgent "super" or fusion program. He was also told that Edward Teller, perhaps the scientist who had given most thought to fusion, had telephoned Oppie for support of the program after the announcement of Joe 1, and been told to "keep your shirt on."

Upon his return to Berkeley, Ernest summoned Robert Serber, who had been close to Oppie as a student and at Los Alamos. He asked Serber to discuss the Russian explosion with Oppie and urge support for an all-out effort to, first, determine if the "super" were possible, and if so, then produce it to maintain American superiority. Serber, himself enthusiastic, agreed to go, shortly, as an emissary to Oppie at Princeton. He was to urge, as an aid to fusion studies, a stepped-up reactor plan for quantity production of neutrons. Ernest promised that if no one else would undertake a crash reactor program, the Rad Lab would put its well-known skills for rapid development to work on it, somewhere in the bay area. Some of the best brains in the lab were already studying it. Seaborg was much interested, but was going to Europe; he would write his support of the plan to the GAC, of which he was a member. It was something the Rad Lab could do to speed up a "super" program. Al-varez, as concerned as Ernest after Joe 1 over the lack of progress with reactors and fusion, discussed this concern with Dean Latimer over lunch at the Faculty Club. They had then gone to Ernest with their worries. Ernest needed no pressure to agree that the problem was urgent; if a fusion bomb were possible to construct, the Russians could do it. If the United States was to maintain its lead in nuclear weapons, there was little time to lose.

Ernest would be in Washington within a few days to discuss radiation warfare; Alvarez was due there on another matter. They would offer their reactor proposal to the AEC. To furnish concrete cost estimates, Reynolds and Brobeck worked overtime; to be up-to-date on fusion progress, Ernest telephoned Teller at Los Alamos. Teller had been the leader in fusion bomb discussions since 1942 when it had been thought, briefly, that fusion of light elements might be the easiest approach to a nuclear weapon. Tremendous obstacles had sidetracked that program for the uranium-plutonium fission bombs, though Teller had continued to study fusion throughout the war, when Oppie believed it certainly possible. Teller had argued mightily for a determined hydrogen bomb program ever since. Comparatively little other effort had gone into the "super"; development of improved and various types of fission bombs had been the main effort at Los Alamos, supported by the commissioners and the GAC.

As a result of the conversation with Teller, Ernest and Alvarez left for Washington earlier than planned, in order first to stop at Los Alamos for more detailed discussion. On October 7 they conferred there with Teller, Gamow, Manley, and Stanislau Ulam, all of whom were hopeful about fusion, providing sufficient tritium was available. It was agreed that a meeting of top physicists be assembled at Los Alamos in November to discuss the problem. Ernest expressed his willingness to get reactor experts to augment his staff and build them as quickly as humanly possible, near enough to the Rad Lab for its talent to be available. Teller suggested heavy water reactors as the easiest to build and by far the most efficient for excess neutrons. Ernest promised, with AEC approval, to get the project under way as soon as he returned to Berkeley. He would endeavor to visit the Chalk River heavy water establishment in Canada, where ex-Rad Lab physicist Bernard Kinsey was stationed, for further briefing on the subject.

In Washington the next afternoon, he found that Commissioner Strauss had already pointed up the urgency of a crash program for the "super," in a memorandum. Ken Pitzer, on leave from California as James Fisk's successor as director of the Division of Research for the AEC, was in favor of a high priority program. He and General James McCormack, director of the Division of Military Applications, would support Ernest's plan to build heavy water reactors. Ernest and Luis were encouraged, during dinner with the Loomises at the Carlton, and at breakfast the next morning with Deputy Secretary of Defense for Atomic Affairs Robert LeBaron, who was also chairman of the AEC Military Liaison Committee. Ernest's appointments at the Defense Department were for another reason, but he urged a crash program for a fusion development there, and told some of the Joint Chiefs of Staff of the brilliance of Kapitza and other Russian scientists and of Kapitza's work with light elements.

He was at lunch when he received a telegram announcing the birth of his sixth child, Susan, the night before, on October 8, 1949. Her name had been suggested by Robert while Ernest was with the family at Balboa.

Alvarez was to give California Congressman Carl Hinshaw data pertaining to air navigation. When the Representative learned that Ernest Lawrence was with him, he called Senator McMahon, who asked the Californians to lunch with him the next day in his chambers at the Capitol. McMahon and Hinshaw strongly favored the project, were interested that the Canadians were far ahead in heavy water reactor technology, and were pleased that Ernest planned to visit the Chalk River establishment. Later, at AEC headquarters, Lilienthal was unenthusiastic; the idea of a super bomb was repugnant to him. Nevertheless he wrote Oppie asking for GAC recommendations in view of the Russian explosion. Other commissioners than Lilienthal approved of Ernest's reactor plan, and, though reluctant to give him sanction for a Chalk River visit, finally approved. Ernest had an appointment in New York the following morning with RCA in connection with his television inventions, and in the afternoon he and Alvarez called on Rabi at Columbia. Rabi, also concerned since the Russian explosion, seemed delighted that something was going to be done to offset it. As Alvarez recalls, Rabi said something to the effect that it was good to see the first team back after four years of playing around with cyclotrons and nuclei. Ernest had a brief visit with Bernard Kinsey and a tour of Chalk River installations before returning to Berkeley.

On October 14, Larry Hafstad arrived in Berkeley and, after conferences, approved a site Ernest had picked on an uninhabited beach near Benicia, northeast of the bay, accessible to Berkeley, and where bay water could be used for cooling. The reactors would be built in units to enable quick changes, Hafstad would go to Chicago for discussions with reactor experts at Argonne, some of whom would be sent to the Rad Lab as soon as possible. Ernest and Alvarez spent the evening with Neylan, who promised the regents' approval of Ernest's recommendation. On the following Monday, the seventeenth, Hafstad phoned that Walter H. Zinn would send some of his reactor people from Chicago to

Berkeley within a week and would come himself after an Oak Ridge meeting he had to attend. Zinn, the best American technical expert on reactors, doubted the advisability of following the Chalk River designs, and suggested one of the more complicated types, such as were under construction at Argonne. Ernest preferred the simple, proven type that could be built quickly. He appointed Alvarez director of the project and had him move to the new Director's Building—which administration and some research people were just beginning to occupy. Everyone pitched in, leaving experiments and accelerator projects, to think about heavy water reactors. Senator William F. Knowland of California visited the laboratory on Friday; he would do what he could to support the program. Pitzer requested that Ernest and Alvarez personally present their plan at the GAC meeting. Teller phoned that the top-level conference on the "super" at Los Alamos would be on November 7. Things seemed to be moving at last.

Alvarez and Brobeck left on the twenty-fifth to see Zinn, the pile expert, in Chicago before going to Washington. Ernest went directly to the Capital with Teller, where they soon learned that Oppie was opposed to any crash program for the "super," including the bay area reactor proposal. Serber, who had been so enthusiastic, not only had failed to convince Oppie, but had been converted to his former teacher's point of view: if the Americans did not build a hydrogen bomb, the Russians would not. Members of the GAC followed Oppie's lead; the advisory committee recommended against the "super" in what Oppie himself described as the "most controversial meeting," at which no minutes were kept. A few days later the AEC commissioners voted four to one against urgency in the development of a hydrogen weapon and asked the President to renounce it, unilaterally. Gordon Dean, who had taken William Waymack's place on the commission, later changed his vote to join Strauss in favoring it. The support of some of the Joint Chiefs of Staff was of no avail. The meeting of physicists for a full-dress discussion at Los Alamos was suddenly cancelled. The fusion program would continue with minimal support; Ernest's reactor program was dead.

Andrei Y. Vishinsky, Soviet Vice Foreign Minister, announced that the Russians had had the atom bomb since 1947 and a few days later asserted that atomic energy was being used in Russia to raze mountains and irrigate deserts. Lilienthal, despite his vote against the fusion program, warned that the Russian explosion made dispersion of our government and industrial facilities imperative. He also announced his resignation from the commission, effective on the last day of the year.

Exhausted by his efforts, depressed and worried over the consequences of what he considered a shortsighted policy, Ernest sought a retreat. "I think he thought of a place the other side of the mountains that might be safe for the children. A place not too far, where he could get away from the telephone and the pressures of the laboratory" Molly said. He found what he liked at Diablo, just over the coast range from Berkeley, and persuaded Molly that they should buy it. The house was not large enough for a family of eight, but the lot was. Hills rose rather abruptly behind the patio, hills with live oak trees on them. Ernest said it would be wonderful for the children and for horseback riding. It was a country club area: they would join a club where there was swimming. Molly consented with the understanding that little would be done toward furnishing the house until Susan was older; the family did not actually live in it until more than a year later. Ernest fixed up the garage as a place in which to relax—and work out television ideas. Often on a Sunday he would insist that they all go to Diablo, "as though there was not a care in the world. He thought there was no concern about food, when they could 'just run into town and get it,' but he often asked people to drop in, and sometimes I'd have twelve or fifteen for a meal. I learned to take food with us because he was always too busy with something else to run into town. But he liked it there. He loved hot weather, provided it was dry heat, and it was often very hot. I have never liked hot weather, and did not like the place chiefly for that reason. Running out there with the family for a day, or a weekend, involved a lot of work for me."

Soon it was a lot of work for Ernest, too. As his television ideas proliferated, the garage became too small and was enlarged—actually into a small shop. Many nights and many weekends, Ernest, and perhaps Jimmy Vale, or even McMillan or Alvarez, were busy there.

When Charles Thomas visited the laboratory in November, he asked Ernest to join the board of directors of the Monsanto Chemical Company. Surprised, but pleased, Ernest protested that it might conflict with his relationship with American Cyanamid. Neylan, whom Ernest entertained with Thomas in San Francisco, protested that Ernest already had too many responsibilities, and that the considerable stipend, as far as he was concerned, was no inducement, since Ernest was the type who would insist that he earn every penny of it. The issue was not resolved until after Thomas's departure from Berkeley, or before the arrival of his letter of gratitude for the "wonderful time with you and your family . . . all my associates are enthusiastic over your joining the board. Don't see any hitch in your relations with American Cyanamid." Rowan Gaither was mildly opposed and Neylan decidedly against Ernest adding the directorship to his duties. "My father confessor advises against it," Ernest finally wrote Thomas.

It had not been difficult to resist the tempting offer. Ernest could not shake off the conviction that a way must be found to facilitate the rapid exploration of thermonuclear possibilities. He "felt it in his bones" that

Russia was working on it. The suggested unilateral renunciation of a fusion bomb would be tantamount to a public invitation for the Soviets to assume whatever superiority we held; if they achieved it, every nation in the world would be at Russia's mercy. It was a situation similar to that with Germany at the start of the war. Balked in his desire to help with a reactor program, he searched for ways in which his tremendous accelerator equipment might be useful. Quantities of neutrons were required, and tritium; perhaps an element other than uranium might prove fissionable, if fusion proved unworkable. The AEC had recognized the scarcity of uranium in the United States and recently had offered profitable inducements for exploration and discovery of the ore, but the country was still largely dependent on the Congo. Such dependence on another continent was a terrifying thought, if uranium or plutonium bombs were to be our nuclear arsenal. During the war Ernest had succeeded in having Donald McLaughlin, now a regent, explore possible sources in Mexico, to no avail.

Herbert York, in a sense Ernest's last graduate student, though he had taken his degree from Segrè in June, had experimented interestingly on the multiplicity of neutron production by the high energy beam of the 184-inch; Ernest now asked him to bombard every element of the periodic table in an unusual way. Each target was placed in a pipe passing through a tank of water through which were distributed indium foils, which were activated by neutrons produced in the target by the beam, giving a means for measuring the total yield of neutrons when bombarded. The results were such—in the York experiments neutrons were multiplied many times—that modification of accelerators for this specific purpose was studied: the cyclotron by McMillan, Thornton, and Dave Judd, and the linear accelerator by Alvarez, Panofsky, and Don Gow.

Perhaps even depleted uranium could be made useful; the experiments were all Ernest could think of that could be done at the Rad Lab. The problem seemed as important as that which inspired the early efforts that had led to the fission bomb.

CHAPTER XVI

To Fuse or Not to Fuse

[1950–1952]

An easel with a blank canvas stood near the wide window that framed
—if one's eyes were shielded from late winter sun, reflected off
west-reaching ocean—trees and rocks and a bit of the bay's crescent
beach, scalloped by surging breakers, and empty of people. Brushes,
tubes of paint, and a palette were on a small table nearby, and there was
a gay little handcart with more paints—and a beret.

Molly thought they had been taken to the wrong room, though it was
one they had occupied before when guests of the Loomises at Del Monte
Lodge. Ernest was puzzled only momentarily; a phone call announcing
their arrival to the Loomises brought their hosts to the room and confirmed his suspicion—he was to try painting. British scientist T. E.
(Bones) Allibone, who had been at the Rad Lab during the war, on a
recent visit had given Ernest the little book *Painting as a Pastime*. He
had mentioned to Manette Loomis, a serious sculptress—she did a fine
bronze head of Ernest—that Winston Churchill made painting seem so
attractive a hobby that he was tempted to try it himself. Manette sensed
that he was serious, that the remark was more than his usual manifesta-
tion of interest in another's vocation. Alfred thought such a hobby
might help his friend to relax. There could be no doubt about his interest now; he wished to get started immediately. But by the time everything was explained, the sun had set, it was cocktail time, and there
were other guests for dinner.

When he failed to appear for lunch on Saturday, Molly and the
Loomises went to his room. There he was, paintbrush in hand and little
daubs of color on his pajamas. A pretty good representation of the scene
from his window was painted on the canvas. He accepted exclamations

of approval with delight, as he had with cyclotrons, or his new Oldsmobile convertible. For a time, uranium shortages, slow progress with
fusion, indeed everything but painting had been put from his mind.
Manette offered a few simple, basic pointers which he grasped at once.
That first painting was finished the day it was started. On Sunday he
packed easel, paints, and the collapsible table in the little cart and all
went off to Point Lobos for the day. He stopped painting only long
enough to enjoy red wine, French bread, and cheese with his hosts—who
had as much fun as he did.

Ernest painted pretty consistently between television experiments at
Diablo, on following weekends—for a while. Once when alone there, he
loaded the little cart, including the wine, French bread, and cheese that
seemed the perfect repast for a working painter, and went into the hills
to paint. He was hot and tired when he stopped for lunch and afterward
decided he had better return to the house. Fatigue, wine, and sun un-
steadied him; he collapsed against the cart, which started careening
down the hill, bumping and scattering its contents until it crashed. His
painting was intact, and he was able to pick up most of the scattered
equipment, but the little cart was damaged beyond repair. Somehow, he
got it and his gear back to the garage. He wrote the Loomises of the
event as a great joke; they sent him another cart.

Diablo was a place of relaxation for a while, whether he went there
alone or with the family as sometimes happened on a Sunday. But as his
television schemes developed, the retreat became the headquarters and
laboratory of that interest; an interest that seemed important and
potentially profitable enough to organize properly. In January, 1950, he
asked Rowan Gaither to represent him in television matters, and in
February the two organized Telecolor Incorporated to exploit the inventions. Rowan was insistent that Ernest should have 75 percent of the
possible profits; Ernest was as firm for equal sharing. They agreed to put
it up to Loomis and to abide by his decision; he judged for equal shares.
In March, they bought the interests Ernest had assigned to Ross Aiken
and Richard Mack. Patent applications were filed. Paramount Pictures
Corporation, already principal stockholder of the Dumont television
enterprise, agreed to finance the corporation. At their suggestion the
name was changed to Chromatic Television Laboratories Incorporated.
More than $1,500 worth of equipment was installed in the Diablo ga-
rage, soon to be considerably enlarged and known as the Diablo Laboratory. Ernest's efforts were not limited to Diablo. He thought of a new
principle while resting on a bunk when John's and Amy's guest at Delta
Ranch. At Balboa in April he worked out another idea; an important
modification of his color television tube occurred to him at the Mayfair
House in New York that same month. And on the last day of April,

while driving to Berkeley from Balboa, an entirely new system was invented.

Neither painting nor television could drive lab problems from his mind for any length of time, or the welfare of his country to which physics might contribute. He was certainly not alone in his concern lest fusion and a hydrogen bomb first be developed elsewhere—and held as a club against the nation—but there was far too little concern in most quarters. He was impatient with much of the debate going on around the nation on the wisdom of further effort, the ethics of the attempt, the belief that it could not be done, or would be too difficult—or, silliest of all, that the Russians could not develop a hydrogen bomb if we refrained. Yet some advocates of these themes, at the close of the war, had asserted that a hydrogen bomb could, and probably would, be made in as short a time as three years. Sanctimonious moral reasoning particularly annoyed Ernest; science was neither moral nor immoral, and scientists must proceed to unravel nature's puzzles willy-nilly; most forces could be considered immoral if used viciously, or even carelessly; every advance in weaponry had been protested, perhaps from the first use of implements for fighting—certainly from the time of the crossbow, against which it was argued that its arrows were propelled with sufficient force to pass completely through an armored man. That a hydrogen weapon, perhaps a thousand times more powerful than the Hiroshima bomb, would be uselessly large was a decision for military experts. If a single bomb could destroy much of Manhattan, and the adjacent New Jersey and Brooklyn harbor and industrial area, would an enemy consider it too large? Opposed to these views, and fellow advocates of deepest inquiry into the possibility of an H-bomb, were highly respected men of affairs, as well as militarists. Omar Bradley, anything but a warmongering general, confided to Ernest that he had been so concerned that Russia might develop a super bomb while this nation complacently moralized that he had taken the liberty of writing to the President.

The theory that the United States was responsible for Russian suspicion and intransigence seemed particularly wrong—in fact unpatriotic—to Ernest. That idea was dealt a devastating blow on January 27, 1950, when Klaus Fuchs confessed that he had passed A-bomb secrets to Russian agents, periodically, while at Los Alamos during the war. He had also later participated in "super" bomb discussions at Los Alamos. On January 31, President Truman, against the advice of the commission and GAC, ordered the AEC to work on all forms of atomic weapons, "including the so-called hydrogen or super bomb."

This was encouraging; perhaps now more scientists would get busy on the problem. Regrettably it would take time to develop reactors for surplus neutrons and tritium—time that would have been saved, Ernest

felt, if reactor programs had been properly encouraged. What could the
Rad Lab do now to help? The experiments of York indicated that tremendous quantities of neutrons could be produced, and perhaps heavy
elements other than uranium be made fissionable in quantity, by powerful, high-intensity deuteron beams. After considerable discussion of the
relative merits of the cyclotron or linear device for the purpose, it was
decided that a huge linear accelerator would be best to function as a
sort of alternate to a reactor—though Reg Richardson, at Berkeley from
U.C.L.A. for two or three days every two weeks, thought Ernest really
favored the cyclotron approach. The AEC, interested in what might result from bombardment of large quantities of materials, and anxious to
determine if plutonium might be produced from depleted uranium or a
substitute, and if tritium could be made without use of a nuclear fuel,
asked Ernest to submit plans for a linear approach to the project. Alvarez was away at the time, so Ernest discussed it with W. K. H. Panofsky
for a day or two before making a decision—on a Friday night. Panofsky
was another linear accelerator expert.

At a hastily called Saturday morning meeting, Ernest proposed a pilot
linear accelerator tube 60 feet in diameter and 87 feet long, to contain
huge drift tubes and more powerful radio frequency than had ever been
achieved. He proposed development of ion sources to inject large numbers of particles, and new focusing techniques, for tremendous beam
currents, in a vacuum of unheard-of capacity. Everything about his plan,
including the goals, seemed utterly fantastic even to the young men accustomed to his ideas; they frankly stared, openmouthed. It was hard to
believe him serious—but they knew that he was.

After some discussion it did not seem so impossible; everyone concluded that such an accelerator would do the job if it could be done at
all. Interest grew, the merits of various appurtenances were discussed as
were material costs—which did not interest Ernest at all. He asked if
anyone saw any advantage in the use of gold for the accelerator's liner
—which effectively terminated cost discussions. Don Gow of Luis' group
thought that, though he was serious, he may have mentioned gold when
he did to direct attention tactfully from costs back to technical concerns.
By lunchtime everyone was enthusiastic over the project, to be called the
Materials Testing Accelerator (MTA), suggested by the Materials Testing Reactor under construction in Idaho. Alvarez would direct the project, Panofsky would make basic designs for the first big tube, "Mark I,"
Gow would handle the modeling program. Interest became so keen, and
the goals seemed so urgent, that activity at the Rad Lab—nights, Saturdays, and Sundays—was reminiscent of early war days.

The university, however, for the same reasons responsibility for other
manufacturing and assembly operations had been considered an im-

proper university function, refused to take responsibility for other than research and consultation assistance to the project. As the AEC was interested in developing private industrial cooperation on the West Coast, the California Research and Development Company was organized to undertake development of the project by the California Research Corporation, a subsidiary of Standard Oil Company of California. This was accomplished after Regent Neylan brought Ernest and Standard Oil Chairman R. Gwin Follis, and his predecessor, Harry Collier, together. It was an ambitious project for a new company, far larger than any ever undertaken by its parent, the California Research Corporation. The pilot plant would be constructed at a onetime naval air station near Livermore, just across the hills from Berkeley, near the edge of the San Joaquin Valley. A full-scale production plant was contemplated for Weldon Spring, Missouri. The project was announced on March 31, 1950, as an AEC classified research program.

Lilienthal left the AEC on February 15. As his successor had not yet been appointed, Commissioner Sumner T. Pike became acting chairman. Conant had refused the position, and the choice was said to be between Ernest and Arthur Compton. The position did not interest Ernest for many reasons; it would involve politics, leaving his laboratories, and residence in Washington. Commissioner Gordon Dean was ultimately appointed chairman.

Ernest continued to go to Washington when he thought it his duty, for nonpolitical reasons that pertained to his field. In March, he managed to take care of his consultant duties in Rochester, Schenectady, and New York, as well as a policy planning meeting at the State Department—for which Dean Acheson thanked him for his time and trouble in coming "to Washington to give the study group the benefit of your ideas . . . they were both stimulating and helpful." And late in April, Ernest attended an all-day Sunday meeting on radiological warfare at the Department of Defense. The subjects of both discussions were above politics and in the national interest. There were politics enough on the Berkeley campus with all the uproar over the loyalty oath. In April, Ernest wrote his old friend Joel Hildebrand, with whom he disagreed about the oath, "just hope and pray, as I'm sure you do, that a way will be found to restore harmony between the president, the regents, and the faculty which is so essential for the University welfare." Jesse Beams, who visited Ernest earlier that year, noted his old friend's distress over an issue he considered trivial.

Ernest entertained Robert LeBaron and some of the Joint Chiefs at the Bohemian Club in the middle of April, and Molly had them for cocktails the next evening before their departure for Washington. There was suspicion among them, too, that urgent pursuit of the "super" had not followed the Presidential order as it should have. They were much interested in the Materials Testing Accelerator studies, LeBaron wrote: "It is always stimulating to our people to visit Berkeley and the comments about the work and the environment are always flattering to you and your staff. We realize that this latest activity at the laboratory is highly speculative and accordingly much too uncertain to include in any future estimates at this time. However, it is a good thing for the defense group to know that new things are in the wind, and that while all of them will not succeed the probability is in favor for success for at least some of them. If this latest adventure measures up to present expectation it will certainly have a far-reaching effect upon the overall program."

During the night of April 23, fire destroyed the engineering and research building on the hill only fifty yards away from the 184-inch cyclotron building. Nine hours later another fire broke out in the plating shop, much farther from an accelerator, but two fires in such close succession provoked accusations of lack of security. Some of Brobeck's Bevatron plans and Panofsky's MTA designs were burned. Harold Fidler, AEC area manager, summoned the FBI. A board of inquiry was appointed; no cause was determined for the first conflagration, and a gas jet that had been left burning was suspected in the second. All was, of course, reported in the press—particularly the rumors of sabotage. Ernest managed to avoid reporters.

It was commendable, he thought, for Strauss to write on security and atomic energy as he did for a July issue of *Life* Magazine. Some of Strauss's attitudes were unpopular with certain physicists, and he asked Ernest to write a letter to the editor in support of his ideas. Ernest refused: "You know how I have felt. . . . I would be of greater usefulness by keeping out of public discussions of current policy questions and tend to my knitting in the laboratory, and also assist you and others who have the responsibility of formulating broad policies by providing whatever technical information I can. I still think I should preserve my amateur standing in public affairs, and leave it to others to carry the ball in influencing directly public opinion." In fact he disagreed with Strauss in one area: Ernest thought too little had been done to bring industry into atomic energy development. "Such propositions as have been suggested by Charlie Thomas have merit."

Public opinion had been suddenly and sharply focused on national security and defense on June 25, by the invasion of South Korea from the north—patent aggression aimed as much at enforcing political doctrine as for acquisition of territory. Ernest was with the Loomises at East Hampton, Long Island, on that Sunday—he and Alfred were discussing a new color television tube when news of the invasion came over the radio. Two days later the U.N. Security Council (then boycotted by

Russia) voted to help repel the aggression. President Truman ordered U.S. forces to assist. The aggression was disillusioning for some of those who had believed in the peaceful intentions of the Communists. And, significantly, Congress was asked, early in July, for $260 million to start a $1.5 billion reactor project. Five huge piles, to be built at Savannah River, South Carolina, would be capable of producing plutonium or tritium—for fission or fusion.

Rabi, in Berkeley for the summer, considered the dual-purpose Savannah reactors the answer to Russian success in making an atomic weapon. Further response, perhaps, would come from the development at Los Alamos of a fission bomb that would require but a fraction of the critical uranium or plutonium mass heretofore necessary for explosion—it soon would be tested experimentally in Nevada. If successful, a thermonuclear device with a fractional bomb as explosive trigger would be tested during Operation Greenhouse in the Marshall Islands. For Greenhouse, York and Hugh Bradner would design major diagnostic experiments. (York, Burton Moyer, and their team had distinguished themselves with their discovery of the neutral meson.) Success of fractional bombs would also relieve some of the worry over the shortage of American uranium deposits, since the ultimate production of the Savannah reactors would mitigate, to some extent, lacks of plutonium and tritium. Nevertheless, Mark I accelerator design progressed; five huge reactors would require much feed material. Ernest thought it imperative that the United States become independent of ore from other countries.

Gow's models for the Mark I devices progressed on a six-days-a-week schedule. One Saturday, while waiting for a piece of equipment to be machined, Gow hooked up a couple of oscilloscopes with miscellaneous electronic gear in radar fashion and brought in a telecast ball game. "Hey, Luis," he called to Alvarez, "we have a very strange wave on the scope!" Alvarez investigated, laughed, and told Gow to leave the assembly as it was. "We'll pull the trick on Lowell Thomas," he said. Thomas was at the lab on a story. Alvarez said it was too bad Ernest was not present and suggested that Gow speak to him about television. Gow was invited to join the TV venture, as a consultant, after MTA models were completed, and, instead of spending Saturdays at the Rab Lab, Gow often spent the entire weekend at Diablo, and many nights as well. He found the project interesting, chiefly because of the opportunity to become better acquainted with Ernest.

"Fascinating to go roaring out to this place all hours of the day or night. Saturdays we'd play ping-pong with Ernest. Might bake something in the oven—we had the run of the house when the family weren't there. Beer was always available, courtesy of Ernest. Sometimes he'd have a bottle of wine at dinner because he thought it relaxing. I remember him saying, 'Nobody under forty should drink and everybody over forty ought to drink.' He kept inventing variations on the color tube. Was very anxious to get it going—always felt it was just around the corner; just one more touch and you had it. On Saturdays, if we were out there first, or he couldn't come out, he might call up on a moment's notice, 'I've got a great new idea. This is really it.' Maybe it would be to grind in V grooves at the end of each piece of glass, or some such thing. 'Let's look at it tonight. I'll be out at ten or right after dinner.' Or maybe it'd be four or four-thirty on a weekday when he called. We'd jump in our cars, maybe Jimmy Vale, Les Cook or Bob Walke and me, and go roaring out to Diablo and try to put something together. Of course we never made it by that night, but maybe the next night we'd be looking at it. It was always this or that minor trouble, but Ernest was always enthusiastic about what we'd done, no matter what. Also quick to recognize defects and deficiencies, and by midnight or two o'clock he'd say, 'Well, what we really have to do is modify this or that, etc.' We'd all leave and try to get home, and it wasn't improbable for Ernest to be back on the phone in the morning. 'I've thought more about this. What we said last night wasn't right. What we have to do is this.' And four-thirty or five we'd be on our way out again.

"This intense enthusiasm was communicated to the group. Always the excitement of getting something done immediately. And the most common entry in the logbook was 'This shop must be kept clean! EOL!' He was just as bad as the rest of us. He'd come into the shop and really get his hands dirty, though he realized in most of these matters that people like Jimmy Vale, particularly, were much better at handling these materials. He loved to run the experiments himself. Once something was set up in a vacuum system, or somehow, he just had to run it, and, as we all joked, it was 'all meters and all Variacs against the stop.' Got so we'd bolt the power supply on a piece of equipment and decide the absolute maximum, and put pins in the handles so they couldn't be turned beyond that point. He always wanted to test equipment to its breakdown point. Standard hour for departure was certainly after midnight during this period. To my wife this wasn't the greatest, but there was a certain amount of enthusiasm. Jimmy Vale probably put in more hours than anybody else."

Vale says: "Well, there were some Saturday nights I wanted to do other things. I have a wife and children. My wife was quite understanding about the whole thing. She met Ernest, was very calm about it. Some of the other fellows' wives were quite bitter. I knew one of them; every time I'd see her she'd rant and rave about her husband spending all his time out there. After we got some bunks in the garage and a regular little kitchen of our own, if it got to be two or three in the morn-

ing, we'd stay out there. It did get to be very hectic because I was working at the lab full time, too. I remember one Friday we worked until
two—all very tired. Ernest went to bed in the house, and somebody else
and I in the garage—in the little bedroom he built. Well, at eight in the
morning there he was pounding on the door. 'Time to get up! Time to
get up!' Don't know how he did it. This was just one small thing in all
his activities, and he never seemed to show signs of tiredness, but of
course he was, obviously. He couldn't even play without going all out. If
we would take a break for ping-pong in the backyard—well, I guess I
was the best player. I'd beat someone pretty heavily. Then he'd play
Ernest and maybe he'd beat Ernest, and then I'd play him, and he'd get
mad sometimes. 'Listen, you're not doing your best. You beat him by a
big margin and he beats me, and then you just barely beat me. Now
when you play with me, I want you to play your very hardest.' This was
typical of him. Even in a game trying his utmost. It was his very nature.
Here's a game and you want to relax and enjoy it, but he couldn't and
expected others to play their hardest, too. He never minded losing; what
bothered him was I wasn't playing as well as I could, easing up because
he was Ernest. He didn't like that."

Rowan Gaither noted the same intensity. One noon, that summer of
1950, before Gaither was to take an afternoon plane for the East, Ernest
thought of something important while they were walking to a restaurant. After a brief discussion, he said, "To heck with lunch. Let's go
to the office and dictate." They were such close friends by that time they
never had serious differences. Actually they never had had, except over
plans for division of possible profits—even then, when Gaither agreed to
put up the money, they forgot to discuss the terms until days later. At
the Bohemian Grove that July—the day Ernest was Hoover's luncheon
guest with General Dwight Eisenhower—he met Rowan late in the evening. Half an hour later he was so excited over an idea that, though it
was after ten, they left the Grove and drove to the laboratory. "What
was exhausting to others was not to him with his enthusiasm and
energy," Rowan said.

Ernest was able to spend a few days with his family at Balboa after
the Grove and before departure for New York the last day of July. The
Blumers, who now had a year-round house nearby, were somewhat
shocked at Ernest's appearance. G.B. commented on his "visible and tor-
tuous temporal artery," but Ernest protested that he was fine. He was
back at Balboa in less than a week and took the entire family to Hollywood for lunch with Paramount Vice-President Y. Frank Freeman at the
studios. The children were ecstatic; they not only watched Bob Hope
make a scene for a forthcoming picture but also had their pictures taken
with him. Then Ernest was off to Yosemite for a weekend directors'

meeting, during which time he invented another TV tube. He went to Diablo to work it out; it was set up two nights later to show Paramount's Bob Dressler who had arrived that day from New York. That was a full day, since he also had Atomic Energy commissioners at the Rad Lab.

He did not get to Balboa again before his family's return to Berkeley on August 20. Ernest and John and their wives held a reception, on the twenty-second, to celebrate the golden wedding anniversary of Carl and Gunda Lawrence. Approximately two hundred guests, including several relatives, joined the festive party on the Lido Deck of the Claremont Hotel. Gunda beamed with pride, not only in her sons, but in Carl. "They were a very devoted, extraordinarily close couple," Molly thought. "Gunda's whole life seemed wrapped up in her husband." There was punch and a beautiful wedding cake of several tapering tiers surmounted by a miniature bride and groom. Champagne was omitted out of consideration for the feminine guest of honor. Carl, later at Ernest's home, toasted his bride with the usual old-fashioned he accepted there, always against Gunda's advice. She never failed to admonish: "Now, Carl, now, Carl, I don't think that's good for you and you might get tipsy." It was gentle remonstrance; she could deny him nothing, particularly now that he was ailing and his sight failing. She worried, too, about Ernest's health, though later that year it was John—rather suddenly and seriously ill—who was the cause of much concern.

An emergency operation to remove his gall bladder was decided upon one morning about two o'clock. Ernest, at the hospital with frightened Amy, impatiently paced the otherwise deserted lobby until he could stand it no longer. "Let's go upstairs and see what they're doing." It sounded like an order. "We can't go up there," Amy remonstrated. But they went and waited near the operating room until a gauze-muzzled nurse came out carrying a tray. She asked Ernest if he would like to see John's gallbladder. He fled without a word. John recovered in good time.

Further alterations on the Berkeley house, including a wide deck off the living room facing the bay and overhanging the hillside, had not been completed when the family returned from Balboa, and, until school commenced, much of the remaining summer was spent at Diablo. "Hot—oh, Lord, it was hot!" Molly remembers. They often dined at the Danville Inn, or the country club, sometimes with guests, unexpected by Molly, after cocktails at the Diablo house. Over the Labor Day weekend there was a constant stream of visitors, including RCA people, for Sunday afternoon and supper. Even after they moved back to Berkeley, most weekends the rest of the year were spent at Diablo, where Ernest, busy in the shop, saw almost as little of his family as at Berkeley.

He conscientiously tried to keep Friday evenings free to take the older children to the movies, an exciting event that often failed in its objective. He always looked in at the laboratory on the way, which the children liked; he also often became so engrossed there that he forgot the movies until it was too late—the children were as uncomplaining about that as Molly. The laboratory was always fun, and the gates, guards, fences, and badges were dramatic, as was their father's importance. A time or two, the older children arrived at the laboratory in sly fashion, when Ernest would forget to leave them at school in the morning. They were as quiet as possible until he parked the car on the hill, when they squealed with delight. He took them back down the hill to school, where their tardiness was blamed on "our absentminded professor father, who forgot us."

Walter Dudziak and Sagane—back at the lab—likely to be at the 184-inch on a Sunday afternoon that winter, missed Ernest if he failed to show up around four-thirty with Eric or Robert. Ernest would spend forty-five minutes or an hour with the physicists before asking them to explain to his son what they were doing. The younger physicists were amazed at how much Ernest knew about their problems. Everyone in the lab, Dudziak is certain, knew that Ernest cared, and that this personal concern was part of his ability with people. He would talk to a machinist or a Ph.D. in the same manner. One day he asked Dudziak why he was all dressed up and wearing a tie, was he going to give a speech? He had meant it as a joke, but when he found it was a fact said, "Good, I'll have to run down and catch it." And he did. "That was a big thing about EOL; everybody knew he cared and so worked harder."

Charles Thomas again asked him to become a Monsanto director. "Rowan and I have reviewed it carefully—reluctantly refuse," Ernest replied. A long letter from Gregory Breit, received the last day of December, asked his assistance in obtaining funds for a new cyclotron at Yale. He felt he could not deny this request. Such appeals for assistance, advice, and recommendations were very frequent. "He was always very generous about other places than Berkeley," Tom Johnson remembers, and "I never knew him to be envious or resentful. The program of high energies—nuclear physics—had a tremendous impact on universities. He had the interests of American science very much at heart." Everyone knew that his word on behalf of a project carried great weight in Washington.

"He had tremendous influence," Alex Hildebrand said, and Norris Bradbury thinks, "He had backers who would back anything that pointed toward a personally desired end." He often did not wait to be asked for recommendations. Earlier in 1950 he had written John Slater at M.I.T. that Stan Livingston deserved to be made a full professor. In

1951, Melvin Calvin wanted to experiment in Norway. Someone advanced $2,500 toward the project's expense, and Ernest gave him another $2,500 from his special fund. Calvin then received a $5,000 prize from the Sugar Research Foundation for his work with radioactive carbon in determining the way in which plants make sugar. He promptly returned $2,500 to each of his contributors—Ernest tore up the check Calvin sent him.

On February 8, 1951, he was honored by the Bohemian Club at a dinner presided over by President Sproul. In his off the record speech Ernest said, "There are those who have the jitters in relation to atomic energy developments—who have a feeling of impending doom—that bombs are going to start falling everywhere, civilization is going to be destroyed and the world is going to be so contaminated with radioactivity that it will be forever uninhabitable.

"There is the school on the other hand, to which I belong, that does not share this view. . . . [We] believe that the advent of the atomic bomb [may be] one of mankind's great blessings—that it provides for the first time in history a technical means of taking the profit out of war, and preventing . . . major aggression. It is generally conceded that the atomic bomb is keeping the Soviets at bay this very minute, and we can continue to make the odds so unfavorable that no one is going to undertake a major conflict.

"The atomic bomb is one of the greatest bargains in history. Last year we spent on the whole AEC program about twenty-five percent of what we spent on TV. As one who is interested in TV, I'm in favor of TV expenditures, but it seems to me far more important to improve as much as possible our military position, atomic-wise, than to provide entertainment for children at home via TV. . . . We can afford to double and redouble our efforts, and we should move as fast as possible toward a truly supreme position.

"Now in advocating these policy matters I am stepping outside my field of special competence. I should stick to fundamental science—and perhaps something in the nature of a family confession is here in order. We scientists have always told each other, and everyone else, that pure science is of great practical importance, but every now and then we wonder if we aren't trying to sell a bill of goods to justify what we enjoy doing, and get paid for doing."

He went on to discuss the Bevatron under construction at the laboratory, from which it was hoped as great strides forward would be made as had been with earlier accelerators. He praised the work of Los Alamos, "in which Californians can take pride, as it is operated by the University of California," and of Stanford's Norris Bradbury, its director, who had resisted the impulse to leave after the war. Their latest accomplishments, which he had just witnessed, he could not discuss, but, "I was reminded of Churchill's famous remark of owing so much to so few." He concluded by suggesting that "things look good, but we can make things look a lot better, and let us hope that we shall be hearing of an ever-expanding construction program for the production of atomic products."

He had reason for his optimism. The Nevada tests had been successful beyond expectation. Indeed it seemed that the explosions, with only a fraction of the critical amount of plutonium, had been of greater intensity than earlier bombs that contained much more fissionable material. In any case, the success of these meant that the number of weapons possible with the available fissionable material was increased many times. As for the "super," he had been led to believe that Teller, Ulam, and other theoreticians at Los Alamos had overcome some of the formidable obstacles in the way of fusion. During Operation Greenhouse on the Pacific Testing grounds in May, fusion on a large scale would be attempted for the first time. John Wheeler and John von Neumann of Princeton were cooperating with Teller's Los Alamos group. Herb York and Hugh Bradner were at work on major instrumentation for the test.

There was, however, still opposition to the "super," passive and overt. The great Einstein issued statements and pamphlets against the program, which he admitted would likely be successful. The moral issues were still debated on the radio; the lack of need for other than fission bombs was argued in journals. The powerful influence of the GAC seemed negative. At Los Alamos itself there was dissension; the impatient Teller disagreed with Bradbury on priorities and methods. If Teller thought the director too conservative, Bradbury found the excitable, emotional, and brilliant theoretician difficult. Teller had twice left Los Alamos after disagreements. Only his determination to unravel the puzzle of fusion had caused him to return, for only at Los Alamos were there facilities to carry out an integrated fusion program. But he remained unhappy there. Obviously Bradbury, as director, had to determine the programs. He was also responsible for furthering A-bomb development—a far more certain objective than any fusion possibilities at the time. The recent tests were indicative of how well and far Los Alamos had carried its fission program.

In any event, the disagreement on administration of the thermonuclear program at Los Alamos prompted Teller's effort to have another weapons laboratory established, with development of the "super," or hydrogen bomb its prime mission. Ernest understood that the Air Force was interested to the extent of holding preliminary discussions for such a laboratory at Chicago. The AEC—at least Chairman Dean—thought it better to build up Los Alamos to explore further the new approach to fusion that had given hope to Teller's group; duplicaion of Los Alamos facilities would be tremendously expensive. The GAC advised against any second laboratory on the grounds that scientific personnel of the proper caliber could not be recruited without depriving Los Alamos, that it would undermine confidence in Los Alamos people, and could do nothing that could not be done better at the New Mexico laboratory. Teller was convinced that a second laboratory would benefit Los Alamos; healthy competition would provide the spur that a secrecy-shrouded—and therefore uncriticized—enterprise needed to remain healthy. As for the GAC, its record of support for any strong fusion program was negative: its hope that a thermonuclear bomb could not be developed had been expressed; its opposition on several grounds, prior to the President's decision, was well known. And it was Teller's opinion —and he had company, including Ernest—that, if the letter of the President's directive had been followed, the spirit had been lacking.

The tremendous obstacles to successful fusion seemed, to many, impossible to overcome; Ernest remembered that the fission bomb had also seemed impossible, and that cooperative effort had surmounted every hindrance. As for moral objections—it would be immoral for science to refuse further understanding of natural forces on any grounds. Who could tell what benefits might come from fusion? Many more applications than that of weaponry were conceivable. If, at Operation Greenhouse, the newly developed fission bomb succeeded in triggering fusion, it would be a strange scientist who could resist further exploration of so exciting a problem, Ernest thought.

He left for Greenhouse May 1 by way of Honolulu, where he was a guest of Admiral John E. Gingrich, a fine host. He reciprocated with a dinner for the admiral and several others at the Royal Hawaiian Hotel the night before departure for Eniwetok, a ten-hour flight from Honolulu. Eniwetok had much the atmosphere of a South Seas resort. A fine officers' club on the beach provided relaxation for Congressmen and visitors. The tropical sea invited swimmers and scuba divers. There were no phones to interrupt conversations with interesting and important men: Congressmen, generals, admirals, and scientists. AEC chairman Gordon Dean was there, and Robert LeBaron. York and Bradner, with the several dozen from the Rad Lab, were busy on the "shot" island, setting up their diagnostic apparatus, when Ernest arrived. There was an open-air movie that night at which the audience was drenched in a sudden unannounced storm. There was concern reminiscent of Trinity, lest the weather delay the test. Teller, who had sounded confident at the briefing, confided his worries to Ernest—who bet him five dollars that the test would be successful. Teller knew that customarily Ernest never wagered or gambled with money. Herb York, who had been soaked

Ernest Lawrence, Glenn Seaborg, and Robert Oppenheimer at a control panel during the conversion of the 184-inch cyclotron magnet from its wartime use as a mass spectrograph to its original purpose as a cyclotron. *(Lawrence Radiation Laboratory)*

E.O.L. on a hill above the 184-inch cyclotron building, University of California, Berkeley. *(Photo by Richard F. Hoorn, Pacific Gas and Electric Company)*

Lawrence and the staff shown with the 184-inch magnet. (*Lawrence Radiation Laboratory*)

Former President Herbert Hoover invited Ernest Lawrence to lunch with General Eisenhower during the Bohemian Grove Encampment, July 23, 1950. *(Photo by Fred G. Clark)*

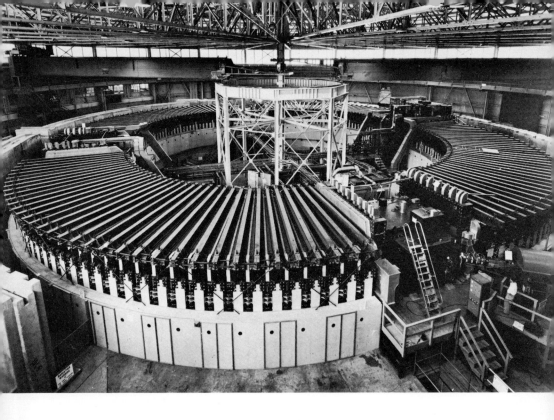

(*Above*) The Bevatron, in which protons may be accelerated to energies of over six billion electron volts. The circular magnet enclosing the acceleration chamber weighs 9,700 tons, the copper coils 347 tons. Particles start the orbit at ten million volts supplied by a linear accelerator, part of which is visible in lower right foreground. (*Below*) *Left to right:* Lady Cockcroft, The Svedberg, Molly Lawrence, Sir John Cockcroft at the Nobel Institute, Stockholm, Sweden, 1951. (*Lawrence Radiation Laboratory*)

Dr. Otto Hahn *(left),* Ernest O. Lawrence, and Donald Cooksey photographed at Point Lobos, California, by Dr. Hanno Hahn in November, 1955.

In May, 1956, members of a University of California Regents' committee accompanied Ernest Lawrence to the Pacific Proving Grounds to witness a hydrogen fusion test. Left to right are University Vice-President James H. Corley; Livermore physicist Harry Keller; Regents Gerald Hagar and Victor R. Hansen; physicists William McMaster and Gerald Johnson, in front of Brigadier General A. D. Starbird; Ernest Lawrence, Carl Haussman, Charles Blue; Livermore Director Herbert York; and Regent Earl J. Fenston. (The man to General Starbird's right is not identified.) *(Photos: Lawrence Radiation Laboratory)*

(Above) From left: Commissioner Lewis L. Strauss; Ernest O. Lawrence; James R. Killian, chairman of the President's Scientific Advisory Committee; and Warren C. Johnson, chairman of the General Advisory Committee, at the presentation of the Fermi Award to Professor Lawrence, October 29, 1957. *(Lawrence Radiation Laboratory) (Below)* Charles A. Thomas congratulates Ernest Lawrence in the presence of Lieutenant General Garrison H. Davidson after the presentation of the Sylvanus Thayer Award at West Point, March 21, 1958. *(Courtesy of Mrs. Ernest Lawrence)*

The Lawrence children in 1958. *From left:* Eric, Mary, Margaret, and Robert behind Barbara and Susan. *(Photo by George Kagawa, Lawrence Radiation Laboratory)*

making last-minute adjustments on the shot tower with its clumsy refrigeration machinery for keeping the tritium and deuterium extremely cold, appeared confident—not only about successful fusion but also that the instrumentation, for which the Berkeley group was responsible, could transmit data to safety in the instant of its annihilation—in fire equivalent to that of sun and stars.

The weather cleared. Chairs had been placed on the beach when observers assembled at the club near dawn. Coffee and sandwiches were served, and dark glasses distributed. The large lagoon was calm; the direction of the "shot" island was indicated—few of the hundreds of small islands of the atoll were visible. Except for the noise of conversation, it was as peaceful as any South Sea island of romance until the departure of observation planes brought the roar of civilization, and the countdown encouraged thoughts of hope, expectancy, or despair for the future. At zero a tremendous ball of fire obliterated thought and vision. A great wave of heat swept over the observers, ahead of the tremendous blast. An expanding cloud appeared to move toward them before it drifted off. It must have been successful; fusion must have been accomplished in such an explosion—if it hadn't, indeed, caused most of it. It was shortly declared an unqualified success, but Ernest knew there were answers not included in the broadcast announcement. When Teller slipped a five-dollar bill into his hand, Ernest knew those answers were affirmative. York's smiling countenance was further assurance. Actually, he learned later, the fusion caused by the fractional fission explosion was far in excess of what had been expected—and the work of the Rad Lab was outstanding in recording the details.

Ernest left the Pacific Proving Ground in an Air Force plane, bound for Japan with, among others, Admiral Arleigh Burke, with whom he had become well enough acquainted to be on a first-name basis. Association of but a few days revealed their common interests in the nation's welfare. Apparently the admiral enjoyed the trip as much as Ernest, for he wrote ten days later: "You made several days most pleasant—and in addition to that I enjoyed meeting you. My only view of Japan will be colored by a dim drizzle offset by your cheerful enthusiasm."

The real purpose of Ernest's Japanese visit was to encourage Japanese physicists, discouraged by loss of their cyclotrons—and loss of face, since nuclear physics was understandably unpopular in Japan. He told the small group at the Nishina laboratory of the fine work of Sagane, and of the esteem in which Yukawa was held in the United States and in the world, as the award of the Nobel Prize testified. He encouraged the establishment of a Japanese Institute of Nuclear Physics and promised to do what he could to gain consent from occupation authorities for the construction of a new cyclotron. He also promised what technical help he and his laboratory might provide. He was a guest at the famous Imperial Hotel, under the auspices of the Occupation, and was taken to the Kabuki theater. He was entertained by geisha. At American headquarters, still agog over the removal of General MacArthur only a month before, he registered his concern for Japanese physicists and requested that permission and help be given to rebuild their cyclotrons. Upon his return to Berkeley, after another couple of days in Honolulu, he wrote letters to Washington in the same interest and later personally pleaded in Washington for Japanese cyclotrons.

He was in Berkeley less than a month before he, Molly, and the Cookseys left for New York and a planned vacation in England and Scandinavia, including a cruise to the North Cape at the top of Norway during the long summer days. Ernest had been invited to the five hundredth anniversary celebration of the University of Glasgow, to be one of a very distinguished company to receive honorary degrees, in his case doctor of laws, during the three-day ceremony. In New York, Don was stricken with influenza and, as he had had virus pneumonia less than a year before, thought it best to wait there for recovery. He and Milicent would join the Lawrences as soon as he was well. Molly and Ernest enplaned for London June 16, and, on the eighteenth, boarded the Royal Scot Express for the journey from London to Scotland. They were met in Glasgow by Professor William J. Duncan of the university faculty, and Mrs. Duncan, whose guests they were for the three days; all honored guests were quartered with academic people. They were soon welcomed by Sam Curran, also of the faculty, who had been at the Rad Lab in 1944–45. There were many other visitors whom they knew. Molly, who had loved academic ceremonial from childhood, when from the gallery she had watched her father present candidates at Yale, considered the Glasgow ceremonies the most exciting and impressive she had seen. She even felt at home in the Duncan household; with their four daughters, there were reminders of Whitney Avenue days in New Haven. There was an impressive commemoration service in the cathedral; equally impressive was the presentation of representatives from universities all over the world—President Sproul was there from the University of California.

The principal oration was delivered by the Right Honorable Lord MacMillan, in an ancient hall; to Molly, its paneled walls teemed with history. The floor was filled with people in the academic dress of many universities and colleges; the scarlet of the Glasgow robes looked particularly rich from the gallery where she was seated with wives of famous guests. On the platform, facing the audience, were the Glasgow faculty and those to be honored with degrees, among whom, besides Ernest, were British Prime Minister Clement Attlee, President Harold W.

Dodds of Princeton, Niels Bohr, representing the Royal Danish Academy, Sir John Cockcroft, José Ortega y Gasset of Spain, Freya Stark—all the names were notable. Molly "thoroughly enjoyed it, the dark old hall, and all the scarlet robes. The names of the people that were read off were pretty impressive, too, and that degree really meant a lot to Ernest."

They returned to London after the ceremonies, where they were to have a chauffeured Cook's Tour car for their stay, but Paramount Pictures representative James Perkins also met the train and persuaded them to accept a company car and driver. Perkins' wife Isabella, a Berkeley girl, was a member of a fine tennis club right in London, where they watched tournament games, and Isabella and Ernest played. They were driven to Oxford to be entertained at the Clarendon Laboratory, and they lunched at the home of Franz Simon, who showed off his Balliol College. It was their first overseas trip together, and the first abroad for either since the war, and it was all fun.

The M/S *Stella Polaris* crossed the North Sea to Bergen and up the rugged, fjord-cut Norwegian coast to the North Cape, where there was no night, but a continually visible sun circling the horizon. There was a good deal of rain during the two-week cruise, and cold weather beyond the Arctic Circle, but it was spectacularly beautiful all the way. The clouds broke completely when they went ashore at Trondheim, to visit the fine cathedral, parts of which dated from the eleventh century, and where Norwegian sovereigns are crowned. They broke their sight-seeing several times that afternoon to telephone to see how the children were faring at home with Dixie, helped by the young wife of a medical student. In the far north, they visited a Lapp encampment with many mangy reindeer. Even in the high-walled fjords, there was no real night. In one of them they sailed very close to a glacier. Though little given to consideration of ancestry and the past, Ernest wondered aloud to Molly about this rugged land of his forebears. At the university in Bergen, where physicist Bjørn Trumpy was the rector, they dined on ptarmigan, in a restaurant reached by a funicular railway up the steep slope of the fjord.

The two-day drive across Norway from Bergen to Oslo by private, chauffeured car was an experience in itself, the narrow, winding road carved into and through cliffs. Molly thought that passing busses must crowd them off to tumble down steep slopes. In Oslo, Ernest seriously thought of attempting to visit Telemark, where there were remote relatives, after a man had come to the hotel to talk about his ancestors. The press was much interested in the famous atomic scientist whose four grandparents had been born in Norway. But there was insufficient time to seek out ancestral valleys, as John and their father had done a year or two before; there were physicists to visit, Gunnar Randers and Odd Dahl, one-time co-workers with Tuve, and a reactor under construction to look at. Also, the Cookseys caught up with them in Oslo, and the four left by chauffered car on a beautiful summer morning for Fjällbacka on the west coast of Sweden, where Professor The Svedberg met them on the shore and took them to his charming island summer home, where his family made them welcome for an afternoon and night. Physicist Svedberg promised to be in Uppsala to greet them at the university there in a few days.

It was fine weather on the drive through beautiful Sweden for two more days; after irreparable car trouble they finally clanked into Stockholm, where the driver could not find the Grand Hotel for some time. Professor Manne Siegbahn and his son Kai had come from their summer residence to welcome them. The cyclotron in the fine laboratory at the Nobel Institute had to be inspected, since designs and help for it had come from Berkeley. A luncheon, with skoals to the honored guests, was followed by a lovely afternoon in the Siegbahn garden. After a cocktail party at the American Consulate, they returned to the Siegbahns' for a gay dinner and more skoals. Never were things pertaining to the atom so toasted within a half day! "You must return again for the Nobel ceremonies," urged Siegbahn, and to Molly's great surprise Ernest seemed serious when he replied, "Maybe we will," though it would mean a return in a few months. Ernest and Don were driven in a hired car next morning to Uppsala, where they were met by Svedberg and several of the distinguished faculty and their wives, who had interrupted their vacations to honor Ernest and Molly at a reception and luncheon. Molly and Milicent, as unaware of the planned event as their husbands, had stayed in Stockholm to see the palace, and the hall where the Nobel award dinners were given!

They flew to London for another few days, were met again by Jim and Isabella Perkins, ran into the LeBarons and Keith Glennans at the Mayfair Hotel, and had a gay impromptu party. The next night they drove to Newberry for dinner with the T. E. Allibones (he had been with Oliphant's group at Berkeley during the war) at the Chequers Hotel, at which another guest was Sir Alexander Fleming, the discoverer of penicillin. At Harwell they saw the national atomic laboratories and spent the night with the Cockcrofts, returning to London next day by way of Birmingham. They arrived on the twentieth in New York, where Molly and the Cookseys shortly left for Berkeley. Ernest stayed a few days in the East for consultant duties, meetings with AEC people in Washington, and conferences in New York with Paramount officials, in which he was joined by Rowan Gaither.

Ernest spent only a couple of weekends at Balboa that summer, despite good intentions and promises, and forfeited on an agreement, signed with Margaret and Mary, that he would spend two complete weeks there or give each of them a cashmere sweater. He was at Diablo most of his free time during August, where he now employed a machinist and a technician; it had become obvious that television design and manufacturing were more than a spare-time operation. Neither he nor his consultants, all lab people, had realized the gap between a laboratory mock-up and production. Gaither made no pretense of production knowledge.

Another exciting period ensued, during which Ernest—with what Gow calls "a real stroke of genius or flash of insight"—proposed the "post deflection focusing." Everyone associated with the enterprise considered this great. "There were slight traces of this idea," Gow said, "just traces, in the notebook four months back. Then all of a sudden there it was, and he just wrote it all—the equations and solutions. He called Jimmy Vale that afternoon and they made it up; in forty-eight hours they had a color picture. Within a few more days the thing operated so well you could say, 'Look how this works!' It changed the whole picture. Paramount and everybody took it very seriously, and Ernest, typically, estimated that it would cost practically nothing . . . ."

George Badger, one of the permanent technicians, packed up the new tube and chassis for transportation to New York—it happened to be September 4, 1951, when transcontinental TV was inaugurated with President Truman's San Francisco address on the Japanese Peace Treaty. When the treaty was signed four days later, by the United States and forty-eight other nations, Ernest was in New York with Vale, technicians Badger, Cooke from Diablo, and the new model. It was an odd-looking laboratory device, its vacuum sustained by continuous pumping, but the picture on the glass plate was good, the color and brightness were excellent. Slight defects could be attributed to the fact that it was practically homemade. Paramount executives were delighted; they returned again and again to look at it; they held a public showing for physicists and engineers. The Diablo crew were kept in New York for three weeks instead of a planned few days. Ernest, convinced that minor flaws could easily be worked out, exuded infectious enthusiasm. Paramount put up more money. A production plant was leased in East Oakland, a production manager, Howard Patterson, who had been associated with RCA, and others were sent west. Gaither hired Crawford Cooley, the son of a law partner, as business manager, and Morgan Gunst left his job with the Rad Lab administration to help run the new Chromatron West Coast Development Laboratory on Thirty-seventh Street in Oakland.

Diablo was seldom visited, its garage-machine shop emptied for the Oakland Laboratory—which was just as well; Diablo neighbors had begun to complain. It also required much less driving time for Ernest.

He had to make periodic trips to Livermore, where the huge Mark I accelerator was nearing completion. Perhaps it would never be useful for anything but experiment; and the MTA production plant in Missouri would never be necessary. The huge Savannah reactors should ultimately be able to supply sufficient tritium for a "super" program, or plutonium, if fission bombs were to be relied upon—fission bombs requiring much less material than had been thought necessary when concern over shortages had made Mark I a great hope. Uranium ore had been discovered in increasing abundance; hopefully the country would be self-sufficient in natural ore. Whatever his hopes for the huge accelerator, he would forego them gladly if there were sufficient materials otherwise.

Actually there were increasing grounds for optimism, however slow the progress. A contract had been let for a reactor powered submarine. There were new people on both the AEC and GAC; commissioner Thomas E. Murray was a pro-"super" man, and Willard Libby of the GAC favored it. Though majorities on both bodies were still opposed to a second weapons laboratory, Chairman Dean discussed it with Ernest at a Nevada test and suggested the possibility of establishing it at the Livermore facility. In November a Livermore weapons laboratory was considered at a Joint Congressional Committee meeting as well as by the AEC. Ernest thought the beneficial results of industrial laboratory competition might well be repeated in two weapons laboratories but was not particularly anxious that it be under Rad Lab supervision—as Gordon Dean apparently was. The new commissioners and scientific advisers also seemed aware of the importance of reactors.

Ernest had found interest in reactors in England and Scandinavia. F. Perrin, the French High Commissioner for atomic energy, had been enthusiastic about them at Saclay, the French atomic energy complex, when he visited the Rad Lab late in September, the day Norwegian physicists Gunnar Randers and Odd Dahl concluded a three-day visit. Oliphant and his wife visited from Australia; there was no doubt where he stood. And earlier in the year Frank Spedding of Ames, Iowa, who had played a vital role in the Manhattan Project, had visited both the Lab and Livermore. Tom Johnson would soon become the new AEC director of research—he had phoned to ask Ernest's advice before acceptance. Tom was to phone for advice many times in the future, particularly on questions relating to university programs.

On November 15, it was announced that Ed McMillan and Glenn Seaborg had won the 1951 Nobel Prize in chemistry. As proud as though they were his sons, Ernest decided that he would accept the invitation to attend the ceremonies he had missed in 1939. Molly had no compunction about going to Stockholm this year, but when the young woman who had helped Dixie while they were away during the summer left, she seemed unable to find a replacement. For the first time, Ernest concerned himself with a domestic problem of this nature and asked Bill Bigelow, of the Rad Lab personnel office, to find them a maid. Bennie Lincoln, a trim and attractive colored woman with an eighteen-year-old son of her own, was soon hired, and Ernest and Molly left San Francisco on a night plane for New York on the twenty-third, arriving on November 25 in London, where the Perkinses again saw that they were well cared for until the twenty-eighth when they went to Oslo for the dedication of the Kjeller pile, then to Copenhagen for a day and a night as guests of the Bohrs at Carlsberg Castle, the mansion that had been given to the state by the brewery family to be the lifetime residence of Denmark's most outstanding citizen. At the Bohr's dinner party one of the most interesting guests to Molly was Mrs. Eugenie Andersen, United States ambassadress.

In Paris for a few days, they were royally entertained by Paramount executives and their wives, who dined them in the Champs Élysées and on the Left Bank, and, though the weather was generally chilly and overcast, with some rain, showed them much of Paris and took them on an all-day trip to Versailles. On that journey, Molly remembers a charming restaurant in a small town associated with French Impressionist painters, fine examples of whose work were displayed in a nearby small gallery. Ernest was more interested in visiting Saclay and a luncheon with a large group of scientists, which Perrin had assembled. Ernest spent half a day in the Phillips laboratories in Holland with Dr. H. B. G. Casimir. After lunch with the Casimirs, Cornelis Bakker, influential in European efforts for a joint-nation nuclear laboratory, drove them to Amsterdam—a bitterly cold ride for Molly, alone without a lap robe, in the rear seat of the car, while the men in front discussed physics. The Bakkers had a large dinner party for them and took them on a boat tour of the canals and harbor. Cornelis walked with them along a canal and showed them Amsterdam's famous red-light district, where "the girls" sit behind street-level windows. After a short flight to Copenhagen, they went by train-ferry to Malmö and Stockholm, arriving a day ahead of the McMillans, whose unscheduled stop of thirty-some hours in Newfoundland for plane repairs caused a big stir in the Stockholm press. Frequent bulletins were issued on the progress of the McMillan journey to the Nobel ceremonies, as December 10 approached. Ed and Elsie arrived on the evening of the ninth, barely in time for the first big formal dinner.

Pride welled up again as Ernest, on the platform with previous winners, witnessed the King's bestowal of awards on Ed and Glenn—and when Glenn to everyone's delight started his acceptance address in Swedish. Ernest's own illustrated, long-delayed Nobel lecture on the evolution of the cyclotron paid tribute to Sweden's Professor Ising, from whom Wideröe had caught the principle explained in drawings that had inspired Ernest. Elsie, who was amused that Ed was paired with Molly for the main dinner, wrote of the ceremonies to Ed's parents, and hers, ". . . now with two Nobel sons-in-law . . . Ed came all the way to Sweden to take in his sister-in-law, Mrs. Lawrence. . . . I must tell you Moll says the queen will never forget Ernest or myself. As she turned to Ernest he said how much he had enjoyed the bon bons at the table, in fact, he had a pocket full of them to take home to the children. The queen said 'How wonderful, I must remember to have fancy papers on them as we did in the old days so one can take them home. But,' she added, 'I am worried about your pocket.' 'Please don't,' said E.O.L. 'See,' at which he drew out neatly folded menus filled with bon bons. The queen really twinkled. The queen's head lady-in-waiting then joined us and said the queen wished especially to meet the Nobel sisters." Elsie also mentions that Ernest followed the event with a cocktail party for McMillan, Seaborg, Cockcroft, Walton, and their ladies at the Grand Hotel: "a truly fitting ending to another epic evening." Ernest and Molly flew directly home, except for a six-hour wait in London. Not long after their return, they held a reception at their home for Ed and Glenn.

Early in the new year Ernest was notified that he had been elected a foreign member of the Royal Swedish Academy, the august body that selects Nobel Prize winners in physics and chemistry. And in his own country, in December, he had been awarded the William Proctor Prize of the Scientific Research Society of America, which was presented to him by Karl Compton, recipient of the society's first award.

It had been pretty well determined, by December, 1951, that a second weapons laboratory would be established, and that it would not be at Chicago, where Teller was a professor. Members of the GAC were excited over a new idea of Teller's, still classified, which made the H-bomb possibility "sweet," in Oppie's term, even to those who had been most doubtful. The AEC was impressed by the work of young men from the Rad Lab at the Greenhouse tests, and felt that Teller could be happy in a Lawrence operation, if he could not have the laboratory he wanted at Chicago. Also there was the existing facility at Livermore, and, with decreasing need for the Materials Testing program, part of the area and some of its people could be transferred to the Rad Lab for work related to fusion.

On New Year's Day of 1952, at a reception at Carl Helmholz's house, Ernest told York, "Herb, come into my office sometime soon. I'd like to talk to you." York had no idea what Ernest wanted to talk about. He had given Herb advice in fatherly fashion periodically since his wartime arrival in Berkeley at the age of twenty-one, with a new master's degree from Rochester. York had then wondered if it might be wiser to enlist in a special engineering detachment; it would mean a cut in salary, but there were all the future ex-soldier benefits to consider. He had mentioned it to Ernest, who first agreed that it might be a good idea, but had called him into his office the next day. "Herb," he had said, "what you've got to do is to stand on your own two feet, and don't make any plans on getting assistance from anybody else. You can perfectly well arrange all that yourself. You don't need any special welfare. You'll be at Berkeley when the war's over, and don't worry."

York had also, later, been called in and exposed to the Lawrence temper; he had been embarrassed when asked the solution to a problem, to give Ernest an answer not his own, and so had said he had forgotten. "He knew damn well I hadn't. He couldn't stand a lie; he just became furious! His eyes turned red, and his jowls shook, and he said, 'If you don't want to cooperate with me, I don't need you here.'" Another time Ernest said something would not work, that York did not understand a problem. York had acceded to Ernest's argument, but, when he left, decided that he had been right and Ernest wrong. He mentioned to Cooksey that he had given in too easily, because he could not argue with Ernest—he was too overcome with awe. York was shortly summoned to Ernest's office and asked, in very friendly fashion, to explain his point again, after which Ernest agreed that York was correct.

There were other times when Ernest had been annoyed with York, though not again as angry as when he had fibbed. After that he had been greeted by a grinning Segrè. "I understand Lawrence is real mad at you," the professor said. "That's okay, you're fine! He's fired me six times!" "Segrè has an almost idealized version of the Latin temper," York explained. He was so pleased. He regarded it as proof that I was a regular fellow, because he'd already been fired six times."

Again Ernest might remind York that one has to be lucky to be successful, to have enough ability to take advantage of luck, but lucky in being in the right place at the right time. "If I got too big a head, or, exactly the opposite, if I showed some lack of confidence, he'd say, 'Well, you're as good as anybody who lives in this place, or that place.' Sort of fatherly, or a master-student relationship. He often admonished us, if one asked for something, or complained, 'Why, if you say that, people are going to think you're a spoiled brat!' Even to McMillan or Alvarez, and of course to me—to anybody. He never said, "I'll think you're spoiled!' It was always others who would think it. . . . Yet what others thought, or might think, never made him change his mind . . . just decide he wouldn't bother . . . others so hopelessly lost . . . just ignore them . . . and he certainly never sought publicity."

Ernest's interest and concern for his younger people was now somewhat different than in the prewar era. Then he had tried to find jobs for them. After the war there was a demand for scientists, especially for those with nuclear or Rad Lab experience. There were choices now, and he wanted to see his bright young men make the most of them. For example, Roger Hildebrand, who had done a fine piece of work in connection with the MTA project, was offered what sounded like a good job with the Bureau of Standards. When he asked Ernest's advice, it was, "No, that's not good enough for you." Not long after, there was a well-paying industrial offer. Ernest said, "Now you don't want that!" But later when there was a position with the University of Chicago that Roger was excited about, Ernest said, "Now you're talking!" Whenever York worried about his future security, Ernest would say, "Don't worry about it! Don't fuss about that! You don't have to worry about these things."

"Some people thought all this domineering; that the Rad Lab was a one-man show, but in fact it wasn't at all. For instance, a man like Segrè, who would hardly ever be willing to take advice and instruction, could work in the laboratory with Ernest's support. Ernest would make room for a person like that. He knew Segrè wouldn't take any instruction from him, so he never gave him any. He still provided him with all the support he needed. I think Segrè was really a great admirer of Lawrence, felt that he was really doing a great job—but that it would be so much greater if he would do it differently. I always did what Ernest wanted, followed his advice, because as I've said I was very fond of him, and because he had such good insight into these things—and because he had such a load on his shoulders. I've certainly never had reason to regret it. I was always anxious to listen to him when he wanted to talk."

York was quite unprepared for what Ernest wanted to talk about in January, 1952. When he went to his office a few days after the party, Ernest came right to the point. "You think there ought to be a second laboratory? You know, on the hydrogen bomb." York was not sure, had not thought enough about it. He knew that Teller was interested in one. "I was a little naïve myself. I didn't know about all the politicking that was going on in Washington." Ernest explained his idea of a new weapons laboratory. It would be at Livermore, would occupy about a third of the area, which would be fenced off from MTA work. It would start modestly. "Let's start a small group . . . in support of Los Alamos and controlled thermonuclear work. Let's start small and see what happens." Except for Teller and a few he might want to bring with him, it would be staffed at first with some of the young men who had been at Eniwetok and some from the MTA project. After a couple of days of thought and further conversation with Ernest, York flew to Chicago to talk with Teller.

Teller's concept of the new laboratory was as different from Ernest's as it could be—"They were poles apart." He wanted a big laboratory at the start, many notable people put in charge of various groups. He had long lists of plans. York returned to Berkeley and reported to Ernest. "It was frankly clear Ernest couldn't see that for beans. He was only willing to sort of step in slow." York then flew to Washington. He had never met top AEC people, but through a friend arranged for "an accidental or casual date, which was sort of childish, but it worked out. They [the AEC] wanted Teller in a laboratory where he could work and be happy, and they wanted it at Livermore under Lawrence. Well, the problem was to keep Lawrence and Teller apart for a while. If they discussed it together too soon, there just wouldn't be a second laboratory. Their ideas were too far apart."

For several weeks York went back and forth between Chicago and Berkeley, never telling either Teller or Ernest anything that was not true, and never telling either all that the other had said. He would explain to Teller how Ernest wanted to start out gradually, put a ceiling over the project at the beginning, but that he did want a big laboratory eventually. Then he would go back to Berkeley, tell Ernest how anxious Teller was to get going, and that he had some ideas about certain necessary people, what Teller said he had to have, and how he thought they should start. Back and forth he went. Teller finally told York it sounded like a big plan to sabotage his whole idea, that it had to have a much higher floor under it. Ernest insisted that none of that was necessary, "no big names and no big plans." Bright young men would do as well as some of those who had already made names for themselves—and perhaps better. "You get a bunch of bright young fellows and they'll learn it all. Those that have famous names—that's not because they're any better, it's only because they're a little older."

York thinks Ernest achieved more, with initially less important people, much of the time. "There were probably more untried people around Berkeley, and around him, than at any of the other places." When York had arrived at the Rad Lab during the war effort, Ernest's principal associates had all been sent to help other projects. "The senior man . . . was Frank Oppenheimer and he wasn't a senior, but a fresh

Ph.D., as I was a fresh master's degree. . . . He did the whole thing with new people. He judged people himself, as opposed to letting their reputations be the criteria. Very few people can do that."

Ernest was ill that spring and avoided travel as much as he could. He did attend a project meeting at Los Alamos, with the regents of the university present. He discussed with Bradbury the new laboratory and its relationship with Los Alamos and attended a big dinner party given by the Bradburys in Santa Fe in honor of the regents and attended by New Mexico's governor. Though Ernest appeared his usual buoyant self, he was obviously not well; he tired readily and was easily upset. Regent Pauley invited him to Palm Springs for a rest, and, during a necessary trip East in April, Rowan Gaither took him to Florida for a few days on the yacht of Barney Balaban, the president of Paramount.

But when he returned to Berkeley, he was at the TV lab many nights and weekends. At Livermore, experimental operation of the huge Mark I accelerator began in March. Though he had, after the first year, relinquished the chair at weekly MTA meetings of lab, California Research and Development Company, and often AEC people, to Alex Hildebrand, he was briefed on them by Chester Van Atta, and much concerned. Decisions had to be made on the new laboratory. He had invited Teller to Berkeley in February, but there had been no satisfactory conclusion on program and personnel. Teller then still hoped to have the new laboratory in Chicago; Ernest had a verbal agreement with AEC chairman Dean to establish it at Livermore.

Neither of the physicists, in their talks, expected it to replace well-established Los Alamos, which had technical excellence, but which both felt was somewhat handicapped by set ideas and which, in any event, had no room for expansion. Ernest thought another weapons laboratory might supply a new impetus; that since all Los Alamos work was highly classified, there could be very little constructive criticism—a little competition might be helpful. The competition both Teller and Ernest were worried about was Russian; unknown progress there could assume "nightmarish" proportions, in Teller's expression. Ernest certainly had no idea of duplication of Los Alamos. Teller was in Berkeley again in the spring. There had been little change in the ideas of either, and Ernest was a little annoyed. "He just doesn't understand our way of doing things. We'll start our laboratory as we see it, Teller or no," he told York. Teller, certain that Ernest did not intend to establish a proper second laboratory, was ready to walk out on a Livermore laboratory.

York, too, was tired of the argument by that time: "Actually, Chick Hayward . . . at a party . . . came over and said 'You've got to talk with Teller. He's going to leave.' I said, 'I've done nothing but talk for days.' Hayward said, 'But you've got to talk to him.' So I talked with Teller, and he . . . wasn't going to have anything to do with it. I don't remember what it was that persuaded him, but he finally decided to stay."

Teller said, "When the decision was made in favor of Livermore, I came here. I did talk to a number of people in Washington about the need for a second laboratory. This took quite a bit of talking. I kept out of any argument where the location would be. I had nothing to do with its being located here. I think after the need was established Washington made a review of various places, and I think that Ernest, understanding the problem, and his willingness to do whatever was necessary, was decisive."

Ernest called York to his office again. "Do you think you could run this laboratory?" York was flabbergasted. He had never run anything before except a small group, as co-leader of the several dozen Rad Lab men at Eniwetok. It struck him as tremendous audacity—who else would take the major responsibility for a new lab and then ask a thirty-year-old man with no experience to run it? York could only answer that he "didn't know, but would think about it." In a couple of days he told Ernest that he was willing to try it, if Ernest thought it was worthwhile.

"It certainly was a matter of great guts, whatever else it was, and this importantly relates to the question as to how domineering a person he was, or was not. Two points: First of all, he was against having any more organization than was absolutely necessary, and therefore, at Livermore, the shops were to be organized, the engineering departments were to be organized, and so on—but not the scientists. There were to be no titles among the scientists. . . . He contended that there is no higher title than professor in the Radiation Laboratory. 'What's all this problem about being a division head, or a group leader? That's all nonsense! You've got the best title there is, professor of physics at the Radiation Laboratory—what are you fussing about?' That was his first order; the only other, which came later, was that we were not to advertise for people—that was too undignified for the Radiation Laboratory. We could recruit but not advertise. And there was to be no organization. Those were the only two orders he ever gave me."

Contracts for the new laboratory were negotiated with the AEC on July 1, 1952, though there had been a previous letter of intent, and recruiting had begun. A portion of the Livermore area was fenced off for the Rad Lab group, and work began in Berkeley before the Livermore Laboratory was ready for occupancy in September. It was an interesting group that took over, one of which Ernest approved. Gordon Dean later testified, at the Oppenheimer hearing: "Practically all of them came immediately out of school. They were young Ph.D.'s and some not Ph.D.'s. We did not get in that laboratory any of the people, as I recall, that we originally thought of as being available for use on a thermonuclear project, like [F.] Seitz—oh, the names slip me. None of those people went to Berkeley. What they did was under Lawrence's administration with Teller as the idea man, with York as the man who would pick up the ideas, and a whole raft of young imaginative fellows; you had a laboratory working entirely—entirely—on thermonuclear work. . . . I think it worked largely because of Teller getting along very well with Dr. Lawrence. These things are a question of human relations. They got along extremely well."

But by the time the second weapons laboratory at Livermore was negotiated, fatigue and general malaise, accompanied by frequent colonic bleeding—and the insistence of John, backed by John's assistant at Donner, Dr. James Born—had forced Ernest to undergo a complete medical examination. Electrocardiogram diagnosis indicated a normal heart; there was mild hypertension. Tuberculin tests were positive—John remembered that when Ernest, ill with a cold and bad cough, had visited him in Rochester in 1931, it had been discovered that he had had tuberculosis in the past. There were now no active lesions revealed by X ray. Rectal bleeding, which Ernest had thought to be from hemorrhoids, was diagnosed by Dr. Dexter Richards, Jr., in April, as early ulcerative colitis, which was confirmed in May by Dr. Joseph Sadusk, Jr., while Ernest was in Oakland's Peralta Hospital for a diagnostic survey. Dr. Sadusk had suggested that, as no ulcer was discovered, the bleeding might be caused by either bacterial colitis or a possible parasitic dysentery. Ernest was discharged on May 10, with a prescribed schedule of medication, vitamins, and more rest.

Bradbury spent the twelfth at the laboratory. Rich dinners for other visitors were often followed by recurrences of the bleeding. Suggested rest and relaxation periods were easily postponed. There was a less gala twentieth wedding anniversary than he had planned for Molly, but she received his usual remembrance of red roses on May 14. There was excitement at Livermore on the nineteenth when the Mark I produced a beam. Many other evenings were spent at the Oakland TV plant. The Rad Lab itself was a never-ending source of interest and concern; he still took personal interest in every problem. "His reactions to individual experiments had much to do with our interest," Roger Hildebrand remembers of the years following the war.

John finally persuaded Ernest, with Sadusk's blessing, to consult Dr. Albert Snell of Palo Alto, whom he considered among the best specialists in the country for treatment of little-understood colitis. Snell advised reduction of activities and pressures, restricted diet, and no alcohol! For the rest of the summer there was little recurrence of the trouble—and a tendency to forget Snell's recommendations. The Diablo place was sold, but the Oakland TV operation—now with nearly a hundred employees —was always a temptation, and surely there was no harm in going there for a look around in the evening! There were elaborate dinners, including one at the Pacific Union Club for Gordon Dean and Bob LeBaron, given by Gwin Follis of Standard Oil. Ernest introduced Dean at a Lakeside Talk at the Grove encampment. Cornelis Bakker returned the Lawrence visit to Holland and was entertained, including a day and a night at Yosemite. Neylan had a dinner for Baruch, who said of Ernest, "He is the most level-headed of scientists." There was a small celebration for Donner Pavilion, the new ten-bed investigation hospital of Donner Laboratory. A protracted Eastern trip involved much activity and entertainment in Washington and New York. On September 11, in Chicago, Ernest was presented with the Faraday Medal of the Institute of Electrical Engineers of London, by Sir John Hacking, at the centennial of the American Institute of Electrical Engineers. Colonic trouble flared again before the trip was over.

Though there was much to do in Berkeley after his absence, he was sure he could adhere to the prescribed regimen of diet and rest—more or less. But there were always factors over which he had no control. The disturbing illness of the popular Rad Labber William Twitchell upset him; no one seemed quite certain of the cause or nature of the malady that confined him to a hospital. The fusion group had moved to Livermore in September and was doing all right, but MTA presented problems; it seemed evident that there would be no full-scale production plant in Missouri, now that sufficient native uranium was available, and tritium and plutonium would be coming from the Savannah reactors. There was criticism of the entire project as an unnecessary boondoggle; fine hindsight, but what if ores had not been discovered in the nation? Opposition to Operation Ivy, the first thermonuclear weapon test in the South Pacific, scheduled for November 1, was distressing. Oppie, whose term on the GAC had expired in June, thought it "utterly impractical to postpone the test but" that "we nevertheless owed it to the Secretary of State [to tell him] what we thought was involved in holding it at that time. . . . We thought they [the Russians] would get a lot of information out of it." Bush thought it improper to hold the test just prior to a presidential election. Some of the commissioners agreed. President Truman finally overruled all objections: ". . . political considerations should never be tolerated in the nation's atomic program."

Ernest did not attend this test of the hydrogen bomb that left, in place of Elugelab Isle, a great crater beneath the sea, demonstrating beyond all expectation the complete effectiveness of the weapon. Ernest was in Balboa, trying to recover from recurrences of his ailment. He was sure they were caused less by entertainment and excitement than by pressures and concern, whether for a very sick colleague from his laboratory, or the nation's welfare. He could not escape those, wherever he went. Molly joined him on the fifth, to help keep him pacified and away from laboratories, TV plant, and long-distance phone calls. He asked Cooksey and Reynolds on the sixth to represent him at forthcoming Los Alamos conferences and postponed consultant meetings in the East. He had been specially invited to Kodak president Albert Chapman's home in Rochester and regretted making excuses, particularly since the last time in Rochester he had begged off from one dinner with his good friend Chapman to go to the home of assistant director of research John Leermakers for *kumla*—sort of a Norwegian dumpling he had liked since boyhood—prepared so well by Mrs. Leermakers. Rochester visits were always fun, whether at the Chapmans', research head Cyril Staud's, or with any of the numerous ex-associates from Oak Ridge days who were still with the Eastman company.

In Schenectady, too, after consultations, there was always entertainment and friendship at G.E. vice-president Guy Suits's home—where Ernest and Suits once spent hours with aboriginal boomerangs and then designed better ones—and where there was sailing on the lake. Or with Coolidge and other G.E. scientists he had known and liked for so long. It made him restless just to think about it—and he found it hard to accept the fact that he was not up to it even for a few weeks.

He kept an appointment with Juan Trippe, president of Pan American Airways, and Yale trustee, but begged off flying with him in his personal plane to Washington and New Haven. He set out by train, on December 6, for New York, from where he planned to go to Oak Ridge for a laboratory directors' meeting, but he was so tired when he arrived that he called Cooksey from the Loomis apartment and asked him to take Thornton to the Oak Ridge meeting in his stead. Cooksey would then go to Miami Beach and meet Ernest at the Roney Plaza.

Ernest limited a Washington stopover to a night and a morning before continuing by train to Florida. He felt well enough the day after arrival in Miami Beach to rent a car and drove with Cooksey to Key West and back. It was Don who was in bed for the next two days with a bad cold. They dined with Barney Balaban, and spent the day and night of the eighteenth on his yacht, cruising up the Inland Passage to Palm Beach, where they entrained for New York on the twentieth.

They arrived in New York Sunday evening and from the Loomis apartment went to call on Commissioner Thomas Murray. They flew from New York on the twenty-third, arriving in San Francisco late that evening.

Christmas at the Lawrences was somewhat marred by the illness of Carl, now practically blind, but cheerful. Ernest's condition appeared to have improved; there was still some evidence of colitis, but, as he informed his father-in-law, no actual ulcer had been found. This moved G.B. to quip on a Christmas message: "I hope your play of Hamlet, with Hamlet left out, is on the mend. . . . Your hardest job will be to learn to relax."

CHAPTER XVII

A Sort of Grandfather

[1953-1954]

D r. Blumer was right; it was more difficult for Ernest to relax than to wrestle with a major problem. Responsibilities as head of laboratories involved in education, pure research and the technical application of research for purposes of war and peace were concrete; these concerns delegated to him—or patriotically assumed as a citizen with particular knowledge and skill—had definite ends. Relaxation seemed negative, passive—it was hard to remember that rest is necessary to revitalize tired organs. Thus, he was unable, in Berkeley, to confine himself to a normal workweek, let alone one broken by at least half a day's rest, as doctors recommended. Even elsewhere he felt deeply the tangible responsibilities of a specially informed patriot. He was intensely patriotic, perhaps narrowly so in that he recognized no shades, but only black or white.

Increasingly frequent requests for consultation came from Congressmen, the State and Defense departments, and ranking officers of the individual services. It was still the director, as much as his laboratory and its marvelous and powerful machines, who attracted important visitors to Charter Hill. "Ernest was probably the busiest man in the country" Gow thought. "It was fantastic! There were Very Important People re defense matters, VIP's re basic science, VIP's re color TV, and VIP's re God knows what else, in and out of his office in an absolutely steady stream. The director's office was a mad house. . . . If I had to see Ernest, I'd desperately urge the matter with Eleanor about nine in the morning. She'd think she could work me in around four-thirty—for about five minutes. . . . He was having this bowel trouble, too."

Even at Balboa, where during the past fall he had spent the longest unbroken period he had ever stayed there, it had been a rare day when he had not been on the telephone to Berkeley, Washington, or New York. Painting, boating, and swimming failed to detract from his concerns for long. He often felt—and Molly at times concurred—that "champing at the bit" to be back in action was harder on his health than laboratory, office, and Oakland TV plant. He even wondered about problems of which he might be unaware because of absence from his desk.

John was convinced that only complete withdrawal from all concerns for a month or two would rid Ernest of his trouble, whether it actually was preulcerative colitis or came from some other cause. It was obvious that he could not be kept quiet for a sufficient period at Balboa, a Florida beach, or, even if he would go, at any resort abroad where he could use a telephone. He flatly rejected the suggestion of a cruise ship—too much socializing. How to get Ernest to relax seems to have been discussed in New York and Washington, as in Berkeley. Close associates were aware that, for all his seeming vitality and cheerful aspect, he was under constant and terrific pressure. That Ernest Lawrence should cancel appointments for reasons of health, as he had at the end of the year, was so startling as to be noteworthy to Easterners, accustomed to having him breeze in radiating vitality. Evidences of fatigue, even of aging, were increasingly hard to conceal; his hair had grayed, his eyes and face at times belied the boyish enthusiasm he still displayed. He became increasingly irritable over delays, minor obstacles, and failures to comprehend, which would have bothered him little in past years. At Livermore he had even slapped a group leader who had protested his instructions. The man had been right and had reported to California Research and Development official J. Q. Cope and given notice of quitting. Alex Hildebrand had been elected to explain the matter to Ernest. Much ashamed of his action, Ernest asked Hildebrand to assemble everyone who had been present at the incident, to witness his apology to the wronged man. His ailment flared up at this time, perhaps before the event.

It was Gwin Follis who offered a solution to the problem of enforced rest, away from all concerns; an extended trip with Molly on big Standard Oil tankers. These ships had comfortable accommodations. Ernest and Molly, as passengers, could be alone as much as desired, and free of telephones for two-week periods, as they circled the globe. The prospect appealed to Ernest, but he doubted the propriety of acceptance, considering his association with the company's subsidiary at Livermore. He asked Neylan's opinion.

"Despite taking it easy for some time before Christmas, I have not fully recovered from the attack of ulcerative colitis of last spring. John, on whom I depend for medical advice, feels I should get away from the lab . . . should make possible a complete healing of the colon and a hundred percent recovery. . . . Now is the time to do it."

Neylan was pleased. "Endorse the idea just one thousand percent. . . . Need not suggest what [MTA] project meant to security of the country but three essential points stand out. One, they [Standard Oil] undertook a very great responsibility, largely on the basis of your being the guiding scientist; two, they undertook it without profit or hope of financial reward; three, your continuing relationship is a very substantial element in the successful discharge of their commitment and responsibility. . . . I not only see no basic criticism but on the contrary am delighted Follis able [to get you away for essential rest]. I gladly assume full responsibility as the Chairman of the Atomic Projects Committee [of the regents] and as your personal friend in urging [that nothing interfere with the trip]."

Once Ernest had agreed to it, arrangements were made for them to take passage on a tanker expected to sail from its New Jersey port on January 24, 1953. The hospitalization of his father during the first week of the year caused temporary indecision, but Carl improved and was released to Gunda's care, so this ceased to be an obstacle. Ernest's own condition was quiescent enough at a January 7 examination for doctors to report it the "most nearly normal . . . seen to date. Some minor ulceration—still microscopic blood." That there might be a physician available on the journey, Dr. John Sherrick, who had delivered five of the Lawrence children, was invited to accompany them. And at the last possible moment, Margaret was included in the party.

Molly disapproved of her removal from school, but Ernest, concerned over her interest in a handsome young man—whom he had ordered from the house when he found them roughhousing—thought it unwise to leave her without a parent, after waiting up for her until three one morning. On that occasion, when he discovered that she had, supposedly, gone to a movie—with Molly's consent—he felt angry and betrayed. Anger became worry when she had not returned by one, then two A.M. Molly, who had tried to placate his anger with assurances that Margaret could take care of herself, was also worried by that time—there might have been an automobile accident. Both met Margaret as she entered her room from the fire escape! That evening, as though nothing had been amiss so early in the day, and, as though on the spur of the moment, he cordially asked Margaret to join them on the trip. Margaret, trying to keep a straight face, was happy to accept; she had no more interest in the handsome young man other than to display him before girl friends.

That her father was decidedly old-fashioned about his daughters, particularly where males were concerned, they had long known. On several occasions, he had "raised the roof," even with fourteen-year-old Mary, who reacted to discipline or scolding with defiance. Margaret, somewhat in awe of her father, and anxious not to worry him, usually avoided argument—and tried to circumvent confrontations. Molly had warned him of this possibility after a stormy session one Sunday afternoon when he had discovered Margaret and a boy in bathing suits innocently stretched out in the sun on a blanket on the lawn below the deck. "What's wrong with it?" Molly had asked. "Would you rather they would go elsewhere, than here in the open?" But the standards of Pastor Rasmussen and Canton were set; women, like so much else, were good or bad; there were no degrees of one or the other, at least in the eyes of observers. Their reputations had to be guarded; he could best see to that if Margie were with them. He was as confident as Molly that Dixie, with Bennie Lincoln's help, could properly supervise and care for the younger children and feed Eric, now at the university.

He sold his Oldsmobile and ordered a Cadillac convertible—light "pastoral" blue at the children's insistence—at cost through the Yosemite company—to be delivered upon his return. He went East a week before the others, to attend to business, and for a final check by Dr. Dana Atchley in New York. Molly, Margaret, and Dr. Sherrick joined him on January 23, and they sailed from Barber, New Jersey, the next day, on the *Paul Pigott,* of Liberian registry, bound for the Near East—all four "signed on" as members of the crew, the customary practice with ships not licensed to carry passengers. Ernest was amused to be listed as ship's doctor, while Dr. Sherrick was purser, and Molly and Margaret, stewardesses.

Their accommodations, filled with flowers and bon voyage gifts, were anything but crew's quarters. In fact, as Ernest wrote his parents, there was "truly luxurious comfort." He and Molly not only had a large bedroom and bath, but a large, well-furnished living room, including a radio-phonograph capable of reception from Europe, Asia, and America. Margie and Sherrick each had a bedroom and private bath. A good Italian cook offered to prepare anything Italian or American they wished to eat.

Departure with such comfort held promise for a pleasant journey, but the first two days at sea were anything but promising or pleasant. Rough seas and wind rolled and pitched the ship; all were sick, Ernest less so than the others. Bad weather was encountered only those first two days—after which everyone else relaxed and put on weight during the two-week voyage. They dined each night with the officers, all Italians, in their dining room. Ernest usually had steak "prepared just as I like it" and only pureed vegetables; Sherrick was supposed to see to that. There were days when he had steak twice, "to make up for what I won't be overeating in Arabia and India." Molly and Margie were more venturesome and enjoyed the fine Italian preparations that were offered. They had cocktails every afternoon at five, often with the captain as their guest.

Captain Cattarinich was an intelligent, largely self-educated man with a genuine interest in physics, who plied Ernest with questions in understandable English—Ernest later sent appropriate physics books to him. The captain permitted his guests the freedom of the bridge, and Ernest thoroughly investigated the engine room. Otherwise Ernest did a good deal of reading and painting; a copy of a picture in his cabin and a remembered Palm Springs desert scene, Molly thought worth preserving. He had fun with the shortwave radio and with his many cameras, both Eric's and John's 16 mm. movie cameras, a 35 mm. Nikon, a polaroid, and a stereorealist camera which Barney Balaban had given him on departure; Molly enjoyed the longest complete rest from household duties and children (for whom she was homesick) she had had.

The ship anchored at Sidon, Lebanon, some time after midnight on February 7. Representatives of the Arabian Pipeline Company were on board to meet them at breakfast, after which the "ship's doctor, purser and two stewardesses" were paid off with a dollar apiece, taken ashore, and driven up the coast to Beirut. It was difficult to sift legend from fact in the ancient city, which they eagerly "saw on foot," after their days of shipboard confinement. They were driven over the Lebanese mountains next morning to more ancient Damascus, in Syria. The road was slippery with snow in high places, and, though the distance was less than sixty miles, it seemed twice that long. There was not time enough in Damascus for Molly; she had to fight the disinterest of the men for enough of it to watch the gold- and silversmiths, and made them wait at the weavers' while she bargained for beautiful brocades. Ernest, in a hurry as usual, never agreed with her that schedules throughout the trip were often too tight, or that they attempted to cram too much into too little time. They walked through old Damascus, said with some authority—it is mentioned with Abraham in Biblical Genesis—to be the oldest still-inhabited city of the world, and through "the street called Straight"; all the places with religious history were impressive, "even if you aren't religious." The names recalled to Ernest Canton's Lutheran Sunday school, and Pastor Rasmussen.

The day after their return from Damascus, they were unable to find space on the Arab Airways plane to Jerusalem. A six-seat biplane, with wire struts between the wings, that Molly thought looked like a cockleshell, was chartered for them. She could not believe that they could be taken anywhere in such a "puddle jumper." The pilot, beyond middle

age and very British, had a competent manner, and the one other passenger, a Jordanian Army officer, assured them of safety; he had often
taken the three-hour flight to Jerusalem in the biplane.

The plane took off all right, and Molly recognized the coast as far as
Sidon before altitude was gained to clear the mountains. Soon they were
in brilliant sun above unbroken heavy clouds. For what seemed a noisy
eternity, they cruised in the glare above the monotonous, billowy
expanse—monotonous until Ernest noticed that the sun, visible for the
first hour or so from the windows on one side, was now pouring into the
craft through the opposite windows. He knew that Jerusalem was almost
directly south of Beirut, so that if they were still over land—mountains
—there could be no good reason for the 180-degree change of direction.
The pilot assured him that all was well, but, when he again reversed his
course, even the Army man was convinced that the pilot was lost. Ernest, maintaining exterior calm, tried to question him; there was petrol
for three and a half hours; he had no weather information; the squawky
radio made no sense. Molly, certain that they would soon end in wreck-
age on a foreign mountain, remembers thinking that at least it would
likely be sudden and that they would all go together. She stopped
worrying to wonder who would look after the orphaned children at
home.

Suddenly there was an opening in the clouds; the plane almost dived
through it, and Molly recognized the Damascus valley, and the city in
the distance behind them. The plane sputtered to a landing at Amman,
in Jordan. The pilot said it was merely a fuel stop, but when everyone
was happily on solid ground, Ernest turned to him. "This is as far as we
go. Where can I get an automobile?" The Britisher was furious. He insisted that he had never been lost—but the Lawrence party went on
from Amman by car. The frantically worried guide, who had been hired
to meet them in Jerusalem, greeted them like long-lost relatives. He had
been certain the little plane had been shot down over Israel. Though of
Arab origin, the guide was a devout Roman Catholic, and had gone to
one of the famous Jerusalem churches to light candles and pray for the
Lawrences.

The return to Beirut was less frightening. Large planes stopped at the
inadequate Jersualem airport only long enough to discharge or take on
cruise passengers, and, on the day the Lawrences were scheduled to
leave, bad weather kept them from even such brief landings. They set
out again by car, in rain that soon turned to snow and sleet. As Syrian
visas had been used on their first visit to Damascus, they stopped at the
French consul's home in Amman; he urged them to remain in Amman
overnight, but Ernest wished to push on. While the consul fixed their
passports, his wife served welcome, hot tea. They reached the Jordan-

Syrian border late at night, and, though Ernest told Molly and Margie to remain in the car while the men went inside the building, the soldiers insisted that everyone get out. When passports had been examined and passengers scrutinized, it seemed that permission to continue was contingent on taking a soldier, as evil appearing as the driver, who wanted to ride with them. Ernest, as Molly remembers, "haughtily refused and got away with it." Very late, they reached Damascus, where fortunately rooms in a good hotel had been secured. The following morning an Arabian American Oil Company plane took them to Beirut, from whence, next day they were taken to the famous ruins of Baalbek.

On February 16, a company plane flew them across northern Arabia to Dhahran on the Persian Gulf. They were comfortably quartered at the Awali guest house on Bahrein Island. There were many Americans in the oil-rich area and much entertaining of the welcome guests. Ernest toured the refineries, and all had various trips into the desert, including one north to the Sheikdom of Kuwait, which, in spite of its tremendous wealth, seemed, to Molly, an unsightly oil company town. They left the evening of the twenty-third for Karachi, Pakistan, on a British commercial flight. Seated in front of Molly and Ernest, and next to Dr. Sherrick, was British labor politican Aneurin Bevan. He was recognizable from pictures in the press, and his importance was made obvious by fussing stewards. Bevan tried to strike up a conversation with quite untalkative Sherrick by baiting him about Americans. Sherrick remained aloof even after Ernest was introduced and had some conversation with the Briton.

They arrived at Karachi in the night and were whisked to the Hotel Metropole where turbaned servants, moving quietly on bare feet and appearing suddenly and unexpectedly, created an air of mystery. The large, rather bare, rooms were comfortable and comparatively clean, with rough-tiled floors. Balconies off the rooms overlooked a court, and a variety of strange smells rose from the kitchen, several floors below. Though sensitive to smells—he used to say that he could tell the kind of store he was passing with his eyes closed—Ernest was interested enough not to mind the odors. Of what use was complaint about something he was powerless to alter? Anyway, they were medicinal smells to which he most objected.

Karachi offered an introduction to what is called "The East"; not only odors but also dirt and extreme and dreadful poverty were everywhere evident. They saw people sleeping in the streets between airport and hotel, and the next day observed children picking over and eating garbage. Flies were everywhere. The Lawrences were almost hesitant to eat, though the food served was tasty enough. Ernest had been cautioned by Dr. Atchley about the "diarrhea belt" in India and the Tropics and had been supplied with opium pills. He had been warned to return to America at once if these were not effective, but caution could not overcome curiosity in sampling the strange foods.

After a day in Karachi, they left by Air India for Bombay, where, again in the dark of early morning, they were met by Paramount representatives, whisked to the Taj Mahal Hotel for a few hours' sleep, and returned to the airport the same morning to enplane for Colombo, Ceylon. Though it was night all the time they were there, Ernest decided he would not return for the scheduled week there after Ceylon. The poverty was too apparent and distressing; unpleasant aromas finally got to and disturbed him. As Herbert York had decided, when a plush, excellent restaurant in San Francisco was once chosen over an "interesting place" in the Mission District, Ernest preferred elegance to color.

Instead of four scheduled days in Ceylon, they spent almost two thoroughly enjoyable weeks on the lovely, lush island—all under the auspices of Paramount. The journey had been referred to as the round-the-world trip, but now it became, and remained, the Ceylon Trip. They saw much of the island. There was an interesting day and night in the jungle, when all were crowded into a Jeep-type vehicle and bounced over narrow tracks to observe wild animals in their natural habitat—elephants, deer, a species of elk, and wild and dangerous water buffalo. They slept in a small wooden shelter in a forest. Their chief guide, Sir Chetampalam Gardner, a polite Tamil Indian, was obviously a Ceylon personage. They were entertained at the American consulate and with a Sunday picnic on an island in a large lake.

Molly thought the Galle Face Hotel, overlooking the esplanade along the sea, fascinating, but was horrified in market areas to see meat hung in the open sun, covered with flies. All thought the Ceylonese very handsome people; no emaciated beggars were in evidence, and neither did any native seem to be fat. It was a paradise compared with the malnutrition and grim squalor of the Near East. For all her reading, Margaret had not realized the conditions in which much of the world's population barely exists, and how little women are regarded in many places, nor, perhaps, had Ernest. He was as thrilled as she was on the location of a major Paramount motion-picture production to meet Vivien Leigh, Dana Andrews, and Peter Finch, and to watch them act before the cameras. The site was a tea plantation on which had been erected a false palace, the marble facade of which was simulated by linoleum. The remarkable and colorful Kandy Dancers, of the city of that name were watched almost as eagerly. None of the party wanted to leave Ceylon—unless it was Ernest, who would have been impatient anywhere after a dozen days.

From Madras, they were taken to see the fascinating Mahamalla-puram cliff carvings—great figures and miniature temples carved into the rock. President Dr. Rasendra Prasad of India, with a retinue of nearly a hundred, was viewing them that day, and the Lawrences were introduced by one of their Paramount escorts. Prasad invited them to join him for tea by the ocean, and tables for all were quickly set up on the shore. Ernest enjoyed conversation with the president.

A few days were spent in New Delhi, during which they were driven to Agra for an afternoon and night; Molly considered the Taj Mahal, "one of the few places that lives up to one's expectations, so beautiful you can think of nothing that compares with it." Yet even here they were aware of the hunger of people. Ernest was appalled that such abject and extreme poverty could exist side by side with extreme wealth and luxury—and that nothing seemed to be done to alleviate the misery. He thought of the benefits—water, power, light—such a nation might reap from controlled nuclear reaction. Yet he visited no laboratories in India; his old friend Saha's institute was in Calcutta, where his former student Nag was at the university, but they avoided that city. (Later that year Ernest was elected an honorary fellow of the Indian Academy of Sciences.)

From New Delhi they flew back to Arabia for another few days at Dhahran, and more American parties. They were flown to Hofuf, where the Emir entertained them in his palace with the Arabian coffee ceremony, which was interesting, despite the clear amber, heavily cardamom-flavored brew, which Molly thought tasted like a well-known mouth wash. It was great fun for her and Margie afterward to bargain in the market for coffeepots. A company plane took them to Beirut for a few more days, after which Ernest was delighted to board one for Rome and "civilization." He might even have been willing to stay with the company plane going on to the United States.

He relaxed in Rome, under auspices of Paramount people, a delightful headquarters for several days. They enjoyed the best restaurants and the sights for which Rome is famous. They drove to the Italian Riviera, visited Rapallo, and San Remo—where Margaret was forbidden entrance to the casino. On the way back to Rome, in Pisa the famous marble leaning tower, used by Galileo in the sixteenth century for experimental demonstration, had special significance for Ernest. They visited the galleries and churches of Florence during two days there. In Aquapendente (hanging waters), at a little restaurant off the main road to Florence, they found San Francisco symphony conductor Pierre Monteux and his wife, on opposite sides of the table, their poodle seated on a chair between them. From Rome they were driven down the coast to Naples, the ruins of Pompeii, and to Salerno. They crossed the Tyrrhenian Sea from Naples to Sicilian Palermo, where they boarded the tanker *A. N. Kemp*, and eleven days later docked at Barber, New Jersey, were again paid a dollar each in wages, and signed off. The Loomises and Gaithers were waiting in New York. Molly, anxious to see the children, left the following day with Margie and Dr. Sherrick. Ernest, with Rowan Gaither, just elected president of the Ford Foundation, had conferences at the Paramount offices. He went to Rochester, Schenectady, and Washington, before returning to Berkeley early in April, in time to entertain Manne and Karin Siegbahn, who had been such fine hosts in Sweden.

There could be little doubt that the two months had been beneficial for Ernest. He looked rested and had put on weight. He was much less upset by irritations at the laboratories or the Oakland plant—where he appeared the first night of his return. Jimmy Vale thought he had mellowed considerably. "For a while after the trip," he said, "when he'd come down, we'd tell him about something and he'd just shake his head and say 'Yes, yes, it's a tough problem,' and walk off and talk to somebody else. Whereas before the cruise, he'd say, 'What's the matter? Why aren't half a dozen people working on this?' He was like this for four or maybe six months before he was at it again. All of a sudden one day it was again, 'Well, let's get to work on it. We're not going to solve it sitting here.'"

It was the same at Livermore. He would talk things over with York and Teller, look around at what was being done, say a few words of congratulation or encouragement, perhaps make a suggestion, get back into his new Cadillac—with the top down—or the Ford station wagon Ira Sandefur usually drove, and off they would go, Ernest's hair blowing in the wind. Ira had been selected from lab employees to drive him after Loomis had offered to pay for a family chauffeur to save Ernest the strain—and prevent accident, particularly on drives to Livermore. Molly objected to a family chauffeur—as she did, mildly, to the Cadillac—as a possible source of false values in the children's minds, but agreed that a personal driver for Ernest, at the laboratory, was highly desirable. Ira was devoted and always available, whether for late hours or a few days. Ernest once bought him skis and put him in the hands of a Yosemite instructor during a weekend directors' meeting.

For most of the summer he was careful about rest, diet, and hours of work. Eleanor, at the Rad Lab just ten years on June 21, and who, as Ernest's personal secretary since the war, screened visitors, calls, and prevented interruptions, was aware of his attempt to adjust to a less strenuous routine, and to remain calm in the face of irritations and difficulties. She was helpful in many quiet ways; Cooksey substituted for him more and more with visitors and routine duties. He did not go to Balboa with the family on June 22. There had been a delay in that departure while Molly found a replacement for Bennie Lincoln, who left to start a foster home for infants. Maggie Tyous (later Williams), was hired to go to Balboa with Molly and the children. Ernest joined them later; he was at Balboa for several short periods that summer. When in Berkeley he played tennis two or three times a week and in general lived a well-ordered life. But he could not avoid participation in exciting laboratory events.

Johnny Foster, Jr., the son of Ernest's old McGill friend John Stuart Foster, and now a young Livermore physicist, telephoned one evening from Nevada to report, in some excitement, that a particular nuclear test of his responsibility had gone well. Ernest said, "Fine, I'll be there." He had retired, but got up, flew to Las Vegas, and appeared at the test site early next morning, without fanfare. He sat down quietly with Johnny, Herb York, and Mark Mills, and learned about it in detail. "I'm just a country bumpkin in this business," he said. Johnny was sure that after a few minutes Ernest knew more about it than they did and is convinced that this sort of action on Ernest's part added tremendously to the incentive and drive of others.

Another night Ernest shivered and waited at the proving ground for a shot, which when fired gave no nuclear yield. Ernest said, "Now let's sit down and see what happened." All points were reviewed and checked, even of those who were certain their aspects had been okay. In a short time the cause of the failure was found in a most unlikely area. "In such instances he never took refuge in personality things, or bawled one out, or said, 'Look, I want you to fix it.'" Johnny Foster remembers: "[He] always quietly sat to check and see what happened—just sort of rolled up his sleeves. But he used to also say that making a bomb of this kind was not like making a car. 'If you got a lemon car, okay, too bad, get another. But a nuclear bomb has to go off; you can't take a chance on a lemon!'"

He was delighted over growing international recognition for John and Donner Laboratory, as evidenced by a request in July, from the Vatican, that John fly to Zagreb, Yugoslavia, where Cardinal Stepinac was seriously ill with polycythemia, a disease involving too great an increase of red blood cells. John had first treated a polycythemia patient with radioactive phosphorus in 1938. The patient was still living, at the age of seventy, and the disease had been similarly controlled successfully in many others. Donner Laboratory had enlarged to nearly twice its original size, and its Pavilion for hospitalized patients was almost completed.

The Korean armistice, signed on July 27, seemed hopeful for international relations—for a few days. Premier Georgi Malenkov boasted on August 8 that "the United States no longer has a monopoly on the production of hydrogen bombs." There was a good deal of doubt about the veracity of the Russian's boast. And indeed it was a boast, and a courageous one; no hydrogen explosion then had taken place in Russia, but the United States soon had evidence that four days after Malenkov's statement a thermonuclear bomb, in which lithium had been an element, had been detonated in Siberia. Lithium fusion was still experimental in American science. In the opinion of scientists such as John von Neumann, of the GAC, soon to become an AEC commissioner, the rapidity with which the Russians had overtaken the United States was possible because "they began their thermonuclear program before we started ours." This he believed due to scientist spies, such as Fuchs, who had been in on early thermonuclear discussions at Los Alamos. Ernest, alarmed, was thankful that a start, however late, finally had been made; progress, he knew, had been made in America. He reminded colleagues: "It's a good thing the advice of some people wasn't taken."

The tempo of his activities automatically increased. He could not, he said, relax in a sailboat, spend time water skiing or lounging on a beach, when there was danger of the nation being blackmailed by another's H-bomb. At Livermore everything possible was being done to exploit fusion possibilities; much progress had been made at Los Alamos. A lithium bomb would be tested early in 1954 at Eniwetok, if protesters against it failed to have it cancelled. There was much hysteria over testing and fallout—encouraged by a few good scientists whom Ernest thought naïve or misguided. No one in Washington with whom he talked in October failed to understand the necessity to test a bomb that might restore weapon equality with Russia. No one could now honestly say the Soviets were simply following the lead of the United States, of necessity. At Livermore and the Rad Lab Ernest constantly encouraged new ideas, insistent that from them would come weapon superiority, not only in the next month or next year but also in a decade. "You have to keep generating ideas and getting people with ideas, or you go under, because from concept to production takes at least four years." He walked around as of old, talking with everyone—engineers, mechanics, the men on the job. "He could really enthuse people, and get them going night and day," Duane Sewell, Livermore director of scientific operations, said, restating what had been said so often for twenty-five years. "His feeling of expectation from, and confidence in, another was the best sort of encouragement."

Study of thermonuclear power for peaceful purposes had also been a vital part of the Livermore program almost from its inception. Indeed, prior to the founding of the second weapons laboratory, highly secret work on the release of energy through controlled fusion had been carried on at the Rad Lab, and Ernest encouraged it and support for it elsewhere, notably the good work at Princeton. He had insisted, as he had with reactor programs, that nondefense applications of controlled fusion be considered second only to weaponry, as vital to national interest. The development of fusion as a source of industrial power would be a most important aid to peace; fusion would utilize fuel of practically unlimited supply and was potentially so cheap that light and power could be made available in any area of the world. It also had a tremendous advantage over fission in that it produced no long-lasting, highly dangerous waste products. For these reasons, if for no other, testing of thermonuclear devices was very important; theory by itself was insufficient for development; only practice could advance it rapidly.

Ernest felt that those who opposed testing were tragically in error, not only as concerned national defense but also for world peace and the elevation of the conditions of the world's deprived masses. High-sounding phrases could be misleading; certainly the Russians would not cease experimentation because of them. The public was being needlessly and dangerously frightened by talk of fallout dangers; obviously there was relatively very little radioactive debris from a proper fusion explosion —only the small fission trigger produced dangerous particles. Testing could reduce fallout almost to the vanishing point, he thought. For all the furor, the fallout from the nuclear test explosions gave less radiation intensity than the difference between the natural cosmic radiation intensity at a mile-high city like Denver and one at sea level. The Cold War was frightening enough; encouragement of further, needless fear of radiation could only stultify efforts to prevent really terrible atmospheric contamination following nuclear bombing by an enemy encouraged by a United States inferior in armament.

On December 8, 1953, President Dwight D. Eisenhower startled the U.N. with the courageous Atoms for Peace Program—a step beyond disarmament. "It is not enough to take this weapon out of the hands of soldiers," he told the assembled diplomats. "It must be put into the hands of those who will know how to strip its military casing and adapt it to the arts of peace." He proposed that involved nations contribute from their nuclear stockpiles to a United Nations International Atomic Energy Agency, in ratios to be determined by negotiation. He said that he expected Congressional approval of a plan to encourage international study of peacetime uses of nuclear energy, to open channels for discussion, get rid of the fear, and "make positive progress towards peace." He spoke of the awesome power of hydrogen weapons and noted that the American stockpile of atomic weapons had the explosive equivalent "of all bombs and all shells that came from every plane and every gun in every theater of war in all the years of World War II." He warned that any attack against the United States would meet with quick and resolute reaction, but that the United States was determined to do its best toward solution of the "fearful atomic dilemma . . . [so that] Man shall not be dedicated to his death, but consecrated to his life." It was a tremendous statement, which stunned even Soviet delegates into applause. Ernest hailed the President's goal; perhaps more spirited support for industrial cooperation would result.

Much had been said about industrial cooperation; only six months before the President's U.N. address, the National Security Council had warned the AEC that development of nuclear power by the United States "is a prerequisite to our maintaining our lead in the atomic field." But for all the talk, little had been done. Ernest had argued for it with Lewis Strauss, chairman of the AEC since Dean's departure in June. The concern of Strauss with security had, Ernest thought, made him too hesitant in this respect. There were industrialists willing to gamble—all important leaps forward involved some risk. He was soon drawn into high-level discussions concerning the Atoms for Peace Program. Efforts to solve challenging problems of controlled fusion received added impetus, though such projects for peaceful applications as were later embodied in "Sherwood," controlled fusion, and "Plowshare," application of nuclear explosions to industrial use, were not publicly discussed. Livermore was heavily involved in both, though the Plowshare project was not authorized until several years later. Ernest early had encouraged serious discussion by Teller, York, and Harold Brown at Livermore over "bomb" usages for industry. Oilman and regent Edwin Pauley early discussed with Ernest the possible use of a nuclear blast for recovery of depleted oil wells.

Completion of the Bevatron, from which much of the crew had for a time been diverted to early MTA work, was now in sight. In October, the AEC gave approval for the construction of the Heavy Ion Accelerator, called the Hilac. These machines all would be in the service of pure science, so necessary to the understanding of nature, whose mysteries seemed to increase with every advance. In the continuing transuranium studies, elements 99 and 100 were produced toward the end of 1953, and others beyond atomic number 100 were theoretically prophesied.

Ernest was as actively involved as ever—television, Livermore, Rad Lab, and national concerns left little time for thought of rest and care for health until there was evidence of a recurrence of his ailment in November. Serious attention to it was postponed for an important visit of Assistant Secretary of Defense Donald Quarles. It did not completely subside, even after holiday relaxation, though he looked and felt well. Confidential notice, received just after Christmas, that Oppenheimer's clearance for secret information had been suspended, caused strong mixed emotions, followed by increased trouble. Ernest consulted his physician, was given a new diet, and again warned to reduce activities and attempt to avoid pressures in matters over which he had no control. Whether or not they were consciously of the New Year variety, his resolutions were to make greater effort to comply with medical advice and to continue care after the recurrence again subsided.

He stopped spending *every* night at the recently leased TV tube production facility at Emeryville—a plant larger than that at Oakland. For a few weeks he also reduced time spent at the laboratories, arrived later mornings and stayed away more afternoons. The death, on January 20, 1954, of Howard Poillon, so much more than a helpful aid with Research Corporation funds in the early days of little money for cyclotrons, and a very real friend and valued adviser, was saddening, but also a relief—Poillon had been ill and irrational for months. That, for one who regarded his benefactor with affection as a person, and with respect as an adviser, had been more than grievous. He wished that Poillon could have shared the excitement when the Bevatron, first on the vacuum pumps January 21, reached the billion-volt mark in February. Poillon had displayed faith when most others had laughed at 20,000 volts.

Ernest went to Honolulu for a couple of days before joining Strauss for the March 1 Castle Tests at Eniwetok. The explosion of that first thermonuclear bomb capable of delivery by plane, but detonated on a tower, was an awesome event. Approximately twice as powerful as had been estimated, it was the equivalent of twelve to fourteen million tons of TNT! Its fission trigger debris was carried more than 165 miles downwind from Eniwetok, and beyond the area considered dangerous, which had been cleared of ships. The device so far exceeded estimations that it was, at first, incorrectly reported to have been out of control. It was to achieve notoriety chiefly because of the contamination of the Japanese fishing trawler, *Fortunate Dragon,* beyond the restricted zone. Inhabitants of two islands, considered well outside the dangerous area, were hurriedly removed to Kwajalein for medical observation. The magnitude of the result, from so comparatively small a bomb, did much to alleviate Ernest's concern over Russian superiority. In fact, the explosion had been so great and its effects so far reaching, the test of a much larger thermonuclear bomb, which also could be carried by plane, was postponed because of risks involved. Much construction on the atoll might well be lost in the greater explosion, natives from far islands would have to be removed, and a much larger possible danger zone would have to be cleared of ships.

He dallied again in Hawaii after the test, attempting to relax and more fully regain the health he had enjoyed after the Ceylon trip. There was a good deal of partying with Navy people, but he rested, played tennis, and swam. He kept in touch with the laboratory by

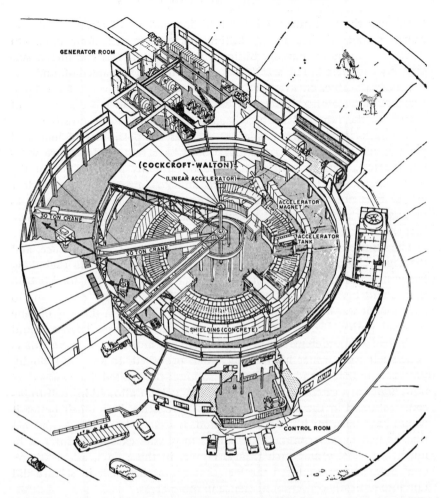

The Bevatron, by means of highly sophisticated devices, *i.e.*, phase stability, frequency modulation, etc., overcomes the mass-velocity ratio problems of very high speeds and can produce energies beyond six billion electron volts. Note size compared to bus in lower left. (*Lawrence Radiation Laboratory*)

telephone; the Bevatron produced a billion and a half electron volts on March 5 and climbed to 4.7 billion during the next four days. On April 1, with more than six billion volts energy, it was considered successfully completed. The search then began for long-dreamed-of, and theoretically possible, elusive particles—and perhaps discovery of the bond that held all together in the nucleus. It was easier to relax knowing of success at the lab, and he had been less concerned over possible Russian superiority since the Castle test. Besides the possibility of increased yield, much had been learned that would have remained obscure without the test. Reports continued to bear testimony to the value of the test; experimentation to learn more and to improve thermonuclear events must now proceed; fusion devices could gain in sophistication as progressively as had those of fission, following the Trinity and Japanese blasts. Fusion now presented the exciting challenge.

The Oppenheimer situation was unfortunate—for Oppie, science, and the country. Ernest was deeply torn between bonds formed in their long friendship and association, personal respect and admiration for his brilliance, and his strong feeling that Oppie's influence as a consultant to government was unwise—had been in fact an obstacle in the way of sane national policy. Ernest had no doubt that the country's defense would be in bad shape defensively if Oppie's advice, and that of those others Ernest felt were under his influence, had prevailed. It was, he thought, unfortunate that it had prevailed for so long; the United States was only now, hopefully, catching up. If only Oppie had not allowed himself to become confused in the attempt to solve all problems, how much better it would have been for him and the nation. It seemed but a short time ago that he had largely confined his talents to physics except for interest in music, art, poetry and such things. Oppie, in those days, asked advice, even of Ernest—recognized the fact that accomplishment in science did not automatically confer omniscience in other areas.

Ernest tried to place the time and cause of the change; was it involvement with other academic areas on the campus? Was it close associations with classicists, linguists, and social scientists? Ernest knew many of them casually and in most cases respected them—but not because their methods were scientific. Did Oppie's change in attitude come with, or follow, marriage? He remembered how politically naïve Oppie seemed at election time in 1936, and that by 1940 he was an ardent and articulate advocate of a third term for Franklin Roosevelt and extension of New Deal policies. Was it only because of the involvement of German relatives with Naziism? That need not have induced sympathy for Communism in such a mind as Oppie's.

He wondered if he might have helped his friend in those days—but he himself, though always a voting citizen, had had little time for politics. He had depended on his father, close to men of the soil, and politically wise from personal experience, and on Poillon, man of affairs and respected businessman. Ernest had scorned the idea that a country of such wealth as the United States could not afford to spend to get back on its feet—or to remain preeminent; he remembered arguments on that with conservative, New England, Mabel Blumer. His mother-in-law never could be persuaded that, since we owed the national debt to ourselves, it would not bankrupt us to borrow as necessary. He remembered someone—could it have been Oppie?—telling him that he was a New Dealer only as it applied to government handouts, that otherwise he was well to the right. He had been too busy with the laboratory to worry about such things; his politics involved support of what he considered was right and a vote against what he thought was wrong. Details were for politicians. Oppie had tried to embrace everything—not only nationally, but internationally as well, and had protested arguments that all that was outside of their competence. Perhaps esteem for this broad view had encouraged him. Perhaps Ernest, as sometimes with his children, had been too harsh in ridicule of foolish conduct or ideas, for he had laughed and scolded at much; in fact had prevented—at least in the Rad Lab—Oppie's efforts to involve laboratory people in causes ranging from migrant workers and Spanish loyalists to union activities. Yet, when war approached and Ernest had brought his colleague's tremendous talent to bear on the uranium-fission problem, Oppie had cast these concerns aside—not only verbally but in writing—and had devoted himself solely, diligently, and brilliantly to the project.

This change too had been remarkable, from a wild-haired, retiring, cartoonist's idea of a mathematical scientist, to a neat and socially gracious individual, apparently at ease with men of affairs and military men. Perhaps he had enjoyed, and given too much importance to, the acclaim which followed the success of the bomb. Was not a certain arrogance, which before the war had been noticeable chiefly to less brilliant students, directed after Los Alamos toward security people, even toward some colleagues, and felt by many nonscientists? ("He is arrogant, all right, but I know of no one with more right to be," a colleague who wished to remain anonymous said.) Several important industrialists and businessmen, whom Ernest respected, had complained that Oppie deliberately talked down to them; that if he were so intelligent he must be aware that his generous use of foreign language phrases and recondite terms made communication difficult with people who did not understand them. A few highly successful men of business had argued with Ernest that Oppie wished to impress rather than to communicate. True, these were not academic men, but they were nonetheless responsible citizens, whom Ernest thought much better equipped for practical affairs than most scientists. He appreciated their advice highly. Ernest had often defended Oppie against such charges on the grounds of his brilliance as a theoretician, and for his seemingly almost impossible accomplishment of keeping penned-up, temperamental, highly individualistic and brilliant men relatively content and on the job at Los Alamos. However, Ernest had little sympathy with the tendency among many scientists to consider themselves superior to businessmen, military leaders and security people, and the rules and regulations lesser men must respect; the assumption that, because one was a good scientist, he automatically knew best the directions in which lay the welfare of the nation—and, indeed, the world. This was, Ernest thought, the supreme arrogance of which too many scientists were guilty: that because they had split and controlled the atom, built a most powerful weapon, and acquired increased understanding of nature's forces, they were thereby a chosen people, more capable than others of directing affairs of state, defense, and even the economic uses of power. No philosopher, Ernest remembered that from mythological times the gods always repaid pride with a fall.

He had deeply hoped that Oppie, though opposing views and some bitterness had fractured their close friendship, would accept the removal of his clearance for secret information quietly. Such clearance was continually withdrawn for a variety of reasons, usually because classified information as no longer necessary for one's work. There was, normally, no stigma attached to the procedure, and, had Oppie remained silent, none but officials and involved administrators need have known of any change in his status or reasons for it. It would not affect his position as director of the institute or his income; he could devote his whole attention to physics and his job. Oppie, however, had elected to protest and had requested a hearing before a personal security board. Was this further indication of fatal arrogance, as had been suggested? Clearance and consultation by government were not rights inherent in citizenship, to be demanded. The hearing began on March 4. Though it was intended that it should be privately conducted, Ernest was certain that it could not be kept from the press and would, therefore, be detrimental to both Oppie and science. He was aware of much that was against Oppie in security files; he had brushed much of it aside as inconsequential when urging his assignment to Los Alamos; Oppie must know much more that could be used against him—it was upsetting and depressing to think of the headline material that would be exposed and that in any case was beside the central point—the soundness or lack of soundness of his advice and influence. So Ernest saw it.

The phasing out of the MTA project as a source of no-longer-necessary substitute materials had unfortunate aspects. Ernest did not hesitate to give up an unnecessary project any more than one that failed to function, but more than himself and his laboratory was involved in this. He had expected MTA to establish California Research and Development as a West Coast company capable of participation in large nuclear development projects. Perhaps MTA had been too large and complicated for a new organization—it would have been difficult for one well established. It was unfortunate that for them it must seem a failure. Though responsible, they had lacked final authority, which had led to some confusion in Rad Lab-Company relations. But the fact was that with increased national production of uranium—and Ernest was at first the only one on the project with access to reliable statistics—there appeared, to CRD men, to be vacillation in the project's goals. Need for plutonium and tritium was a classified matter—the entire project had been restricted from the start, and changes therefore often seemed arbitrary to uninformed CRD people.

Some scientists elsewhere had considered it a fiasco from the start—Rabi had early told Panofsky that he was wasting his time. Panofsky never thought so even after shutdown. It would have been vital had not American ore deposits beyond expectation been discovered. Ernest felt that science gained substantial dividends in addition to the insurance provided against shortage; it had opened new fields of research, provided new techniques for the production of high-energy, highly intense beams—already of value in the Sherwood program for study of various aspects of fusion. Vacuum technology had been greatly developed, as had very high-power shortwave oscillator tubes, also useful for Sherwood, the early warning network and in other important classified areas. The training of many engineers and technicians in neutron physics, electrical discharge phenomena, and vacuum engineering was very important—certainly in the Livermore fusion programs. In the Rad Lab, the resulting A-48 would produce beams a quarter of a million times the intensity of those common in synchrocyclotrons. The fact of the matter was simply that substitute materials were no longer needed, and, with sufficient uranium, reactors were cheaper producers of plutonium.

Ernest's sole regret was the sense of wasted effort some CRD men felt; it was unfortunate that because of the nature of the project much of the operation had to be conducted in nonbusinesslike fashion, with resultant misunderstandings. The refusal of Alex Hildebrand to join the Rad Lab staff at the conclusion of his CRD responsibility was understandable. His fine sense of responsibility for people he had brought to the project on the assumption that it would be permanent—many of them had built or purchased homes in the area—made him somewhat bitter. Ernest was fond of Alex. He had been at the Lawrence home for dinner, and their family association was a long one. Alex's brother Roger regretted his decision, certain that association with the Rad Lab would be a happy one for Alex.

Design of new accelerators for the Rad Lab and Yale followed the successful completion of the Bevatron. AEC contracts for these had been signed in February. Ernest's cooperation in obtaining the large accelerator grant for Yale had been secured by Breit almost four years before; now Professor William Watson, director of Sloane Laboratory, arrived for a short visit; Professors Robert Beringer, M. S. Malkin, and Robert Gluckstern came to work at the Rad Lab with Van Atta and others on design of the Hilac. Dean E. W. Sinnott, of the Yale Graduate School, wrote of the pleasant anticipation of "close association with you and your Lab over the next year or two while designing accelerators" —a collaboration that progressed well. Beringer and company were at the Rad Lab about a year.

On April 19, at a dinner address before the World Affairs Council in Los Angeles, Lewis Strauss announced the intention of President Eisenhower to arrange an international conference of representative men from every area to explore "benign and peaceful uses of atomic energy." It would be the first such convention ever held, and the idea—previously suggested privately by Alan Waterman of the National Science Foundation, and by Rabi—was adopted by the U.N. It would be held in Geneva in 1955; Rabi would plan details.

Pleasure in this all-out attempt toward international control and development of peaceful applications of atomic energy was somewhat overshadowed by the insistent request of Strauss that, as a necessary duty, Ernest appear for questioning at the Oppenheimer Hearing. From the first, that affair in Washington had been anything but private. Much press coverage was intemperate in tone. The proceedings were termed "McCarthyism," "symptomatic of hysteria," and "persecution"; Strauss was accused of conducting a personal vendetta in retaliation for opposition to his views; a great scientist, it was said, was being subjected to trial because his honest opinions happened to be mistaken. Nowhere was it indicated in the press that the hearing was not a trial and that it was called at Oppenheimer's request. Ernest reluctantly agreed to appear in Washington following a weekend meeting of AEC laboratory directors at Oak Ridge, in late April. Luis Alvarez also was asked to appear, as were Wendell Latimer, Ken Pitzer, and Teller, all of Berkeley, and presumably against reinstatement of Oppie's clearance, since the requests were from the AEC.

The Oak Ridge meeting was held at Topoca Lodge in the Smoky Mountains in beautiful spring weather. Naturally, the Oppenheimer affair was the chief topic of conversation, aside from formal meetings on laboratory matters, as it was whenever scientists gathered. The first group Ernest joined, Tom Johnson, Walter Zinn, Lee Haworth, Clarence Larson, and Alvin Weinberg, before a scheduled session at Topoca, was disturbed over press reports—testimony had been revealed by Oppenheimer and his counsel, much to the dismay of Personal Security Board members who feared trial by the press would be prejudicial to the inquiry. Much of the complex scientist's past had thus been revealed by reporting in full the letter of information on which the hearing was based, and in Oppie's own long statement; examination by counsel exposed more. A great deal of sympathy—in much of which Ernest shared—was expressed for Oppie, in whatever group, whenever his name was mentioned. It was painful to see a man's life picked apart and exposed, but, Ernest said, he had asked for it. It was argued that he had to defend or clear his honor—his loyalty. Ernest had no conviction of disloyalty and would have been the first to attest to Oppie's brilliant mind; perhaps it was because of the efforts of that mind to encompass so much in addition to natural science—philosophy, poetry, social and political (so-called) science, ideas and ideals and sentiment—that he was often lost in the resulting morass, unable to determine which of conflicting directions to take. Suddenly becoming a public personage had made him aware of the importance of what he said, and he had strayed from science. A scientific adviser should be a scientist—not a moralist. Later events had proven much of his advice incorrect, and his persuasive, almost hypnotic influence made it dangerous, particularly in the halls of power where decisions had to be made realistically—not mystically. Ernest's views were not shared by all his colleagues at Topoca Lodge; should not a scientist be moral? Must he advise against his convictions? Was not a widely ranging mind more likely to find correct answers? Was it a crime to be wrong, granted that sometimes he had been? It was not criminal to be wrong, Ernest agreed; it would be worse than criminal for the United States to be confronted with an H-bomb, having none ourselves.

There were remarks Ernest thought intemperate; colorful language, with frequent references to persecution, martyrdom, vendetta, and such, were hardly scientific, even if uttered by scientists. Most discussions were reasonable, quiet, and tended toward objectivity even in disagreement, the essence of which fell into one of two patterns generally, which had begun to develop even before conclusion of the war in "to drop or not to drop the bomb" arguments. Disagreements had developed further during Congressional struggles to get an atomic energy bill, in arguments toward international control, and in the H-bomb controversy. Leaders in the two camps, and others, had not always been consistent: Oppie had been most vocal among the scientists for use of the bomb against Japan—Ernest most strongly opposed. After the war Ernest became a leading advocate of the H-bomb, Oppie most influential against it.

Rowan Gaither said: "Ernest's drive made him controversial, particularly after he made a sort of end run against the Advisory Committee when it voted against the hydrogen bomb. Of course they were wrong, as history has shown, but before that there was his insistence that a scientist be a scientist and not a politician, that his chief concern should not be with moral implications of the use of the bomb, but to act and respond as a scientist to his country's demands—even though as a whole man he might be against the result. He was very intolerant of anything that would obstruct or delay fusion and was influential in the reversal of the decision against a strong effort. I think this indirectly led to the second lab at Livermore.

"It was in the hydrogen controversy, perhaps, that the really significant departure of two points of view of science occurred. There was U.C. at Berkeley versus M.I.T. and Caltech—not institutional differences—but differences of individuals, and certainly not all individuals in these places, and as it slopped more and more over into moral considerations, the infighting became dirty. It made me think of what happened in Greece and Rome—though Ernest did not think in historical terms. They had all worked together for the A-bomb and differed radically on the H-bomb."

Differences had lessened considerably after the Russian detonation of a fusion bomb. There was little scientific support now for unilateral surrender of atomic superiority, or for the case that Russia would not develop one if America did not, or could only develop one by copying what had been done by the United States. Only those who were present at the Topoca Lodge discussions know, or could remember, all that was said off the record, but there were reasonable and respected colleagues who apparently clarified, for Ernest, reasoning behind some of Oppie's advice that had seemed erratic, and there was a clearer understanding of Ernest's point of view, which some had considered chauvinistic. All deplored the damage to science and the scientific image; some thought it would be compounded if Oppie was not cleared. Someone pointed out that apparently the only derogatory testimony would come from Berkeley people. Ernest emphatically assured them that he had no part in any personal vendetta, that the Berkeley scientists referred to he knew to be seriously concerned over the nation's welfare. It was true that since Oppie's departure from the GAC—that had nothing to do with clearance, had been routine—his influence on governmental decisions was comparatively minor and, except when he was called as a consultant, more public than private. How much less complicated it would have been just not to have him called for consultation! The stormy debate bound to result among conflicting camps would hurt not only science but also the AEC and the whole security system. Only those opposed to the United States and its policies could possibly benefit from further cleavage in American scientific ranks.

For whatever reasons, Ernest telephoned to Alvarez in Berkeley and asked him not to testify. Luis was surprised—as was Strauss, in Washington, when he learned of it. Strauss phoned Alvarez to say that refusal would be ducking responsibility. After a good deal of soul-searching, Alvarez flew to Washington and the hearing, ". . . one of the very few times that I did something Ernest told me not to do. It was a very rare thing . . . and later he said something—that I'd done something courageous, that he approved of it . . . that he wished he hadn't given in to pressure. He didn't say these things, but I was well enough tuned [to him] to know that he admired what I did. It was a difficult thing."

It was also a difficult time for the scientists at Topoca Lodge: Zinn became ill, Tom Johnson fell and fainted, and Ernest suffered the worst single attack of colitis he had endured up to that time, which effectively resolved any question of his appearance at the Oppenheimer hearing. He became so weak that he was unable to tour a portion of the Union Carbide and Carbon plant as planned, and he left almost immediately for Berkeley. Lest there be accusations of feigning illness to avoid the hearing, he had called Haworth, Larson, and Johnson to his room to witness the quantity of blood he had lost. Alvarez thought—and said Strauss concurred—that Ernest used the illness to avoid an unpleasant duty. Others say he would never have used an excuse: "It just wasn't in him to do that." Robert Bacher is of the opinion that, had Ernest testified, much would have been cleared up and understood by those who misjudged his attitude toward Oppie.

Clearance was not reinstated for Oppenheimer; the majority report of the Personal Security Board recommended against it, and the commissioners thereupon voted that he "be denied access to restricted data" —though all but one of them was emphatic that there was no evidence of disloyalty. Their majority report stated that important agencies of the government "at one time or another have felt the effect of his falsehoods, evasions, and misrepresentations"; mentioned his "persistent and willful disregard for the obligations of security"; and his "persistent and continuing association with communists," including a recent meeting in Paris with an individual claimed to have once been an intermediary for a Soviet consulate. Commissioner Henry Smyth alone voted to reinstate Oppie's clearance. In a separate, concurring opinion, Commissioner Murray elaborated on his reasons for considering Oppenheimer also disloyal.

A furor followed. Oppenheimer was said to be a martyr, deserving of more gratitude from a country he had served so well; to accuse him of failure to give good advice was hindsight; the whole affair was said to be McCarthyism at its worst.

What shocked—and deeply hurt—Ernest were the falsehoods; if he had not considered Oppenheimer disloyal, he certainly had not thought him dishonest. That so fine a scientist could, to use Oppie's own words, tell "a tissue of lies" or "cock-and-bull story," that "the whole thing was a pure fabrication," was utterly disillusioning. Honest opposition to the H-bomb program could be charged to naïveté, perhaps to continuing associations with those who had influenced him toward radicalism —and which he had assured Ernest had been given up—these could be forgiven. How rationalize dishonesty? To dismiss it as a trifle of the past in a man so intelligent as Oppie was impossible for Ernest with his rigid definitions of truth and falsehood. And it was not the past that caused the majority of the Security Board to "regretfully conclude that Dr. Oppenheimer had been less than candid in several instances in his testimony before this board." If there was any satisfaction that Oppenheimer's influence had been removed—it could, of course, not be removed entirely by the denial of clearance—the revelations brought Ernest bitter disappointment.

Furor over the Oppenheimer affair added to the already considerable fear in the nation of spies, atomic war, and fallout. Ernest thought much argument against fallout implied that it would be a greater woe than conquest by bombs or the threat of them. He was well aware of radiation damage—had been for years. Dr. Hardin Jones of Donner, one of Ernest's advisers on radiation hazards, thought Ernest understood fallout—and problems with Russia that must be considered along with it—better than others. "Ernest worried about the backwash of weapons, radiation, and the strength of the country in their proper relationship," is Jones's opinion. "He did more than anyone else to promote studies of radiation effects."

Nor did Ernest confine concern of radiation effects to fallout; he discussed precautions in use of dental X-ray apparatus and procedure with his dentist, Dr. Arthur Jensen, and himself refrained from too frequent dental X-ray surveys, because he did not wish to use up his "exposure quota." Molly made a nuisance of herself in shoe stores where foot X-ray machines could overexpose playful children and were operated by unskilled people. The machines disappeared from Berkeley shoe stores before they were banned elsewhere. Faulty apparatus and careless use of X rays was more likely to be disastrous than fallout. Yet he was also concerned lest antitest hysteria should frighten people against the proper use of radiation in diagnosis and therapy. Proton beams for therapy were initiated at the Rad Lab in 1954. Under John's direction, they were carefully directed at patients' pituitary glands with such precision that only the gland received the full dosage, a safer procedure than pituitary surgery, many thought.

Ernest was awarded the Medal of the American Cancer Society at its 1954 annual meeting, "For his pioneer work in the development of the cyclotron, from which has come much of our vast store of knowledge regarding isotopes and their uses; for his distinguished discoveries in and contributions to the field of medical physics, which, while seeming far distant from the bedside of the cancer sufferer, are intimately related in some form or another to almost all patients receiving diagnosis or treatment for a malignant disease . . . an appreciation for your efforts, all of which have been primarily expended for the benefit of mankind." Particularly gratifying was the congratulatory letter of the great and respected De Hevesy from Stockholm: ". . . hardly anyone made greater contributions to cancer research than you. In these days when many erroneously consider the construction of the pile to be responsible more than any other step for the progress in the field of tracer research, the cancer society very properly recalls that not being the case. The decisive step was the construction of the cyclotron. I vividly recall what an event it was when we were put into the position to replace our very modest samples prepared with the aid of neutron sources by your marvelous preparations which you so generously put at such an early date at our disposal."

In his reply Ernest recalled the personal pleasure he had had in following De Hevesy's "pioneering investigations in which you used radioactive material that came from here." Then followed a paragraph expressive of thoughts, which for some time had recalled to Ernest Rutherford's remark of the early thirties, that he had become a sort of grandfather, looking after his young men at Cavendish. "Nowadays in the laboratory most of my satisfaction in research is vicarious. Somebody has to run the laboratory and help provide facilities and my pleasure more and more is coming from following the researches of my associates."

Pleasure in following the work of his associates had a rather drastic consequence, after more Castle series tests in May; not because Livermore aspects were less than successful—failure is necessary for achievement, he told his people, and in this case proved the value of testing. Personal consequences included a recurrence of the colonic trouble that had subsided sufficiently after the flare-up at Oak Ridge to permit the flight to Eniwetok, with the hope that rest in Honolulu afterward might further allay it. He did not tarry in Hawaii, however, but returned to Berkeley where examination disclosed the presence of a tapeworm apparently picked up in the South Pacific. He was hospitalized for treatment, after which, as he wrote to Strauss, "following doctor's order," he was "taking off long weekends."

He might have remained away from the Rad Lab the following weekend but not from the Emeryville TV plant. Except for a short visit at the rest home where his father lay blind and hopelessly paralyzed, he spent most of Saturday with Gow and Vale demonstrating "how easy it is to clean color fields with external magnetic fields." In spite of problems with it, he was excited and confident about his tube. He wrote Lawrence Haugen: "The industry is in quite a stew about the color television tube development. CBS & RCA are making a tremendous drive to get a tube into production, while we are proceeding on a much more relaxed and easy pace. We are not moving nearly as fast, of course, as the big companies but I think in the long run we will come out on top because our tube is basically the best answer to the problem."

Ernest was back in the hospital again before another weekend, with pneumonia. Neylan phoned the hospital and was shocked at the lack of vitality in his voice. He was well enough on the Fourth of July to fly to Balboa in a rented plane with Eric at the controls—Eric had stayed in Berkeley for a summer job—and later in the month to introduce Strauss—who was a guest of Hoover at the Grove—for a Lakeside Talk. Ernest had Bradbury as guest at the Summer Encampment, and "unburdened himself about Oppie" to the Los Alamos director. He was proud that he had managed to avoid New York or Washington in 1954, until he flew East on August 8. He considered such avoidance as evidence that he was "taking it easy." He had not been back long before he went to Seattle with Cooksey for a Physical Society meeting, and to see Fred Schmidt and his cyclotron at the University of Washington. He did not stay for the conclusion of the meetings, but returned to Balboa, where he received word of his father's death on the morning of August 26. He flew to Berkeley with Molly that day.

Carl had been hopelessly ill for about five months, during which, as he apparently suffered little, Ernest had been more concerned about his distressed mother. Immediately following Carl's stroke she had insisted that he remain at home; there were nurses around the clock. A month of this had been too much for her, however, and Carl had been moved to a hospital. Gunda immediately wanted him back home where she could help care for him. Since he was only partially conscious most of the time, his last illness had been very trying for the devoted wife, particularly when he became irrational, and after his death she was completely lost. Her sons considered a suitable home, where she would not be alone and might find friends; Gunda protested this, nor would she allow anyone to live with her. Ernest worried about it aloud to Neylan, who told him to leave his mother alone; if she wished to remain in the apartment without a companion, she should be allowed to so long as she was able. "You've got to respect her independence!" he said, and Ernest saw the wisdom of the advice. Gunda usually spent weekends, or Sundays, with one of her sons and his family. Molly and Amy, one of whom saw her almost every day, continued to take casseroles or other prepared food to her, as they had during Carl's illness.

Jim Born, John's assistant director at Donner Laboratory, who had supervised the care of Carl, received criticism for keeping him alive during his last three or four months of unconsciousness. Ernest and John, however, were grateful that Jim, in addition to the skills of a physician, had contributed friendship and kindliness to the welfare of their parents. They insisted that Born accept a monetary gift, which he put into bonds "for my children's education, and I think your father would approve." Born, who after earning a degree in law at the University of Wisconsin had continued there for another eight years and a medical degree, was particularly well qualified as an administrative aide in a growing medical laboratory. He was also well regarded as a physician by Rad Lab people.

Ernest was asked to aid in the organization of the nuclear research center in Europe in which participating nations would cooperate and their scientists take part. To be located near Geneva, the center would make available the necessary equipment for high-energy physics research, the expense of which would be prohibitive for a small country. "CERN" would be patterned somewhat after the idea of Brookhaven, in which universities of the Northeast shared and cooperated. Before he left for Geneva in September, Ernest decided his top associates should have official recognition for what, in fact, they were. The only titles among his scientific personnel had been from the beginning that of associate director for dependable Cooksey, and later assistant director for engineer Brobeck, yet the laboratories had grown until, in 1954, there were 2,500 on the payroll. McMillan, Seaborg, Alvarez, and Teller were told to assume official titles as associate directors. At Livermore one day Ernest suddenly turned to York. "Well, Herb, why don't you start calling yourself director out here?" York was surprised and impressed. "He could well have decided to get somebody else, after the Castle Tests." But Ernest had continued to support York and the laboratory as he ran it—it had been a pretty complete delegation of authority from the beginning. For more than the first year at Livermore, York, following government instructions, had written a program for the laboratory. When he had taken it to Ernest for signature, York was told to sign it himself, though Ernest did sign his approval, under York's signature. After that York signed all basic program and direction documents, and Wally Reynolds signed administration papers involving buildings, material, and financial requests. Reynolds also had unusual authority; Ernest, impatient with administrative details, relied on him to an unusual degree. Wally always followed directions if they were given, and, if Ernest was not explicit, Wally understood that he did not wish to be bothered.

Ernest also decided about this time that York should not have to wear a badge at Livermore, as everyone else did but Ernest—which in effect was the mark of the director. Before he left for CERN he wrote to Harold Fidler, San Francisco manager of AEC operations, requesting that the new titles be used in official papers and letters, adding that, of course, John had long been director of Donner, and Joseph Hamilton director of Crocker Laboratory.

Representatives of CERN nations were heartened by Eisenhower's announcement of a world atomic pool—without Russia if she continued to balk beyond patience. CERN participants were eager and excited: a good European nuclear laboratory, equipped for high-energy physics, should make valuable contributions. As he always had been, Ernest was happy to see—and help—others acquire equipment that would enable them to experiment on the highest levels. John, who had been in Milan, was driven by early Rad Labber Lorenzo Emo to Zurich to meet Ernest. They found him in excellent spirits, though, as Emo remembers, somewhat ill. Ernest drove to Geneva with them, over Grimsel Pass, stopping a night at Interlaken, in good weather "with wonderful views," he wrote home.

After a final CERN meeting, and an evening with its chosen head, Stanford's Felix Bloch, who was a native of Switzerland, Ernest and John flew to London. Ernest kept a dinner appointment with T. E. Allibone, who would be at the Rad Lab again for a few days in November. At John's insistence, they returned to New York by ship, and his ailment subsided again. He was well enough a month later to make another short unpublicized trip to Europe. It was no secret at the laboratory that he had flown off without his wallet and necessary papers, which Molly—on a Sunday night—airmailed to New York, too late. They reached him in London. Upon his return, minor ulceration was discovered in his colon, and a new daily treatment was prescribed.

Ernest was heartened to be granted basic TV tube patents in an unprecedented ceremony, in which the papers were presented to him personally, by the Commissioner of Patents, in Washington. It was a long time since his initial idea—and thirty years since he and Sam Jacobsohn had talked of patents at Yale—and he had learned that commercial production involved much more than a workable idea. The Emeryville plant was a hive of activity with, as Gow said, "sheets of stainless steel coming in one door, glass in another, and problems everywhere." The Oakland Laboratory had been closed; research continued at Emeryville alongside small-scale production, but the distance between New York administration and California research and production caused unforeseen difficulties. Ernest, however, was optimistic.

Besides Allibone, there were several foreign scientists at the laboratory in November, including a French group from Saclay, where a proton synchrotron was to be constructed. Ernest, as always, directed that all possible help and cooperation be available; engineering drawings, photographs, and unpublished notes were furnished. He personally tried to make the visitors welcome in other ways. Molly appreciated Maggie's presence of mind when notified late on a Friday afternoon that the French physicist Louis Leprince-Ringuet had been invited to dinner. Maggie thought it likely the Frenchman might prefer fish on Friday to the meat already cooking. Molly rushed in time to the market; the fish was appreciated and pronounced excellent. More than once, in Molly's absence from the house when Eleanor phoned announcing dinner guests at the last minute, Maggie simply substituted a future night's roast for planned hamburger. "She had a great fund of common sense and imperturbability in time of domestic crisis," Molly said. "She got good training for our menage when she worked for Dr. Lee in Palo Alto—even more unpredictable than Ernest about extra people for dinner. She and the children are good friends—they, too, respect the self-reliance with which she often cared for them single-handed."

Scientists everywhere were saddened, on November 28, by the death of Enrico Fermi, just five days before the twelfth anniversary of the activation of the world's first atomic pile. It had been planned to present him on this anniversary with the AEC's first award for outstanding contribution to nuclear science. Because of serious and rapidly spreading malignancy, of which he had learned during the last summer, the award had been made earlier—just twelve days before his death at the age of fifty-three. Ernest said, "Professor Fermi was a truly great man of science who contributed mightily to our understanding of nature. His contributions in the development of atomic energy are monumental, and America and all the world share the loss of this great man with his bereaved family."

On December 8, Ernest and Molly went to Los Alamos where, after meetings, Ernest helped Strauss formulate a television address on Atoms for Peace which the commissioner delivered the following Sunday, and which Ernest and Molly saw in New York with the Loomises and Gaithers. These friends had joined them on Saturday in General Courtney Whitney's Waldorf Towers apartment, where Ernest was given the Raymond E. Hackett Award, including a sizable check, in the presence of a small group that included General and Mrs. Douglas MacArthur. There were few others who knew of the award given by the Rock Ledge Institute which arranged that there should be no publicity.

During the last week of December, for the first time, the American Association for the Advancement of Science held its principal annual meeting on the West Coast. It was also the first time all sessions had ever been held on a single campus. Over 6,500 members attended the Berkeley meetings. Photographed together were five of California's six Nobel laureates: Ernest, McMillan, Seaborg, Giauque, John Northrup, and Wendell Stanley. It was fifteen years since Ernest had won the first Nobel Prize to be awarded to anyone at California—or any state university—and no faculty anywhere else had so many Nobelists as were now at Berkeley. One Berkeley professor complained good-naturedly that his children asked why he possessed only a Ph.D., when the fathers of their friends had Nobel Prizes.

CHAPTER XVIII

The Peaceful Atom

[1955–1957]

Ernest became increasingly involved in the issues of international disarmament and the nonmilitary uses of atomic energy during 1955. Always an advocate of peaceful applications, he had been heartened by the President's Atoms for Peace proclamation, but little had been accomplished internationally since that dramatic statement, and too little progress had been made in industrial applications at home. He had shied away from the disarmament question publicly, there had been too much loose talk throughout the nation—even advocacy of unilateral action, to add to the controversy. Disarmament seemed an ideal impossible of attainment while rigid barriers prevented assurance against deceit. If that assurance were possible, the United States would, of course, put away its arms. What a boon it would be: banishment of the fear that gripped people everywhere, and the transfer of so much effort and money to constructive pursuits! Peaceful use of atomic energy and real disarmament could make the earth the paradise it ought to be, if *people* would permit it.

He felt therefore that need for rest and dislike of committees were insufficient excuses for refusal of Presidential assistant Harold Stassen's request for him to serve as chairman of a special task force of his disarmament committee. Completely nonpolitical and unpublicized, the Stassen Committee was charged by the President to study disarmament and recommend policy. The assignment required much time in Washington—initially most of January—and several trips across the Atlantic. In addition to meetings of his own group, there were periodic conferences with other task force chairmen of the committee, particularly, for Ernest, with

James Fisk, of the communications group, and Generals James Doolittle and Bedell Smith of Air and Army special subcommittees.

Ernest's task force was, initially, to consider all aspects of inspection and detection, if possible to find foolproof methods of ensuring good faith in the event agreement was reached, even if, as in the past, inspection was denied behind the Iron Curtain. The President hoped to reach accord of some nature at a summit meeting, at last agreed to by Russia, in July. He and the British and French heads of state would attend. If shown that clandestine violations could be detected in every instance, perhaps at least tentative agreement might be reached. Though never, in the early months of 1955, entirely free from symptoms of illness, Ernest attacked the problem vigorously in spite of misgivings that its solution might affect experiments he considered most useful.

Early in February, when he went to Yosemite for a directors' meeting, he took Margaret and Robert along for the weekend. Though he seemed "peppy and cheerful," Margaret thought his attempts at extended skiing rather ludicrous, until she realized that he was not strong nor even very well. He needed more rest than a Yosemite weekend. He found it hard to avoid a good deal of entertaining when in Berkeley—and he did enjoy it—not only for the Loomises later in the month, or various scientists and Lowell Thomas, but also for the entire laboratory in a large French restaurant—DiBiasi's was much too small now for a lab party. He tried to be more selective about accepting invitations, but so often he felt "obliged" to attend functions Molly thought he could avoid. She protested again his lack of care of himself, accused him of availability to everybody, whether of government or science; the thousand and one demands made upon him need not all be recognized. "I thought he was treating himself as though he was expendable. I told him if he didn't take care of himself someone else would be doing the things he was doing. We had a long discussion, one day, just out of the blue. My outbursts always cleared the air. He assured me I didn't know how many things he did turn down. There were some things he had to do. His Washington business was for the President. He would get a lot of rest on a forthcoming Atoms for Peace trip to Japan."

There was no noticeable slackening of pace after their discussion; there were more trips to the East, Operation Teapot tests in Nevada, laboratory affairs, and the television plant. He thoroughly enjoyed one April journey when he ducked out of Washington for a day on the nuclear-powered submarine *Nautilus*. Commander Wilkinson called for him at his New London hotel for breakfast on board the submarine, which cast off at eight. He not only had a complete tour of the *Nautilus,* but, thanks to Admiral Rickover's suggestion, was allowed to operate the forward vanes and experience a dive and an underwater cruise before returning to New London at five in the afternoon. "A day that I shall never forget," he wrote "Rick" Rickover. "I wish I could tell you how much I appreciate your kindness and the special trouble you went to to make it possible for me to have such an experience."

The next day he crossed the country for lunch and discussion with an associate of the Rockefeller brothers, Najeeb Halaby, in Palm Springs. Halaby, who had first flown a jet plane across the United States, was entertained a day or two later with Laurance Rockefeller, after a tour of the Radiation Laboratory under the guidance of Ernest, McMillan, Alvarez, and Seaborg. Rockefeller—who offered to back Ernest with up to a quarter of a million dollars in any desired project—wrote of his Berkeley visit that there were two things he would like to know how to do. First, how to help Ernest Lawrence, and second, how to get Ernest's favorite restaurant to move to New York.

Early in May, Ernest went to Japan on an Atoms for Peace mission organized by John J. Hopkins, chairman and president of the corporation that had built the *Nautilus*. Hopkins, inspired by the President's U.N. speech, had proposed an atomic Marshall Plan to enable all nations to acquire the benefits of atomic energy. Matsutaro Shoriki, member of the Japanese Diet, newspaper owner, and president of Nippon Television, invited Hopkins, Ernest, and Lawrence Hafstad to assist in formation of an Atoms for Peace committee and to help allay Japanese opposition and fear of anything atomic. Vernon Welsh, Hopkin's assistant as vice-president of General Dynamics Corporation, arranged details for the Americans. The trip was "quite breathless" as Larry Hafstad wrote; there were few restful moments from arrival at Haneda Airport on May 6, and immediate press conferences there and at the Imperial Hotel, through a dozen very full days of conferences with, and talks to, government ministers, industrial leaders, physicists, and medical, biological and agricultural researchers. The Hopkins party met the Prime Minister the first morning and was entertained by him later in the week. They inspected research and technical institutes, and Ernest found time to visit Shoriki's television station, before he and Hafstad lectured at Science Institute Hall. There was an evening of public lectures in Hibya Park which Communist elements threatened to disrupt. The huge assembly overflowed the hall, until there were more people outside than within. Welsh worried that Ernest, his tall figure so easily identifiable, circulated carelessly among the crowd, well behaved for the most part, but pressing near the building's entrances. The speeches were all well received and loudly applauded whenever Atoms for Peace was mentioned.

In his address, Ernest said that he considered it a special privilege to return to beautiful Japan, to enjoy again the fine hospitality which he had experienced four years before, and to renew acquaintanceships with distinguished colleagues and friends, one of whom, Dr. Yoshio Fujioka, interpreted the address for him. He mentioned his friendships with Sagane, Yasaki, and Yukawa, who had contributed so much to the advancement of knowledge. He spoke of the biological and medical aspects of nuclear science, and of Japanese physicians prominent in the field. It was, however, nuclear science, "rather specifically its vital importance for the future of fundamental science," that he stressed. "We sometimes forget that nature is infinite and that we must always strive for a deeper knowledge of the laws of nature and that there is no end of this endeavor. To me it has been a wonderful experience to see how fundamental scientific research, where the only objective is always to understand a little more deeply, opens up vast new practical developments in completely unexpected directions."

He cited Roentgen's discovery of X rays, the result of efforts to understand electrical discharge in a vacuum tube; he concluded with discussions of practical applications of products from the cyclotron, the original purpose of which was pure research, and of recent experiments at the Rad Lab in therapeutic destruction of the human pituitary gland— normally requiring a difficult surgical excision—by high-energy beams from the 184-inch cyclotron. Slides illustrated the method of rotation of a patient so that only the gland received the full destructive dose. He expressed hope that the future of this science, still in its infancy, might contribute to health and happiness. "As a member of the older generation of scientists who has been privileged to observe at close hand the bounty that nature has in store for those who seek her truth, it is my privilege and duty to do all I can to urge ever more generous support of fundamental scientific research the world over, for the well-being of all mankind."

The Japanese press devoted hundreds of columns to the mission, was laudatory of the speeches, and appeared to have dropped resistance and fear of a Japanese atomic energy program. Conferences with representatives of the scientific, religious, cultural, and educational fields, after the lectures, had a more optimistic air. The last meeting with the members of the Japanese Atomic Energy Commission was most fruitful; there was eagerness to arrange for enriched uranium for reactors from the United States. On May 14, the Americans were flown to Osaka; the last evening and night were spent in Kyoto, the ancient capital of Japan, which had remained unbombed throughout the war, where they were entertained by famous geisha.

Molly met Ernest in Honolulu on the return journey, for a pleasant vacation together. They were entertained by the Commander of Joint Task Force Seven, Admiral Charles B. Momsen, and his wife, and

spent an afternoon at Regent Pauley's Coconut Island, a short distance
from the city. They visited several islands; near Hilo the volcano goddess
Pele put on "an unusually good show." Gordon MacDonald of the Volcano Observatory took them closer to the eruption than tourists are
usually permitted—so close that Molly was a little worried. "But he
knew what was safe and what wasn't. We went out on cooling cinders
that had come down the day before. . . . We could watch the erup-
tions, streams and masses of stuff would shoot into the air and rivers of
molten lava come down, quite within sight—actually down to the road
where we walked. The volcanologist knew just how long it took to reach
certain points, but there was hot material so near us we could feel its
heat. The wall of burning red and white hot material about four feet
high, well, it was more like a river; trees fell and traveled with it. We
walked around and took pictures. Ernest was fascinated; I was sort of
nervous, but MacDonald said, 'Don't worry. It's one of those slow-
moving things. I'll tell you when it's time to get back.' " That was but
one of many interesting experiences of their week in the islands, a week
in which Ernest actually relaxed; he seemed rested when they returned
to Berkeley on the evening of May 27.

There were ten days in Berkeley—highlighted by the visit of Mark
and Mrs. Oliphant, traveling around the world. Oliphant was always
excited by the Rad Lab—and there was always much for the old colleagues to discuss. Ernest then flew to New York and was in Washington
on June 20 for the presentation of the Barnard Medal to Merle Tuve.
He returned by way of Los Angeles to visit Regent Pauley. Among other
matters, he told Pauley that York and his wife were to leave on a deserved vacation trip which should be extended to a circuit of the globe.
Dr. and Mrs. York left on July 1 for six weeks—and went around the
world.

Professor Birge retired on July 1 and was succeeded as chairman of
the physics department by Carl Helmholz. Birge's secretary, Rebekah
Young, who had been in the office when Ernest joined the department,
retired the same day. Among the events in honor of their long tenures
was a party for both professor and secretary, given by Rebekah's nonaca-
demic university friends, to which the physics staff was invited. Birge did
his best to create the impression that the party was solely for Rebekah,
as she said, "not wanting me to feel too uncomfortably insignificant as
co-honoree with a person of his eminence." But it was for the faithful
secretary as well as for the distinguished professor that Ernest attended
the party. Birge, as emeritus professor, would have an office in Le Conte
Hall and be available; Rebekah would be missed. It was said—and no
one could dispute it—that never had a chairman anywhere presided
over a physics department of such phenomenal growth. Ernest had much

respect for the more statistically minded physicist, and Birge certainly was proud of Ernest and the Rad Lab, which only a month before his retirement had commenced construction of yet another accelerator, the Hilac heavy ion accelerator that had been planned with the Yale crew. Reconstruction of the 184-inch that would enable it to reach still higher energies was also under way—and during the past year element 101, the ninth of the transuranium group, heavier than uranium, had been artificially created.

Ernest had planned, as so often before, an extended vacation at Balboa with his family during the summer, but, after a couple of days there, he suddenly decided to have the front section of the old house remodeled. The kitchen had been made more convenient with new steel cabinets and a dishwasher, but, except for painting, little else had been done at Balboa. With his usual enthusiasm, he called in carpenters —and the front of the house was torn off. Before the summer was over, plans were altered until the entire house was scheduled for reconstruction. He saw paneled interiors at another house and decided on that for certain rooms. Plans were changed as necessary to incorporate other ideas he picked up, as interest made him observant wherever he went. Ralph Chaney recalls that Ernest usually paid little attention to decor; he never mentioned or seemed to notice the fine Oriental objects and decoration most people exclaimed over in the Chaney home. People absorbed his interest, not the room—it was still observed that one felt he had Ernest's sole interest—before he plunged into physics, or television, or national safety. Now walls, ceilings, fixtures were studied.

An architect was brought in late, and a builder, both on a cost-plus basis. Ernest was absent much of this time, and it was rather difficult for Molly, but the children had a tremendous time, as more and more of the old structure was demolished—until Molly sent them back to Berkeley with Maggie and moved to her parents' house nearby. "It was impossible to sleep there"—but someone had to supervise.

Margaret remembers: "Dad's thought was to use most of the old house which actually slanted from its foundations. He said, 'Why not just support it with a few steel beams on each side and then we could knock the walls every which way as desired.' I remember telling him makeshift remodeling jobs invariably cost more than tearing all down and starting over, but Dad was convinced his scheme would work, so it was remodeled piece by piece. One morning, late no doubt, Mary and I were rudely awakened by a face at an open door, saying 'You'd better get up, your room is next.' The front of the house was torn off by then, and we climbed down a ladder to the remnants of the first floor. We lived in literally half a house for over a month. Dad rarely came down. I think he had a few go-arounds with the contractor about how it could be done in an easier manner, but he got a kick out of it, particularly some of Robert's humor, like the time he got a big pail of magenta paint and in large letters, across the board wall protecting us against the elements and the public—because the whole front of the house was gone—wrote 'CONDEMNED.' I remember one night Mother and I were in the living room in our coats trying to read. There were holes in the board barrier stuffed with curtains, and some couple strolling around the island seemed concerned and stopped outside. The woman said, 'Oh, George, these poor unfortunate people, trying to hold on to their home which has been condemned.' Obviously Mom and I had difficulty controlling laughter.

"But the whole project was very important to Dad. He desperately wanted a place where he could get off to himself and away from the constant confusion and noise of us kids and our numerous friends. Of course he never complained of illness. If we had been more alert, we would have realized that some of the difficulties we had getting along with him were due to the fact that he was not well, but we just didn't know he was really ill. We had wonderful times with him, boating, water skiing, swimming. He did all these things like a happy inexperienced kid; he drove the boat like a madman, which we all loved—except Barbara, who wouldn't go with him unless Mom came along."

Molly had to return to Berkeley for the start of the children's schools and her own community commitments. Work on the house dragged on throughout the winter. Ernest and Molly made occasional trips to inspect it or to confer with architect and builder. It was not finished until the following May. Ernest had periodically paid out a thousand or more dollars, but, as arrangements had been verbal, he was badly shocked to learn the total cost. Margaret had been right; it would have been far cheaper to tear the old house down and start over. As it was, he felt that advantage had been taken of him, and he asked Bill Douglass, the laboratory attorney, for advice. Everything was settled amicably; it had been an experience, he had learned a lesson, and in the future such arrangements would be written. Anyway, it was a fine, attractive, and comfortable house at last; he would spend much more time in it now. His and Molly's bedroom occupied the whole front of the second floor and had a wide, enclosed porch facing the bay.

Early in August he was in Geneva as a scientific representative at the long-delayed Atoms for Peace Conference, which followed the summit meeting. Dag Hammarskjöld, the U.N. Secretary General, had asked Ernest and Professor Vladimir Veksler, of the Russian Academy, to lecture on accelerators on the same evening. Ernest therefore called on Veksler as soon as he arrived in Geneva and invited him to dinner so that they might coordinate their lectures. Veksler accepted with apparent pleasure, and, since Seaborg would be with Ernest, Veksler agreed to bring A. P. Vinogradov, the Russian expert in transuranium chemistry.

Consequently, on the first night of the conference, which opened August 8 in the magnificent hall of the Palais des Nations, Ernest, Seaborg, and Professor John Turkevich of Princeton, acting as interpreter, called for the guests at the Hotel Metropole. The Russians preferred to follow in their own car to what Ernest had been told was Geneva's finest French restaurant. After a few toasts, Ernest and Veksler discussed their lectures. Veksler said his phasotron—similar to the Bevatron—produced ten-billion-volt protons, and that its magnet weighed 36,000 tons—four times as much as the steel in the Bevatron. He spoke of government interest in their scientists, of their high pay—even compared with that of industrialists—and of the financial support accorded science by the Soviets. Ernest found his guests courteous, friendly, and apparently uninhibited in conversation. It was an enjoyable, profitable evening and seemed to verify his thesis that exchange, however brief and limited, could only promote understanding.

Their lectures the evening of the eleventh were illustrated with slides, and it was apparent that Russian scientists "knew what they were doing," at least as far as accelerators were concerned. One of the younger Russians said that he had never heard the word "cyclotron" before coming to the conference, that where he had studied, the circular accelerator was referred to as a "Lawrence." Veksler regretted that Ernest had been unable to attend a conference in Moscow, just preceding the Geneva affair, to which he had been invited too late. Ernest, too, would very much have liked firsthand observation of Russian scientific work. Many other invited scientists had had to decline for the same reason. Rabi told Ernest that during meetings to select the ten conference speakers, the Russians followed each of their proposals by pointing out with emphasis that the nominee was a member of the Academy of Sciences of the U.S.S.R. Rabi had been equally emphatic, when he nominated Ernest, that Professor Lawrence was a member of the Soviet Academy of Science, and everyone had laughed.

Ernest felt that the conference, attended by nearly 1,500 scientists, marked a stride forward in surmounting Cold War barriers—for scientists anyway—and that science soon again might enjoy the free international communion it had known before the rise of totalitarianism. Certainly the Americans had shown their sincerity and goodwill. They released much heretofore secret information, and a complete, swimming-pool-type reactor was flown to Geneva from Oak Ridge for display in action. It became the conference's most popular exhibit. This open reactor enabled observers to look down into the water and to see the blue glow of radiation as it demonstrated controlled fission. The exchange between delegates, curious about each other, that occurred at social affairs, was as valuable as formal sessions, Ernest thought, in dispelling suspicion. He was amused at certain Europeans who, recently critical of American secrecy, were now as critical of American generosity which they thought might endanger the security of the free world. Free world scientists had much to discuss with each other, as well as with Russians. Niels Bohr, Cockcroft, and De Hevesy were others among the ten principal speakers, as were Willard Libby and Hans Bethe of the United States. Laura Fermi, invited by Strauss, was delegation historian. H. J. Bhabha of India was president of the conference; delegates included scientists from every area. Numbers of nonscientific people came for the exhibits. Ernest asked an Italian, who had introduced himself and had struck up a conversation, if he was a scientist. "No, just a schoolteacher." "Wonderful!" Ernest said, "I'm a schoolteacher too."

With John, who had been involved in a committee on medical aspects, Ernest flew to Spain for three days following the conference, before returning to America. He reported on the conference and what he had learned of Russian science at the first university meeting of the Berkeley fall semester, held out of doors on the campus to accommodate the crowd. He had one regret, after receipt of a letter addressed to him in Geneva and forwarded to Berkeley after his departure. It was an invitation to dine with Rolf Wideröe, whose article in a magazine had inspired the cyclotron.

Somewhat later, at a symposium honoring the twenty-fifth anniversary of Sproul as president, Ernest discussed the growth of the physics department at Berkeley in the quarter century of President Sproul's tenure. Whereas the total department budget in 1930 had been $104,850, and the staff had consisted of a faculty of sixteen with twenty-four teaching assistants, in 1955 there were thirty-four faculty members, fifty-four teaching assistants, and twenty readers, with a budget of $511,494 exclusive of the much larger Radiation Laboratory and medical physics sums from research grants of the Federal Government. Enrollment had doubled during the twenty-five-year period. By 1955, 10 percent of the National Academy's roster of member-physicists were from the University of California. Ernest spoke of Sproul's support and of Professors Leuschner and Lewis, who had done so much to promote the physical sciences, and of the work of Chairman Birge and others of the physics department. He cited the debt owed to Robert Oppenheimer, who, within the department, had developed the leading theoretical school of the country, and, after sketching the history of the cyclotron, he credited his associates past and present in the Rad Lab, and concluded with the first public announcement of the recent discovery of the long-sought negative proton by Segrè, Owen Chamberlain, C. E. Wiegand, and T. Ypsilantis, with important help from Lofgren, who was in general charge of the Bevatron, from which billions of electron volts had made the identification possible. Notice of the discovery of this "nuclear ghost which had haunted the world's physicists for generations," as Ernest described it, precipitated a flood of congratulatory messages.

On October 26, Ernest introduced Sir John Cockcroft at a luncheon meeting of the National Industrial Conference Board in New York, and two days later, at Yale, he spoke at the dedication of the Willard Gibbs Research Center. In the latter address, he spoke of days as recent as those of Josiah Willard Gibbs, when physicists, chemists, and biologists were known as natural philosophers. "The great scientists of earlier times were interested in all aspects of nature. Now we are in the age of specialization, perhaps at times overemphasized; accelerator programs provide solution to overspecialization in that they unite scientists from various disciplines in fine teamwork." He spoke of the recent excellent collaboration of Yale and Berkeley in the design and construction of the new heavy ion accelerators.

Ernest had nearly delayed the ceremonies. While walking toward the podium with President Whitney Griswold and Pan American President Juan Trippe, he spotted a familiar face in the crowd of two or three thousand people, and excused himself from his escorts to visit the old South Dakota friend. It was Ferdinand Smith, to whom Dean Akeley had suggested dropping physics for baseball. Ernest exchanged stories with Smith until President Griswold politely requested permission to take Dr. Lawrence to the stand.

Two weeks later, at a California regents dinner meeting honoring regents emeriti, Ernest spoke again of the history of the cyclotron and of the help the regents had been since that early day when Regent Ehrman had taken him to lunch and said, "Dr. Lawrence, don't you worry about the budget. It's our problem to find the funds. You just push ahead with the experiments." Succeeding regents and administrators, Ernest said, including President Sproul, Vice-President Corley and Secretary-Treasurer Underhill, had been important not only because of their financial support but also in the sense of security their confidence had given to those in the Rad Lab.

Of the many visitors to Berkeley in the latter months of 1955—and they included generals, admirals, government officials, and international figures—the one who meant most to Ernest was Otto Hahn, with his son Hanno. The anti-Nazi physicist, who had split the uranium atom in Germany on the eve of the war, had been invited by Ernest while at the Geneva Conference, and, through Rowan Gaither, the Ford Foundation had arranged the journey and stay in the United States. After his Berkeley lectures, Hahn was taken by Ernest to Yosemite, to Palm Springs, and to the Ed Janss Ranch—where Hahn was allowed to fly a plane, with a pilot beside him. Hahn's gratitude to Ernest, Gaither, and the Foundation was profuse. Ernest had urged on Gaither the importance of scientific exchange and the usefulness the Ford Foundation might render to science and engineering: "We've got to get more good engineers in the United States; we don't have enough." Gaither said the grants and formulation of science programs of the Foundation owed much to Ernest.

Shortly after the first of the year, 1956, Ernest went East, ostensibly on consultant matters—he did visit Eastman, General Electric, and American Cyanamid people—but actually for unpublicized meetings that concluded an October classified assignment to his Stassen Task Force. He verbally reported conclusions to Stassen before dinner at the former governor's Chevy Chase home. On his return to Berkeley, he found a letter from President Eisenhower expressing gratitude and "earnest commendation for adding another chapter in your distinguished career of service. . . . Your effort may conceivably turn out to be of great and historic significance. . . . I'm glad that you have agreed to continue to serve as needed in this matter." Another from General Walter Bedell Smith expressed appreciation for support and wholehearted cooperation that made possible "the accomplishment of a project of great personal significance to the President and are deserving of the highest praise." It was not long before Ernest's Scientific Task Force was again—in February—asked to consider, in the President's words, ". . . the problem referred to as 'disarmament.' "

Ernest and Molly had hoped to entertain the Loomises and Gaithers in the refurbished Balboa establishment, in the middle of March, after a Rand Corporation meeting in Santa Monica, but they realized, after an earlier March visit, that there was too much to be done before house guests could be comfortable. They postponed selecting rugs, linoleum, and furniture. They did serve cocktails on the upstairs porch of their unfinished house but stayed at a marina motel. The house, to all intents "new" and designed to their taste, was not occupied until after Ernest's return from the May Redwing tests at Eniwetok.

Ernest was much interested in the preparations at Livermore for Operation Redwing, as in all Livermore activities, which became increasingly fascinating, whether directly applicable to weapons, or the Sherwood Projects for peaceful uses of fusion—still classified, since much of the information was basic to both military and peaceful applications. Methods of handling plasmas, gases made up of charged particles, many thousands of degrees beyond the melting point of any solid container —in magnetic fields—were exciting, as were efforts to "pinch" plasmas to heighten further the possibility of fusion. Operation Redwing, however, was notable as the first test in which a fusion bomb was actually dropped on a target from a plane. It was successful but, however much more powerful and sophisticated, did not carry the thrill of the Trinity test, eleven years earlier, when Ernest had been impelled to jump up and down for joy. Evidence that this was not diminution of youthful enthusiasm was apparent after a helicopter ride which York arranged for him. "It was just as if he was a young kid out to do it, and when he got back he just bubbled about what great sport it was—a very youthful approach."

There was time for a few days with Molly at Balboa, after Redwing, most of them occupied with final details of the remodeling and furnishing—and settlement of differences with builders. He was satisfied, however, that it was now a place where he could relax, even with the children and their playmates tearing through the house. That front upstairs room was a dead end; he could seclude himself there without interfering with healthy play. Household sounds could be shut out, even though beach noises—swimmers, motorboats, and all manner of shouts and calls—could not. He assured Molly that he would now use the Balboa house much more—as soon as he returned from Europe. He missed Eric's graduation in political science. From the university, Eric would go to Naval Officer Candidate School at Newport, Rhode Island.

Ernest arrived on June 11, in Geneva, where he found a car provided by the Ford Motor Company waiting for his personal use—thanks to Gaither. It had been driven from Belgium by Mrs. Walter McKey, wife of the Ford director for Europe, who was in America. He found Mrs. McKey pleasant company at dinner, a time or two, and the use of the car most helpful, particularly in getting to CERN, or to the home of its new director, Cornelis Bakker. The Bakkers entertained a large number of scientists from various conferences assembled in the Swiss city; one met American and foreign colleagues everywhere. There was a pleasant afternoon with Stan Livingston, who had come for one of these affairs. They discussed, with some amazement, the extent to which accelerators had developed and how far afield they had spread! Actually high-energy physics, teamwork in science, the big laboratory—most of the amazing growth of science, from atom bomb, fusion, and tracer techniques to transuranium elements and artificial cosmic ray particles, could be said to stem from the early cyclotrons.

Stan thought Ernest actually surprised that it had all gone so far and so fast and that its influence had been so important in so many areas. It was as though he had never reflected on, never really assessed, his influence and that of his laboratory. It seemed to Stan, noting the deference everywhere accorded him, that Ernest's importance was "because of his being a personality." His infectious enthusiasm, still most evident, continued to inspire those around him. "His own farseeing view—the things that he was enthusiastic about, were things that were important, and pulled people into the field. I feel that he was really a major personality in science . . . perhaps this inspiration to others was the major contribution."

Inspiration was certainly a big factor in Ernest's wide influence, but it was only one factor—for example, in Warren Weaver's assessment. "I never knew another scientist, indeed any other person, who so absorbed others and made them greater than they were. He pulled others into his orbit." Perhaps Oppenheimer best expressed this influence in other fields than physics, when he spoke of Ernest's early recognition and "this really very farseeing support of the use of physical means in biological studies. Things are happening now in regard to genetic codes, and so on, that were not done in Berkeley—were not what Ernest had in mind, but they are direct consequences of techniques to which he gave such impetus. And when he got the Nobel Prize, this is one of the things in the citation, and rightly so." Others, who knew of his influence at Geneva, including the Indian Bhabha and the Dutch Bakker, spoke of his stature as a "scientific statesman," and that assessment was increasingly and independently being made in the United States, beginning with the President.

Ernest managed a brief stay at Balboa after Geneva, though it was incidental to a trip to Los Angeles with Seaborg for a conference with Walt Disney, also attended by Randy Hearst, on the possibility of animated films for science education—and a meeting with Pauley, now chairman of the Board of Regents. Pauley offered rest and relaxation at Coconut Island for as long as Ernest and Molly might wish to stay in Hawaii. It was tempting, but Ernest had accepted the invitation of the Secretary of the Navy for a cruise around the Horn on the refurbished aircraft carrier *Franklin Delano Roosevelt*. Ernest's old friend, Chick Hayward was in command—because, Ernest said, he was the only captain in the Navy who was a Democrat. "They couldn't have a Republican in command of the *Franklin Delano Roosevelt*." At ceremonies when he assumed command of the ship, Hayward was presented with a beautiful package, which, divested of its fancy wrappings, was found to contain an ordinary lifesaver, on one side of which was lettered "Theodore Roosevelt," and on the other, "I like Ike." Hayward was certain that Ernest had "put the boys up to it." He also thought the trip would be good for the tired physicist and had suggested that he be among the guests. Ernest was unable to leave with the ship from Bremerton; he joined the cruise in Chile. On his flight from Miami to Panama, his seatmate, Mr. Nichols, was a California alumnus who had established a business in Lima, Peru. Ernest spent a day in Panama before continuing to Lima, where Nichols and his wife and Julian Smith met him. Smith of Cerro de Pasco Corporation, had been notified of his arrival by mining engineer and regent Don McLaughlin. Between them, they provided a fine time and thorough sight-seeing in Peru, including flights to Cuzco and Machu Picchu. Ernest flew over the high Andes for a quick visit in Buenos Aires with the Argentine AEC and back across them to Valparaiso where he met Hayward, just before the captain was to place a wreath at the statue of Arturo Pratt, naval hero of the Chilean war with Spain.

Ernest was given the admiral's quarters on the huge carrier for the interesting and relaxing voyage. Once he had satisfied his curiosity about the intricacies of the great ship, he leisurely painted or read—or just loafed and studied the sea, or the wake. He talked to various assemblies of officers, crew, and other guests about challenges to the free world, atoms for peace, and problems involved in the proper inspection so essential to any disarmament agreement. There were interesting discussions with others among the dozen and a half civilians, among whom were Norris Bradbury of Los Alamos, and two businessmen with whom there was continuing friendship after the cruise, James MacWilliams Stone and Vladimir A. Reichel. There was much good-natured horseplay; Ernest and Bradbury were elected to judge the ship's company's beard contest. At the southernmost point of the cruise, below the Horn and almost to the Weddell Sea, where cold-water tests were undergone, the announcement came over the radio that Hayward had been selected an admiral. Ernest got a cake baked in the shape of an admiral's hat and carried it to the table himself. Hayward, who had been injured with hot engine oil when his plane was hit during World War II, guessed he was the only one-eyed admiral in the service. In previous talks with Ernest, he had discussed leaving the Navy because of the eye trouble, or to accept more remunerative work. Ernest always protested with reasonable persuasion that Hayward must not quit. "We have to have knowledgeable people in the service." Now he could congratulate him that each decision to remain had been correct.

Though he had talked a good deal with hearty Mac Stone of going ashore for celebrations in Trinidad and Barbados, Ernest left the ship in Rio de Janeiro to fly home. He was rested; why prolong the indolence when there was so much to do? His flight from Rio was delayed, for which Ernest later was glad, since he thereby crossed the fascinating Amazonian jungles in daylight. After two days in New York, he flew to Los Angeles for a weekend with the family at Balboa. He was at the Rad Lab before August 10 to greet General Doolittle for consultations pertaining to the Stassen mission. He thought it important to be in

Berkeley for the visit of Veksler and a group of Russian scientists. Personally, with McMillan, he showed Veksler the Rad Lab complex, from the Old Rad Lab wooden building, Crocker and Donner laboratories on the campus proper, to the Bevatron and other accelerators on the hill, crowned by the dome of the 184-inch cyclotron. He entertained them at home and elsewhere, confident that their common interests and friendship would be helpful to wider general understanding. Veksler, particularly, was a strong advocate of international cooperation among scientists. Ernest thought him very likeable, as well as a fine scientist.

The house was less crowded with only the younger children around, but Ernest missed those who were away, though Margaret, in her junior year at Stanford, was frequently at home for weekends. Fifteen-year-old Robert, now the young man of the family, spent much of his time downstairs in his "bunkroom," the old laundry room which Molly had refurbished with paint, double decker bunks, home varnished unfinished furniture, and drapes and bedspreads patterned with cowboys and bucking broncos. The little girls, Barbara and Susan, were usually around when Ernest was at home; just nine and almost seven, they could still be cuddled, tossed, and jostled. Margaret treasures a "marvelous photograph Eric took of Barbara and Susan snuggled in their father's arms in his living room chair." Mary was in Portland, Oregon, at Reed College, her own choice after deliberation, of which Ernest was proud. He noted that its academic standing was high, which was easy to believe, remembering Brady and other students whose undergraduate work had been at Reed. He would have been happy if his older children, particularly Eric, had been interested enough in science to make it a career.

Margaret remembers the educational aims he thought every young person should have: work hard, as hard as necessary to be the best in the field—plenty of time later to reap the benefits and have fun. "He had strong prejudices as to what kind of learning and careers were important, that is, science!! If you have a strong scientific education, you can do anything. Don't major in engineering if you want to be an engineer; if you want to be an engineer, major in physics and learn engineering on the job, or on your own. Don't be a dentist, be a doctor, and so on. Philosophy is dead, humanities are secondary to science." It was hard for him to understand Eric's serious devotion to photography—though it had been Ernest's idea to construct a darkroom for Eric in the loft of the garage—but Eric's interest in the Navy could be heartily approved. Mary's often rebellious independence had, he thought, asserted itself well in choosing a college. She had a fine mind. Robert, always smiling and somewhat harum-scarum, had to be urged to pay enough attention to high-school studies, if he were to get into college. Molly had threatened not to pay his doctor bills if he persisted in being a daredevil—to which he had replied, "But, Mother, it's such fun, and sometimes you get away with it."

In September, Ernest was elected a trustee of the Rand Corporation, of which Rowan Gaither was chairman of the board. Rowan had no hesitation in advising Ernest's participation in organizations of national importance, though he was still zealous in attempting to prevent involvement in less worthy associations that would demand much time and energy. Regent chairman Pauley also endeavored to save Ernest's health and energies, not only by frequent offers of Coconut Island for rest and vacations but also the use of his personal plane for trips in California—sometimes simply to bring him and Molly south for a day at his home, and perhaps to see a professional football game, or to and from Balboa. Ernest, as he had before this fall, asked for a rain check for Coconut Island; he felt rested, and he never considered most laboratory duties as work. It was a pleasure to be with old friends of Oak Ridge days, Clarence Larson, George Felbeck, and Lyman Bliss at Parma, Ohio, for the dedication of new Union Carbide and Carbon Corporation laboratories on September 18, and it was always heartening to see laboratory expansion in industry. He was in Berkeley for the event of 1956 at the Rad Lab; in September the anti-neutron was discovered by a team which included Bruce Cork, O. Piccioni, Y. Lambertson, and W. Wenzel. That was the principal topic during a Teller-hosted nuclear panel at the Rad Lab early in October.

The Hungarian revolt of October 23 crushed hopes of radical change in Russian attitudes, considered possible after the death of Stalin. Jimmy Vale remembers that Ernest was ". . . particularly disturbed by it. He thought it a pity we didn't give any real help. Really very upset over it, though he realized what might have happened if we had gone over to interfere. I don't think Teller, though Hungarian, had anything to do with Ernest's feelings." American international intentions again were plainly demonstrated on the twenty-sixth when, with eighty-one others of the United Nations, agreement was reached on an International Atomic Energy Agency for peaceful use of the atom, and the United States offered it eleven thousand pounds of uranium 235. Because he considered international goodwill so important, Ernest accepted the request of Herbert Hoover, Jr., Assistant Secretary of State, to join a scientific advisory committee for the Brussels Exhibition, and agreed to attend a five-day November meeting in Belgium as scientific adviser.

Pro-and-con argument over testing and fallout in the current presidential campaign was very injurious, Ernest thought, internationally as well as at home. Fallout danger still was vastly overestimated by many opponents; incorrect statistics were used in a demagogic manner. As for testing—he couldn't imagine a good scientist in opposition. Experiment must be continuous, never static.

Alfred Loomis explained Ernest's point of view: "If you want to find the truth, you must continue experiment. You don't know what you will find, perhaps a completely physical fact that will revolutionize concepts of nature. Not necessarily revolutionize concepts of weapons for war, but a way to create a proper environment of heat [for fusion], and only by testing can that be done. I can't imagine him not believing in testing, because he knew the fields were unlimited in possibilities, and to arbitrarily stop is like saying 'What's the use of building the Bevatron? We don't need to know any more about it.' He knew as much about fallout as anybody, but he approached it as a scientist, not as a political weapon. Nobody can foresee without experiment how new scientific knowledge can be applied to peaceful or to utilitarian purposes. That's why he wanted Livermore. He felt there should be more courage in experimentation, and not just continue it, as always had been done. He knew big jumps ought to be taken here and there to see if we could open up new things, so they had some failures, but they learned from them how to be successful. Failure can supply most useful information. Any laboratory will test something to destruction to find out how far they are from failure. Does it take ten times the force to cause failure, or only twice the force? Experiments which cause failure are often the most crucial of all."

Mac Stone, fellow guest on the Cape Horn cruise, was emphatically vocal on political use of testing and fallout hysteria at his San Francisco hotel, before politics was banished as a subject at his dinner party. Stone, a hearty extrovert, then entertained guests with stories of Ernest on the cruise, between each of which he'd shake his head and practically shout, "The best Goddamn egghead I ever met," or "He's great, great, a real human animal—not one of your ivory tower birds!" He related how Ernest, contrary to Navy regulations, had liquor up in "the admiral's country—which was all his. Hayward and I would go up there before lunch or dinner and find him sitting there, maybe with his feet up on something, with a glass of scotch in his hand. He'd say, 'Don't worry—doctor's orders.' Hayward got so nervous when an orderly or anyone knocked, I thought he was going to hide under the chair or something. But whoever came in, Ernest would just sit there with his medicine in his hand and say 'doctor's orders.' I didn't have a drink until we hit the beach at Rio. . . . He was the most normal egghead I ever saw—except he thought there was only one good school in the country. A regular prune-picker he was—just one school—Berkeley!"

The next day, Sunday, Ernest took Stone and his guest Sue Heyman to the Berkeley tennis club for doubles. "Ernest gets this ringer on me —a pro from the tennis club—and by God, we played on concrete! Can you imagine that! Tennis ought to be played on a lawn! Then afterward he asked us to go to his house for something impromptu and very special, 'tube steaks.' Said he was surprised I hadn't tried them, they were so good. Well, we had them. They were *wieners*." While Ernest mixed cocktails, Stone asked if he really believed that testing was safe and important, and fallout "a phony issue." Ernest said, "Absolutely." Stone then tried to persuade him that it was his duty as a loyal American citizen to say so, so that everyone would know. Teller had tried previously to get Ernest to make a statement to counteract antitest advice given to Adlai Stevenson. Ernest had refused, insisting that scientists should keep out of partisan politics, that it was his principle to avoid public statements. As cocktails were downed, Stone demanded to meet Teller, who was then invited to come to the house. Teller refused to argue with Ernest, but Stone persisted and Ernest finally agreed to issue a joint statement with Teller.

After it was written, they called Daniel Wilkes of University Public Information, who arrived after Stone had left, and sat down at the table and threshed out a proper statement for release, Molly and Wilkes moderating somewhat what the men had planned to say. Wilkes thought the timing poor, two days before the election, which he thought Eisenhower would win in a landslide. He stressed that morning papers would dislike breaking an already set page late Sunday night for a statement on the subject. Wilkes got the idea that Ernest agreed with him, but, "feeling no pain" at the moment, thought it would please Strauss, who had much earlier urged that he make his views on the subject known to the public. Teller didn't approve the statement as written and went upstairs and wrote a stronger, longer one which Wilkes argued could only be taken politically. Ernest, after thorough discussions in which Molly joined, chose Wilkes's draft, which was phoned to the morning papers.

The statement mentioned the physicists' long and close connection with nuclear weapons, the H-bomb test program, and other facts— Ernest refused to include his participation on the Stassen policy committee. It was, however, pointed out that the belief that detection methods were infallible was an unfortunate misconception; there were no known methods of certain detection; it was impossible to maintain "a fast-moving scientific and technical nuclear weapons program without tests"; one can never be certain that a device will work until it is tested; the country could fall far behind technically without continuing tests; radioactivity produced by testing is insignificant, as shown by the National Academy of Sciences' study. Finally, "We are convinced that no matter who is elected President, tests will continue to be carried on with scrupulous regard to public health."

Reactions were immediate and vigorous, pro and con. Much criticism from opponents of testing decried the issuance of such a statement the day before the national election. But congratulatory telegrams and letters far outnumbered those that were critical. "Of course they did," Teller said. "The point is that this whole fallout scare is something which is completely ridiculous. Really completely ridiculous, and I think ninety-nine percent of the scientists know it." Oppenheimer remembered that he "had the gravest misgivings when Stevenson raised this issue during his campaign, because I loved the fellow, but the one on the inside had all the advantages. It was sure to be loused up, because of the fact that Stevenson couldn't possibly do the necessary homework."

Ernest asked Jimmy Vale to set up television at Amy's Los Baños ranch, so that election centers and headquarters across the country could be watched as returns came in. Vale drove Ernest to Los Baños and back, the night of November 6, "Just chatting about things, the kids, different things, no business. He seemed more mellow. I said, 'I'm an FDR man myself.' Ernest replied 'I was, too, but toward the end there were some mistakes.' "

He stayed no longer than necessary in Europe as American scientific adviser for the Brussels Exhibition meeting. He hurried back to New York for conferences with Paramount people, and on to Berkeley. The TV business was in trouble, not only with Chromatic; color TV had not been accepted well by the public. Gow remembered: "People were starting to move out. Instead of clamor for sample tubes, you couldn't give them away. With Chromatic there were strong differences between financial control in New York and the technical end in Berkeley. Difficulties of communication and resultant hard feelings between individuals put Ernest under a great strain. Perhaps I was more aware than others, perhaps had a little better perspective—I was right in the middle of the battles. It was a difficult period. The fault was not entirely on one side or the other. Once somebody at Paramount told Ernest something which he repeated at a press conference; it was my bad luck to find out it wasn't so. There was a very unpleasant scene at Paramount. I had to tell Ernest what went on. He recognized that in a sense he had been had a little. We made a point of this with Paramount people, that there was one thing they couldn't do, that this man's scientific reputation could not be compromised on things of this kind. On the other hand, they didn't understand that when Ernest said such and such a thing would work, he meant that he and his people could invent around and make it work. Ernest disliked having anything to do with arguments over which guy was right and which was wrong. He could not control New York and felt guilty that millions of dollars had been put into it without much to show. I think he was seeking a way out, to get it off his back—but in a clearly honorable way.

"Then he suddenly proposed a relatively new idea which was entirely technical. Had a big meeting with all the consultants and the Emeryville management. We started looking at sample pictures on a tube Vale and I had thrown together using this new principle. Ernest asked how we liked it. It was very interesting because all of us who knew Ernest at the lab were perfectly confident that it would work out. Management people looked a little bit pessimistic. Suggestions were made. Craig Nunan, director of research, was silent until Ernest asked what part he was going to play in the new program, and Craig said, 'None! I'm leaving!' This, I think, was the morale crash point of the operation, and the only time I've ever seen clean-cut defiance of Ernest. It was a shocking thing! He was particularly hurt. Just sat there, dead silence in the room—an intensely dramatic moment—and then the organization really started to come apart at the seams. New York pretty much lost confidence. Not in the *basic principles* and not in *Ernest,* but in the facility out here."

Efforts were made to interest others in taking over Chromatic. Ernest was most cooperative, hoping Paramount could recover the millions they had put into it. There were manifestations of considerable interest in getting it, too—from Columbia Broadcasting Company, the Philco people, and others. Ernest made a special trip to Holland with Borge Hansen-Møller, who had been brought in to help, in January, 1957, to see Philips officials. Borge wished to go by ship, and they sailed on the S.S. *United States,* though Ernest had at first refused to "waste" four and a half days crossing the Atlantic—until John advised it.

Once aboard, Ernest said, "Sorry, Borge, my brother says I have to rest. So I'll be in the cabin most of the time." He did remain in his cabin until about four each afternoon, when he came on deck "for air." Rested and invigorated, he would appear for dinner and would dance half the night—at least once until three in the morning. He won the captain's prize for dancing—a bottle of champagne—and then insisted on treating others to the bubbly wine. His watch was still on California time when they arrived in London, where he made a five-minute motion-picture talk for the Institution of Electrical Engineers of London about the Faraday Medal, which he had received in America in 1952. Ernest and Borge then flew to Amsterdam, where Casimir had a Philips car to meet and take them to Eindhoven. Ernest thought the discussions and preliminary negotiations went very well. They were returned to London in Mr. Philips' private plane, and Ernest stayed a few days at Claridge's, where John, who had been at a meeting in Paris, joined him. They visited the Harwell and Manchester laboratories before returning to New York.

A contradictory situation developed at Paramount, according to Gow. Paul Raiborne, a Paramount vice-president, and chairman of the board of Chromatic Television Laboratories, continued to believe as he had from the very beginning—that Chromatic was a very valuable property. Whenever an interested firm attempted serious negotiations, Raiborne invariably offered unacceptable terms. The strain of hope and frustration affected Ernest, who finally realized that little could be accomplished with divided control. An arrangement was ultimately worked out whereby the Emeryville facility, and a license to manufacture tubes for military purposes, were sold to Litton. Tubes for entertainment purposes would be further developed in New York. Ernest profited from the arrangement, and remained as consultant to both Litton and Paramount. The New York laboratory ultimately became Paramount's Autometric—a successful operation that would have been impossible without Chromatic. The color tube continued to be made on a small scale, and Paramount's faith in its virtues held.

Loomis thought Ernest very tired after the London-Eindhoven trip though he maintained his buoyancy. Ensuing conferences in New York tired him more, though Loomis and Gaither thought he should take the television business less seriously; there was no reason for him to assume responsibility for Paramount's production problems and the poor market. It seemed that at least some of the Paramount officials were less eager than Ernest to unload Chromatic, except in an unusually lucrative arrangement. Before returning to Berkeley from the Holland trip, the Loomises persuaded him to join them for a few days in Jamaica. For almost a week he relaxed, played tennis, and swam at Montego Bay. He wrote Mary that he "got a diploma as a graduate of a water skiing school, which simply meant that I finally learned how to get up out of the water." More delightful than Jamaica, the atmosphere, and the warmth that, for him, was always relaxing, was the rapport with Alfred; the long and close friendship embraced such mutual understanding that there was little need for explanations, whether of national affairs, science, or personal problems. It would have been good to prolong the visit but he left to spend a weekend with Eric, then stationed near Jacksonville, Florida. He then flew to Los Angeles, for a few days with Molly at Balboa.

Though he had told Eric he was "fine" and, in the letter to Mary, wrote that he was "in tip-top form," his colitis had again become aggravated. He was convinced that its cause was stress, perhaps this time due to the Chromatic situation, though concern about the increasing general confusion over fallout, the fear of nuclear bombing of American cities, and the general hysteria may have been responsible. Indulgence may have been contributory; he had never cut alcohol from his diet as had been advised from the first, though he did not drink excessively for a big man. John von Neumann's death from cancer on February 8 distressed him, as did the death of Crocker Laboratory Director Joe Hamilton ten days later. Von Neumann, brilliant mathematician, had invented computers that stripped months from the length of time otherwise necessary for hydrogen bomb calculations. Hamilton's studies of thyroid metabolism had led to widespread use of radioiodine in the treatment of hyperthyroidism. Both men might have contributed much more had they lived a normal span of years.

Ernest was in Washington again for a March 1 conference with Governor Stassen and his group. On the second, he went to Swarthmore for dinner with Swann and his old professor's new wife, before going to New York and consultant duties. He found time for an enjoyable evening with Juan and Betty Trippe and a short visit in New Haven, before he returned to Berkeley in time for a party—attended by more than a hundred Rad Lab men and wives—honoring Lewis and Mrs. Strauss. He was soon in Washington, after appointment by the president to an advisory group to the just-established Gaither Committee. Gaither's panel of prominent men was asked to evaluate aspects of national security relative to defense, including proposals for the construction of bomb shelters.

On March 20, Ernest and Molly flew to Portland where he was to lecture at Reed College on the twenty-second. Mary joined them for dinner, and the next day and evening was spent with the Bradys at Corvallis. Brady was surprised to find Ernest bitter about Oppenheimer; he had regarded them, when Oppie was at California, "as the most powerful team in physics, the experimentalist and the theoretical man. I reminded him of this and he said, 'Yes, I got Oppie that job in the first place. I guaranteed him. I could excuse almost anything except lying to the security people. This I could hardly believe—I can't understand it.' " Ernest was surprised—and a bit nervous—to find what he thought would be an informal talk for students was one of a series of scheduled lectures open to the public, but he seemed at ease when he spoke. Brady, who was pointed out as an early student who had worked on the first cyclotron, considered the talk a clear and simple summary of accelerator development, "up to and including discovery of the antiproton." Brady overheard faculty members say that it was one of the outstanding lectures of the year. Ernest was impressed by Reed—he gave the honorarium for his lecture to the physics department—but had some doubts about the apparent free and easy atmosphere; beards and such casualness as he observed were not as common on most campuses as they were soon to become. Brady was reassuring.

Though Ernest's colitis had subsided, John took him to Dr. Snell on March 29. No new symptoms or worrisome signs were found. He repeated to Snell his conviction that stress and strain caused the trouble; he had, he said, regulated his activities accordingly. Snell said, that if he had not known the past history, he would have called the "whole thing negative." What Snell might have considered "regulated" was not always apparent; there was a great deal of activity at Livermore and at the Rad Lab, where the Hilac was nearing completion—it had nitrogen ions at full energy on April 11. Ernest drove Molly and the children to Balboa at the start of their Easter vacation, flew back the following Monday to be at the lab, and returned to Balboa again for the Easter weekend, after which he drove the family home to Berkeley!

Governor Stassen phoned on April 23, asking Ernest to accompany him to London early in May for discussions with British officials; he was there two days. Upon his return, Molly met him in New York to go to Hot Springs, Virginia, for a Business Adivsory Council meeting at The Homestead, where they were guests of Charles Thomas for the weekend. Ernest addressed the council on radiation hazards both in testing and in industrial applications, following Strauss on the program. The talk was very well received, which did not surprise Thomas. "People could understand Ernest, knew exactly where he stood on everything. . . . He didn't preach humanitarianism perhaps, as some did— he had it." With his TV responsibilities out of the way, Ernest succumbed to Thomas's urging and agreed to serve on the Monsanto Board if no conflicts would be involved with other commitments. He checked this possibility with Gaither's help. Rowan also went to St. Louis to discover clearly what Ernest's responsibilities would be. Ernest and Molly flew from Hot Springs to San Francisco with Ted Peterson, president of Standard Oil of California, in his private plane.

Ernest was in Berkeley for only four days—including May 14, his twenty-fifth wedding anniversary, before he again flew East for a day at Eastman in Rochester. After a few hours in New York City, he flew to Knoxville and Oak Ridge. He was in Washington on the twentieth to appear before a subcommittee of the Joint Congressional Committee on Atomic Energy and returned to Berkeley that night. On May 22, the Vallecitos Laboratory of the General Electric Company was dedicated near San Jose, California. The project was important to him not only because it was a G.E. operation in which, as a consultant, he was concerned, but because it was another step forward in industrial atomic cooperation with government. In his dedicatory address, he stressed the company's part in the American tradition of free enterprise, pointing out that its

research laboratory, about half a century old, had produced ample proof
that discoveries in pure science are "fountainheads of boundless progress."

He had to fly out again that night, with Teller and Livermore's Mark
Mills, to appear before the Joint Congressional Subcommittee on Military Applications. The Congressmen became so engrossed in the scientists' discussions that the meeting extended beyond the intended limit,
and the questions strayed from the original matter to related subjects.
Impressed legislators thought the President should hear the scientists at
firsthand, and Congressman Sterling Cole telephoned the White House,
where the scientists were asked to meet President Eisenhower the following morning.

Teller thought Ernest so awed to be in the White House and in the
presence of the President that he had difficulty in speaking. He asked
Teller to initiate the conversation, but, as senior member of the trio, it
was Ernest the President first addressed. "This awe was something I just
could not imagine," Teller said. "Ernest's ease with authority had always been assumed; the regents to him were like close friends." Ernest's
ease and first-name associations with generals, admirals, and industrial
tycoons was usual; with the President the old stammering appeared until he lost himself in the subject and recovered. "It is a fact that he
could hardly bring up a word. I mean he was all tight and excited." But
what Mills reported to his wife were Ernest's command of the subject
and lucid explanations. The President was particularly interested in
methods by which radioactive debris had been reduced in newer bombs,
so that with the next series of tests there should be less than 4 percent of
the contamination produced by a similar current bomb. The scientists
thought that, in three to five years, fallout could be reduced still further, perhaps almost entirely eliminated. The President, impressed, requested his press secretary to arrange a conference with White House
correspondents. Strauss wrote Ernest that the great response of the press
was due to the fact that Ernest and Teller were such personalities.

Ernest stopped in St. Louis on his return to Berkeley on June 26. He
met other Monsanto directors at a fine Thomas dinner and was formally
elected a member of the board. Thomas said Ernest "was stimulating to
the whole enterprise. When he went around to various laboratories and
plants he gave a tremendous lift to chemists, and all the others—talking
with them, lunching, just asking questions. And he was so honest, when
I told him he had to take forty thousand dollars of insurance in our
company program, he said he couldn't because he wasn't an employee. I
said he was just that, earning fifteen thousand dollars a year as a board
member, and I made him sign it—including the hospitalization. It was a
fine association. Sometimes he'd arrive here very early in the morning.

I'd come down to the office and find him lying on the couch in my office. He'd jump up as though he'd had a full night's sleep. . . . He would have made a good executive in the organization. Always went from A to B directly but he was not a corporation man—things were black or white with Ernest; everything else was red tape so 'why horse around with it?' " The next time he attended a Monsanto board meeting, he stayed at the home of Chairman of the Board Edgar Queeney, with whom he had been acquainted since 1949.

Ernest broke his toe in a Las Vegas shower bath on July 4, after the Mercury tests, the most extensive to date in the United States. There had been a great hullabaloo from the start—indeed long before the first shot, cries of alarm were world wide. Improved safety measures—more accurate weather forecasts and better understanding of wind patterns in relation to fallout—kept danger to a minimum. Much was learned through the use of balloons rather than towers as supports for nuclear devices; for the first time a nuclear-armed air-to-air rocket was tested successfully; troops were dug in; shelters—even clothing and packaging materials—were tested; and, above all, in Ernest's mind, a variety of small nuclear weapons for defense purposes was proven. The toe injury was hardly sufficient excuse to beg off a television appearance which Strauss urged him to make—because, Strauss said, his White House appearance had proved him such a good public personality. But for Ernest it was reason enough to stay at home and let Cooksey write Strauss, "He wants to beg off the TV appearance. For the long run he is convinced he should remain as far as possible a non-controversial figure and thinks his usefulness is enhanced without publicity."

He was able to entertain Charles and Mrs. Thomas at Disneyland on the eleventh, and to go with Don to the Bohemian Grove encampment on the eighteenth. A week later he was again in the East for meetings of both the Stassen and Gaither committees and personal affairs. He presented his case on fallout at a medical meeting at Lake Arrowhead, California, the middle of August. Donner Laboratory's John Gofman followed with a discussion of medical aspects of the problem. Al Graves of Los Alamos explained control of fallout in current tests. Bradbury and Ernest participated in the general discussion that followed. Their case was clear enough for the doctors, but other statistics were used by opponents of testing to "prove" quite opposite results; there were reputable scientists with that view, too. It was little wonder the public was confused. No one could doubt, however, that much more fallout—plus death and destruction—would cover the land if U.S. weakness encouraged an enemy nuclear Pearl Harbor.

Regent chairman Pauley was an interested observer at the Arrowhead meeting. He mentioned, somewhat humorously, a vital concern of the

Board of Regents: a successor to President Sproul had to be found. An editorial in the San Francisco *Call Bulletin* suggested that they could do no better than to "put administration of the University in the capable hands of Dr. Ernest O. Lawrence, one of the great scientists of our time, humanitarian and really great intellectual giant." Ernest, as Pauley knew he would, "just laughed that one off." He did not even think about it. He did get pleasure out of telling Jesse Beams and Tom Johnson about it when they visited the lab for three days, on AEC matters, with Keith Glennan and Warren Johnson.

Ernest left New York with York on September 1 for Lisbon, where they "loafed" until the morning of the fifth when they joined Cooksey on a plane for Rome, which he had boarded in New York. The three were joined by Teller in Naples, where Admiral "Chick" Hayward took over for a Sixth Fleet special orientation cruise. Navy planes flew them on the sixth to Athens and then to the flight deck of the carrier *Randolph*. On the seventh they transferred to the U.S.S. *Salem* to witness further maneuvers, and the following day they boarded the submarine *Sailfish* at Suda Bay, Crete. It was Ernest who finally persuaded Teller to enter the submarine, after which Sixth Fleet Commander Admiral J. Brown found a sword and dubbed Teller "Sir Don Quixote." Other demonstrations on an LST concluded the cruise, after which they were flown back to Naples with a few hours' stopover in Athens to see some of the classic ruins. After calling on Admiral Robert P. Briscoe of NATO, they were flown to London, via Paris, for two days, and a visit to Harwell, and then across the Atlantic on a VIP DC-6.

Ernest and Don were in Nevada on September 19 for the first AEC underground nuclear explosion, from which Ernest went to Los Angeles for a formal supper at the Pauley residence in Beverly Hills in honor of new regent and Mrs. Philip L. Boyd. A few days later, at Regent McLaughlin's home in Berkeley, he renewed acquaintance with Pedro Beltran, publisher of *La Prensa* of Lima, who, with Mrs. Beltran, a San Franciscan and Stanford graduate, had entertained Ernest on his way to join the Cape Horn cruise. At the Lawrence home, Beltran rewarded Robert's efforts in high-school Spanish by an offer of a job the following summer with the Beltrans in Peru.

In spite of all his activity—trips back and forth across the country, to Europe, to tests, besides increasing Government committee responsibilities—Ernest's health seemed good. Though he was often aware of colitis symptoms, the ailment was rather quiescent. He still managed, when in Berkeley, to play tennis a couple of times a week—several Thursdays he put off important people to keep a tennis date with Walter Dean of the Federal Land Bank. If it were doubles, Ernest and Dean usually played against Hal Davis, a San Francisco photographer, and public accountant

Vannoy Davis. On other days he and Dean would oppose each other, or there might be singles with Mel Gruhn of Redwood City. Gruhn and Ernest were once partners in tournament play at Palm Springs, which Ernest almost missed because of a Los Alamos meeting. According to Gruhn, Ernest got the military VIP plane to drop him at the Palm Springs airport, where Mel and his wife, Honey, met him. When Ernest got off the plane, "which was loaded with brass," he was without a racket—either forgotten in the first place, or left at Los Alamos or on the plane. They barely had time to equip him for the match, which they won, whereupon they proceeded to Ernest's quarters, where there was a not-forgotten bottle of fine bourbon. Ernest struggled in vain with a tray of ice cubes. "I never could make these things work," he told Honey. "You do it." With one adroit twist she freed the ice, amazed at the scientist's ineptitude; he beamed admiration for the lady's dexterity.

His most frequent associate at the tennis club was Dean, whom he called "Coach." Dean was quite competitive and thought that Ernest had become somewhat lackadaisical in later years, and urged him to play harder. Ernest merely laughed at such comments and said he did not care so much about winning—though he liked to. He told Dean that half the fun now was managing to avoid or overcome obstacles to getting away from the lab to keep a date, "but he loved the game, the exhilaration and the exercise." He sometimes got Dean's "goat a little —never played with a guy who hit so many balls out. Sometimes wouldn't position himself but camped between service line and back-court line, and would just sweep, forehand and backhand. He'd take them or pick balls up, or out of the air, and usually get them in. He loved to hit balls that way. He was like an old shoe, no side or swank, always informal—not like your idea of a scientist. If we saw a strange or bearded character on the street, I'd point him out as 'another scientist,' and he'd just laugh."

Sometimes Ernest would take Barbara and Susan to the club to swim while he played, which they loved almost as much as going to the laboratory with him. Perhaps "lackadaisical" and "camping" evidenced fatigue, or lack of sufficient energy for the continuous fast pace tennis demands. Dean had no idea of Ernest's chronic complaint.

At home he fell asleep almost the minute his head was on the pillow. He had always been able to go to sleep easily, but there was a difference now in the type of fatigue. Molly often felt deprived of the only opportunities for private conversation in long periods of time. When he accused her of making decisions about the children, that should have been his, or in which he should have been consulted, she agreed completely. She added that it was a fact she resented more than he did, but that she had to because he just wasn't there—even when he was at home, he didn't have time. That discussion ended without a satisfactory conclusion. Some nights later, when he went to sleep immediately, Molly awakened him. "Ernest I've *got* to talk to you!" She was not sure that he had heard, until after a few seconds he suddenly sat upright and, with pleading look, asked, "Molly, you're not going to leave me?" She assured him that the idea had never crossed her mind, that she would be lost without him, but that there were certain matters that simply had to be discussed, and that her sole complaint was that, with all the demands made on him, there was no time left for his family.

It was as Oppie had noted of former years, but heightened by increased responsibilities; "Ernest's rapid engulfment, the rapid public character of his life, indeed rather hard. . . . He was always on the move, and his sense of priorities was not compatible with raising a family. He was fond of his children, naturally, devoted to Molly, but it was rough for her. . . . Never a hint of it's being impossible, never a hint that she couldn't make out. But sometimes the sense that she was a little crushed, not so much by him as by the wind that he and his life made—by the reality of his devotion to the laboratory and all it stood for—that was the central thing in his life. It was a monument!" Yet more and more, particularly since the onset of colitis, he wanted Molly with him on his trips, some of which she felt were of too short duration, and would allow too little opportunity for them to be together, to make it worthwhile to leave the children. Her mother advised that if Ernest needed her, or wanted her, she ought to accompany him whenever she could.

She accompanied him on an Eastern trip early in October. They were in Chicago on the fourth—the day the first man-made satellite, "Sputnik," was launched by Soviet scientists. It was the subject of most of the conversation at the guesthouse in Oak Ridge the next day, and at the Aebersold's dinner. There was no question but that it was a triumph for the Russians, who at the end of August had announced the successful test of an intercontinental ballistic missile. The veracity of the missile announcement had been questioned, but there was no doubt about the orbiting Sputnik, over which Ernest found Washington agog the next day. The capital was still worrying about it two weeks later when he was again in Washington for Rand and other meetings. He was present, too, for the presentation of the first Atoms for Peace Award to Niels Bohr, in the great hall of the National Academy of Sciences. At a small luncheon for Bohr in his office, Strauss announced, privately, that the President had approved the recommendation of the GAC and the AEC that the Fermi Award—medal, citation, and $50,000—be given to Ernest. The public announcement was made on the twenty-ninth, when Ernest was a guest at a small party given by General Courtney Whitney in New York, and where Ernest again had a chance to converse with General Mac-Arthur. He left the next day to attend a regents' meeting at Los Alamos.

The Russians launched Sputnik II on November 3, with a live dog as passenger. "Let us hope that there will be a rapid turn from complacency, and that all Americans will close ranks and get busy on what needs doing in the circumstances," Ernest wrote to Strauss. But when General Curtis LeMay visited the laboratory on the sixth, Ernest did not get a hopeful picture of the American missile program. It was hard to believe that American science, with the advantage of American industrial competence, could fall behind the Communists in areas in which most Americans were proud of superiority. He was not at liberty to discuss the Gaither Report, which was submitted to the President on the seventh, at one of the largest National Security Council gatherings in history. Though never published, the report stressed the committee members' concern that top echelons of the Government failed to realize the extent of the threat to the United States, as did both the Pentagon and the CIA.

On the seventh, Molly, Ernest, and the Cookseys flew to New York, where Ernest and Molly just had time to catch a night train for Rochester, where they spent the day and evening of the eighth. Don and Milicent spent that day at Brookhaven. Ernest and Molly returned to New York on the ninth, taxied to the Gaither residence, and avoided Alfred Loomis until the evening, when with the Gaithers, Cookseys, and a few other of the Loomises' most intimate friends, they surprised Alfred on his seventieth birthday, at a party given by his biologist son Farnsworth and his wife, at the Colony Club. Ernest and Molly returned to Berkeley the next morning.

On the twenty-first, Ernest spoke at the Welch Foundation Conference in Houston, Texas. He had planned to speak, he said, about recent discoveries in the laboratory, but with two Sputniks circling the earth, science and the national welfare were much more on his mind—as he hoped it was on the minds of his listeners, concerned as they were with scholarship. He stressed the importance of teachers in the problem of keeping abreast, if not ahead, of other nations, with allusions to the influence of Dean Akeley on his life as a scientist, and to the seriousness with which education and science are taken in Russia. He pleaded for short-range programs of drastically stepped-up research and development for defense. He said that arguments against expenditure, even in emergency —and he considered the present a time of emergency—reminded him of the bartender, who with his brother John, was the last to leave the torpedoed and sinking *Athenia*, early in World War II. Just as they were about to step into a lifeboat, the Scottish bartender said, "Excuse me, sir, I forgot to lock the bar." He actually went back and locked it before leaving the doomed ship. Ernest stressed the theme again in California, briefly, before Strauss, the principal speaker at the dedication of the second G.E. Vallecitos project, this one an atomic power plant at Pleasanton. He wished there were more such venturesome corporations. Had there been, Russia might not now have such an advantage.

Molly joined Ernest on November 29 for another short Eastern trip to receive the Fermi Award. They took a sleeper plane to New York and on December 1, with the Gaithers and Loomises, went to Washington where Ernest had a suite at the Carlton for his guests, including the Cookseys, whom he, Alfred, and Rowan met at the Washington airport. Strauss gave a luncheon for the party at the F Street Club before the ceremony at three in the afternoon, December 2. The presentation was to have been made by the President at the White House; because of his illness, it was made by Strauss before a large gathering of friends and officials, which due to a chance meeting in the hotel elevator, included California Governor and Mrs. Goodwin Knight and Senator Knowland —who had asked what Ernest and Molly were doing in Washington. It was the second Fermi award presentation—for contributions in nuclear energy and atomic physics. Ernest told of a congratulatory letter he had received, in which a friend had quipped that the substantial monetary value of the award had finally brought understanding of what Ernest meant when he said that one could never tell when pure science would produce practical results.

It was his twentieth major award in twenty years and pushed the total amount of prize money for the same period over the 100,000-dollar mark. Included among these were the highest prize of the National Academy of Sciences of the United States, the international Nobel Prize, and awards from England, France, and Belgium that celebrated contributions to physics, engineering, biology, medicine, and international service, none of which had been specifically and consciously sought. In addition to these were fourteen honorary degrees, a number of memberships in learned societies, significant of achievement, and many fellowships.

With all of them he was humble—not the false humility assumed for show—and eager to give credit for the part played in his success by colleagues of the Rad Lab. Robert Oppenheimer observed that "a man who is a great friend of mine—someone that I saw a lot . . . when the cyclotron began to upheave—it sort of mushroomed—said to me, 'Is Ernest an ambitious man?' I remember never having a satisfactory answer to that question. It seemed to me that action, movement, ambition were quite harmoniously matched, and when you say ambitious you mean someone who wants a prize. Ernest liked getting it; he liked working for it more than he wanted the prize."

On a sleeper plane returning to San Francisco, after Molly had retired, Ernest and George Parkhurst, Standard Oil of California vice-president, talked of the ceremony, and such subjects as could be discussed in voices loud enough to be heard over the noise of the plane. When unable to induce the stewardess to serve more than the permitted two drinks apiece, they tried bribery; no matter what the offer, the young lady was adamant. Parkhurst asked if a check for $50,000, guaranteed negotiable by the United States, would influence her. She allowed the possibility, if either could produce one, whereupon Ernest handed her the prize check he had been given earlier in the day. She was flabbergasted—but unyielding.

Ernest and laboratory colleagues were on a "Wide Wide World" national television broadcast from the laboratory the following Sunday. The Sunday after that he took four visiting Soviet scientists, three of whom were laboratory directors, with his family on an all-day drive to Big Basin, Big Trees, Monterey, and finally to Trader Vic's for dinner. The Russians also enjoyed an evening at the Lawrence home, where they had cocktails and buffet supper after a day at the laboratory. Margaret, Mary, who was home from Reed, and Robert enjoyed talking with them as did even Barbara and Susie. The visitors pronounced it a wonderful family.

One reason for the Russians' presence was a nuclear conference at Stanford. Ernest was to attend a reception and banquet there, and, as Molly did not wish to go, he took Margaret. At Palo Alto he left her with a group of young nuclear physicists and went off to talk with others. One of the young men brought her a drink—which she carefully manipulated from her father's notice. There were more drinks after dinner, and, when Ernest came to take her home, he said, "Margie, you'd better drive because I've had several drinks." Margie drove home all right but held her breath when he kissed her good night.

He had become very unhappy about Mary at Reed College; for all its high standing and demand for good student work, permissiveness in other areas, the belief that a student should be allowed to say what he thinks and do what he wants, troubled him. He had not been aware of the freedom allowed students, only of Reed's academic status. Though he had been a little disturbed by the shaggy beards, and casual dress, and attitudes among the students at the time of his lecture, he was well aware of Mary's independent nature and inclination to rebel against conformity and the status quo. Somewhere after that he heard loose charges and rumors, in the fashion of the McCarthy period, and his concern approached alarm. He determined that she should not continue at Reed and hoped to accomplish her withdrawal without conflict—he knew that Mary would stand up to him. Before she had chosen Reed, she had talked of continuing her education in Europe. So he told her, in December, that it would be a good time to go to school in Switzerland, since John was there on sabbatical leave with Amy, and their cousin Mark was studying at the *Ecole Internationale*. Would she not like to seize the opportunity to attend the University of Geneva? Mary understood the ruse at once and said so. Nevertheless the idea was attractive, and she agreed to the plan—though she was incensed at what she considered an unjust attitude toward Reed, as was James Brady when he learned of it.

The family, except for Eric, was together in Berkeley for Christmas. With John and Amy away, they did not wish to leave Gunda and she did not wish to go to Balboa. She was quite well and had been for some months at a residence for elderly women in Oakland. Ira drove her to church on Sundays and occasionally took her other places. Once, when Mac Stone was in town and they had played tennis in the afternoon, Ernest asked Mac to join him for dinner. Stone had a date with his mother and suggested that Ernest get Gunda and join them. Ernest said, "That would be fine, except that I haven't time to go out and pick her up." Mac could not get over that. "Imagine this brilliant guy. It never occurred to him that he could send for her! Well, he did, and the four of us had a wonderful time. His mother was a real honey."

CHAPTER XIX

Lawrencium

[1958]

"Talent is that which is in the power of man, genius is that in whose power man is," Dean Akeley quoted James Russell Lowell in a New Year letter to Ernest. The dean, ninety-seven in 1958, considered his famous onetime student a genius on grounds far broader than the invention of the cyclotron: "that was just a machine, though the most significant instrument for the advancement of science in the last hundred years." Ernest had gone beyond science and engineering, Akeley said, was actually a scientific statesman, as his speeches showed. "Character" was the key. Akeley was "pleased by the nice things you said about me at Houston," and wrote elsewhere of Ernest, "The longer he lived, the greater he became." He was proud that he had discovered and nurtured this genius in the classroom; "that is the business of a teacher, to unearth genius." Dean Akeley thought his former pupil's genius also evident in men, particularly the young, whom he had attracted to his laboratory and inspired to their own high achievements— two of them also had won Nobel Prizes. Ernest was amused at the idea of being considered a genius; the old teacher's extravagance could be blamed on affection, age, and perhaps the fact that, since retirement as dean of engineering, more than twenty years ago, he had been teaching philosophy. Nevertheless the approbation from Akeley now pleased him almost as much as it had as a student. How fortunate the day he had been persuaded, almost against his will, to study physics with the dean—or was the lucky day the one when he had gone to Akeley, the "rare bird" of the campus, for wireless equipment?

But he was wasting time looking backward and staring so long out over the campus and the bay toward the Golden Gate, with its great span hung from two towers. If they had not insisted on giving him such a plush office, with such a view from the wide windows, he might get more done; perhaps he was getting old himself. He would not get through the pile of "personal" mail or get around to all the projects in time to meet Molly and get to Yosemite before dinner, if he spent time "dreaming." He hurried through the mail—answers could wait for Monday—and only got as far as the huge Bevatron, down below and across the road from his office, before leaving for Yosemite, with Molly at the wheel. It was a good weekend.

Molly did not join him on a short trip to Acapulco with Randy and Catherine Hearst. The result of a sudden invitation, for days on which she was committed to attending important Community Chest budget committee meetings, she declined. Ernest was hurt that her strong sense of obligation to civic duty should outweigh his desire that she accompany him, and Molly felt guilty—which would have been the case whichever way she decided. Ernest wrote of "three days of wonderful hospitality with Dr. and Mrs. Prinzmetal of Beverly Hills." With Hearst and the doctor there was deep-sea fishing—he enjoyed lounging on the boat in smooth seas under a warm sun—and it was equally pleasant on the beach, with a little swimming sandwiched between longer rests and good talk. There was just enough gaiety in the evenings for balance. The three days between the trip down and back was just the right length of time, he thought, and he did look better when he returned, his face a healthy tan.

When Neil McElroy had replaced Charles Wilson as Secretary of Defense in the Eisenhower Cabinet, he asked Charles Thomas for advice about scientists. Thomas had suggested that McElroy wait until he could be in Washington with Ernest. When Thomas and Ernest visited McElroy, the Secretary had described a particular need. Ernest without hesitation had said, "Herb York." Consequently York was asked to join James Killian's committee as director of research, Advanced Research Projects Division of the Institute of Defense Analyses, and chief scientist of the Advanced Research Projects Agency for the Secretary of Defense. York, unaware of the Washington meeting, consulted Ernest about it and was surprised to be advised to take the position. "Before, it had always been, 'No, sir!'; now he thought it was probably the right time. My whole career is based on being supported—pushed if you accept the word—by Lawrence. And what I learned from him, too." Before he had been in Washington a year, the President appointed York the first Director of Defense Research and Engineering of the Department of Defense —the result of a proposal formulated by John Wheeler and others, and backed by Ernest, which was submitted to the Senate Preparedness Subcommittee. Wheeler wrote of it to Ernest in January, 1958:

"I have discussed it with a number of responsible colleagues. They agree that a National Defense Laboratory is a necessity.

"Granted the right leadership, I believe a number of good people will join in the enterprise full time on an emergency basis. Herb York in my opinion would make an outstanding director.

"This is to ask on behalf of Eugene Wigner, Oskar Morgenstern and myself if you would lead this delegation to call on Secretary McElroy to put to him the necessity of such a project initiation laboratory. I will phone you to get your answer."

Ernest was not in Berkeley when Wheeler phoned, nor did he receive the letter until early in February. He and Molly had joined the Loomises and Gaithers in New York on January 27 and had flown to Jamaica for a week on Montego Bay and a wonderful and relaxing rest. Manette Loomis says no one would have known, in Jamaica, that Ernest had ever been ill. "He looked well, kept telling us he felt wonderful. Drinking and dancing and having the time of his life; just enjoying it so, and Molly, too—he had to drag Molly home. He was such a good dancer—not up to date, you know—but he had good rhythm, which is what most scientists don't have. A fast dancer but good, very good. It was such fun to be with him. We really enjoyed it." Ernest and Molly left the delightful place and company for New York to meet Mary and to see her off for Geneva on February 5. Then to Washington, where Ernest spent most of one day in the new AEC establishment in Germantown, and another at the Pentagon. There was a little optimism this time; the United States had put "Explorer 1," its first earth satellite, into orbit on the last day of January.

Shortly after their return to Berkeley, Molly went to Balboa to be with her mother, who had undergone surgery for cancer. Molly telephoned Ernest of Mabel's progress; the night before her release from the hospital, he spoke encouragingly to Mabel herself and hoped to see her "well as ever" in a week or so when he planned to be in Balboa. It was therefore most startling to Molly, her mother, and G.B., as they approached the Blumer home, returning from the hospital next day, to see Ernest in front of the house. Mrs. Blumer remembers the shock of his unexpected presence. "There was Ernest standing on the front porch, large as life. He was *big*, and, I guess, aggressive-looking. Awfully impressive standing there. I said, 'If he grabs me, I think I'll scream.' I was sore and everything hurt me. He came running out with his big smile, and Molly told him to be careful, and I said, 'It is all right Ernest, we're delighted to see you, but I'm a little shaky.' I managed to get out of the car, and he said, 'Well, Mabel, you're standing on your own two feet and you are smiling just the way I wanted to see you, so everything is better now. I just had to come too!' . . . Imagine, he came down from

Berkeley just on the spur of the moment to welcome me home from the hospital. People were always ready with private planes or anything he could ever want."

He had had the opportunity to fly to Los Angeles with Regent Pauley and had taken Robert along. Pauley had also put a "very sporty" Chrysler at their disposal, which delighted Robert almost as much as the flight down and back in a private plane with two most cooperative pilots. He and his father had the cabin to themselves on the way back, next day. Mabel's statement was almost true; there usually was someone ready to help him achieve what he wanted—and always there had been at least one of the regents who took special interest in him and his work. There was criticism on the campus over Ernest's close relationships with regents. When ex-president Sproul was asked if he hadn't at times resented Ernest's bypassing of administration in going directly to regents, he boomed with hearty exaggeration, "Hell, he made me, why should I object!" York's answer to the criticism was, "That was just another part of his disdain for organization, for formal organization. You have to remember he did that in *both* directions. He was impatient with red tape. Administration people are often red-tape men. There was nothing special in bypassing them; he did it the other way, too, right down to the janitor." The regents were proud of Ernest and his great laboratory, as Ernest was proud of their concern for science and the laboratory. When he learned that, on their own initiative in 1958, they had appropriated additional funds for science and engineering, he wrote them of his appreciation. He often said there was too little appreciation of all they had accomplished through the years, "which in such large measure is responsible for the greatness of the university."

When Ernest learned that Mabel was to have daily X-ray treatments following the operation, he telephoned to request that she not have them; it was **too dangerous; he wouldn't stand for it;** if the doctor had been thorough, she should not need them. Mabel phoned her surgeon who said that the operation was complete. He, too, thought X rays would not be good for her. Mrs. Blumer remembers that the X-ray man was furious, that he said, "Well, some ignorant fool has got hold of her and made her say this, as though I didn't know more than some darn fool son-in-law." The surgeon asked if he knew who that son-in-law was. "No, and I don't care!" The surgeon said, "He's Professor Ernest Lawrence, and I don't think you can say that he is exactly ignorant." The next time Ernest saw her, he said, "Oh, Mabel, you are just as spry as you ever were." Mrs. Blumer continued: "He always made you feel so good—take those birthday suppers! Barbara was born on the eighth, and he was born on the eighth, and I was born on the seventh, of August, so we'd have this triple birthday party, and Ernest would always come dancing in. 'Isn't it swell we're all together again?' And no matter what the kids gave him, if it was only a shoehorn or a comb, he'd dance around and say, 'That's just what I wanted' and would really mean it. He'd always do so much to please people."

He felt more like his old self that March. Everything seemed to be improving, from the state of the nation's health to his own. He remarked that the laboratories functioned as well during his absence as when he was there—which Cooksey noted was not always the case, and when true it was because something of his presence remained. Cooksey would retire next year, and Ernest wondered who could replace him; he knew how important he had been in the success of the whole Rad Lab complex—and to him personally. Cooksey might be finicky, but that very fussiness was part of his value. Would Ernest be able to be away so freely with another lieutenant? He thought himself blessed with good men! Everyone at Livermore in Deputy Director Mills's group, for example, exercised particular care in preparation for the Hardtack open shot tests at Eniwetok, because Ernest wished them to go exceptionally smoothly for scheduled U.N. observers. He would not attend this test series. On March 18, he and Molly flew to New York for the President's presentation to him at West Point of the Sylvanus Thayer Medal of the Association of Graduates of the United States Military Academy. He was busy during two preceding days, each concluded by dinner with the Loomises and Gaithers. They had a night at a theater, too, and he was glad that Molly—so often at home with children in bygone years—had become a real member of this group at last.

On the twenty-first they drove through a heavy, exciting snowstorm to West Point for the Founders' Day luncheon, at which the presentation was to be made before the Cadet Corps and distinguished guests. Few of the invited guests arrived, however, held back or marooned by what newspapers reported as "the worst snow storm of the year and one of the worst in many years." President Eisenhower, detained in Washington because of takeoff and landing hazards, telephoned remarks he had expected to make personally, which were read for him by General W. D. Crittenberger. Reviewing Ernest's accomplishments, the President said, "As a statesman of the atom you have sought its beneficent application not only to physics—but to biology, medicine, and technology. . . . Today the men of West Point pay tribute to your contribution to our nation and to all humanity, for your achievements as scientist and as a statesman of science." Ernest "with the true humility of the great scientist," reported the association's journal Assembly, paid tribute to the memory of Thayer. "It was through his influence that the Academy was established as an engineering school, indeed, as the first scientific school in the country."

The selection committee, among whose members were General of the Army Omar Bradley, Generals Jacob Devers, Lucius Clay, and Alfred Gruenther, had been requested to nominate as first recipient of the Sylvanus Thayer Award "that citizen of the United States whose record of service to his country, accomplishments in the national interest, and manner of achievement, exemplify outstanding devotion to the principles expressed in the motto of West Point—Duty, Honor, Country."

Molly returned to Berkeley the following day, and Ernest and Charles Thomas, who had managed to get to West Point for the ceremony, went to Dayton, Ohio, for a Monsanto directors' meeting, and a tour of the Mound Laboratory, which was involved in peaceful applications of atomic energy. Ernest left Berkeley again on April 6 with Teller, who had taken York's place as director at Livermore, for an important Seattle meeting, where they would also be guests of honor with Senator Henry Jackson at a Boeing Company reception and dinner. After a briefing on the Boeing meeting in Berkeley on the eighth, Ernest asked AEC area manager, Harold Fidler, to become his assistant director when Cooksey retired in 1959. Ernest said that he was aware that leaving a good position and Government service would entail some sacrifice on Fidler's part, but as he must know what the Rad Lab position entailed, he could weigh the advantages of one against the other. For his part, Ernest would see that Fidler need have no worries as to future security as assistant director of the Rad Lab. Fidler was too thrilled that Ernest would ask him to weigh anything very objectively. He had observed Ernest at close range from the first days of the Manhattan District.

In spite of all the activity and banqueting, Ernest felt "fit as a fiddle," as he wrote John in Geneva. But it was short-lived. He had barely finished dictating the letter when he was stunned by news that Mark Mills had been killed the night before when a helicopter from which he was inspecting preparations for an Eniwetok test was upset and crashed in shallow water during a sudden rainsquall. Livermore's Harry Keller had nearly drowned, and two Army officers escaped unhurt. Ernest took the death of Mills as a personal tragedy; it was followed by severe recurrence of colitis, accompanied by the excretion of much blood and mucus. Convinced the flare-up was attributable to the Mills accident and concern for Mark's family, he left that day for Santa Monica and a Rand board meeting, after which he rested at Balboa for a few days. His condition improved somewhat, though he was weak and pale when he returned to Berkeley on the eleventh to attend memorial services for Mills at the San Ramon Valley Congregational Church, near Danville, on April 12. The church was packed, and, by Polly Mills's request, there were "only gay spring flowers, no lilies."

Ernest remained in Berkeley during meetings of the American Chemical Society, though he did not attend a session. After discussion with Calvin, he had enabled the Russian chemist A. N. Nesmeyanov and his wife to participate in the meetings by inviting them to Berkeley as his personal guests, with expenses paid from New York. There was a cocktail party for the Russians at the Lawrence home, attended by distinguished delegates and university chemists. He stressed, to American colleagues, the importance of conversations between scientists of the East and West held in an atmosphere unclouded by politics or specific conference aims, pointing out again that science should not be political or subject to barriers. Robert Bacher, at that time a member of the President's Science Advisory Committee, considered Ernest the most vigorous proponent of exchange of scientists and large-scale exchange of students as a basis for understanding. "We can only win by this—only gain by such an exchange," Ernest repeatedly asserted. It was important enough to him to excuse postponing complete rest, as he did when asked for a date when "you expect to be in Washington" to participate in a meeting of the State Department's Policy Planning Staff; he went to Washington after the Russians' departure.

He returned to Berkeley in time to see Eric, home on the carrier *Ticonderoga* after a five-month tour in the Far East with the Seventh Fleet. Ensign Eric was still determined to make photography his profession and to study graphic arts at the Art Center School in Los Angeles at the conclusion of his Navy duty. Ernest did not now try to discourage this desire, which Eric had long cherished, other than to warn that photography was not likely to be profitable as a career. One should, of course, work at what he enjoyed if possible; he could remember no opposition from his parents—though his ambitions had always been toward medical or natural "real" science, which they had recognized as of as much importance as teaching.

His mother, apparently victim of a minor stroke late in April, and suddenly confused, was missed at family dinners, to which Ira had often brought her. He wrote John in Switzerland that she was "slowly losing ground but everything is being done to keep her comfortable and happy." Nurses and attendants were necessary for several days, but she made a surprisingly good recovery, Ernest noted, before his departure again for Washington early in May, for the annual Carnegie meeting and conferences with AEC people and Governor Stassen. The AEC wanted him to assist in entertaining U.N. observers at a "clean" H-bomb test to be held sometime during the summer, both in Berkeley where analyses would be made after the demonstration and in the South Pacific. Strauss also hoped that he would attend some sessions of the Atoms for Peace Conference at Geneva in September—as an adviser without the burden of delegate duties—after which he could go to

Yugoslavia for the dedication of a cyclotron and a nuclear laboratory in Zagreb. There was also a strong possibility that he would be summoned to Europe by Stassen early in the summer, probably on short notice.

In New York he shopped in secondhand bookstores for old *New York Times* crossword puzzle books Molly might have missed or worked long enough in the past to have forgotten, and on Fifth Avenue for a mink stole for her birthday on the fifteenth. The stole had been recommended by Elsie, whom he found chatting with Dixie one noon when he had unexpectedly come home for lunch in Molly's absence. Asked for advice about a birthday gift, both had recommended a mink stole. He protested that he had already given her a fur jacket, after a particularly frigid trip some years before; anyway mink was too showy for a faculty wife. Elsie hooted; many faculty wives had mink! She added, rather tartly, that his was an odd attitude for a man who drove a new Cadillac convertible every year. Ernest protested that his Cadillacs were not expensive, procured as they were through the Yosemite company, and sold after one year's use, for cost, or very little less. They were nevertheless flashy Cadillacs, Elsie pointed out. He bought the mink. When he arrived in Berkeley, the weekend before her birthday, he was so excited about it that he could not resist telling Molly that it was coming, explaining that he had not had her initials put in the lining until he was sure she approved the style and color, which she did. It was delivered on the fourteenth, as were the red roses she had received on each of their twenty-five former anniversaries. He saved the crossword puzzle books for her birthday next day.

On Mother's Day—when Polly Mills and her children had been invited for dinner, and Polly had been shocked by Ernest's advice that she should marry again—he promised Molly a leisurely summer, with much time at Balboa. Except for the possible hurried trip to Europe, of very short duration, and one or two flights to the South Pacific, he would not have to leave the country until fall. He might even forego the September Geneva Conference. They would go to Balboa right after the annual combined birthday party for Molly, Elsie, Don, Wally Reynolds, and Carl Helmholz, for which the Cookseys and McMillans were hosts this year. He had to stay in Berkeley until the seventeenth in any case, to greet Prince Bertil of Sweden at the laboratory. He and President Sproul had welcomed Prince Bernhard of the Netherlands on the thirteenth.

They reached Balboa on the eighteenth for what started out to be a quiet and beneficial week. He was free of symptoms of the colitis that had flared so badly the previous month and had recurred periodically since. Rest and relaxation would take care of it! By the middle of the week, telephone calls from Washington interrupted the serenity; the

President wanted Ernest to serve with James Fisk and Robert Bacher at a Geneva Conference of Experts to Study the Possibility of Detecting Violations of a Possible Agreement on Suspension of Nuclear Tests. Molly protested that he was in no condition to undertake the task, particularly since he would have to be in Washington for weeks of preparation before the meeting. Ernest, somewhat depressed over the idea, nevertheless felt it his duty to accept. When the President specifically requests one, he cannot refuse. It was most important; after years of effort to get the Russians to discuss the subject properly, Nikita Khrushchev had agreed to allow Soviet and Western experts to consider technical aspects of nuclear test suspension. And it was urgent; the President wished to allow the Soviet Premier as little time as possible in which to change his mind.

By the weekend, when Ernest and Molly drove to Camarillo for a Yosemite directors' meeting and party at the Conejo Ranch, Ernest was committed; briefings would begin in Washington on June 2. During the drive to Berkeley from Camarillo on the twenty-fifth, he persuaded Molly to accompany him, since the Geneva Conference might last for weeks. She could see Mary; the little girls would be all right at Balboa with Dixie (Maggie did not care to stay at Balboa), and the Blumers were just a few steps away. Robert would be in Peru, Eric at sea, and Margaret expected a job in Washington or Chicago, if her plans to work in Italy for the State Department failed to materialize.

On the twenty-seventh, Ernest flew to St. Louis for a Monsanto directors meeting. Though in a hurry to return, he managed to call on Arthur Compton, seriously ill with heart complications. He discussed the Geneva Conference and the problems of testing and inspection. As a scientist, he disliked the possibility of a ban on experimentation; however, if that were the condition of international control, and a halt to nuclear weapons competition, he must assent to it—provided adequate inspection, or guaranteed detection of violations, were incorporated in any agreement. Compton understood the difficulties, particularly for so strong an exponent of experiment as Ernest. Cheered by Ernest's spirit, he thought him in excellent health—was almost envious of it. He was to return to a hospital in a few days for another month and hoped after that to regain his vitality.

Ernest was back in Berkeley the twenty-ninth. He appeared to have recovered from his most recent flare-up. John, nevertheless, was unhappy, on his return from Europe, to learn of Ernest's insistence on participation in the Geneva talks. His advice against it made no more impression than had Molly's pleading. Ernest told him flatly that nothing could stop him from accepting the President's request that he take part in the conference. John phoned Dr. Snell after Ernest had left for Washington

early in June. The doctor thought the Geneva venture would probably be all right in spite of the recurrence; that the chronic trouble
would remain localized to the lower segment of the descending colon
which, he said, had looked better when last thoroughly examined, about
a year before, than it had in 1953. In view of recurrent flare-ups since
the April attack, he advised a colon X ray (Ernest did not have time)
and recommended a hydrocortisone preparation. The best John could
do for his brother was to obtain a supply of the medicine.

The briefings were intense and held under confining security arrangements. The guarded rooms were left only for meals and sleep each day
until Friday night, June 6. Ernest, exhausted, took a sleeper plane west,
but, after loafing all Saturday at Balboa, insisted on attending a party at
the Brobecks' that night. He went again to Washington on a sleeper
plane Monday night—fortunately he slept and rested well on these
flights—for more intense and trying sessions, but he returned to Berkeley the night of the thirteenth, too late to attend Robert's graduation
from high school. "He was as near exhaustion as I had ever seen him,"
Molly said. "The buoyancy he still managed to display in public just
wasn't there, at home. I didn't realize how sick he was; I thought he was
just completely tired." Sunday, the fifteenth, Ira drove them to Palo
Alto for Margaret's graduation, *cum laude,* from Stanford. They did not
arrive in time to find seats shaded from the hot afternoon sun, and
Ernest was soon most uncomfortable. The event seemed interminable
even to healthy Molly. Ernest, who became increasingly miserable, managed to endure it until after Margaret's name was called, she had
paraded across the front of the amphitheater, and received her diploma,
when Ernest and Molly hurriedly left. He regretted that Ira had not
been asked to wait nearby with the car, especially after they walked
across the campus to Jordan House—where Margaret lived—only to find
it locked. Ernest by that time was—*and looked*—very ill; he was extremely thirsty and urgently in need of a rest room. Fortunately Ira soon
appeared with the car and drove them to town for facilities and refreshment—after which Ernest felt well enough to take Margaret to dinner
in San Francisco.

He left for Washington the next night—via sleeper plane—for another intensive week, broken only on the nineteenth for the presentation to Polly Mills of a posthumous award for Mark, in the presence of
their children, his mother, and several notables. Ernest had asked Polly
if she would like to have him attend, which had pleased her so that he
also took Teller, Bacher, and an adviser from Livermore, Harold Brown,
with him. After the ceremony, Ernest had a dinner for Polly, her family,
and some of the guests—about twenty people in all. Toward the end of
the week, Russian threats of boycott posed the possibility that the con-

ference would not be held. It was decided that the American experts would ignore whatever tactics the Soviets had in mind and be ready in Geneva on July 1, as scheduled. Ernest remained in Washington for the weekend. On the twenty-fourth, before his evening departure for New York, he visited Merle Tuve in his laboratory. "We helped start this and have to do what we can about it," Ernest said. "The President asked, so I must go."

Bacher said of those briefings that the three scientists practically lived together and developed genuine interest in and respect for their differing views—though there was actually no great difference among them. All three had the same worries, which were considerable. Charged to determine the technical difficulties in the way of inspection and control, they discovered, for instance, that much seismological information which had been thought reliable was incorrect. Bacher, who thought it a most interesting month, gained much respect for Ernest's judgment and deep interest in the problem. Ernest did not understand why certain scientists misinterpreted and quoted things against him—but did not let it worry him, Bacher observed. Neither he nor Fisk realized that Ernest was ill; that he was more careful of himself than he had been before they ascribed to Ernest having learned that there were limits even to what he could do. "He was not well but deliberately went off on this mission he thought important—but that is how he operated."

Molly joined him in New York on the twenty-fifth. He looked so tired, she again tried to dissuade him from going, even suggesting that it might be better for the country if a completely well person took his place. He would have none of it. "He seemed to take this more seriously than anything he had ever done, and yet, he told me, they were not even certain that the Russians would show up; they had made it so uncertain. But he said, 'We are going and hope they show.' "

Gaither had arranged that the Ford Foundation make it possible for Leonid Tichvinsky, of the Berkeley faculty, to accompany Ernest as personal interpreter and observer of Russian attitudes. Born in Russia, the professor of mechanical engineering had been in the United States for nearly thirty years and was married to a daughter of that Commander Lucci who had been so helpful in the early days. Ernest hoped to understand Russian sincerity or lack of it, and that Leonid could judge by tone and attitude as well as by interpretation. Harold Brown of Livermore also went along as a technical adviser.

Still uncertain of meeting the Soviet experts, the American delegation left Idlewild on June 26, after much news photographing of the three scientists at the airport. Through a mistake, the scientists were put on the wrong plane; there were no berth accommodations for the long trip. Bacher and Fisk were concerned, since it was evident that Ernest needed to stretch out and sleep, and they thought that Molly, at least, should be able to sleep, too. It was a long night before they stopped in Lisbon, for breakfast. Ernest was then so exhausted it was difficult for him to disguise it. Molly thought Fisk and Bacher also appeared drawn and tired. It was then that she learned "how really dreadful the pressures had been during those conferences of the past month." All were glad to reach the Hotel du Rhône in Geneva. Ernest perked up when Mary came from her *pension* for dinner. Amy and Mark were still there. Fortunately there was a long weekend before the conference started on July 1, though Ernest went to an office which he was to share with Bacher for part of Monday. There were parties almost every evening, one of the first a large affair attended by many physicists in Geneva for one or another of several conferences—McMillan and others from Berkeley were there for a High Energy Conference.

Ernest considered many of these social affairs as important for international understanding as formal meetings. He talked with Russians who had been at the Rad Lab and at his house; he happily greeted Americans he had not seen for some time—Karl and Elizabeth Darrow, the Robert Wilsons, and many others. At a huge garden party given by CERN director and Mrs. Bakker, on the outskirts of Geneva, he talked briefly with Oppie. Oppenheimer remembered: "There was, I would say, a sense of disengagement, but certainly not hostility. . . . It was certainly not unpleasant . . . after 1953–54 we saw almost nothing of each other . . . at Bakker's there were a couple of hundred people milling around and I said, I must have said, how glad I was that he had come to the meeting. . . . I heard from Bacher how extraordinarily devoted and sweet he was during this period, although I imagine that he himself had some grave doubts—but was apparently quite willing to subordinate these doubts to the mission."

It was not easy to submit his belief as an experimentalist to any taboo on testing, nor his intensely patriotic—some called it too nationalistic—concern for absolute insurance of compliance with agreements reached. Nor was it easy to be patient with vacillation and dissimulation. The Russians appeared, but at the first official session Delegate Fedorov insisted that, as a preamble to any technical discussion, it be stated that the purpose of the conference was absolute cessation of nuclear tests, though he understood as well as the Westerners that the meetings were for the study of the possibilities of detection *if* an agreement—yet to be reached—was violated. The first three conference days were wasted in fruitless discussions, entirely beside the point. N. N. Semenov, Nobel Laureate in chemistry, who arrived a day late, maintained that all he had heard in many places in several countries was the cry for cessation of experiment and the prohibition of nuclear weapons, yet when Ernest attempted personal discussion with him, Semenov apologetically said he understood no language but Russian. He was less strident and more cordial at private meetings, away from comrades and microphones. Semenov and his wife—the only woman with the Russians—were invited to dine with Ernest and Molly on July 11, following the Western Delegation reception. Semenov accepted and asked permission to bring a young associate—who turned out to be the English-speaking Soviet First Secretary of Foreign Affairs. Tichvinsky, who accompanied Ernest and Molly to the dinner, thought he gleaned more about Russian attitudes from Mrs. Semenov than from the men. She was a native of old St. Petersburg; her cousins had attended the same private school Tichvinsky had finished in 1916. She was adroit, however, in avoiding comment on sensitive subjects about which he, as an ex-Russian, was curious. Semenov, also of prerevolutionary schooling, appeared enigmatic and was awkward at the dinner because, Tichvinsky thought, he found it difficult to be natural in the political Russian's presence, since "even the devil would be honest with EOL." The only delegate with whom Tichvinsky had a chance for private talk was astounded that anyone could have been happy in the United States for as long as Tichvinsky had lived there. He refused to believe, for example, that there had been over eighty Soviet vetoes at the U.N. Geneva was the first foreign city he, and many of the Russian scientists, had ever visited.

As delegates, the Russians did their best to make early meetings non-technical and tailored for preconceived political results. It was trying for all the Westerners. Ernest was most complimentary, in speaking to Molly, over Fisk's handling of the difficult job of delegation chairman: his tact, restraint, refusal to become angry, and his patience. He developed much respect for the abilities of Harold Brown of Livermore. Molly thought Fisk, Bacher, and Brown also showed much fatigue after the first week—a six-day week of late hours. There was much for Molly to do while Ernest was busy. If Mary was occupied with classes or her own activities—she went off to Germany a few days after their arrival— there were many friends from Berkeley and elsewhere among those whom the conferences had drawn to Geneva. The Darrows invited her on a cruise of the lake that had been arranged for CERN Conference delegates; there was always something, or she could explore and find much of interest on her own. She remembers best the few times Ernest was present and not too tired—a party on a large open deck on top of a university building, on a beautiful sunny day when Mont Blanc was visible, not frequently possible from Geneva; watching the American Fourth of July celebrations in the mist at the Parc des Eaux Vives through protective glass at a place where Barney Balaban's brother Harry and his wife took them; cocktails at the Balabans' apartment on one of their first evenings in Geneva; dinner at the American Consul's home, with Mary along and a young consulate secretary for her escort; dinner at the home of Dr. and Mrs. David Weddell, he the representative of one of the drug companies associated with American Cyanamid.

Ernest had little time or energy for activity unrelated to the meetings, except those functions he considered almost obligatory for good relations. He had looked forward to a purely pleasurable Sunday outing on the thirteenth with the Jerome Powells, to whom they had been introduced by Amy, who had known Virginia Powell in California. Ernest seemed well enough, if tired, when the Powells picked them up at the hotel, Molly remembers. "We went to Chamonix—up the long lift, and he seemed suddenly very exhausted and quite uncomfortable while we were up there. It was very cold and quite high. I realized that he was anxious to get down again. It was just too much, and I thought he had caught cold. It seemed to develop into the flu, and after a day or two he stayed in bed to avoid pneumonia." Bacher and Brown kept him informed of developments: Tichvinsky, who had the next room, reported every evening. Bacher was surprised that the illness lingered. "He just didn't seem to get well, though he didn't seem terribly sick, when I was present." Molly was not entirely deceived by his cheerful efforts to appear only slightly ill. His cough was harsh and there was afternoon fever. When he did not improve, Molly, fearing pneumonia again, called in a physician recommended by the Weddells on Thursday, the seventeenth. Dr. Bernard Wissmer noted that Ernest was cheerful and did not seem acutely ill, despite fever. He found moderate tenderness along his whole colon, but no serious respiratory symptoms; medication was prescribed. Ernest told him that he frequently had relapses when under tension. Dr. Wissmer called on the nineteenth, twentieth, and twenty-first; Ernest was somewhat better each day—except for the fever. Ernest wanted to attend the reception at the Polish Embassy on the twenty-second, the Polish National Holiday, but sent Molly to represent him, escorted by Tichvinsky—who thought most of the "Poles" in the receiving line were Russians. Ernest managed to take Molly himself to the Russian affair; the Soviets gave the most extravagant party of all.

On the twenty-third he went to Dr. Wissmer's office for a proctoscopic examination. Wissmer was surprised to find "acute condition of ulcerative colitis . . . fever still 102. Wanted to fluoroscope his chest but he refused to be exposed to X rays. Gave shots of liver and placenta extract." Ernest was in bed much of the time from then on. On one of his better days he wanted to walk all the way along the lake to the park. Molly thought it too far, but he was insistent. He nearly collapsed on the way back. After that he was unable to walk more than a little in their rooms, except to go to Wissmer's office; meals were served in their sitting room. There were many callers, some of whom advised him to go home, but he refused. He put on a good front, particularly when Bacher and Brown came to discuss the agenda. It was deceptive to most, but Molly knew that he was very tired and sick. She tried to make him see the advisability of returning to Berkeley; in pajamas and robe, he drew himself up, painfully, to his full height, stared intensely at her and said, "I could never live with myself if I left before this conference is over!"

After the visit of a Nobel committeeman from Stockholm and a long discussion of physicists' qualifications for the Prize, he was particularly tired. The next day he went to Dr. Wissmer's office and received injections of liver and placenta extract, and penicillin. Wissmer then had telephone consultations with John and Dr. Snell, in the United States. The injections were repeated on the twenty-sixth; the doctor decided to start "a complete checkup with analysis" on the following Monday, the twenty-eighth. He "strongly suggested [that Ernest] stay away from conferences to avoid nervous tension." On Sunday, Molly rented a car and she, Ernest, and Tichvinsky drove around the lake. They had lunch in a quaint place that overlooked the water. On Monday morning he felt worse. "This is it," he told Molly. "We're going home tonight." He telephoned the consulate himself; they were unable to secure reservations before the following evening. He went to Dr. Wissmer's office for injections and announced that he was leaving for home, though the doctor noted "real subjective improvement." There was afternoon temperature; he was restless to get away, once the decision had been made, and Molly was very much worried.

The consulate reserved berths on a Swissair plane and arranged to have their baggage loaded ahead of time; everything was to be expedited so that Ernest and Molly could remain at the hotel until the last minute and step from the car to the plane. When they were called, Tichvinsky dispatched a wire to Cooksey and accompanied them to the airport. But, through a mistake at the airport, they were summoned too soon; departure was late. "Ernest spent hours there before the plane left. He was tired and in pain. Finally, the airport manager was called by one of the consulate men and we were taken to the medical officer's room, where there was a couch on which he could lie down. He seemed really sick, but, when we finally went to the plane, he brightened a little, thinking he could get in the berth at once—but they wouldn't make it up until a seven-course dinner had been served to all passengers. The plane was near Lisbon before he could lie down. He took sleeping pills and slept quite well all the way to New York. A Paramount man was there with a car, though it was early morning; someone in Geneva had sent word. Ernest was very much upset because he knew the man but could not think of his name."

The State Department had also sent someone, and a car. They were whisked through customs without delay. Though Molly had been worried over their late arrival and the missed San Francisco connection, they were able to board a San Francisco flight almost immediately. Ernest perked up at once. He looked better, said "Everything is fine now," and stretched out in the roomy, comfortable seat in the central compartment of a Constellation. Molly, too, believed that everything would now be all right. She would get him home to a familiar doctor. He seemed better and rested well as the plane droned on across America. It was good to see Ira waiting at the airport in the late afternoon, while it was still light for the drive home. Ernest remarked that the house was empty; the younger children were, of course, still at Balboa. He telephoned to John, who took him to Peralta Hospital in Oakland the next day, July 31. Dr. Sadusk's report noted: "temp 101, pulse 120, blood pressure 120/90, well developed male who seems acutely ill, prostrated, skin warm and dry . . . picture is one of an acute fulminating relapse of a chronic idiopathic ulcerative colitis . . . rule out significant upper respiratory infection."

Once he was settled in the hospital, Ernest felt much better and seemed progressively to improve. Physicians were quite sure that, although his condition was serious, he would recover quickly, after which he must have a prolonged rest. He was allowed to check on laboratory affairs and showed much interest—though Cooksey was frankly alarmed on his first visit to the hospital, and Eleanor Davisson found him "so pale and thin that he doesn't look like himself at all." Teller, allowed only one visit, was warned to avoid controversial subjects and confine his conversation to progress at Livermore. McMillan and Alvarez were careful not to excite him. He was optimistic, he told Chick Hayward, in Bethesda Naval Hospital in Maryland, over the phone, joked about their troubles, and bet that he would be the first one out.

"He asked me to bring his paints down on the second day. Often after that when I went to his room, he'd be standing up, painting; always said he felt fine. On Sunday, the third of August, he seemed so much better that I asked him if he would be upset if I went to Balboa to see the family. I didn't tell him that Dixie thought Susan not well. He was a little reluctant but finally guessed it was 'time somebody checked up on the kids' and said he would be down in a week or so—just as soon as they let him out of the hospital. I fully expected that he would." Molly drove to Balboa on the fourth. She telephoned Ernest when she arrived; he sounded very cheerful, as he did on succeeding nights.

Robert returned from Peru, and Dixie, anxious to get away, was released. By Thursday, Susan was very sick, with a frighteningly high fever. It was Mabel Blumer's birthday, and the following day would be Barbara's—and Ernest's fifty-seventh. Though he couldn't attend, the usual party had been planned from the day of Molly's return, though Dixie had already had one children's celebration. It was a party of sorts that was held. Barbara recalled her last birthday, when Ernest had let her ask any children she wished for a wonderful day at Marineland. Everyone talked with Ernest on the telephone, even Susan, who he realized was not well. Molly sensed that he did not feel as well as he had on previous nights, but Ernest assured her he was all right; that she should "get Susan well." But nothing seemed to help Susan, not even the prescribed antibiotics. "She was such a skinny little thing anyway," as Molly said. Molly had been up with her much of the night before, and was again, following the party. Worry for the child displaced worry for the man—said to be improving.

Don Cooksey failed to see the hoped-for-improvement on his second visit to the hospital. Added to concern for his friend was concern for the great laboratory of which that friend was the vital force. He went from the hospital to the director's office on the hill, for a private conference with Wally Reynolds on the future of the Radiation Laboratory, if it became necessary for Ernest to be out of touch with it for a long period of time. Who could be considered the best possible successor? Ernest would be the last one to want an outsider appointed. Don eliminated himself as a possibility; he was due to retire, a younger man was desirable. Don and Wally went to the hospital the next morning, and, after a short conference, Ernest—who seemed somewhat better—telephoned Clark Kerr, president of the university since July 1, to request that Edwin McMillan immediately be named deputy director of the Radiation Laboratory, with authority to act in Ernest's stead. Ed was appointed that day—a week before his co-holder of the Nobel Prize and fellow associate director of the Radiation Laboratory, Glenn Seaborg, officially became chancellor of the Berkeley campus.

Ernest did not respond well to medication; there appeared to be little actual improvement since his hospitalization. Dr. Sadusk discussed surgery with John, who hoped that Ernest would improve soon enough that surgery need not be forced; it would be so much better if Ernest agreed to it. The only time it had been mentioned, Ernest had flatly refused to consider it—not because of the operation itself—but because of following complications. The prospect of life without a colon—and therefore without a normal eliminative process—seemed impossible for him even to think about. For him, he was certain, it would mean almost complete retirement from activity, no matter how successfully substitute means could be managed. Yet there was no doubt that his condition was rapidly deteriorating. Dr. Snell, summoned for consultation, agreed that it was serious.

Elsie took it upon herself to telephone Molly; she thought her sister ought to go to Ernest as soon as possible. "Nobody else is going to say so, apparently, but I think he is a very sick man," she said. Molly was able to get plane reservations. Her sister Bertha came to help. Susie was bundled up; Robert and Barbara somehow got ready. The fire was turned off under the pot roast. "We just walked out," Molly said. Bertha's husband drove them to the airport. They arrived in Berkeley late in the evening. Molly was unable to get Susan's pediatrician until early the next morning when Susan's crisis was over—she had had paratyphoid, Dr. Long said. Maggie came to help. Molly went to the hospital as soon as the pediatrician left the house.

Ernest was more listless than she had ever seen him, after a forced smile and an attempted cheerful greeting. She noticed that his paints had not been touched since her last visit; he asked her to pack them up and take them home. It was disturbing that Dr. Sadusk seemed upset over a disagreement with Dr. Snell; he was obviously unhappy over Ernest's condition. John thought it best that Ernest be moved to Palo Alto, closer to Dr. Snell. On the thirteenth he was transferred to Palo Alto Hospital; Robert went with him in the ambulance. He arrived at the hospital very tired, fevered, and dehydrated from continuous bloody diarrhea. He was given a blood transfusion and ACTH almost as soon as he was in his room. Surgeon Blake Wilbur saw him that afternoon. Ernest had sharp chills during the night and looked "pretty washed out in spite of transfusions," Snell noted the next morning.

But Ernest remembered an upcoming Monsanto directors' meeting and dictated a letter to Thomas: "Expect to be in the hospital a few weeks and then to Balboa for a few weeks to recharge my batteries. Will see you in September." Molly came daily and spent most of these visits in the hospital corridor while nurses attended or doctors examined him. For several days there was much bleeding, which was stopped only temporarily. Each day there were fluctuations. On some days he would show interest in reports from Geneva, sent daily by Tichvinsky, or in opinions of the meetings from Navy Captain J. H. Morse. There appeared to be progress; he was confident Fisk and Bacher would do all right, and he remembered Brown's excellent help. One day he would greet Molly cheerfully: "Well, I've got this thing licked!" The next day there might be increased bleeding and a very listless patient. John, often at Palo Alto, seemed puzzled, but not overly worried, Molly thought.

Finally she went to Dr. Snell's office and demanded frankness. "I'm worried about your old man," Snell said. "How do you feel about an operation?" It was a shock, but she was readily convinced that surgery offered the only satisfactory solution. Snell was generally reassuring, however; he wanted to wait another week; with blood transfusions, and other things that were being done, Ernest would be in much better condition for surgery. Molly thought that Ernest himself should be convinced of the necessity or wisdom of surgery, and should agree to the drastic operation of his own accord. She knew how he would resist it, and better than anyone else how it would alter his way of living for the rest of his life—which Snell said should be many years—in a way which a person like Ernest would find awkward.

Molly discussed it with Ernest. He seemed to have no resistance. She explained that he would get used to any complications, that it would make little difference in his life. He agreed that surgery seemed the best solution and wistfully guessed he would have to give up tennis. Molly protested that she saw no reason why he should. He did not see how he could change clothes in the locker room or take showers—he tried to shrug, hopelessly. Molly suggested that all he had to do was take a sweater along and come home for his shower. "I tried to reassure him that it wouldn't bother me at all." He was quiet for a while, and then he said, "You know I wish I'd taken more time off. I would have liked to, you know, but my conscience wouldn't let me." This startled Molly. "I always thought he wanted it that way. He always said he thought life couldn't be long enough for all he wanted to do. He'd never been able to just sit; he didn't know how to do nothing. He said, 'You know I could have died in Geneva.' I said, 'I suppose it's possible. I certainly thought you should have come home sooner, but you didn't want to.' He admitted it; by that time he knew he was very sick. There were days that followed when I didn't stay with him more than a few minutes. He didn't care, he was too exhausted to care, to respond. I kept things from him that would have bothered him. Mary had smashed up her car in Geneva. She wasn't hurt; she was coming home as expected anyway, to enter the university. At first I brought important or interesting mail to him, or papers for his signature. I remember one of the last things he signed was his contract for the next year at the university. I thought a personal letter from President Eisenhower might cheer him; the President hoped for his quick recovery, wrote that he realized it had been a personal sacrifice for Ernest to accept the job with all of his other heavy tasks, that he was grateful, and that the country was further indebted to Ernest. Mail for him came to the hospital, too, all sorts of cards, plants, and flowers. Polly Mills sent a beautiful arrangement of orchids. Trader Vic sent meals. Jack Neylan phoned every day. He always asked if he could have their cook fix something special and take it over to him. Mr. Pauley wanted us to go to Coconut Island for his convalescence. People were phoning the house all day long, and I would remember to take messages to him. Once he had made up his mind to have the operation, he wanted it done at once, but they had to wait, which was an extra ordeal."

On August 22, after three relatively good days, he was considerably worse. There was a good deal of nausea, a very rapid pulse, and a temperature of 104. Intravenous solutions were administered in addition to transfusions. The next day the Geneva Conference closed, successfully and in a cordial atmosphere, according to the papers. He evidenced no reaction when Molly told him. Saturday, the twenty-third, was a bad day followed by a bad night. Surgery was scheduled for Wednesday, the twenty-seventh; intravenous fluids and transfusions were continued. The night of August 26 was one of his better ones at Palo Alto Hospital. He had no fever in the morning and was less toxic; heart and lungs were all right. Across the country, that morning, the twenty-seventh, President Eisenhower's first question of Robert Bacher, at the White House to report on Geneva, was about the condition of Ernest Lawrence. The President was told, as Bacher had been, that Ernest was fine—recovering.

Molly was at the hospital early but was not allowed in the room with Ernest, under sedation all morning. The operation, scheduled for nine, was delayed; Dr. Wilbur had other surgery. She saw Ernest for a minute or two near noon, before he was taken to surgery; his eyes opened; he was conscious enough to speak but too softly to be heard. She kissed him and wished him luck. "I'll be here when you wake up." Already worried by the delay, Molly became too nervous to sit alone; she went to the surgery floor. John, in and out of the operating room, tried to reassure her. She was shown the excised colon when it was brought from the operating room; she knew, from her studies, that it would have been impossible to heal; not an inch of it was unaffected. There was only one small ulcer, but the entire mucous lining was involved, much of it entirely gone; only small islands of mucosa remained. The interlining, which normally would have been pale pink in color, was thickened and an angry red—what was left of it. Small wonder there had been so much bleeding. There was no indication that healing had started after the weeks of treatment: "It was just raw. At first I felt that no one could live with all that removed. Then I was relieved that they had taken it out, because I don't believe it ever could have healed."

Other contributing disease was discovered; most serious was severe atherosclerosis of the superior mesenteric artery, which supplied blood to much of the abdominal area. John wondered how Ernest had kept going at all, or had managed to play tennis as recently as early summer; he could not possibly have had sufficient blood in his lower trunk. Medication had likely never reached the area. Probably the only possible prevention would have been considerable restriction of activities as long as ten years earlier, or before the war, in which case he certainly would not have been happy.

Molly continued hopeful, but it was difficult to believe that he could survive after he left surgery, where he had been for five hours. "The doctors said he was unconscious, but I was certain he spoke to me: 'I'm ready to give up now,' and again, 'Molly, I can't make it.' He begged to be given something for his pain, but for some reason they did not want him to have anything. I could hardly bear it when they said that he just thought he was in pain and was not actually conscious. They had needles all over him for transfusions, intravenous fluids; they gave oxygen. They had poured blood into him for days, five pints, and eight pints of albumen just prior to, and nine pints of blood during, surgery. This was continued after he returned to his room. Dr. Wilbur came in and made a slit in his leg for another needle. They put a drug in the intravenous fluid to help bring up his blood pressure. About ten o'clock, Dr. Lee said he could feel a pulse at last, that things were looking up.

"I told John I desperately needed some coffee. Dr. Snell told me to go and get it, that nothing was going to change. Ira, who had driven me down and was still waiting, went with us, as the hospital dining room was closed. At a nearby place that was open, we all ordered something, but I couldn't touch it. I think I knew. We went back. Before we entered the lobby, poor Ira could see something was going on, and he went tearing up the stairs two or three at a time without waiting for the elevator. When I got out of the elevator, I knew at once, by the way the nurses looked at me. I don't know why, but I couldn't go in the room with him. It had been bad enough to see how he had looked before. The doctors came out and told me he was dead—but I already knew. Then it was hours before they got through fussing around and let us go. John must have known earlier; he had called Amy and wouldn't leave until she arrived. I wanted to go home. It was about two in the morning when we left."

Ira was badly shaken. "Coming back from this lunch place, I could see this activity in the window up there, and I figured maybe she shouldn't be there. I went in, and how bad I felt—just hopeless. You want to do something—but there is nothing. I waited in the room and let the nurse and the doctor tell her. I couldn't do anything—so I got all his personal items and ran back with them to the car. I think she sort of expected it, and so did John, though of course they didn't tell me this. She certainly held her composure well. It was about three hours before we started back." Ira, always a very careful driver, drove off at terrific speed. Molly asked him to slow down a bit, after which he drove much too slowly.

It was good to have Elsie in the house, and Robert, already informed of his father's death—John had phoned Elsie and asked her to go to the children. Elsie had found Barbara and Susan asleep on the floor, waiting for their mother, and had just put them to bed. Robert was awake; he had told Elsie he knew something terrible had happened before she spoke of it; it was very hard on him. When Molly arrived she tried to explain that his father could never again have been a well man. She tried to comfort him and get him to bed. With John, Amy, and Elsie, she drank coffee and smoked countless cigarettes. She phoned Margaret in Chicago; a radiogram was dispatched to Mary on a ship in the Atlantic. Hospitalized Admiral Hayward, notified by Eleanor Davisson, phoned Admiral Burke, Chief of Naval Operations, who radioed the commander of Carrier Division Three, "Request you give emergency leave to Lt. Eric Lawrence due to the death of his father. The Navy has lost a good friend in his father and anything you can do to expedite getting him ashore will be appreciated." Eric was flown home at once. Charlotte Gaither would meet Mary in New York when her ship docked; Rowan and the Loomises took a morning plane to San Francisco. To John fell the task of telling his mother.

Molly agreed to a memorial service but refused to allow a public funeral. Someone had suggested that the memorial be held in the Greek Theater on the campus. When Elsie had to ask her about it, Molly was furious, said it was not to be a spectacle. The First Congregational Church, the largest in Berkeley, was agreed upon, and there at ten o'clock on Saturday morning, August 30, the memorial was held. Prior to the service, Ira drove Molly and the children, except Mary, who arrived too late, to the mortuary for a few private minutes. At the memorial service Ernest's close Radiation Laboratory associates served as ushers for some five hundred people who heard President Clark Kerr deliver a glowing, sincere eulogy. ". . . whatever high honors the world can offer to science, Ernest Lawrence received. . . . These are just some of the honors of his lifetime—but he will go on being honored as long as the history of science continues to be written.

"Manlike creatures have lived on this planet for at least a million years. Throughout these million years they have constantly groped to understand more about and to control better the world about them. A few of them have shot some ray of light into the great unknown darkness of ignorance and illuminated a new area for all future generations. One of the strongest of these beams of light was created by Ernest Lawrence, and men forever after will see farther and understand more because of it. Each of us and each of our children owe to Ernest Lawrence a debt beyond price. For, by his expansion of our understanding, by his reduction of our ignorance, he has added a little to the human dignity of each of us and something more to the meaning of life. . . . And in the men and women he gathered around him—in their enthusiastic expeditions into the unknown, in their intriguing concepts and effective works to bend the atom to man's good—is the continuing spirit of Ernest Lawrence."

Dr. Vere Loper, pastor of the church, spoke of his insight, warmth, humility, enthusiasm, generosity, leadership, courage, and patriotism. Citing the remark of Themistocles after the Battle of Marathon, "The victory of Miltiades will not permit me to rest," Dr. Loper concluded, ". . . the trophies of Ernest Lawrence will not permit us to rest."

Indeed his spirit would be both goad and inspiration for generations yet unborn. President Eisenhower, in his second letter to the Lawrence home in as many weeks, expressed his personal loss, and that of the nation, but stressed the benefits to mankind of Ernest's accomplishments for the future. "Very importantly, he has left thousands of students to carry on his work—dedicated to him and to the objectives he was attempting to achieve."

The President announced annual AEC awards for scientific accomplishment by men under forty-five years of age, to be named for Ernest, who had accomplished so much when young, and who had so much faith in the capabilities of the young.

Lewis Strauss wired from Geneva where, among men of several nations, fifty-three Rad Lab and Livermore scientists had gathered, and where a large Rad Lab exhibit of fusion devices was a center of attraction, "First plenary session conference on peaceful uses of atomic energy tomorrow will be dedicated to Ernest." The National Academy of Sciences, soon to hold the third Berkeley meeting in its history—it was at the first, in September, 1930, that the initial cyclotron, of glass and sealing wax, supported on an old kitchen chair with the aid of a clothes hanger, had been announced and exhibited—paid a rare tribute by establishing an Ernest O. Lawrence lectureship. The Radiation Laboratory was officially renamed the Lawrence Radiation Laboratory. University regents announced plans to build a Lawrence Hall of Science—high on a slope above the laboratory—to be a living, functioning memorial to ". . . help raise the scientific literacy of our nation." Young scientists of a new generation at the Rad Lab discovered element 103 and named it Lawrencium.

Thus in education, in men, in the ever-greater accelerators, even in the Table of Elements, some indestructible entity of Ernest Lawrence continues.

HONORS, AWARDS AND MEMBERSHIPS OF ERNEST ORLANDO LAWRENCE

Awards and Medals:

Elliot Cresson Medal of Franklin Institute, 1937
Research Corporation Prize and Plaque, 1937
Comstock Prize of National Academy of Sciences, 1937
Hughes Medal of Royal Society (England), 1937
Nobel Prize in Physics, 1939
Duddell Medal of Royal Physical Society, 1940
William S. Dunn Award, American Legion, 1940
National Association of Manufacturers Award, 1940
Holley Medal, American Society of Mechanical Engineers, 1942
Copernican Citation, 1943
Wheeler Award, 1945
Medal for Merit, 1946
Medal of Trasenter, Association of Graduate Engineers, University of Liège, Belgium, 1947
Officier de la Légion d'Honneur, France, 1948
Phi Delta Epsilon Annual Service Award, 1948
William Proctor Prize of the Scientific Research Society of America, 1951
Faraday Medal, 1952
American Cancer Society Medal, 1954
Enrico Fermi Award, 1957
Sylvanus Thayer Award, 1958

Honorary Degrees:

Sc.D., University of South Dakota, 1936
Sc.D., Stevens Institute of Technology, 1937
Sc.D., Yale University, 1937
Sc.D., Princeton University, 1937

LL.D., University of Michigan, 1938
Sc.D., University of Chicago, 1941
Sc.D., Harvard University, 1941
Sc.D., Rutgers University, 1941
LL.D., University of Pennsylvania, 1942
Sc.D., McGill University, 1946
Sc.D., University of British Columbia, 1947
Sc.D., University of Southern California, 1949
Sc.D., University of San Francisco, 1949
LL.D., University of Glasgow, 1951

Memberships:

Member

American Representative at Solvay Congress, Brussels, 1933
National Academy of Sciences, 1934
American Philosophical Society, 1937
Phi Beta Kappa
Sigma Xi
Gamma Alpha
American Scandinavian Foundation, 1942
Board of Foreign Scholarships, U.S. Department of State, 1947
Newcomen Society, 1948–1951
Physical Society of Japan, 1954
California Alumni Association
Alumni Association of University of South Dakota
Board of Trustees: Carnegie Institution of Washington, 1944
                               Rand Corporation, 1956

Foreign Member

Royal Swedish Academy of Sciences, 1952

Honorary Member

Bohemian Club (California) , 1940
California Academy of Sciences, 1940
Academy of Science, U.S.S.R., 1943
Royal Irish Academy, 1948

Fellow

American Physical Society
American Association for the Advancement of Science
American Academy of Arts and Sciences

Honorary Fellow

Leland Stanford Junior University, 1941
National Institute of Sciences of India, 1941

The Institute of Medicine of Chicago, 1941
Royal Society of Edinburgh, 1946
The Physical Society, 1948
Indian Academy of Sciences, 1953

Sources

Selected Bibliography

Baxter, James Phinney. *Scientists Against Time*. Boston: Little Brown & Co., 1952.

Bulletin of the Atomic Scientists. 1945 through 1958.

Cattell, J., ed. *American Men of Science*. Seventh Edition. Lancaster, Pa., Science Press, 1944.

Compton, Arthur H. *Atomic Quest, A Personal Narrative*. New York: Oxford University Press, 1956.

Glasstone, Samuel. *Sourcebook of Atomic Energy*, Second Edition. Princeton: D. Van Nostrand Co., 1958.

Groves, Lt. General Leslie R. *Now It Can Be Told, The Story of the Manhattan Project*. New York: Harper & Brothers, 1962.

Hewlett, Richard G., and Oscar E. Anderson, Jr. *The New World, 1939–1946*. University Park: Pennsylvania State University Press, 1962.

Knebel, Fletcher, and Charles W. Bailey, II. *No High Ground*. New York: Harper & Brothers, 1960.

Lamont, Lansing. *Day of Trinity*. New York: Atheneum, 1965.

Laurence, William L. *Dawn Over Zero*. New York: Knopf, 1946.

Lawrence, Carl G. *Autobiography*. Unpublished.

McMillan, Edwin M. "Particle Accelerators," Part XII, Vol. III, *Experimental Nuclear Physics*, edited by E. Segrè. New York: John Wiley & Sons, 1959.

Seaborg, Glenn T. *The Transuranium Elements*. New Haven: Yale University Press, 1958.

Smyth, Henry De Wolf. *Atomic Energy for Military Purposes:* The official *Report on the Development of the Atomic Bomb*. Princeton: Princeton University Press, 1947.

South Dakota State Historical Society. *South Dakota Historical Collections*. Volume XXII, 1946.

Stimson, Henry L. "The Decision to Use the Atomic Bomb," *Harper's Magazine*, 1947.

Strauss, Lewis S. *Men and Decisions*. New York: Doubleday & Co., 1962.

United States Atomic Energy Commission. *In the Matter of J. Robert Oppenheimer*. Washington, D.C.: Government Printing Office, 1954.

Wilson, Robert R., and Raphael Littauer. *Accelerators*. New York: Anchor Books, 1960.

Scientific papers and articles of Ernest O. Lawrence and other staff members of the Radiation Laboratory, University of California, Berkeley.

General Sources

The following sources were used throughout: speeches by Ernest O. Lawrence; material from his personal files; his reports to the Research Corporation, the Rockefeller Foundation and the University of California; files in the Department of Physics and the Radiation Laboratory; the voluminous correspondence which passed (over a period of thirty years from 1918) among Carl and Gunda Lawrence and their sons Ernest and John, most of which was saved. Lawrence family scrapbooks and collections of clippings, often undated and without indications of specific periodicals, were examined. The Associated Press and United Press were often indicated as sources. *The New York Times,* the *New York Herald Tribune,* the *San Francisco Chronicle,* the *Oakland Tribune* and the *Berkeley Daily Gazette* were consulted for general background material. Issues of the *Canton Argus Leader* and of the *Sioux Valley News,* both published in Canton, South Dakota, for the period 1900–1950, were read for the same purpose, as well as for specific references to the Lawrence family.

In addition, particular sources used in individual chapters are specified below:

Chapter I Born Grown Up: 1901–1918

Personal interviews by the author with Clarence Anderson, Horace C. Ellis, Harold Graneng, Mr. and Mrs. Robert Hipple, Franklyn Hyde, Judge and Mrs. Verne Jennings, Mrs. Ardis Johnson, Dr. and Mrs. John H. Lawrence, Oliver Laxon, Ben and Gus Noid, Oliver E. Overseth, Rena Overseth, Jenny Paulson, Paul Paulson, Francis Pinckney, Mr. and Mrs. Ernest Rowe, Al Swanholm, Arthur Tobiason, Merle Tuve, Lester Wegner.

Correspondence between the author and Verne Kennedy.

Unpublished talk by Mary Cooper Frankberg.

Pierre, S.D., report cards of Ernest O. Lawrence.

Teaching certificate issued to Ole Lawrence by Dane County, Wisconsin Territory, March 11, 1846.

Chapter II Young Man in a Hurry: 1918–1922

Personal interviews by the author with Lewis and Mrs. Myra H. Akeley, Charles Barrett, E. P. Churchill, Edward and La Rue Dwight, H. F. Frankenfeld, Leo Heck, Oren House, A. L. Lawson, Walter W. Ludeman, Marion Akeley Miller, Oliver E. Overseth, Helen Parsons, Arthur Tobiason, Merle Tuve.

Correspondence between the author and Lewis and Mrs. Myra H. Akeley, H. F. Frankenfeld, Stanley Tobiason.

Correspondence of Ernest O. Lawrence with Ruby Patterson, Merle Tuve.

Other correspondence: Edward Freeman to John H. Lawrence, P. M. Glasoe to Carl Lawrence, Ferdinand Smith to John H. Lawrence.

Andrade, E. N. da C. *Rutherford on the Nature of the Atom.* New York: Doubleday & Co., 1964.

South Dakota Educational Association Journal, April, 1938.

Volante, University of South Dakota student publication, 1919–1922.

Chapter III   Cut-and-Try: Fall, 1922–Spring, 1925

Personal interviews by the author with Charles Barrett, Gregory Breit, Arthur Compton, Donald Cooksey, Mr. and Mrs. Edward Dwight, Edward Freeman, Elizabeth Cooksey Hamilton, Lawrence Haugen, Norman Hilberry, Thomas H. Johnson, Dr. John H. Lawrence, Leonard Loeb, Anne Cooksey Maes, Joseph Morris, Oliver E. Overseth, A. L. Swanholm, W. F. G. Swann, Merle Tuve.

Letters of Samuel Jacobsohn.

Correspondence between the author and William J. Buchta.

Correspondence between Ernest O. Lawrence and H. A. Erikson, Iwao Fukushima, Lawrence Haugen, Kuma Kawasaki, Ruby Patterson, Merle Tuve.

Jaffe, Bernard. *Michelson and the Speed of Light.* New York: Anchor Books, 1960.

Ernest O. Lawrence. Address at the inauguration of Arthur H. Compton as Chancellor of Washington University, St. Louis, Mo., 1945.

Chapter IV   Not Work—Great Fun: June, 1925–August, 1928

Personal interviews by the author with Jesse W. Beams, Raymond T. Birge, Mabel Blumer (Mrs. George), Arthur Compton, Donald Cooksey, William D. Coolidge, William Hamilton, Lawrence and Margaret Haugen, Albert W. Hull, Thomas H. Johnson, Mrs. Ernest O. Lawrence, Dr. John H. Lawrence, Leonard Loeb, Mrs. Edwin M. McMillan, Joseph Morris, Oliver E. Overseth, Al Swanholm, W. F. G. Swann, William Watson.

Correspondence between the author and Leonard Loeb.

Correspondence of Ernest O. Lawrence with Raymond T. Birge, Mary Blumer, Karl Darrow, Elmer E. Hall, L. G. Hoxton, Leonard Loeb, Ernest Merritt, F. A. Osborn, Ruby Patterson, Peggy Read.

Chapter V   How to Get a Million Volts: August, 1928– October, 1930

Personal interviews by the author with Jesse W. Beams, James Brady, W. D. Coolidge, Niels E. Edlefsen, Mrs. Walter Frederick (Christine Brooke), Lawrence Haugen, Curtis Haupt, Joel Hildebrand, Albert Hull, Henrietta Jenkins (Mrs. Francis A.), Thomas H. Johnson, Victor Lenzen, M. Stanley Livingston, Leonard Loeb, Lauriston C. Marshall, Robert Oppenheimer, Linus Pauling, C. Donald Shane, David H. Sloan, Robert Gordon Sproul, W. F. G. Swann, Milton White.

Correspondence of Ernest O. Lawrence with Raymond T. Birge, Mary Blumer, Lawrence Haugen, Leonard Loeb, Northwestern University.

Papers of Donald Cooksey, Robert Gordon Sproul.

McMillan, Edwin M. "Particle Accelerators," in *Experimental Nuclear Physics*, Vol. III, Part XII, ed. E. Segrè. New York: John Wiley & Sons, 1959.

Chapter VI   Proton Merry-Go-Round: October, 1930– Early 1932

Personal interviews by the author with Raymond T. Birge, Mrs. George Blumer, James J. Brady, Donald Cooksey, Mr. and Mrs. Lawrence Haugen, Malcolm G. Henderson, Henrietta Jenkins, Charles C. Lauritsen, Victor Lenzen, M. Stanley Livingston, Leonard Loeb, Robert Oppenheimer, Milton White.

Correspondence of Ernest O. Lawrence with Joseph W. Barker, Mary Blumer, William Buffum, Donald Cooksey, Frederick G. Cottrell, W. V. Houston, F. N. D. Kurie, Robert Oppenheimer, Howard A. Poillon, John C. Slater, David Sloan, Merle Tuve.

Other Correspondence: James J. Brady and Donald Cooksey.

Chapter VII Vintage Year: 1932–Fall, 1933

Personal interviews by the author with Jesse W. Beams, Raymond T. Birge, Dr. and Mrs. George Blumer, James J. Brady, Sir John Cockcroft, Donald Cooksey, Herbert M. Evans, Malcolm C. Henderson, W. V. Houston, William L. Laurence, Charles C. Lauritsen, Mrs. Ernest O. Lawrence, Dr. John H. Lawrence, J. J. Livingood, Edwin M. and Mrs. McMillan, Joseph Morris, Sir Mark Oliphant, Robert Oppenheimer, Linus Pauling, David H. Sloan, Dr. Robert Stone, Merle Tuve, Milton White.

Correspondence of Ernest O. Lawrence with Raymond T. Birge, Mary Blumer, James J. Brady, James Chadwick, Sir John Cockcroft, Donald Cooksey, R. H. Fowler, Rudolf Ladenburg, Sir Mark Oliphant, Robert Oppenheimer, Lord Ernest Rutherford.

Papers of Sir John Cockcroft.

Compton, Karl. *The Technology Review*, January, 1933.

Chapter VIII Alchemist's Dream:
October, 1933–December, 1935

Personal interviews by the author with Paul C. Aebersold, E. Amaldi, Sidney W. Barnes, Jesse W. Beams, Mrs. George Blumer, Sir John Cockcroft, Donald Cooksey, Lee A. DuBridge, Sidney M. Ehrman, Herbert M. Evans, John Stuart Foster, Sr., Malcolm C. Henderson, George de Hevesy, Charles C. Lauritsen, Mrs. Ernest O. Lawrence, Dr. John H. Lawrence, Victor Lenzen, J. J. Livingood, M. Stanley Livingston, Leonard Loeb, Mrs. Edwin M. McMillan, Joseph Morris, Sir Mark Oliphant, Dr. Langley Porter, Dr. Robert Stone, Merle Tuve.

Correspondence of Ernest O. Lawrence with Paul C. Aebersold, Kenneth T. Bainbridge, Jesse Beams, Niels Bohr, James Chadwick, Sir John Cockcroft, Donald Cooksey, R. H. Fowler, G. Gamow, George de Hevesy, R. Joliot, Franz N. D. Kurie, Paul Langevin, William L. Laurence, Victor Lenzen, Joseph Morris, Mark L. Oliphant, Howard Poillon, Lord Ernest Rutherford, Merle Tuve.

Chapter IX Heart's Desire: 1936

Personal interviews by the author with Raymond T. Birge, Vannevar Bush, Donald Cooksey, James B. Conant, Mrs. Ernest O. Lawrence, John Francis Neylan, Robert Oppenheimer, Robert Gordon Sproul.

Correspondence of Ernest O. Lawrence with Vannevar Bush, George D. Birkhoff, Karl Compton, James B. Conant, Howard Poillon.

Notes and memoranda of Raymond T. Birge.
Papers of Robert Gordon Sproul.

Chapter X: The Club: 1930's

Personal interviews by the author with Philip H. Abelson, Paul C. Aebersold, Luis W. Alvarez, Raymond T. Birge, Sir John Cockcroft, Arthur H. Compton, Donald Cooksey, Lee A. DuBridge, Lorenzo Emo, John Stuart Foster, Sr., George Kenneth Green, Malcom C. Henderson, Hardin B. Jones, Martin Kamen, Bernard B. Kinsey, Barbara Bridgeford Laslett, L. Jackson Laslett, Dr. John H. Lawrence, Victor Lenzen, J. J. Livingood, M. Stanley Livingston, Leonard Loeb, Wilfrid B. Mann, Edwin M. McMillan, Basanti Nag, Henry W. Newson, Sir Mark Oliphant, Robert Oppenheimer, Frances Randolph, Winfield Salisbury, David H. Sloan, Arthur H. Snell, Dr. Robert Stone, Robert L. Thornton, Milton White, Robert R. Wilson, Chien-Shiung Wu, Rebekah Young.

Correspondence between the author and Dr. John H. Lawrence.

Correspondence of Ernest O. Lawrence with Hans Bethe, Karl Compton, Donald Cooksey, L. Jackson Laslett, Sir Mark Oliphant, Hugh Paxton, Lord Ernest Rutherford.

Oliphant, Sir Mark. "The Two Ernests," *Physics Today*, September and October, 1966.

Time, November 1, 1937.

Kerr, Clark. Address to National Academy of Sciences, November, 1958.

Snell, Arthur H. Address at the Los Angeles Conference, held at the University of California, April 16, 1962.

Remarks at closing party for 60-inch cyclotron, Claremont Hotel, Oakland, California, July 7, 1962.

Chapter XI   Your Career Is Showing Promise: 1937–1939

Personal interviews by the author with Philip H. Abelson, Paul C. Aebersold, Dr. Walter C. Alvarez, Jesse W. Beams, Raymond T. Birge, Mrs. H. B. Blumer, Arthur H. Compton, Donald Cooksey, William D. Coolidge, Lee A. DuBridge, Martin D. Kamen, Mrs. Ernest O. Lawrence, Alfred Loomis, Edwin M. McMillan, Sir Mark Oliphant, Robert Oppenheimer, Helen Griggs Seaborg, Emilio Segrè, Charles Seymour, Arthur H. Snell, Robert Gordon Sproul, Dr. Robert Stone, W. F. G. Swann, Merle Tuve, Warren Weaver, John A. Wheeler.

Correspondence of Ernest O. Lawrence with Alex Allen, Dr. Walter C. Alvarez, Jesse W. Beams, Niels Bohr, Arthur H. Compton, Donald Cooksey, Lee A. DuBridge, Ludvig Hektoen, Lise Meitner, Sir Mark Oliphant, Howard Poillon, H. P. Rainey, Charles Seymour, Arthur H. Snell, Dr. Robert Stone, W. F. G. Swann, Merle Tuve, Warren Weaver.

Other Correspondence: Kenneth T. Bainbridge and Donald Cooksey, Donald Cooksey and Charles Seymour.

Papers by:
Niels Bohr and John A. Wheeler
Karl Compton
Robert Gordon Sproul
Dr. Robert Stone

Chapter XII   "Leaping Ahead": 1940–1941

Personal interviews by the author with Luis W. Alvarez, Dr. George Blumer, Gregory Breit, Vannevar Bush, Arthur H. Compton, James B. Conant, Donald Cooksey, Karl K. Darrow, Lee A. DuBridge, George de Hevesy, Martin Kamen, Dr. John H. Lawrence, Alfred Loomis, Wilfrid B. Mann, Edwin M. McMillan, Sir Mark L. Oliphant, Robert Oppenheimer, Glenn T. Seaborg, Emilio Segrè, Arthur H. Snell, Warren Weaver.

Correspondence between the author and Sir Mark L. Oliphant.

Correspondence of Ernest O. Lawrence with Dr. Glen Bell, William B. Bell, Lyman J. Briggs, Vannevar Bush, Karl Compton, James B. Conant, Robert Cornog, Karl K. Darrow, John Dunning, Ludvig Hektoen, George de Hevesy, Frank B. Jewett, Sir Mark Oliphant, Howard Poillon, Norman F. Ramsey, Franz Simon, Warren Weaver, Archie Woods.

Correspondence between John Dunning and Donald Cooksey.

Seaborg, Glenn T. Address at the University of California, Berkeley, February 21, 1966.

Robert Gordon Sproul papers.

Chapter XIII   The Race: 1942–July 16, 1945

Personal interviews by the author with Luis W. Alvarez, Rexford W. Barton, Wilfred S. Bigelow, William M. Brobeck, William Brower, Vannevar Bush, Melvin Calvin, William Chambers, Ralph Chaney, Albert K. Chapman, Arthur H. Compton, James B. Conant, Richard Connell, Dr. and Mrs. Donald Cooksey, William D. Douglass, Priscilla Green Duffield, George Everson, Harold A. Fidler, Lt. Gen. Leslie R. Groves (Ret.), W. T. Hanson, John C. Hecker, Roger H. Hildebrand, Frederick Howard, Edward D. Hudson, Leon O. Jackson, Henrietta Jenkins, Martin Kamen, Clarence Larson, Dr. John H. Lawrence, Robert S. Livingston, Edward J. Lofgren, Donald H. Loughridge, John Manley, Edwin M. McMillan, C. E. K. Mees, C. E. Norman, Sir Mark Oliphant, Frank F. Oppenheimer, Robert Oppenheimer, William E. Parkins, Jr., Wallace B. Reynolds, J. Reginald Richardson, George O. Robinson, Glenn T. Seaborg, C. Donald Shane, Lloyd P. Smith, Frank H. Spedding, Chauncey Starr, Edward W. Strong, Edward Teller, Charles A. Thomas, Lowell Thomas, Cornelius A. Tobias, Robert Traver, Robert M. Underhill, James T. Vale, T. Gentry Veal, Julian H. Webb, Herbert F. York.

Correspondence between author and R. S. Shankland.

Correspondence of Ernest O. Lawrence with Vannevar Bush, Albert K. Chapman, James B. Conant, James Ellis, Robert Gordon Sproul.

Laurence, William L. Press dispatches.
Notebooks of C. Donald Shane.

Chapter XIV   Crossroads: July, 1945–December, 1946

Personal interviews by the author with Dean and Mrs. Lewis E. Akeley, Luis W. Alvarez, Robert F. Bacher, Morris E. Bradbury, William M. Brobeck, Vannevar Bush, Melvin Calvin, Albert K. Chapman, Arthur H. Compton, Donald Cooksey, Patricia Durbin, Herbert M. Evans, Paul Fine, H. Rowan Gaither, Jr., Lt. Gen. Leslie R. Groves (Ret.), Mrs. Ernest O. Lawrence, Dr. John H. Lawrence, Alfred Loomis, W. G. Malcolm, Lauriston C. Marshall, Edwin M. McMillan, John Francis Neylan, Sir Mark Oliphant, Robert Oppenheimer, W. H. Panofsky, Lewis L. Strauss, C. Guy Suits, Charles A. Thomas.

Correspondence of Ernest O. Lawrence with Vannevar Bush, Albert K. Chapman, W. G. Malcolm, Mark L. Oliphant, Robert Oppenheimer, Richard Pearce, C. Guy Suits.

Pearce, Richard. Press dispatches.
Truman, Harry S. Memoirs, Vol. I, Years of Decision. New York: Doubleday & Company, 1955.

Chapter XV Berkeley Is Mecca—Ernest the Prophet: 1947–1949

Personal interviews by the author with Luis W. Alvarez, Sidney W. Barnes, William M. Brobeck, Margaret Lawrence Casady, Albert K. Chapman, Donald Cooksey, Ann Eggers, H. Rowan Gaither, Jr., Dr. John W. Gofman, Lawrence R. Hafstad, Admiral J. T. Hayward, Thomas H. Johnson, Hardin B. Jones, David L. Judd, Mrs. Ernest O. Lawrence, Mrs. John H. Lawrence, John Leermakers, Alfred Loomis, Donald H. Loughridge, W. G. Malcolm, Edwin M. McMillan, John Francis Neylan, Frank F. Oppenheimer, Robert Oppenheimer, Edwin W. Pauley, Kenneth S. Pitzer, Lloyd P. Smith, Robert Gordon Sproul, Lewis L. Strauss, C. Guy Suits, W. F. G. Swann, Charles A. Thomas, Robert M. Underhill, James T. Vale, Warren Weaver, Vernon M. Welsh, Herbert F. York.

Correspondence of Ernest O. Lawrence with William B. Bell, Albert K. Chapman, W. G. Malcolm, C. Guy Suits.

Brooks, Harvey. Remarks at conferring of Ernest O. Lawrence award, June 27, 1960.
Chew, Geoffrey. "Academic Freedom on Trial at the University of California," in *Bulletin of Atomic Scientists*, 1950.
Stuart, George R. *The Year of the Oath*. New York: Doubleday & Company, 1950.
United States Atomic Energy Commission. Statement Concerning Soviet Atomic Weapons, February 5, 1953.

Chapter XVI To Fuse or Not to Fuse: 1950–1952

Personal interviews by the author with Luis W. Alvarez, Hugh Atterling, Barney Balaban, Jesse W. Beams, H. J. Bhabha, Ward Blackmon, Norris E. Bradbury, Hugh Bradner, Gregory Breit, Albert K. Chapman, Mr. and Mrs. Donald Cooksey, A. Crawford Cooley, Robert Dressler, Walter F. Dudziak, H. Rowan Gaither, Jr., Dr. John W. Gofman, Morgan Gunst, Jr., Admiral J. T. Hayward, Alex Hildebrand, Joel Hildebrand, Roger Hildebrand, Thomas H. Johnson, Elmer Kelly, Mrs. Ernest O. Lawrence, Dr. and Mrs. John H. Lawrence, Robert LeBaron, John Leermakers, Alfred and Manette Loomis, John Manley, Dr. and Mrs. Edwin M. McMillan, Burton J. Moyer, Thomas E. Murray, W. K. H. Panofsky, Kenneth S. Pitzer, Paul Raiborne, J. Reginald Richardson, Glenn T. Seaborg, Helen Griggs Seaborg, Emilio Segrè, Frank H. Spedding, Cyril J. Staud, Lewis L. Strauss, C. Guy Suits, Edward Teller, Robert M. Underhill, James T. Vale, Herbert F. York.

Correspondence between the author and former President Harry S Truman.

Correspondence of Ernest O. Lawrence with General Omar Bradley, Gregory Breit, Admiral Arleigh Burke, Albert K. Chapman, Joel Hildebrand, Robert LeBaron, Manne Siegbahn, Cyril J. Staud, Lewis L. Strauss, C. Guy Suits, The Svedberg.

Medical Reports on Ernest O. Lawrence assembled from various sources and in the files of Donner Laboratory, University of California.

Chapter XVII A Sort of Grandfather: 1953–1954

Personal interviews by the author with Luis W. Alvarez, Robert F. Bacher, Barney Balaban, Robert Beringer, Dr. George Blumer, Dr. James L. Born, Margaret Lawrence Casady, Donald Cooksey, Lorenzo Emo, Harold A. Fidler, John Stuart Foster, Jr., H. Rowan Gaither, Jr., J. D. Gow, Leland J. Haworth, George de Hevesy, Alex Hildebrand, Arthur L. Jensen, Thomas H. Johnson, Hardin B. Jones, Elmer Kelly, Mariette Kuper, Clarence E. Larson, Charles Lauritsen, Mrs. Ernest O. Lawrence, Dr. and Mrs. John H. Lawrence, Alfred Loomis, Louis McKeehan, Thomas E. Murray, John Francis Neylan, Robert Oppenheimer, George Parkhurst, Howard Poillon, Ira Sandefur, Duane Sewell, Dr. John Sherrick, Walter Starr, Lewis S. Strauss, James T. Vale, Herbert F. York.

Correspondence of Ernest O. Lawrence with Dr. Dana Atchley, Dr. George Blumer, President Dwight D. Eisenhower, Clarence E. Larson.

Medical reports on Ernest O. Lawrence, Donner Laboratory.

Chapter XVIII   The Peaceful Atom: 1955–1957

Personal interviews by the author with Luis W. Alvarez, Robert F. Bacher, Jesse W. Beams, Pedro Beltran, Felix Block, Dr. George Blumer, Norris E. Bradbury, James J. Brady, Vannevar Bush, Melvin Calvin, Margaret Lawrence Casady, Owen Chamberlain, Ralph Chaney, Frank Collbohm, Donald Cooksey, Walter Dean, William D. Douglass, Walter F. Dudziak, Lorenzo Emo, John S. Foster, Jr., Mary Lawrence Freeman, H. Rowan Gaither, Jr., J. D. Gow, Morgan Gunst, Jr., Lawrence Hafstad, Borge Hansen-Møller, Admiral J. T. Hayward, Leland Hayworth, Carl Helmholz, George de Hevesy, Dr. Arthur L. Jensen, Thomas H. Johnson, Clarence E. Larson, Eric Lawrence, Mrs. Ernest O. Lawrence, Dr. John H. Lawrence, Robert LeBaron, M. Stanley Livingston, Edward Lofgren, Mr. and Mrs. Alfred Loomis, Dr. and Mrs. Edwin M. McMillan, Thomas E. Murray, John Francis Neylan, Sir Mark Oliphant, Robert Oppenheimer, W. K. H. Panofsky, George Parkhurst, Edwin W. Pauley, T. Gerald Pickavance, Polly Plesset, Vladimir A. Reichel, Glenn T. Seaborg, Emilio Segrè, Harold E. Stassen, J. MacWilliams Stone, Lewis L. Strauss, C. Guy Suits, Edward Teller, Charles A. Thomas, James T. Vale, Vladimir Veksler, Warren Weaver, Vernon Welsh, John A. Wheeler, Rolf Wideröe, Daniel M. Wilkes, Herbert York, Rebekah Young.

Correspondence between the author and James J. Brady.

Correspondence of Ernest O. Lawrence with Dean Acheson, T. E. Allibone, Vannevar Bush, Frank Collbohm, President Dwight David Eisenhower, Laura Fermi, H. Rowan Gaither, Jr., J. D. Gow, Otto Hahn, George de Hevesy, Herbert Hoover, Jr., J. J. Hopkins, Clarence E. Larson, Robert LeBaron, Manne Lindholm, Gordon MacDonald, John Francis Neylan, Edwin W. Pauley, Isadore I. Rabi, Admiral Hyman G. Rickover, Laurance Rockefeller, Manne Siegbahn, Gerard C. Smith, General Walter Bedell Smith, Harold Stassen, J. MacWilliams Stone, Lewis L. Strauss, C. Guy Suits, Edward Teller, Charles A. Thomas, Juan Trippe, Vladimir Veksler, John A. Wheeler.

Other Correspondence: Ferdinand O. Smith to Dr. John H. Lawrence.

Fermi, Laura. *Atoms for the World*. Chicago: University of Chicago Press, 1957.
Snell, Arthur H. "Geneva Diary, August 8–20, 1955," *American Scientist*, October, 1955.
United States Atomic Energy Commission *Eighteenth Semi-Annual Report*. Washington: Government Printing Office, July, 1955.
Medical Reports on Ernest O. Lawrence, Donner Laboratory.

Chapter XIX: Lawrencium: 1958

Personal interviews by the author with Robert F. Bacher, Mrs. George Blumer, Harold Brown, Margaret Lawrence Casady, Arthur H. Compton, Donald Cooksey, Karl K. Darrow, Eleanor I. Davisson, Harold A. Fidler, H. Rowan Gaither, Jr., Admiral J.

T. Hayward, Randolph Hearst, Mrs. Ernest O. Lawrence, Dr. and Mrs. John H. Lawrence, John Leermakers, Alfred Loomis, Edwin M. and Mrs. McMillan, John Francis Neylan, Robert Oppenheimer, W. K. H. Panofsky, Edwin W. Pauley, Polly Plesset, Wallace B. Reynolds, Ira Sandefur, Glenn T. Seaborg, Robert Gordon Sproul, Walter A. Starr, Harold E. Stassen, Lewis L. Strauss, Edward Teller, Charles A. Thomas, Leonid Tichvinsky, Merle Tuve, John A. Wheeler, Herbert F. York.

Correspondence between the author and Margaret Lawrence Casady.

Correspondence of Ernest O. Lawrence with Lewis E. Akeley, President Dwight David Eisenhower, Eric Lawrence, Margaret Lawrence, Mary Lawrence, Robert Lawrence, Captain J. H. Morse, Edwin W. Pauley, Polly Plesset, Edgar M. Queeny, Lewis L. Strauss, Charles A. Thomas, Leonid Tichvinsky, John A. Wheeler.

Kerr, Clark. Eulogy delivered at memorial service for Ernest O. Lawrence, Berkeley, California, August 30, 1958.

Loper, Dr. Vere. Eulogy delivered at memorial service for Ernest O. Lawrence, Berkeley, California, August 30, 1958.

Tichvinsky, Leonid. Reports to Ernest O. Lawrence from the Geneva Conference of Experts to Study the Possibility of Detecting Violations of a Possible Agreement on Suspension of Nuclear Tests; August, 1958.

Medical reports on Ernest O. Lawrence, Bonner Laboratory and Palo Alto Hospital, Palo Alto, California. Autopsy report, Alta Bates Community Hospital, Berkeley, California.

Index